ASHRAE POCKET GUIDE

for Air Conditioning, Heating, Ventilation, Refrigeration

10th Edition

ASHRAE · 180 Technology Parkway, Peachtree Corners, GA 30092 · www.ashrae.org

ISBN 978-1-947192-77-5 (paperback)
ISBN 978-1-947192-78-2 (PDF)

Product code: 90071 12/22

Library of Congress Cataloging-in-Publication Data

Names: ASHRAE (Firm), author.
Title: ASHRAE pocket guide for air conditioning, heating, ventilation, refrigeration.
Other titles: Pocket guide for air conditioning, heating, ventilation, refrigeration
Description: 10th edition. | Peachtree Corners : ASHRAE, [2022] | Includes index. | Summary: "Comprehensive yet consolidated reference for HVAC engineers with data from the ASHRAE Handbooks and ASHRAE Standards 62.1, 62.2, 15, and 55; revised from the 2017 edition"-- Provided by publisher.
Identifiers: LCCN 2021017597 | ISBN 9781947192775 (softcover) | ISBN 9781947192782 (pdf)
Subjects: LCSH: Heating--Equipment and supplies--Handbooks, manuals, etc. | Ventilation--Handbooks, manuals, etc. | Air conditioning--Handbooks, manuals, etc. | Refrigeration and refrigerating machinery--Handbooks, manuals, etc.
Classification: LCC TH7011 .A38 2022 | DDC 697.9--dc23
LC record available at https://lccn.loc.gov/2021017597

Updates and errata for this publication will be posted on the ASHRAE website at www.ashrae.org/publicationupdates.

CONTENTS

PREFACE

The ASHRAE Pocket Guide was developed to serve as a ready, offline reference for engineers without easy access to complete ASHRAE Handbook volumes.

This tenth edition has been revised in 2022 to include updates from the current editions of the ASHRAE Handbook series as well as from various ASHRAE standards. This edition continues to emphasize basic design information.

The ASHRAE Pocket Guide was first published in 1987. This edition was compiled by Walter Grondzik. Major contributors to previous editions include Carl W. MacPhee; Griffith C. Burr, Jr.; Harry E. Rountree; and Frederick H. Kohloss.

Throughout this Pocket Guide, original sources of figures and tables are indicated where applicable. Due to space constraints, a shorthand for ASHRAE publications has been adopted. ASHRAE sources are noted after figure captions or table titles in brackets using the following abbreviations:

Fig	Figure
Tbl	Table
Ch	Chapter
Std	ASHRAE Standard
Gdl	ASHRAE Guideline
2021F, 2017F, etc	*ASHRAE Handbook—Fundamentals*
2020S, 2016S, etc.	*ASHRAE Handbook—HVAC Systems and Equipment*
2019A, 2015A, etc.	*ASHRAE Handbook—HVAC Applications*
2018R, 2014R, etc.	*ASHRAE Handbook—Refrigeration*

Complete entries for all references cited in tables and figures are available in the original source publications.

1. AIR HANDLING AND PSYCHROMETRICS

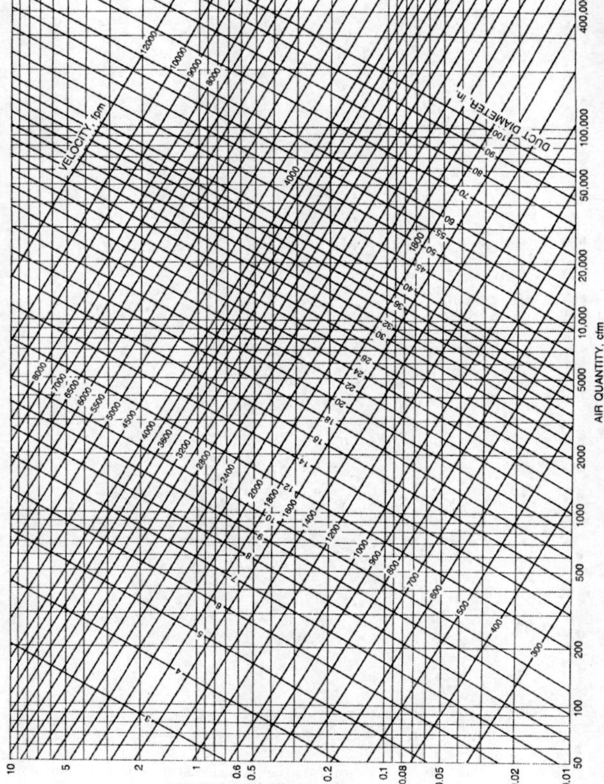

Figure 1.1 Friction Chart for Round Duct (ρ = 0.075 lb_m/ft^3 and ε = 0.0003 ft)
[2021F, Ch 21, Fig 9]

Table 1.1 Velocities vs. Velocity Pressures

Velocity V, fpm	Velocity Pressure P_v, in. H_2O
300	0.01
400	0.01
500	0.02
600	0.02
700	0.03
800	0.04
900	0.05
1000	0.06
1100	0.08
1200	0.09
1300	0.11
1400	0.12
1500	0.14
1600	0.16
1700	0.18
1800	0.20
1900	0.22
2000	0.25
2100	0.27
2200	0.30
2300	0.33
2400	0.36
2500	0.39

$P_v = (V/4005)^2$

Noncircular Ducts

Hydraulic diameter $D_h = 4A/P$, where A = duct area (in.^{2}) and P = perimeter (in.). Ducts having the same hydraulic diameter will have approximately the same fluid resistance at equal velocities.

Fittings

Resistance to flow through fittings can be expressed by fitting loss coefficients C. The friction loss in a fitting in inches of water is CP_v. The more radically the airflow is changed in direction or velocity, the greater the fitting loss coefficient. See *ASHRAE Duct Fitting Database* for a complete list. 90° mitered elbows with vanes will usually have C between 0.11 and 0.33.

Round Flexible Ducts

Nonmetallic flexible ducts fully extended have friction losses approximately three times that of galvanized steel ducts. The loss rises rapidly for unextended ducts; with a correction factor of 2 if 90% extended, 3 if 80% extended, and 4 if 70% extended. For centerline bend radius ratio to diameter of 1 to 4, the approximate loss coefficient is between 0.82 and 0.87.

Table 1.2 Duct Leakage Classification[a]

Duct Type	Predicted Leakage Class C_L	
	Sealed[b,c]	Unsealed[c]
Metal (flexible excluded)		
Round and flat oval	3	30 (6 to 70)
Rectangular		
≤ 2 in. of water (both positive and negative pressures)	12	48 (12 to 110)
> 2 and ≤ 10 in. of water (both positive and negative pressures)	6	48 (12 to 110)[c]
Flexible		
Metal, aluminum	8	30 (12 to 54)
Nonmetal	12	30 (4 to 54)
Fibrous glass		
Round	3	na
Rectangular	6	na

[a] The leakage classes listed in this table are averages based on tests conducted by AISI/SMACNA (1972), ASHRAE/SMACNA/TIMA (1985), and Swim and Griggs (1995).

[b] The leakage classes listed in the sealed category are based on the assumptions that for metal ducts, all transverse joints, seams, and openings in the duct wall are sealed at pressures over 3 in. of water, that transverse joints and longitudinal seams are sealed at 2 and 3 in. of water, and that transverse joints are sealed below 2 in. of water. Lower leakage classes are obtained by careful selection of joints and sealing methods.

[c] Leakage classes assigned anticipate about 25 joints per 100 linear feet of duct. For systems with a high fitting to straight duct ratio, greater leakage occurs in both the sealed and unsealed conditions.

Table 1.3 Recommended Ductwork Leakage Class by Duct Type

Duct Type	Leakage Class C_L, cfm/100 ft^2 at 1 in. of water
Metal (flexible excluded)	
Round	3
Flat oval	3
Rectangular	6
Flexible	6
Fibrous glass	
Round	3
Rectangular	6

$$\text{Leakage Class } C_L = Q/\Delta P_S^{0.65} \quad (1.1)$$

where

Q = leakage rate, cfm/100 ft^2 surface area

ΔP_s = static pressure difference, inches of water between inside and outside of duct

Table 1.4 Duct Sealing Requirement Levels

Duct Seal Level	Sealing Requirements[a]
A	All transverse joints, longitudinal seams, and duct wall penetrations
B	All transverse joints and longitudinal seams
C	Transverse joints only

[a] Transverse joints are connections of two duct or fitting elements oriented perpendicular to flow. Longitudinal seams are joints oriented in the direction of airflow. Duct wall penetrations are openings made by screws, non-self-sealing fasteners, pipe, tubing, rods, and wire. Round and flat oval spiral lock seams need not be sealed prior to assembly, but may be coated after assembly to reduce leakage. All other connections are considered transverse joints, including but not limited to spin-ins, taps and other branch connections, access door frames, and duct connections to equipment.

Table 1.5 Duct Leakage per Unit Length

Unsealed Longitudinal Seam Leakage, Metal Ducts		Leakage, cfm per ft Seam Length at 1 in. Water Pressure	
Type of Duct/Seam		Range	Average
Rectangular	Pittsburgh lock		
	26 gage	0.01 to 0.02	0.0164
	22 gage	0.001 to 0.002	0.0016
	Button punch snaplock		
	26 gage	0.03 to 0.15	0.0795
	22 gage	NA (1 test)	0.0032
Round	Spiral (26 gage)	NA (1 test)	0.015
	Snaplock	0.04 to 0.14	0.11
	Grooved	0.11 to 0.18	0.12

Per Section 6.4.4.2.1 of ANSI/ANSI/ASHRAE/IES Standard 90.1, ductwork and all plenums with pressure class ratings must be constructed to Seal Class A. Openings for rotating shafts must be sealed with bushings or other devices that seal off air leakage. Pressure-sensitive tape must not be used as the primary sealant unless it has been certified to comply with UL-181A or UL-181B by an independent testing laboratory, and the tape is used in accordance with that certification. All connections must be sealed, including but not limited to spin-ins, taps, other branch connections, access doors, access panels, and duct connections to equipment. Sealing that would void product listings is not required. Spiral lock seams need not be sealed.

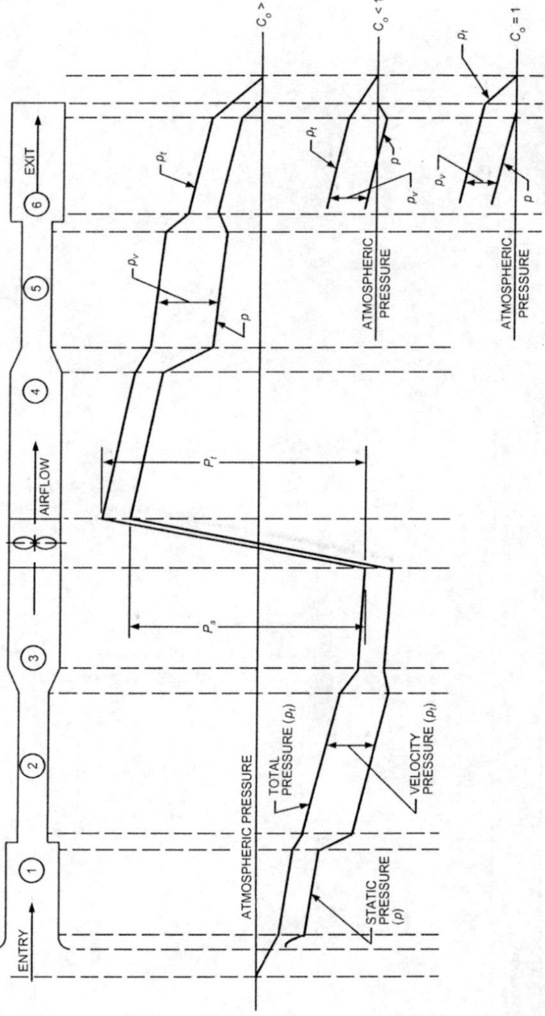

Figure 1.2 Pressure Changes During Flow in Ducts [2021F, Ch 21, Fig 6]

Table 1.6 Equivalent Rectangular Duct Dimensions for Equal Friction and Airflow* [2021F, Ch21, Tbl 3]

Circular Duct Diameter, in.	Length of One Side of Rectangular Duct *a*, in.																			
	4	5	6	7	8	9	10	12	14	16	18	20	22	24	26	28	30	32	34	36
	Length Adjacent Side of Rectangular Duct *b*, in.																			
5	5																			
5.5	6	5																		
6	8	6																		
6.5	9	7	6																	
7	11	8	7																	
7.5	13	10	8	7																
8	15	11	9	8																
8.5	17	13	10	9																
9	20	15	12	10	8															
9.5	22	17	13	11	9															
10	25	19	15	12	10	9														
10.5	29	21	16	14	12	10														
11	32	23	18	15	13	11	10													
11.5		26	20	17	14	12	11													
12		29	22	18	15	13	12													
12.5		32	24	20	17	15	13													
13		35	27	22	18	16	14	12												
13.5		38	29	24	20	17	15	13												
14			32	26	22	19	17	14												
14.5			35	28	24	20	18	15												
15			38	30	25	22	19	16	14											
16			45	36	30	25	22	18	15											
17				41	34	29	25	20	17	16										
18				47	39	33	29	23	19	17										
19				54	44	38	33	26	22	19	18									
20					50	43	37	29	24	21	19									
21					57	48	41	33	27	23	20									
22					64	54	46	36	30	26	23	20								
23						60	51	40	33	28	25	22								
24						66	57	44	36	31	27	24	22							
25							63	49	40	34	29	26	24							
26							69	54	44	37	32	28	26	24						
27							76	59	48	40	35	31	28	25						
28								64	52	43	38	33	30	27	26					

Table 1.6 Equivalent Rectangular Duct Dimensions for Equal Friction and Airflow* [2021F, Ch21, Tbl 3] ***(Continued)***

Circular Duct Diameter, in.	Length of One Side of Rectangular Duct a, in.																			
	4	5	6	7	8	9	10	12	14	16	18	20	22	24	26	28	30	32	34	36
	Length Adjacent Side of Rectangular Duct b, in.																			
29								70	56	47	41	36	32	29	27					
30								76	61	51	44	39	35	31	29	28				
31								82	66	55	47	41	37	34	31	29				
32								89	71	59	51	44	40	36	33	31				
33								96	76	64	54	48	42	38	35	33	30			
34									82	68	58	51	45	41	37	35	32			
35									88	73	62	54	48	44	40	37	34	32		
36									95	78	67	58	51	46	42	39	36	34		
37									101	83	71	62	55	49	45	41	38	36	34	
38									108	89	76	66	58	52	47	44	40	38	36	
39										95	80	70	62	55	50	46	43	40	37	36
40										101	85	74	65	58	53	49	45	42	39	37
41										107	91	78	69	62	56	51	47	44	41	39
42										114	96	83	73	65	59	54	50	46	44	41
43										120	102	88	77	69	62	57	53	49	46	43
44											107	93	81	73	66	60	55	51	48	45
45											113	98	86	76	69	63	58	54	50	47
46											120	103	90	80	72	66	61	56	53	49
47											126	108	95	84	76	69	64	59	55	52
48											133	114	100	89	80	73	67	62	58	54
49											140	120	105	93	84	76	70	65	60	56
50											147	126	110	98	88	80	73	68	63	59
51												132	115	102	92	83	76	71	66	61
52												139	121	107	96	87	80	74	69	64
53												145	127	112	100	91	83	77	71	67
54												152	133	117	105	95	87	80	74	70
55													139	123	110	99	91	84	78	72
56													145	128	114	104	95	87	81	75
57													151	134	119	108	98	91	84	78
58													158	139	124	112	102	94	87	81
59													165	145	130	117	107	98	91	85
60													172	151	135	122	111	102	94	88

*Table based on Equation 25 of Chapter 21 of 2021 *ASHRAE Handbook—Fundamentals*.

Table 1.7 Equivalent Flat Oval Dimensions* [2021F, Ch 21, Tbl 4]

Circular Duct Diameter, in.	Minor Axis *a*, in.																
	3	4	5	6	7	8	9	10	11	12	14	16	18	20	22	24	30
	Major Axis *A*, in.																
5	8																
5.5	9	7															
6	11,12																
6.5	14	9,10	8														
7	17	12		8													
7.5	19	13	10	9													
8	22	15	11														
8.5		17,18	13,14	11	10												
9		20,21		12		10											
9.5			16	14	12	11											
10			18,19	15	13												
10.5			21	17	15	13											
11				19	16	14	12	12									
11.5				20	18		14	13									
12				22,23		16,17	15	14									
12.5				25,26	20,21				14								
13				28		19	17	16		14							
13.5				30,31		21	18										
14				33		22	20	18	16,17	15							
14.5				34,36		24,25	22	19									
15				37		27	23	21	19	17,18							
15.5				41					20								
16				44,47		30,32		23,24	22	20							
17						33,35,36		26,27	24,25	21,23	20						
18						38,39		29,30		25,26	22						
19						43,46		32,34,35		28,29	23	22					
20						49,52		37,38,40		31,32	25,27	24					
21						55,58		41		34	28,30	25	23,24				
22						61		45,48		36,37,39	31,33	27,29	26				
23								51,54		40,43	34,36	30	27	26			

Table 1.7 Equivalent Flat Oval Dimensions* [2021F, Ch 21, Tbl 4] ***(Continued)***

Circular Duct Diameter, in.	Minor Axis *a*, in.																
	3	4	5	6	7	8	9	10	11	12	14	16	18	20	22	24	30
	Major Axis *A*, in.																
24								57,60		47	39	32,33	29	28			
25								63		50	42	35	31,32	29			
26								67,70,73		53,56	45	38	34,35	31			
27								76,79		59,62	49	41	37	33			
28										65	52,55	44	40	36			
29										69,72	58	47	43	39	35		
30										75,78	61,64	51,54	46	42	38		
31										81	67	57	49	45	41	37	
32											71,74	60	53	48		40	
33											77,80	66	56	51	44		
34												69	59,62		47	43	
35												73,76	65	55,58	50	46	
36												79	68	61	53	49	
37													71	64	57	52	43
38													75,78	67	60	55	
39													81	70,73	63	59	46
40														77	66,69	62	49
41														80	72	65	52
42															75	68	55
43															79	71	
44															82	74	58
45																77	61
46																81	65
47																	68
48																	71
49																	74
50																	77
51																	80
52																	81

*Table based on Equation (26) of Chapter 21 of 2021 *ASHRAE Handbook—Fundamentals*.

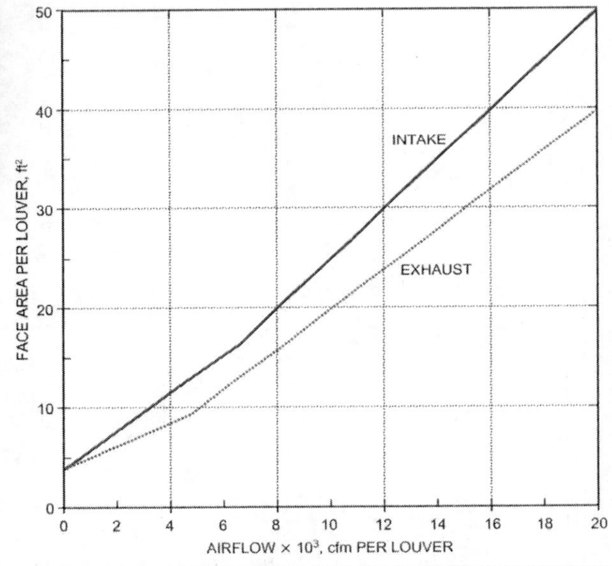

Parameters Used to Establish Figure	Intake Louver	Exhaust Louver
Minimum free area (48 in. square test section), %	45	45
Water penetration, oz/($ft^2 \cdot 0.25$ h)	Negligible (less than 0.01)	N/A
Maximum static pressure drop, in. of water	0.15	0.25

Figure 1.3 Criteria for Louver Sizing [2021F, Ch 21, Fig 18]

Table 1.8 Typical Design Velocities for HVAC Components

Duct Element	Face Velocity, fpm
Louvers	
Intake	
7000 cfm and greater	400
Less than 7000 cfm	See Figure 1.3 for criteria
Exhaust	
5000 cfm and greater	500
Less than 5000 cfm	See Figure 1.3 for criteria
Filters	
Panel filters	
Viscous impingement	200 to 800
Dry-type, extended-surface	
Flat (low efficiency)	Duct velocity
Pleated media (intermediate efficiency)	Up to 750
HEPA	250
Renewable media filters	
Moving-curtain viscous impingement	500
Moving-curtain dry media	200
Electronic air cleaners	
Ionizing type	150 to 350
Heating Coils	
Steam and hot water	500 to 1000 200 min., 1500 max.
Electric	
Open wire	Refer to mfg. data
Finned tubular	Refer to mfg. data
Dehumidifying Coils	400 to 500
Air Washers	
Spray type	Refer to mfg. data
Cell type	Refer to mfg. data
High-velocity spray type	1200 to 1800

Table 1.9 Fan Laws [a,b] [Adapted from 2020S, Ch 21, Tbl 2]
For All Fan Laws: $\eta_{t1} = \eta_{t2}$ and (point of rating)$_1$ = (point of rating)$_2$

No.	Dependent Variables	Independent Variables	
1a	$Q_1 = Q_2$	$\times\left(\frac{D_1}{D_2}\right)^3 \times \frac{N_1}{N_2}$	$\times 1$
1b	Pressure$_1$ = Pressure$_2$[c]	$\times\left(\frac{D_1}{D_2}\right)^2 \times \left(\frac{N_1}{N_2}\right)^2$	$\times \frac{\rho_1}{\rho_2}$
1c	$W_1 = W_2$	$\times\left(\frac{D_1}{D_2}\right)^5 \times \left(\frac{N_1}{N_2}\right)^3$	$\times \frac{\rho_1}{\rho_2}$
2a	$Q_1 = Q_2$	$\times\left(\frac{D_1}{D_2}\right)^2 \times \left(\frac{\text{Press.}_1}{\text{Press.}_2}\right)^{1/2}$	$\times\left(\frac{\rho_2}{\rho_1}\right)^{1/2}$
2b	$N_1 = N_2$	$\times\left(\frac{D_2}{D_1}\right) \times \left(\frac{\text{Press.}_1}{\text{Press.}_2}\right)^{1/2}$	$\times\left(\frac{\rho_2}{\rho_1}\right)^{1/2}$
2c	$W_1 = W_2$	$\times\left(\frac{D_1}{D_2}\right)^2 \times \left(\frac{\text{Press.}_1}{\text{Press.}_2}\right)^{3/2}$	$\times\left(\frac{\rho_2}{\rho_1}\right)^{1/2}$
3a	$N_1 = N_2$	$\times\left(\frac{D_2}{D_1}\right)^3 \times \frac{Q_1}{Q_2}$	$\times 1$
3b	Pressure$_1$ = Pressure$_2$	$\times\left(\frac{D_2}{D_1}\right)^4 \times \left(\frac{Q_1}{Q_2}\right)^2$	$\times \frac{\rho_1}{\rho_2}$
3c	$W_1 = W_2$	$\times\left(\frac{D_2}{D_1}\right)^4 \times \left(\frac{Q_1}{Q_2}\right)^3$	$\times \frac{\rho_1}{\rho_2}$

where
D = fan size
N = rotational speed
ρ = gas density
Q = volumetric airflow rate
P = pressure
η = fan efficiency
W = power

a. The subscript 1 denotes that the variable is for the fan under consideration.
b. The subscript 2 denotes that the variable is for the tested fan.
c. Fan total pressure P_{tf}, fan velocity pressure P_{vf}, or fan static pressure P_{sf}.

Unless otherwise identified, fan performance data are based on dry air at standard conditions 14.696 psi and 70°F (0.075 lb_m/ft^3). In actual applications, the fan may be required to handle air or gas at some other density. The change in density may be because of temperature, composition of the gas, or altitude. As indicated by the Fan Laws, the fan performance is affected by gas density. With constant size and speed, the horsepower and pressure varies directly as the ratio of gas density to the standard air density.

The application of the Fan Laws for a change in fan speed N for a specific size fan is shown in Figure 1.4. The computed P_t curve is derived from the base curve. For example, point E(N_1 = 650) is computed from point D(N_2= 600) as follows:

At D,

$$Q_2 = 6000 \text{ cfm and } P_{tf_2} = 1.13 \text{ in. of water} \tag{1.2}$$

Using Fan Law 1a at Point E

$$Q_1 = 6000(650/600) = 6500 \text{ cfm} \tag{1.3}$$

Using Fan Law 1b

$$P_{tf_1} = 1.13 \times (650/600)^2 = 1.33 \text{ psi} \tag{1.4}$$

The completed P_{tf_1}, N = 650 curve thus may be generated by computing additional points from data on the base curve, such as point G from point F.

$$\text{hp} = \frac{\text{cfm} \times \text{static pressure, in. of water}}{\text{fan efficiency (decimal)} \times 6356} \tag{1.5}$$

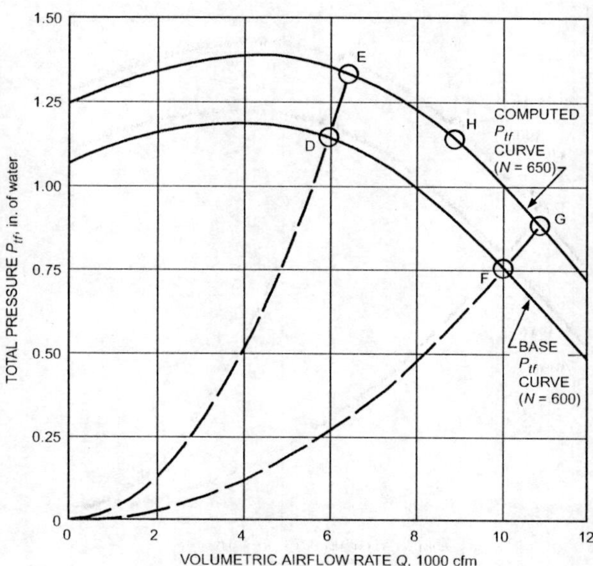

Figure 1.4 Example Application of Fan Laws [2020S, Ch 21, Fig 4]

Table 1.10 Types of Fans [2020S, Ch 21, Tbl 1]

	Type	Impeller Design	Housing Design	Performance Characteristics	Applications
Centrifugal Fans	Backward-Inclined (includes AF, BC, and BI)	Blades inclined away from direction of rotation and can be single-thickness flat (BI), single-thickness curved (BC), or airfoil (AF) contour. Deep blades allow efficient expansion in blade passages. Air leaves impeller at velocity less than tip speed. For given duty, has highest speed of centrifugal fan designs.	Single- or double-inlet scroll design for efficient conversion of tangential velocity pressure to static pressure. Maximum efficiency requires close clearance and alignment between impeller and inlet.	Highest efficiency of all centrifugal fan designs, with peak efficiencies occurring at 50 to 60% of wide-open volume. Fan has a non-overloading characteristic, which means power reaches maximum near peak efficiency and becomes lower, or self-limiting, toward free delivery. Airfoil blades are most efficient, followed by curved and then flat blades.	General HVAC. Used in ducted applications covering a large range of pressures. Airfoil blades can be used for clean air industrial operations. For industrial applications where the environment may corrode or erode airfoil blades, consider using single thickness blades instead.
	Radial and Radial Tipped	Blades are either fully radial (R) or backward inclined with a radial curve at outer edge (RT). Fully radial blades can have back plate and shroud, back plate only, or neither (open). Radial tipped blades normally have back plate and shroud.	Single or double inlet scroll similar to other centrifugal fan designs. Fit between impeller and inlet not as critical as for backward inclined fans.	Higher pressure characteristics than airfoil and backward curved fans. Power rises continually to free delivery, which is an overloading characteristic. Radial tipped blades are slightly more efficient than straight blades. Shrouded impellers are more efficient than nonshrouded.	Primarily for material handling in industrial plants where high duct velocities are required to keep materials airborne. Also for some high-pressure industrial requirements. Rugged impeller is simple to repair in the field. Choice of impeller type generally depends on materials being transported. Impeller sometimes coated with special material.

Table 1.10 Types of Fans [2020S, Ch 21, Tbl 1] ***(Continued)***

	Type	Impeller Design	Housing Design	Performance Characteristics	Applications
Centrifugal Fans *(Continued)*	Forward-Curved	Large number of thin curved blades with outer edge tipped toward direction of rotation. Air leaves impeller with a high tangential velocity. Relies on scroll housing to convert this velocity pressure to static pressure. For given duty, has lowest speed of centrifugal fan designs.	Single or double inlet scroll shaped design necessary for conversion of tangential velocity pressure to static pressure. Fit between impeller and inlet not as critical as for backward inclined fans.	Pressure curve less steep than that of backward-inclined fans. Curve dips to left of peak pressure. Highest efficiency occurs at 40 to 50% of wide open volume. Operate fan to right of peak pressure. Power rises continually to free delivery which is an overloading characteristic.	Primarily for low- to medium-pressure HVAC applications, such as residential furnaces, central station units, and packaged air conditioners. Slower speed and lower tonal noise characteristics allow them to be used closer to occupied spaces. A possible exception is central station air handling units because of low frequency noise that is more difficult to attenuate.
	Plenum/Plug	Single inlet centrifugal impellers can be airfoil, backward curved, or backward inclined. Mixed flow or radial impellers can also be used for specific applications. AF BC BI	No integral housing. The equivalent of a housing, or plenum chamber (dashed line), depends on the application. Due to the lack of a housing, all pressure development occurs in the impeller. The components of the drive system for the plug fan are located outside the airstream. PLENUM PLUG	Similar to housed airfoil/backward curved/backward inclined fans but slightly less efficient due to the lack of conversion of kinetic energy in the discharge airstream. Because plenum and plug fans do not have usable outlet velocity pressure, they should always be selected based on fan static pressure. Both fans are susceptible to performance degradation caused by poor inlet installation and insufficient clearance to surrounding walls.	Plenum fans are used for HVAC equipment such as air handlers. Advantages include flexibility of equipment discharge and potential for smaller equipment footprint. Multiple plenum fans in parallel (fan arrays) can be used to further reduce the axial length of air handling equipment. Plug fans are commonly used for high-temperature process applications.

Table 1.10 Types of Fans [2020S, Ch 21, Tbl 1] ***(Continued)***

	Type	Impeller Design	Housing Design	Performance Characteristics	Applications
Axial Fans	Propeller	Small number of blades (two to six), either airfoil or single thickness curved, attached to a relatively small hub.	Simple circular ring, orifice plate, or venturi. Optimum design is close to blade tips and forms smooth airflow into impeller. Improved static efficiency can be obtained with an extension of the venturi into an expanding conical discharge.	High flow rate, but very low pressure capabilities. Discharge pattern circular or conical and airstream swirls.	For low-pressure, high-volume air-moving applications, such as ventilation through a wall without ductwork or air-cooled condenser fans.
	Tubeaxial	Usually has four to eight blades with airfoil or single thickness cross section. Blades may have fixed or adjustable pitch. Hub is usually less than half the fan tip diameter.	Cylindrical tube with close clearance to blade tips. Free inlet applications should use a bell mouth inlet to minimize entrance losses.	High flow rate, medium pressure capabilities. Pressure curve can dip to left of peak pressure at higher blade pitches. Avoid operating fan in this stall region. Discharge pattern circular and airstream rotates or swirls downstream of fan.	Low- and medium-pressure ducted HVAC applications where straight through flow and compact installation are required. Used in some industrial applications, such as drying ovens, paint spray booths, and fume exhausts.
	Vaneaxial	Typically has more blades than tubeaxial fans. Blades may have fixed, adjustable, or controllable pitch. Hub is usually greater than half fan tip diameter. Most efficient designs have airfoil blades.	Cylindrical tube with close clearance to blade tips. Guide vanes upstream or downstream from impeller increase pressure capability and efficiency.	High pressure characteristics with medium volume flow capabilities. Pressure curve can dip to left of peak pressure. Avoid operating fan in this stall region. Guide vanes correct circular motion imparted by impeller, which improves pressure characteristics and fan efficiency.	General HVAC systems in medium- and high-pressure applications where straight-through flow and compact installation are required. Has swirl-free downstream airflow. Used in industrial applications in place of tubeaxial fans. More compact than centrifugal fans for same duty.

Table 1.10 Types of Fans [2020S, Ch 21, Tbl 1] ***(Continued)***

	Type	Impeller Design	Housing Design	Performance Characteristics	Applications
Mixed-Flow	Mixed-Flow	Combination of axial and centrifugal characteristics. Contoured back or hub; airfoil, curved, or straight blades, either shrouded or not. Airflow through impeller has both radial and axial components.	The majority of mixed-flow fans have a tubular housing for use in ducted applications and include outlet turning vanes.	Characteristic pressure curve between axial fans and centrifugal fans. Higher pressure than axial fans and higher-volume flow than centrifugal fans.	Similar HVAC applications to centrifugal fans or in applications where an axial fan cannot generate sufficient pressure rise.
Cross-flow	Cross-flow (Tangential)	Impeller with forward-curved blades. Typically impeller width is much greater than diameter.	Specially designed housing for 90° or straight-through airflow. Housing causes air to enter the impeller at its periphery, flow through the impeller, and discharge at a different point of its periphery.	Similar to forward-curved fans. Power rises continually to free delivery, which is an overloading characteristic. Lowest efficiency of any centrifugal fan type.	Low-pressure HVAC components (e.g., fan heaters, fireplace inserts, electronic cooling, air curtains) where a long, narrow discharge is needed.

Table 1.10 Types of Fans [2020S, Ch 21, Tbl 1] ***(Continued)***

	Type	Impeller Design	Housing Design	Performance Characteristics	Applications
Other Designs	Inline Centrifugal	Single-inlet centrifugal impellers can be airfoil, backward curved, or backward inclined. AF BC BI	Cylindrical tube similar to vaneaxial fan, except clearance to impeller is not as close. Air discharges radially from impeller and turns 90° to flow through guide vanes. Variations include cylindrical and square housings with or without guide vanes. Square housings can include side discharge.	Performance similar to backward-inclined fan, except capacity and pressure are lower. Lower efficiency than backward-inclined fan because air turns 90°.	Ducted HVAC applications with air discharging in axial direction (e.g., low- to medium-pressure return air systems in HVAC applications).
	Power Roof Ventilators – Centrifugal	Single-inlet centrifugal impellers can be airfoil, backward curved, or backward inclined. AF BC BI	Weather-protected housing with means of mounting to a building opening. Usually does not include configuration to recover velocity pressure component. Radial discharge from impeller can be directed either toward building or away from building.	Less efficient than scroll-type housed fan. Centrifugal units are slightly quieter than axial units.	Low-pressure ducted exhaust systems (e.g., general factory, kitchen, warehouse, some commercial installations).

Table 1.10 Types of Fans [2020S, Ch 21, Tbl 1] ***(Continued)***

Type			Impeller Design	Housing Design	Performance Characteristics	Applications
Other Designs *(Continued)*	Power Roof Ventilators *(Continued)*	Axial	Small number of blades (two to six), similar to an axial propeller fan.	Similar housing to an axial propeller fan with added weather protection and means of mounting to a building opening. Can supply or exhaust air from a building, and housing can direct air either toward building or away from building.	Usually installed without ductwork; therefore, operates at very low pressure and high volume.	Low-pressure exhaust or supply systems (e.g., general factory, kitchen, warehouse, some commercial installations).
		Induced-Flow	Centrifugal backward inclined or mixed flow. AF BC BI MF	Can be scroll or tubular inline with converging cone or nozzle to increase nozzle velocity, which induces additional airflow through outlet. OUTLET AIRFLOW INDUCED AIRFLOW INLET AIRFLOW	Performance similar to BI and MF but with reduced efficiency due to high velocity needed for induction. Outlet airflow greater than inlet airflow.	Typically used for laboratory or hazardous chemical exhaust where dilution is required and tall stacks are not desired.

Table 1.10 Types of Fans [2020S, Ch 21, Tbl 1] ***(Continued)***

		Type	Impeller Design	Housing Design	Performance Characteristics	Applications
Other Designs (*Continued*)	Jet Fan	Centrifugal	Single-inlet centrifugal impellers can be airfoil, backward curved, or backward inclined. (AF, BC, BI)	Rectangular, low profile. Outlet tapers to increase discharge velocity. May contain outlet straighteners and inlet protection guards.	Performance measured and rated in thrust F_t. Designed for high-velocity discharge to add momentum to larger volume of air. Note that performance curves shown are not at a single speed, but at variable speeds N.	Unducted for space-constrained parking garages and emergency fire and smoke evacuation. Comparable initial cost with ducted solutions but more flexibility for exhaust and inlet air locations.
		Axial	Could be bidirectional or reversible in operation; similar flow rates in either direction is common.	Tubular housing may or may not have guide vanes. Typically fitted with inlet and outlet silencers and protection screens. (AIRFLOW)	Performance measured and rated in thrust F_t. Designed for high-velocity discharge to add momentum to larger volume of air. Typically operates at high speed, which necessitates inlet and outlet silencers. Note that performance curves shown are not at a single speed, but at variable speeds N.	Road or rail tunnels, parking garages, and emergency fire and smoke evacuation. Comparable initial cost with ducted solutions but more flexibility for the exhaust and inlet air locations.
		Circulating	Includes small propeller fans up to large-diameter ceiling mounted fans. Typically two to eight blades, either airfoil or single-thickness curved, attached to a comparatively small-diameter hub.	Often unhoused, but can have housing.	Performance typically measured and rated in airflow rate versus input power and impeller rotational speed N. Usually operated at free air with high-volume flow rate. Note that performance curves shown are not at a single speed, but at variable speeds.	Used for generating elevated air speeds to provide cooling of people or animals and prevent stratification of temperature or humidity (e.g., inside warehouses, airports, gymnasiums, barns). Can also be used for drying processes.

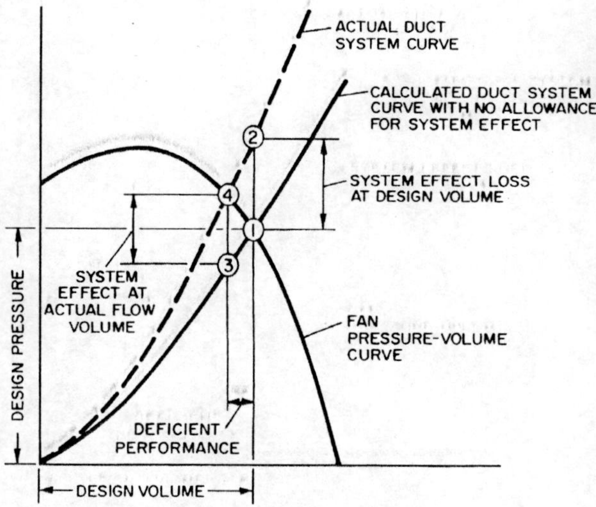

Figure 1.5 Deficient Fan/System Performance

Figure 1.5 illustrates deficient fan/system performance. System pressure losses have been determined accurately, and a fan has been selected for operation at point 1. However, no allowance has been made for the effect on fan performance of system connections. To compensate, a fan system effect must be added to the calculated system pressure losses to determine the actual system curve. The point of intersection between the fan performance curve and the actual system curve is point 4. The actual flow volume is, therefore, deficient by the difference from 1 to 4. To achieve design flow volume, a fan system effect pressure loss equal to the pressure difference between points 1 and 2 should be added to the calculated system pressure losses, and the fan should be selected to operate at point 2.

For rated performance, air must enter a fan uniformly over the inlet area in an axial direction without prerotation.

Fans within plenums and cabinets or next to walls should be located so that air may flow unobstructed into the inlets.

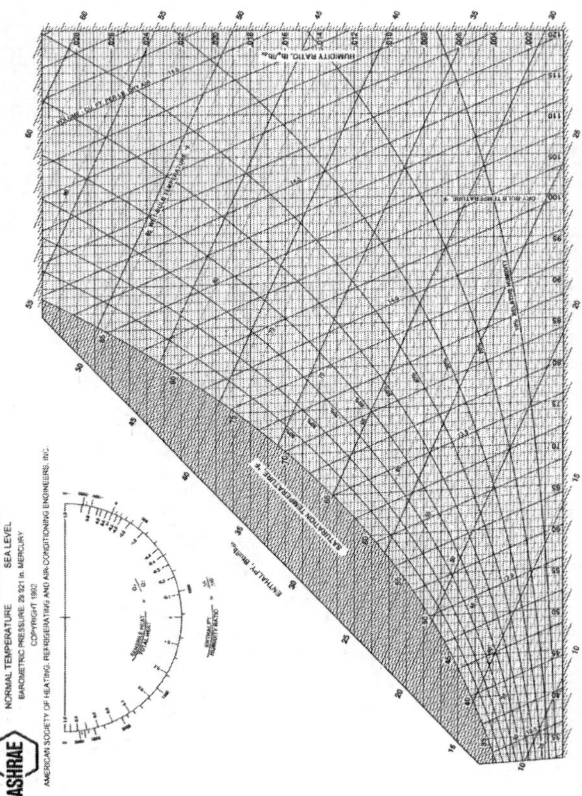

Figure 1.6 Psychrometric Chart for Normal Temperature, Sea Level
[2021F, Ch 1, Fig 2]

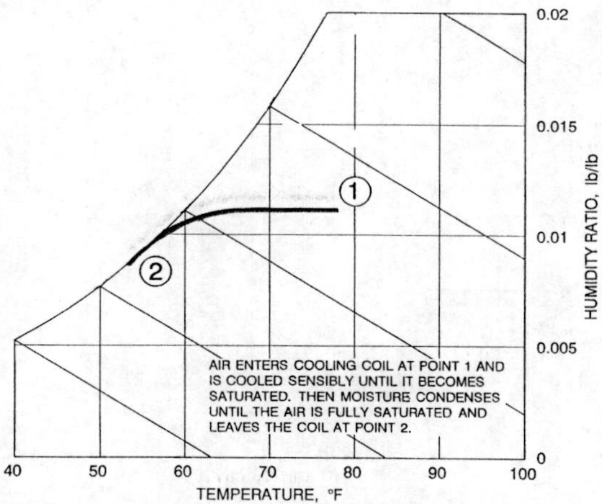

Figure 1.7 Direct Expansion or Chilled Water Cooling and Dehumidification

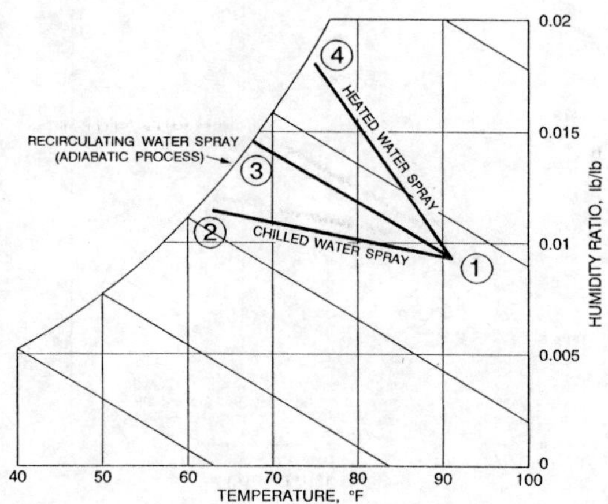

Figure 1.8 Water Spray Cooling

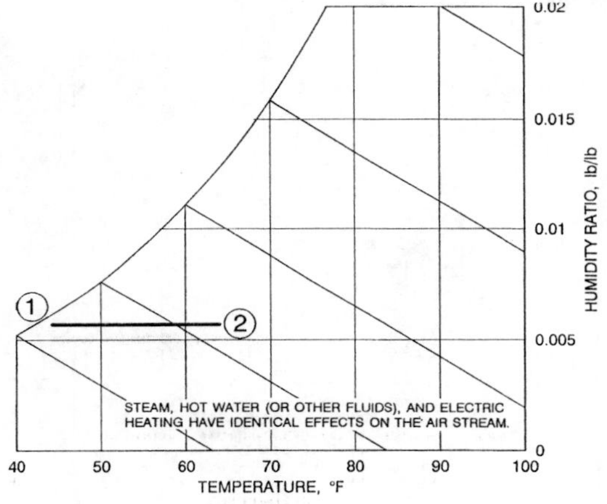

Figure 1.9 Steam, Hot-Water, or Electric Heating

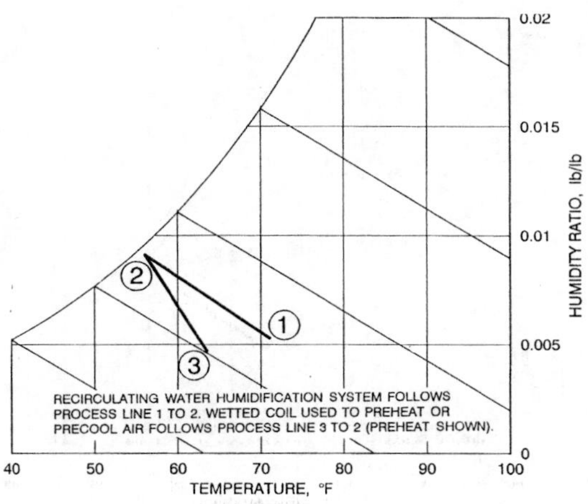

Figure 1.10 Water Humidification

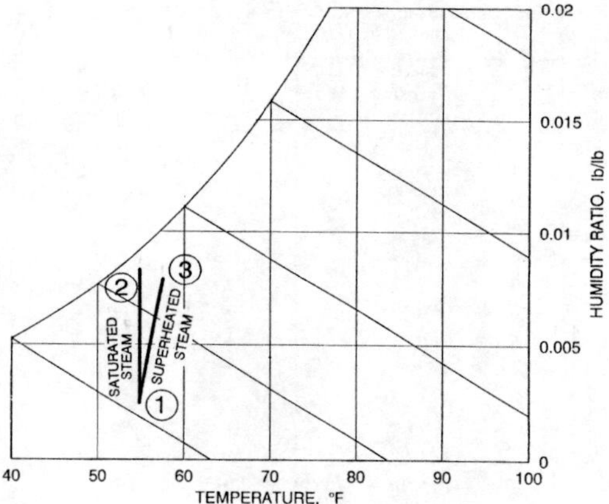

Figure 1.11 Steam Humidification

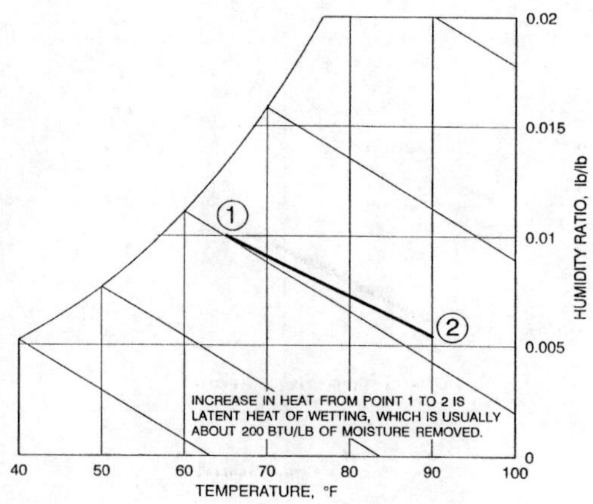

Figure 1.12 Chemical Dehumidification

Table 1.11 Specific Enthalpy of Moist Air at Standard Atmospheric Pressure, 14.696 psia
[Adapted from 2021F, Ch 1, Tbl 2]

Temp., °F	Specific Enthalpy, Btu/lb_{da}	Temp., °F	Specific Enthalpy, Btu/lb_{da}
−80	−19.213	79	42.634
−70	−16.804	80	43.701
−60	−14.390	81	44.794
−50	−11.966	82	45.914
−40	−9.524	83	47.062
−30	−7.052	84	48.239
−20	−4.527	85	49.445
−15	−3.234	86	50.682
−10	−1.915	87	51.950
−5	−0.561	88	53.250
0	0.835	89	54.584
5	2.286	90	55.952
10	3.803	91	57.355
15	5.403	92	58.795
20	7.106	93	60.272
25	8.934	94	61.787
30	10.916	95	63.343
35	13.009	96	64.939
40	15.232	97	66.578
45	17.653	98	68.260
50	20.306	99	69.987
55	23.229	100	71.761
60	26.467	110	92.386
65	30.070	120	119.615
70	34.097	130	156.077
71	34.959	140	205.828
72	35.841	150	275.493
73	36.744	160	376.736
74	37.668	170	532.269
75	38.615	180	793.142
76	39.584	190	1303.297
77	40.576	200	2688.145
78	41.593		

Table 1.12 Standard Atmospheric Data for Altitudes to 30,000 ft
[2021F, Ch 1, Tbl 1]

Altitude, ft	Temperature, °F	Pressure, psia
–1000	62.6	15.236
–500	60.8	14.966
0	59.0	14.696
500	57.2	14.430
1,000	55.4	14.175
2,000	51.9	13.664
3,000	48.3	13.173
4,000	44.7	12.682
5,000	41.2	12.230
6,000	37.6	11.778
7,000	34.0	11.341
8,000	30.5	10.914
9,000	26.9	10.506
10,000	23.4	10.108
15,000	5.5	8.296
20,000	–12.3	6.758
30,000	–47.8	4.371

Source: Adapted from NASA (1976).

Table 1.13 Moisture and Air Relationships*

ASHRAE has adopted pounds of moisture per pound of dry air as standard nomenclature. Relations of other units are expressed below at various dew-point temperatures.

Equiv. Dew Pt. °F	Lb H_2O/ lb dry air	Parts per million	Grains/ lb dry air[a]	Percent Moisture%[b]
–100	0.000001	1	0.0007	—
–80	0.000005	5	0.0035	—
–60	0.000002	21	0.148	0.13
–40	0.000008	79	0.555	0.5
–20	0.00026	263	1.84	1.7
–10	0.00046	461	3.22	2.9
0	0.0008	787	5.51	5.0
10	0.0013	1315	9.20	8.3
20	0.0022	2152	15.1	13.6
30	0.0032	3154	24.2	21.8
40	0.0052	5213	36.5	33.0
50	0.0077	7658	53.6	48.4
60	0.0111	11080	77.6	70.2
70	0.0158	15820	110.7	100.0
80	0.0223	22330	156.3	—
90	0.0312	31180	218.3	—
100	0.0432	43190	302.3	—

a. 7000 grains = 1 lb
b. Compared to 70°F saturated.
* *NUMBERS*, 1985, Altadena, CA, by Bill Holladay and Cy Otterholm.

Space Air Diffusion

Room air diffusion methods can be classified as one of the following:

- **Fully mixed systems** produce little or no thermal stratification of air within the space. Overhead air distribution is an example of this type of system.
- **Fully (thermally) stratified systems** produce little or no mixing of air within the occupied space. Thermal displacement ventilation is an example of this type of system.
- **Partially mixed systems** provide some mixing within the occupied and/or process space while creating stratified conditions in the volume above. Most underfloor air distribution and task/ambient conditioning designs are examples of this type of system.

Local temperature and carbon dioxide (CO_2) concentration have similar stratification profiles.

Air distribution systems, such as thermal displacement ventilation (TDV) and underfloor air distribution (UFAD), that deliver air in cooling mode at or near floor level and return air at or near ceiling level produce varying amounts of room air stratification. For floor-level supply, thermal plumes that develop over heat sources in the room play a major role in driving overall floor-to-ceiling air motion. The amount of stratification in the room is primarily determined by the balance between total room airflow and heat load. In practice, the actual temperature and concentration profile depends on the combined effects of various factors, but is largely driven by the characteristics of the room supply airflow and heat load configuration.

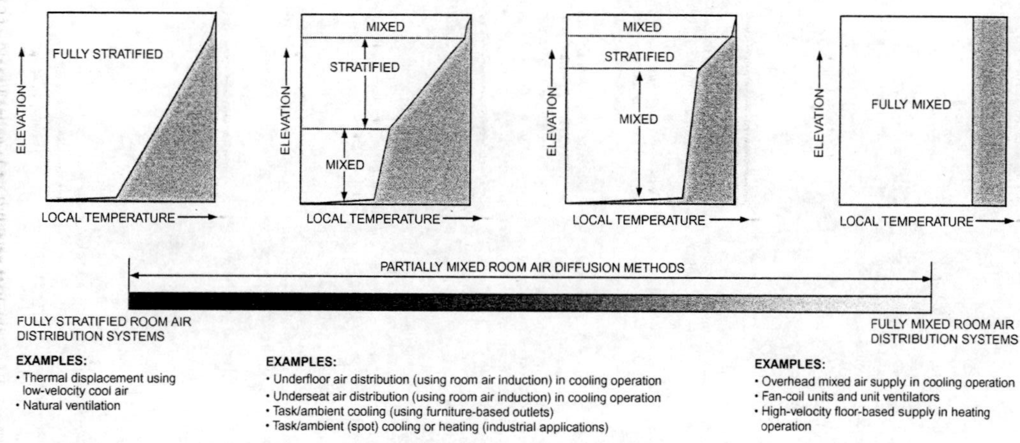

Figure 1.13 Classification of Air Diffusion Methods [2021F, Ch 20, Fig 1]

Principles of Jet Behavior

Air Jet Fundamentals

Air supplied to rooms through various types of outlets can be distributed by turbulent air jets (mixed and partially mixed systems) or in a low-velocity, unidirectional manner (stratified systems).

If an air jet is not obstructed or affected by walls, ceiling, or other surfaces, it is considered a **free jet**. When outlet area is small compared to the dimensions of the space normal to the jet, the jet may be considered free as long as

$$X \leq 1.5\sqrt{A_R} \tag{1.6}$$

where

X	=	distance from face of outlet, ft
A_R	=	cross-sectional area of confined space normal to jet, ft^2

Characteristics of the air jet in a room might be influenced by reverse flows created by the same jet entraining ambient air. If the supply air temperature is equal to the ambient room air temperature, the air jet is called an **isothermal jet**. A jet with an initial temperature different from the ambient air temperature is called a **nonisothermal jet**. The air temperature differential between supplied and ambient room air generates thermal forces (buoyancy) in jets, affecting the jet's (1) trajectory, (2) location at which it attaches to and separates from the ceiling/floor, and (3) throw. The significance of these effects depends on the ratio between the thermal buoyancy of the air and jet momentum.

Jet Expansion Zones. The full length of an air jet, in terms of the maximum or centerline velocity and temperature differential at the cross section, can be divided into four zones:

- **Zone 1** is a short core zone extending from the outlet face, in which the maximum velocity and temperature of the airstream remains practically unchanged.
- **Zone 2** is a transition zone, with its length determined by the type of outlet, aspect ratio of the outlet, initial airflow turbulence, etc.
- **Zone 3** is a zone of jet degradation, where centerline air velocity and temperature decrease rapidly. Turbulent flow is fully established and may be 25 to 100 equivalent air outlet diameters (i.e., widths of slot air diffusers) long.
- **Zone 4** is of major engineering importance because, in most cases, the jet enters the occupied area in this zone. Distance to this zone and its length depend on the velocities and turbulence characteristics of ambient air. In a few diameters or widths, air velocity becomes less than 50 fpm.

Centerline Velocities in Zones 1 and 2. In zone 1, the ratio V_x/V_o is constant and ranges between 1.0 and 1.2, equal to the ratio of the center velocity of the jet at the start of expansion to the average velocity. The ratio V_x/V_o varies from approximately 1.0 for rounded entrance nozzles to about 1.2 for straight pipe discharges; it has much higher values for diverging discharge outlets.

Experimental evidence indicates that, in zone 2,

$$\frac{V_x}{V_o} = \sqrt{\frac{K_{c2}H_o}{X}} \tag{1.7}$$

where

V_x	=	centerline velocity at distance X from outlet, fpm
V_o	=	$V_c/C_d\,R_{fa}$ = average initial velocity at discharge, fpm
V_c	=	nominal velocity of discharge based on core area, fpm
C_d	=	discharge coefficient (usually between 0.65 and 0.90)
R_{fa}	=	ratio of free area to gross (core) area
H_o	=	width of jet at outlet or at vena contracta, ft
K_{c2}	=	centerline velocity constant, depending on outlet type and discharge pattern
X	≥	$(1/K_{c2}H_o)^{1/2}$ = distance from outlet to measurement of centerline velocity V_x, ft

Centerline Velocity in Zone 3. In zone 3, centerline velocities of radial and axial isothermal jets can be determined accurately from Equation 1.8:

$$V_x = \frac{K_{c3} V_o \sqrt{A_o}}{X} = \frac{K_{c3} Q_o}{X \sqrt{A_o}} \tag{1.8}$$

where

K_{c3}	=	centerline velocity constant (see Table 1.14 for generic values)
V_o	=	$V_c/C_d R_{fa}$ = average initial velocity at discharge, fpm
A_o	=	free area, core area, or neck area as shown in Table 1.14 (obtained from outlet manufacturer), ft^2
A_c	=	measured gross (core) area of outlet, ft^2
Q_o	=	volumetric flow rate of supply air, cfm
X	=	distance from face of outlet, ft

The effective area, according to ANSI/ASHRAE Standard 70, can be used in place of A_o in Equation 1.8 with the appropriate value of K_{c3}.

Throw. Equation 1.8 can be transposed to determine the throw X of an outlet if the discharge volume and the centerline velocity are known:

$$X = \frac{K_{c3} Q_o}{V_x \sqrt{A_o}} \tag{1.9}$$

Comparison of Free Jet to Attached Jet

Most manufacturers' throw data obtained in accordance with ANSI/ASHRAE Standard 70 assume the discharge is attached to a surface. An attached jet induces air along the exposed side of the jet, whereas a free jet can induce air on all its surfaces. Because a free jet's induction rate is larger compared to that of an attached jet, a free jet's throw distance will be shorter. To calculate the throw distance X for a noncircular free jet from catalog data for an attached jet, the following estimate can be used.

$$X_{free} = X_{attached} \times 0.707 \tag{1.10}$$

Circular free jets generally have longer throws compared to noncircular jets.

Jets from ceiling diffusers initially tend to attach to the ceiling surface, because of the force exerted by the Coanda effect. However, cold air jets will detach from the ceiling if the airstream's buoyancy forces are greater than the inertia of the moving air stream.

Table 1.14 Generic Values for Centerline Velocity Constant K_{c3}[a] for Commercial Supply Outlets for Fully and Partially Mixed Systems, Except UFAD [2021F, Ch 20, Tbl 1]

Outlet Type	Discharge Pattern	A_o	K_{c3}[a]
High sidewall grilles (2021F, Ch 20, Fig 4)	0° deflection[b]	Free	5.7
	Wide deflection	Free	4.2
High sidewall linear	Core less than 4 in. high[c]	Free	4.4
	Core more than 4 in. high	Free	5.0
Low sidewall (2021F, Ch 20, Fig 7)	Up and on wall, no deflection	Free	4.5
	Wide deflection	Free	3.0
Baseboard	Up and on wall, no deflection	Core	4.0
	Wide deflection	Core	2.0
Floor grille (2021F, Ch 20, Fig 5)	No deflection	Free	4.7
	Wide deflection	Free	1.6
Ceiling (2021F, Ch 20, Fig 2)	360° horizontal[d]	Neck	1.1
	Four-way; little deflection	Neck	3.8
Ceiling linear slot (2021F, Ch 20, Fig 3)	Horizontal/vertical along surface[c]	Free	5.5
	Horizontal/vertical free jet[c]	Free	3.9
	Free jet (air curtain units)	Free	6.0

[a]Generic values shown for example purposes only. See manufacturer's data for specific K_{c3} values.
[b]Free area is about 80% of core area.
[c]Free area is about 50% of core area.
[d]Cone free area is greater than duct area.

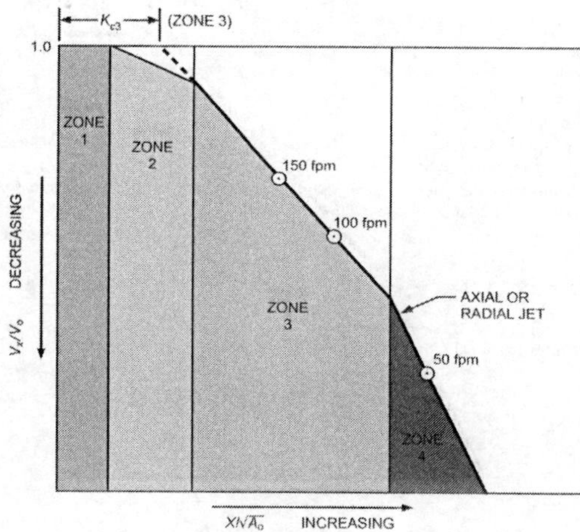

Figure 1.14 Zones of Expansion for Axial or Radial Air Jets
[2021F, Ch 20, Fig 11]

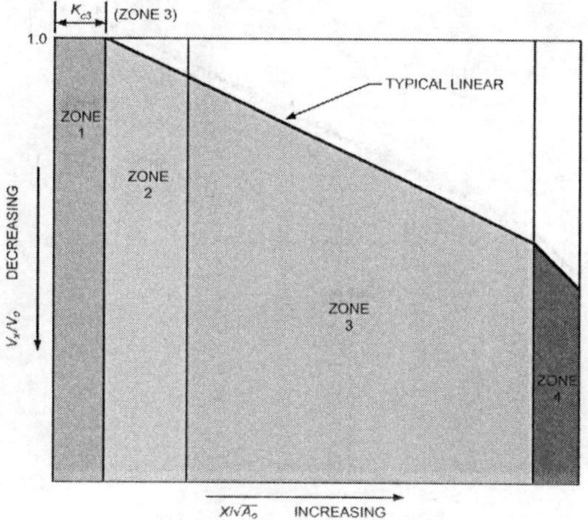

Figure 1.15 Zones of Expansion for Linear Air Jets
[2021F, Ch 20, Fig 12]

Outlet Types and Characteristics

Straub and Chen (1957) and Straub et al. (1956) classified outlets into five major groups (the subgrouping was added in 2017 and was not part of the original research):

- **Group A1.** Outlets mounted in or near the ceiling that discharge air horizontally (Figures 1.16 and 1.17).
- **Group A2.** Outlets discharging horizontally that are not influenced by an adjacent surface (free jet; Figure 1.18).
- **Group B.** Outlets mounted in or near the floor that discharge air vertically in a linear jet (Figure 1.19).
- **Group C.** Outlets mounted in or near the floor that discharge air vertically in a spreading jet (Figure 1.20).
- **Group D.** Outlets mounted in or near the floor that discharge air horizontally (Figures 1.21 and 1.22).
- **Group E.** Outlets that project supply air vertically downward (Figures 1.23 and 1.24). When used in partially stratified systems (e.g., laminar flow outlets, TDV), these outlets use low discharge velocities; in mixed systems (e.g., air curtain units, other downward directed ceiling devices, etc.), they use higher discharge velocities.

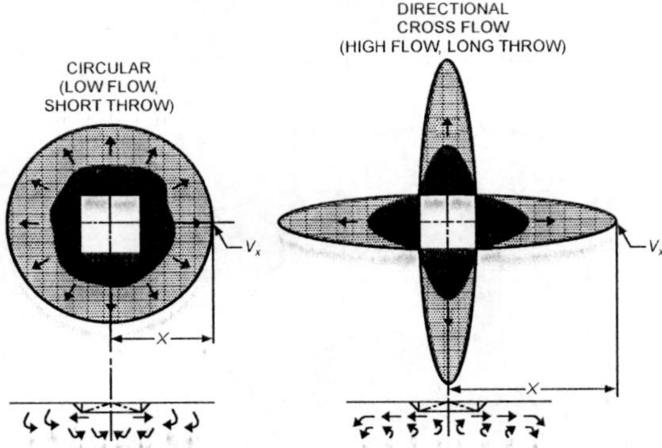

Figure 1.16 Example Airflow Patterns of Outlet Group A1 [2021F, Ch 20, Fig 2]

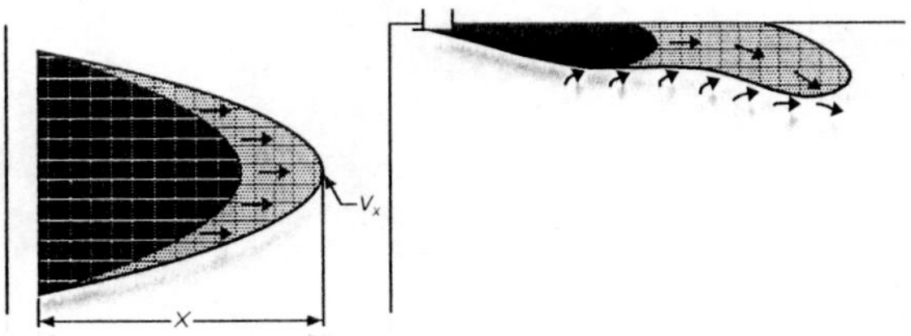

Figure 1.17 Example Airflow Patterns (Nonisothermal) of Outlet Group A1 [2021F, Ch 20, Fig 3]

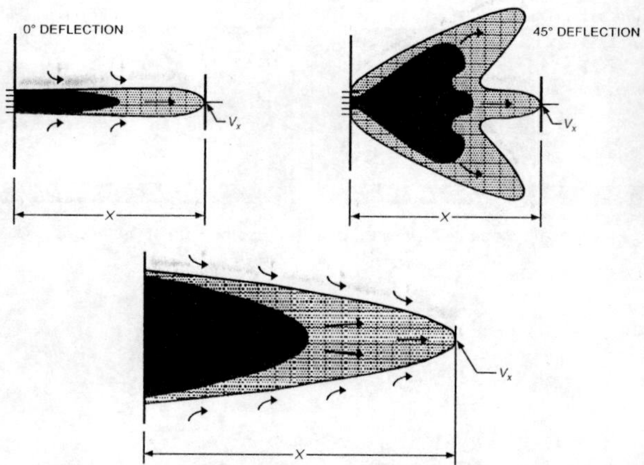

Figure 1.18 Example Airflow Patterns (Isothermal) of Outlet Group A2
[2021F, Ch 20, Fig 4]

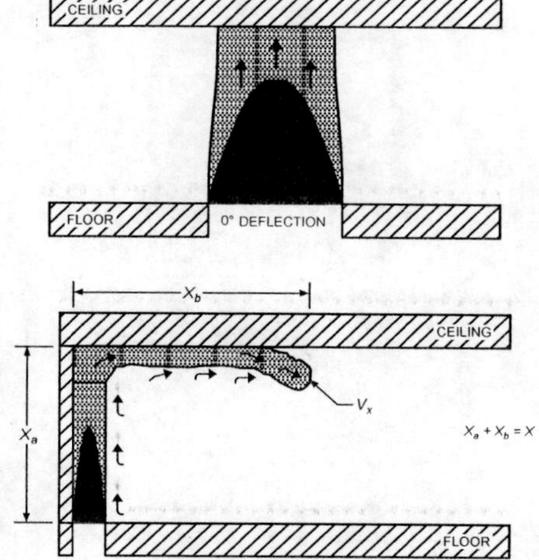

Figure 1.19 Example Airflow Patterns (Nonisothermal) of Outlet Group B
[2021F, Ch 20, Fig 5]

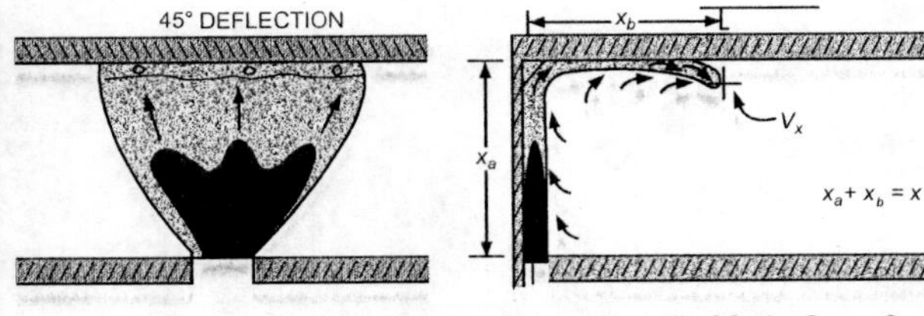

Figure 1.20 Example Airflow Patterns (Nonisothermal) of Outlet Group C [2021F, Ch 20, Fig 6]

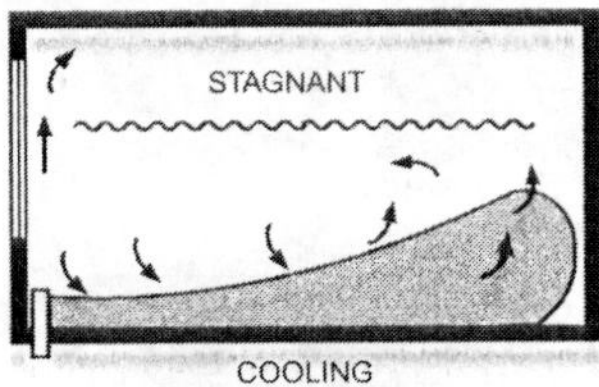

Figure 1.21 Example Airflow Patterns (Nonisothermal) of Outlet Group D (High Velocity) [2021F, Ch 20, Fig 7]

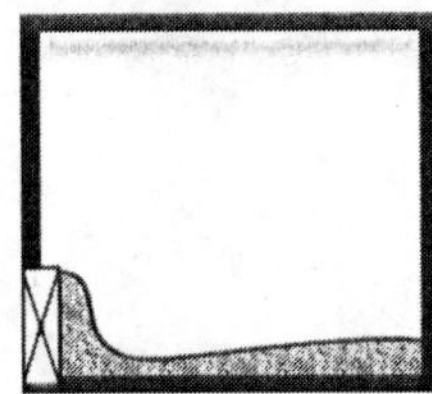

Figure 1.22 Example Airflow Patterns (Nonisothermal) of Outlet Group D (Low Velocity) [2021F, Ch 20, Fig 8]

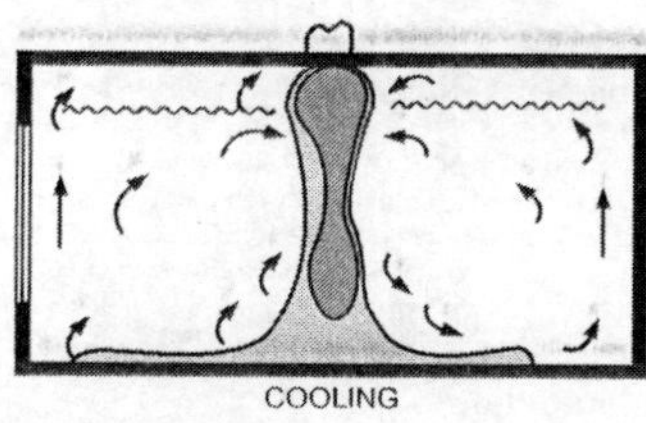

Figure 1.23 Example Airflow Patterns (Nonisothermal) of Outlet Group E (High Velocity) [2021F, Ch 20, Fig 9]

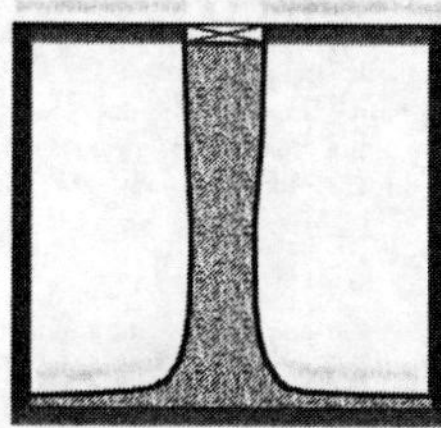

Figure 1.24 Example Airflow Patterns (Nonisothermal) of Outlet Group E (Low Velocity) [2021F, Ch 20, Fig 10]

Room Air Distribution

Air distribution systems affect not only indoor air quality (IAQ) and thermal comfort but also energy consumption over the entire life of a project. ANSI/ASHRAE/IES Standard 90.1 provides energy efficiency requirements that affect supply air characteristics.

Ventilation effectiveness is affected directly by the room air distribution system's design, construction, and operation, but it is very difficult to predict. ANSI/ASHRAE Standard 62.1 provides a table of typical values. As an example, well-designed ceiling-based air diffusion systems produce near-perfect air mixing in cooling mode and yield an air change effectiveness of almost 1.0.

Fully Mixed Air Distribution

In mixed air systems, high-velocity supply jets from air outlets maintain comfort by mixing room air with supply air. This air mixing, heat transfer, and resultant velocity reduction should occur outside the occupied zone. Occupant comfort is maintained not directly by motion of air from outlets, but from secondary air motion from mixing in the unoccupied zone. Comfort is maximized when uniform temperature distribution and room air velocities of less than 50 fpm are maintained in the occupied zone.

Maintaining velocities less than 50 fpm in the occupied zone is often overlooked by designers, but is critical to maintaining comfort. The outlet's selection, location, supply air volume, discharge velocity, and air temperature differential determine the resulting air motion in the occupied zone.

Principles of Operation

Mixed systems generally provide comfort by entraining room air into discharge jets located outside occupied zones, mixing supply and room air. Ideally, these systems generate low-velocity air motion (less than 50 fpm) throughout the occupied zone to provide uniform temperature gradients and velocities. Proper selection of an air outlet is critical for proper air distribution; improper selection can result in room air stagnation, unacceptable temperature gradients, and unacceptable velocities in the occupied zone, possibly leading to occupant discomfort or poor air quality.

The location of a discharge jet relative to surrounding surfaces is important. Discharge jets attach to parallel surfaces, given sufficient velocity and proximity. When a jet is attached, the throw increases by about 30% over a jet discharged in an open area. This difference is important when selecting an air outlet. For detailed discussion of the surface effect on discharge jets, see Chapter 20 of the 2021 *ASHRAE Handbook—Fundamentals*.

Mixed air systems typically use either ceiling or sidewall outlets discharging air horizontally, or floor- or sill-mounted outlets discharging air vertically. They are the most common method of air distribution in North America.

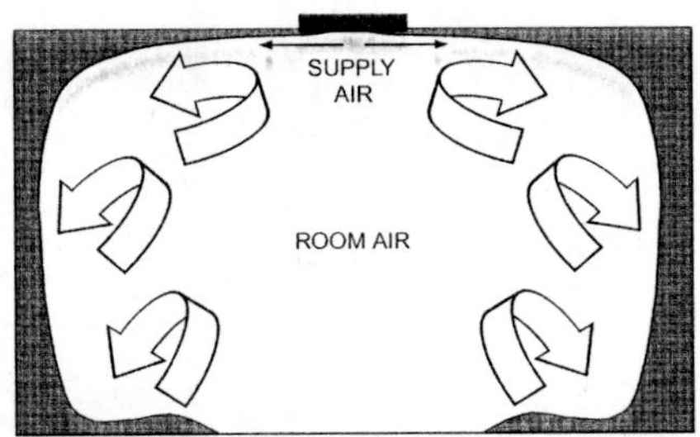

Figure 1.25 Air Supplied at Ceiling Induces Room Air into Supply Jet
[2019A, Ch 58, Fig 5]

Horizontal-Discharge Cooling with Ceiling-Mounted Outlets

Ceiling-mounted outlets typically use the surface effect to transport supply air in the unoccupied zone. The supply air projects across the ceiling and, with sufficient velocity, can continue down wall surfaces and across floors. In this application, supply air should remain outside the occupied zone until it is adequately mixed and tempered with room air.

Overhead outlets may also be installed on exposed ducts, in which case the surface effect does not apply. Typically, if the outlet is mounted 1 ft or more below a ceiling surface, discharge air will not attach to the surface. The unattached supply air has a shorter throw and can project downward, resulting in high air velocities in the occupied zone. Some outlets are designed for use in exposed duct applications. Typical outlet performance data presented by manufacturers are for outlets with surface effect; consult manufacturers for information on exposed duct applications.

Vertical-Discharge Cooling or Heating with Ceiling-Mounted Outlets

Vertically projected outlets are typically selected for high-ceiling applications that require forcing supply air down to the occupied zone. It is important to keep cooling supply air velocity below 50 fpm in the occupied zone. For heating, supply air should reach the floor.

There are outlets specifically designed for vertical projection and it is important to review the manufacturer's performance data notes to understand how to apply catalog data. Throws for heating and cooling differ and also vary depending on the difference between supply and room air temperatures.

Cooling with Sidewall Outlets

Sidewall outlets are usually selected when access to the ceiling plenum is restricted. Sidewall outlets within 1 ft of a ceiling and set for horizontal or a slightly upward projection the sidewall outlet provide a discharge pattern that attaches to the ceiling and travels in the unoccupied zone. This pattern entrains air from the occupied zone to provide mixing.

In some applications, the outlet must be located 2 to 4 ft below the ceiling. When set for horizontal projection, the discharge at some distance from the outlet may drop into the occupied zone. Most devices used for sidewall application can be adjusted to project the air pattern upwards toward the ceiling. This allows the discharge air to attach to the ceiling, increasing throw distance and minimizing drop. This application provides occupant comfort by inducing air from the occupied zone into the supply air.

Some outlets may be more than 4 ft below the ceiling (e.g., in high-ceiling applications, the outlet may be located closer to the occupied zone to minimize the volume of the conditioned space). Most devices used for sidewall applications can be adjusted to project the air pattern upward or downward, which allows the device's throw distance to be adjusted to maximize performance.

When selecting sidewall outlets, it is important to understand the manufacturer's data. Most manufacturers offer data for outlets tested with surface effect, so they only apply if the device is set to direct supply air toward the ceiling. When the device is 4 ft or more below a ceiling, or supply air is directed horizontally or downward, the actual throw distance of the device is typically shorter. Many sidewall outlets can be adjusted to change the spread of supply air, which can significantly change throw distance. Manufacturers usually publish throw distances based on specific spread angles.

Cooling with Floor-Mounted Air Outlets

Although not typically selected for nonresidential buildings, floor-mounted outlets can be used for mixed system cooling applications. In this configuration, room air from the occupied zone is induced into the supply air, providing mixing. When cooling, the device should be selected to discharge vertically along windows, walls, or other vertical surfaces. Typical nonresidential applications include lobbies, long corridors, and houses of worship.

It is important to select a device that is specially designed for floor applications. It must be able to withstand both the required dynamic and static structural loads (e.g., people walking on them, loaded carts rolling across them). Also, many manufacturers offer devices designed to reduce the possibility of objects falling into the device. It is strongly recommended that obstructions are not located above these in-floor air terminals, to avoid restricting their air jets.

Long floor-mounted grilles generally have both functioning and nonfunctioning segments. When selecting air outlets for floor mounting, it is important to note that the throw distance and sound generated depend on the length of the active section. Most manufacturers' catalog data include correction factors for length's effects on both throw and sound. These corrections can be significant and should be evaluated. Understanding manufacturers' performance data and corresponding notes is imperative.

Cooling with Sill-Mounted Air Outlets

Sill-mounted air outlets are commonly used in applications that include unit ventilators and fan coil units. The outlet should be selected to discharge vertically along windows, walls, or other vertical surfaces, and project supply air above the occupied zone.

As with floor-mounted grilles, when selecting and locating sill grilles, consider selecting devices designed to reduce the nuisance of objects falling inside them. It is also recommended that sills be designed to prevent them from being used as shelves.

Heating and Cooling with Perimeter Ceiling-Mounted Outlets

When air outlets are used at the perimeter with vertical projection for heating and/or cooling, they should be located near the perimeter surface, and selected so that the published 150 fpm isothermal throw extends at least halfway down the surface or 4.5 ft above the floor, whichever is lower. In this manner, during heating, warm air mixes with the cool downdraft on the perimeter surface, to reduce or even eliminate drafts in the occupied space.

If a ceiling-mounted air outlet is located away from the perimeter wall, in cooling mode, the high-velocity cool air reduces or overcomes the thermal updrafts on the perimeter surface. To accomplish this, the outlet should be selected for horizontal discharge toward the wall. Outlet selection should be such that isothermal throw to the terminal velocity of 150 fpm should include the distance from the outlet to the perimeter surface. For heating, the supply air temperature should not exceed 15°F above the room air temperature.

Space Temperature Gradients and Airflow Rates

A fully mixed system creates homogeneous thermal conditions throughout the space. As such, thermal gradients should not be expected to exist in the occupied zone. Improper selection, sizing, or placement may prevent full mixing and can result in stagnant areas, or having high-velocity air entering the occupied zone.

Supply airflow requirements to satisfy space sensible heat gains or losses are inversely proportional to the temperature difference between supply and return air. Equation 1.11 can be used to calculate space airflow requirements (at standard conditions):

$$Q = \frac{q_s}{1.08(t_r - t_s)} \tag{1.11}$$

where

Q = required supply airflow rate to meet sensible load, cfm
q_s = net sensible heat gain in the space, Btu/h
t_r = return or exhaust air temperature, °F
t_s = supply air temperature, °F

For fully mixed systems with conventional ceiling heights, the return (or exhaust) and room air temperatures are the same; for example, a room with a set-point temperature of 75°F has, on average, a 75°F return or exhaust air temperature.

The objective of air diffusion is to create the proper combination of room air temperature, humidity, and air motion to provide thermal comfort and acceptable indoor environmental quality in the occupied zone. There are three recommended methods of selecting outlets for mixed-air systems using manufacturers' data:

- by appearance, flow rate, and sound data
- by isovels (lines of constant velocity) and mapping
- by comfort criteria

Table 1.15 Characteristic Room Length for Several Diffusers (Measured from Center of Air Outlet) [2019A, Ch 58, Tbl 5]

Diffuser Type	Characteristic Length L
High sidewall grille	Distance to wall perpendicular to jet
Adjustable blade	
Fixed blade	
Linear bar	
Nozzle	
Horizontal-throw ceiling diffuser	Distance to closest wall, midplane between outlets or intersecting air jet
Round	
Square	
Perforated	
Louvered	
Plaque	
Swirl	
Sill grille	Length of room in direction of jet flow
Ceiling slot diffuser	Distance to wall perpendicular to jet or midplane between outlets
Light troffer diffusers	Distance to midplane between outlets plus distance from ceiling to top of occupied zone

Air Diffusion Performance Index (ADPI)

ADPI was developed as a way to quantify the comfort level in heating and cooling for a space conditioned by a mixed-air system. High ADPI values generally correlate to high space thermal comfort levels, with the maximum obtainable value of 100. Selecting outlets to provide a minimum ADPI value of 80 generally results in a well-mixed space.

Table 1.16 ADPI Selection Guide for Typical Cooling Loads [2019A, Ch 58, Tbl 6A]

Terminal Device in Cooling Mode	Installation	Load, Btu/h·ft^2	Max. ADPI T_{50}/L	Max. ADPI	*T/L* Low Limit for ADPI > 80%	*T/L* High Limit for ADPI > 80%
Adjustable-blade grilles	45° upward blades, High sidewall	8	0.8	98	0.4	1.3
		16	0.9	96	0.5	1.2
	0° horizontal blades, High sidewall	8	1.7	94	1.2	2.2
		16	1.8	88	1.4	2.2
	45° downward blades, High sidewall	8	0.9	76	NA	NA
		16	1	70	NA	NA
Fixed-blade grilles (high sidewall installation)	15° upward blades, High sidewall	8	1.4	96	0.5	2.4
		16	2.1	94	1.2	2.9
	15° downward blades, High sidewall	8	1.9	85	1.5	2.2
		16	2	82	1.8	2.2
Linear-bar grilles (high sidewall installation)	High sidewall	8	1.3	92	0.7	1.8
		16	1.3	88	1.0	1.6
	Sill	8	1.3	94	0.9	1.7
		16	1.3	90	1.0	1.6
Nozzles (high sidewall installation)	High sidewall	8	0.7	96	0.4	2.0
		16	1	89	0.4	1.9
Round ceiling diffuser	Ceiling	8	1.6	99	0.4	3.2
		16	1.9	98	0.5	3.2
Square ceiling diffuser	Ceiling	8	1.8	100	0.8	2.8
		16	1.8	100	0.6	3.1
Perforated diffusers, round pattern	Ceiling	8	1.9	95	0.5	3.3
		16	2.1	95	0.9	3.4
Perforated diffusers, directional pattern (4-way)	Ceiling	8	2.1	100	1.2	3.1
		16	2	95	1.0	2.9
Louvered face diffusers, with lip on deflector blade	Ceiling	8	2.5	100	0.5	4.4
		16	2.6	100	0.6	4.5
Louvered face diffusers, without lip on deflector blade	Ceiling	8	2	100	0.5	3.6
		16	1.8	100	0.4	3.4
Plaque face diffusers	Ceiling	8	1.6	100	0.3	3.0
		16	1.6	100	0.4	3.2
Linear-slot diffusers	Ceiling	8	1.8	100	0.5	3.0
		16	1.8	100	0.5	3.1
T-bar slot diffusers	Ceiling, periphery of a wall	8	1.3	96	0.7	1.9
		16	1.5	90	1.1	1.9
Swirl diffusers	Ceiling	8	1.3	100	0.4	2.4
		16	1.3	98	0.4	2.4
N-slot diffusers	Ceiling	8	1.8	100	1.3	2.4
		16	1.8	95	1.3	2.3

Source: Data developed by Liu et al. (2016) for this chapter from ASHRAE research project RP-1546 (Liu 2016), and air speed limit (70 fpm) extrapolated from data. Additional data point used to create new regressions for ADPI curves to better represent current diffusers/grilles. Table applies to spaces with maximum 12 ft ceiling.

Table 1.17 ADPI Selection Guide for Typical Heating Loads [2019A, Ch 58, Tbl 6B]

Terminal Device in Heating Mode	Installation	Load, Btu/h·ft²	Max. ADPI T_{50}/L	Max. ADPI	*T/L* Low Limit for ADPI > 80%	*T/L* High Limit for ADPI > 80%
Adjustable-blade grilles	45° upward blades, High sidewall	10 to 12	1.1	95	0.6	1.9
	0° horizontal blades, High sidewall	10 to 12	1.6	94	1.1	2.4
	45° downward blades, High sidewall	10 to 12	0.7	84	0.6	0.8
Fixed-blade grilles	15° upward blades, High sidewall	10 to 12	1.8	96	1.2	2.8
	15° downward blades, High sidewall	10 to 12	1.4	88	0.6	2.2
Linear-bar grilles	High sidewall	10 to 12	1.2	94	0.6	1.7
	Sill	10 to 12	1.2	100	0.7	1.8
Nozzles (high sidewall installation)	High sidewall	10 to 12	1.5	92	1.0	2.0
Round ceiling diffuser	Ceiling	10 to 12	1.4	93	1.0	2.3
Square ceiling diffuser	Ceiling	10 to 12	1.7	91	2.5	3.4
Perforated diffusers, round pattern	Ceiling	10 to 12	2.1	90	2.0	2.8
Perforated diffusers, directional pattern (4-way)	Ceiling	10 to 12	2.5	87	2.5	3.4
Louvered face diffusers, with lip on deflector blade	Ceiling	10 to 12	2.6	88	2.5	4.4
Louvered face diffusers, without lip on deflector blade	Ceiling	10 to 12	2.1	88	2.1	3.2
Plaque face diffusers	Ceiling	10 to 12	2.1	93	2.1	3.0
Linear-slot diffusers	Ceiling	10 to 12	1.7	90	1.7	3.1
T-bar slot diffusers	Ceiling, periphery of a wall	10 to 12	1.6	91	1.3	2.0
Swirl diffusers	Ceiling	10 to 12	1.4	100	1.4	2.1
N-slot diffusers	Ceiling	10 to 12	1.9	100	1.5	2.4

Source: Data developed by Liu and Novoselac (2015) for this chapter from ASHRAE research project RP-1546 (Liu 2016), and air speed limit (70 fpm) extrapolated from data. Additional data point used to create new regressions for ADPI curves to better represent current diffusers/grilles. Table applies to spaces with maximum 12 ft ceiling.

Fully Stratified Air Distribution

Fully stratified air distribution systems are characterized by a vertical temperature gradient throughout the space, where the coolest temperature is at the floor level, and the warmest temperature is at the ceiling height. Displacement ventilation (DV) systems are the most common example of a fully stratified air distribution system. DV systems typically use floor or low sidewall (sometimes ceiling-mounted) diffusers delivering low-velocity, cool air across the floor. The low-velocity air, in conjunction with room loads and buoyancy effects, creates the characteristic vertical thermal stratification.

Principles of Operation

DV systems (see Figure 1.26) use very low discharge velocities, with diffusers typically sized to provide outlet velocities between 40 and 70 fpm. In addition to the low velocity discharge, the temperature of the supply air is also different from a fully mixed system, with temperatures generally above 60°F; lower temperatures may be used in industrial applications, exercise or sports facilities, and transient areas where comfort concerns are minimal. This cool supply air is more dense than the ambient air and drops to the floor after discharge, whether from floor, low sidewall, or ceiling mounted locations, spreading across the lower level of the space (typically less than 8 in. in height).

As convective heat sources (Figure 1.26) in the space transfer heat to the cooler air around them, natural convection currents form and rise along the heat transfer boundary. Without significant room air movement, these currents rise to form a convective heat plume (thermal plume) around and above the heat source; as the plume rises, it expands by entraining surrounding air. Its growth and velocity are proportional to the heat source's size and sensible load, as well as the temperature of the ambient air above it. As the plume rises, ambient air from below and around the heat source fills the void. An occupant in a DV system entrains the cool, conditioned air directly into their breathing zone. As the occupant exhales, the spent air, being warmer and more humid than the ambient air, is pulled out of the breathing zone by the rising plume. Convective heat from sources located above the occupied zone has little effect on occupied-zone air temperature.

At a certain height, where plume temperature equals ambient temperature, the plume dissipates and spills horizontally. Two distinct zones are thus formed in the room: a lower occupied zone with little or no recirculation flow (close to displacement flow), and an upper zone with recirculation flow. The boundary between these two zones is often called the **shift zone** (or **stratification height**). The height of this boundary layer between the upper and lower

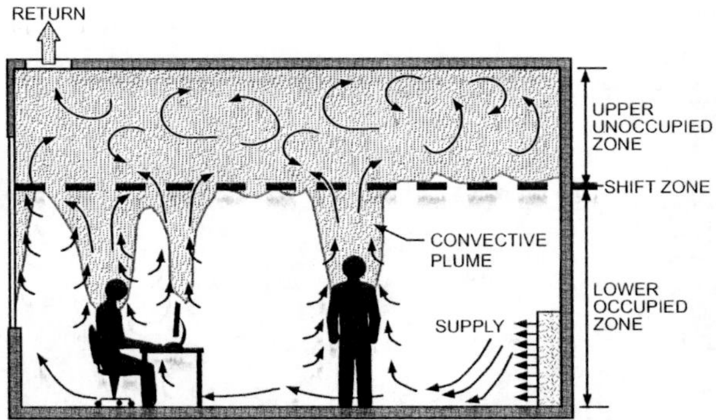

Figure 1.26 Displacement Ventilation System Characteristics
[2019A, Ch 58, Fig 6]

zones is determined based on the convection flow rates of the thermal plumes in relation to the airflow rate supplied by the diffusers. In a DV system, increasing the airflow rate limits stratification and lowers the boundary layer height, with a decrease in airflow providing the opposite effect Actual and simplified representations of the temperature gradient in the space are shown in Figure 1.27.

Outlet Characteristics

Displacement outlets are designed for average face velocities between 50 and 70 fpm, and are typically in a low sidewall or floor location. Return or exhaust air intakes should always be located above the occupied zone for human thermal comfort applications.

Displacement outlets are available in a number of configurations and sizes. Some models are designed to fit in corners or along sidewalls, or stand freely as columns. It is important to consider the degree of flow equalization the outlet achieves, because use of the entire outlet surface for air discharge is paramount to minimizing clear zones and maintaining acceptable temperatures at the lower levels of the space.

Stationary occupants should not be subjected to discharge velocities exceeding about 50 fpm because air at the ankle level within this velocity envelope tends to be quite cool. As such, most outlet manufacturers define an adjacent zone (also called a *clear zone*) in which locating stationary, low-activity occupants is strongly discouraged, but transient occupancy, such as in corridors or aisles, is possible. Occupants with high activity levels may also find the clear zone acceptable.

Unlike mixed systems, outlets in thermal displacement systems discharge air at very low velocities, resulting in very little mixing. As such, design of these systems primarily involves determining a supply airflow rate to manage the thermal gradients in the space in accordance

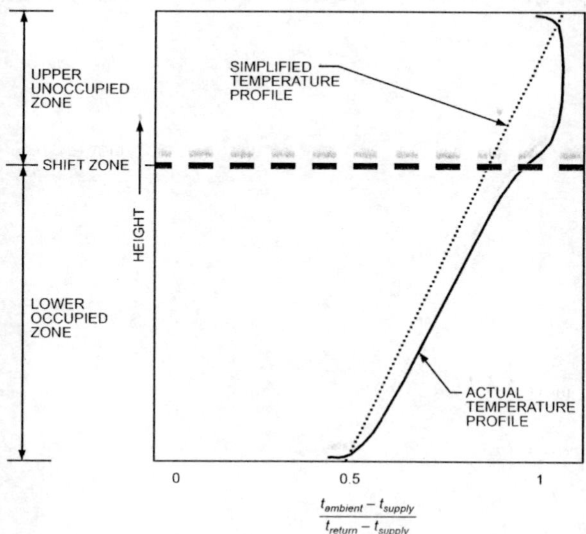

Figure 1.27 Temperature Profile of Displacement Ventilation System
[2019A, Ch 58, Fig 7]

with ASHRAE comfort guidelines. ANSI/ASHRAE Standard 55 recommends that the vertical temperature difference between the ankle and head levels of space occupants be limited to no more than 5.4°F to maintain a high degree (>95%) of occupant satisfaction.

Application Considerations

For heating, either a displacement diffuser with integrated heating or a separate system is generally recommended. Displacement ventilation can be used successfully in combination with perimeter fan-coils, hydronic systems, or radiators and convectors installed at the exterior walls to offset space heat losses. Radiant heating panels and heated floors also can also be used with displacement ventilation. To maintain displacement ventilation, outlets should supply ventilation air about 4°F lower than the desired room temperature.

Thermal displacement ventilation systems can be either constant or variable air volume. A thermostat in a representative location in the space or return plenum should determine the delivered air volume or temperature. If the time-averaged requirements of ANSI/ASHRAE Standard 62.1 are met, intermittent on/off airflow control can be used.

Avoid using displacement ventilation and mixed air systems in the same space, because mixing destroys the natural stratification that drives the thermal displacement ventilation system. Displacement ventilation systems can be complemented by hydronic systems such as chilled floors. Use caution when combining chilled ceilings, beams, or panels with fully stratified systems, because cold surfaces in the upper zone of the space may recirculate contaminants stratified in the upper zone back into the occupied zone.

Partially Mixed Air Distribution

A partially mixed system's characteristics fall between a fully mixed system and a fully stratified system. It includes both a high-velocity mixed air zone and a low-velocity stratified zone where room air motion is caused by thermal forces. For example, floor-based outlets, when operating in a cooling mode with relatively high discharge velocities (>150 fpm), create mixing, thus affecting the amount of stratification in the lower portions of the room. In the upper portions of the room, away from the influence of floor outlets, room air often remains thermally stratified in much the same way as displacement ventilation systems.

Principles of Operation

Supply air is discharged, usually vertically, at relatively high velocities and entrains room air in a similar fashion to outlets used in mixed air systems. This entrainment, as shown in Figure 1.28 reduces the temperature and velocity differentials between supply and ambient room air. This discharge results in a vertical plume that rises until its velocity is reduced to about 50 fpm. At this point, its kinetic energy is insufficient to entrain much more room air, so mixing stops. Because air in the plume is still cooler than the surrounding air, the supply air spreads horizontally across the space, where it is entrained by rising thermal plumes generated by nearby heat sources.

Research and experience have shown that the amount of room air stratification varies depending on design, commissioning, and operation. Control of stratification includes the following considerations:

- By reducing airflow and mixing in the occupied zone, fan energy can be reduced and stratification can be increased, approaching a reasonable target at 3°F to 4°F temperature difference from head to ankle height, which satisfies ANSI/ASHRAE Standard 55.
- By increasing airflow and mixing in the occupied zone, excessive stratification can be avoided, thereby improving thermal comfort.

Figure 1.28 shows one example of the resulting room air distribution in which the room air is mixed in the **lower mixed zone**, which is bounded by the floor and the elevation (**throw height**) at which the 50 fpm terminal velocity occurs. At this elevation, stratification begins to occur and a linear temperature gradient, similar to that found in thermal displacement systems, forms and extends through the **stratified zone**. As with thermal displacement ventilation, convective heat plumes from space heat sources draw conditioned air from the lower (mixed) level through the stratified zone and to the overhead return location. A third zone,

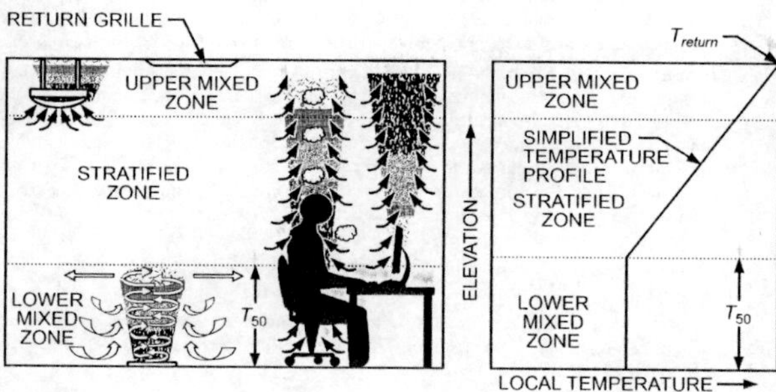

Figure 1.28 UFAD System in Partially Stratified Application
[2019A, Ch 58, Fig 9]

referred to as the **upper mixed zone**, may exist where the volume of rising heat plumes terminate. Although velocities in this area are quite low, the air tends to be mixed.

Outlet Characteristics

One outlet type is a **swirl diffuser** with a high-induction core, which induces large amounts of room air to quickly reduce supply to ambient air velocity and temperature differentials. Supply air is injected into the room as a swirling vertical plume close to the outlet. Properly selected, these outlets produce a limited vertical projection of the supply air plume, restricting mixing to the lower portions of the space. Most of these outlets allow occupants to adjust the outlet airflow rate easily. Other versions incorporate automatically controlled dampers that are repositioned by a signal from the space thermostat and/or central control system.

Another category includes more conventional **floor grilles** designed for directional discharge of supplied airflow. These grilles may be either linear or modular in design, and may allow occupants to adjust the discharge air pattern by repositioning the core of the outlet. Most floor grilles include an integral actuated damper, or other means, that automatically throttles the volume of air in response to the zone conditioning requirements.

Room air induction allows UFAD diffusers to comfortably deliver supply air a few degrees cooler than possible with outlets used for thermal displacement ventilation outlets. The observance of clear, or adjacent, zones above and around the diffusers, where stationary occupants should not reside, is recommended. Outlet manufacturers typically identify such restrictive areas in their product literature.

As with thermal displacement systems, design involves determining a supply airflow rate that limits thermal gradients in the occupied zone in accordance with ANSI/ASHRAE Standard 55 guidelines. ASHRAE Standard 55 recommends that the vertical temperature difference between the ankle and head level of space occupants be limited to no more than 5.4°F if a high degree (>95%) of occupant comfort is to be maintained.

Application Considerations

Some considerations include the following:

- Supply temperatures in the access floor cavity should be kept at 60°F or above, to minimize the risk of condensation and subsequent mold growth.
- Most UFAD outlets can be adjusted automatically by a space thermostat or other control system, or manually by the occupant. In the latter case, outlets should be located within the workstation they serve.
- Use of manually adjusted outlets should be restricted to open office areas where cooling loads do not tend to vary considerably or frequently. Perimeter areas and conference rooms require automatic control of supply air temperatures and/or flow rates because their thermal loads are highly transient.
- Heat transfer to and from the floor slab affects discharge air temperature and should be considered when calculating space airflow requirements. Floor plenums should be well sealed to minimize air leakage, and exterior walls should be well insulated and have good vapor retarders. Night and holiday temperature setbacks should likely be avoided, or at least reduced, to minimize plenum condensation and thermal mass effect problems. With air-side economizers, using enthalpy control rather than dry-bulb control can help reduce hours of admitting high moisture-content air, thus also reducing the potential for condensation in the floor plenums.
- Avoid using stratified and mixed air systems in the same space, because mixing destroys the natural stratification that drives the stratified system.
- Return static pressure drop should be relatively equal throughout the spaces being served by a common UFAD plenum. This reduces the chance of unequal pressurization in the UFAD plenum.

See *UFAD Guide: Design, Construction and Operation of Underfloor Air Distribution Systems* for a more thorough discussion of issues involved with the design and application of UFAD systems.

Air Dispersion Systems

Textile air dispersion systems are low-pressure extended plenum systems with pressurized tubing and air distributed along the path of least resistance. Systems constructed with metal follow the same principles.

Various supply air outlet styles are available: porous fabric weave used as an outlet, microperforations, linear vents, orifices, and nozzles. Many of these air outlet styles can be used together to achieve specific results.

Return Air Inlets

The success of a mixed air distribution system depends primarily on supply diffuser location. Return grille location is far less critical than the location of air outlets. In fact, the return air intake affects room air motion only in the area immediately around the grille. Measurements of velocity near a return air grille show a rapid decrease in magnitude as the measuring device is moved away from the grille face. Table 1.18 shows recommended maximum (to avoid excessive noise) return inlet face velocities as a function of grille location. Every enclosed space should have return/transfer inlets of adequate size per this table.

For stratified and partially mixed air distribution systems, it can be advantageous to place the return air inlet in the ceiling. ANSI/ASHRAE Standard 62.1 allows ventilation effectiveness greater than 1.0 for some stratified and partially mixed air distribution systems in cooling mode if the return air inlet is located in the ceiling.

Supply air short circuiting is normally not a problem if the outlet is selected to provide adequate throw and directed away from returns or exhausts. The success of this practice is confirmed by the availability and use of combination supply and return diffusers.

Table 1.18 Recommended Return Inlet Face Velocities
[2019A, Ch 58, Tbl 1]

Inlet Location	Velocity Across Gross Area, fpm
Above occupied zone	>800
In occupied zone, not near seats	600 to 800
In occupied zone, near seats	400 to 600
Door or wall louvers	200 to 300
Through undercut area of doors	200 to 300

2. AIR CONTAMINANTS AND CONTROL

Contaminants

Bioaerosols

Bioaerosols are a diverse class of particles of biological origin. They include bacteria, fungal spores, fungal fragments, pollen grains, subpollen particles, viruses, pet- and pest-associated allergens, and plant debris. They are of particular concern in indoor air because of their association with allergies and asthma and their ability to cause disease. Chapters 10 and 11 of the 2021 *ASHRAE Handbook—Fundamentals* contain more detailed descriptions of these contaminants.

Bioaerosols range in size from 0.01 to 100 µm. Single bacterial cells are approximately 1 µm or less in aerodynamic diameter; however, they are often transported as larger bacterial cell agglomerates (~2 to 5 µm) or attached to other biological and abiotic particles. Unicellular fungal spores are generally 2 to 5 µm in aerodynamic diameter and multicellular fungal spores are larger than 10 µm. Fungal fragments are typically less than 1 µm in size. Pollen grains range in size from 10 to 100 µm, whereas subpollen particles span ~0.01 µm to several micrometers in size. Individual viruses can be as small as 0.02 to 0.03 µm, but are typically carried on larger particles. Pet- and pest-associated allergens are approximately 1 to over 20 µm.

Air Filters and Cleaners

ASHRAE Air Filtration Standards

ANSI/ASHRAE Standard 52.2 contains minimum efficiency reporting values (MERVs) for air cleaner particle size efficiency. In 2008, the standard incorporated arrestance testing from the discontinued ASHRAE Standard 52.1. Table 2.1 provides an approximate cross-reference for air cleaners tested under ASHRAE Standards 52.1 and 52.2. Currently, there is no ASHRAE standard for testing electronic air cleaners.

Filter Installation

In-service efficiency of an air filter is sharply reduced if air leaks through the bypass dampers or poorly designed filter-holding frames. The higher the filter efficiency, the more careful attention that must be paid to the rigidity and sealing effectiveness of the frame. In addition, high-efficiency filters must be handled and installed with care.

Published performance data for all air filters are based on straight-through unrestricted airflow. Filters should be installed so that the face area is at right angles to the airflow whenever possible. Provide sufficient space in front of (upstream) or behind (downstream of) the filter, or both, depending on its type, to make the filter accessible for inspection and service. A distance of 20 to 40 in. is required, depending on the filter chosen

Filter Types

Major factors influencing filter design and selection include (1) degree of air cleanliness required, (2) specific particle size range or aerosols that require filtration, (3) aerosol concentration, (4) resistance to airflow through the filter, (5) design face velocity to achieve published performance, (6) change-out cycle requirements, (7) energy consumption requirements, (8) special disposal mandates, and (9) resistance to certain conditions (physical, chemical, or biological).

Common air cleaners are broadly grouped as follows:

In **fibrous media unit filters**, the accumulating dust load causes pressure drop to increase up to some maximum recommended or predetermined value before changing filters. During this period, efficiency normally increases. However, at high dust loads, dust may adhere poorly to filter fibers and efficiency drops because of offloading. Filters in this condition should be replaced or reconditioned, as should filters that have reached their final (maximum recommended) pressure drop. This category includes viscous impingement and dry air filters, available in low-efficiency to ultrahigh-efficiency construction.

Renewable media filters are fibrous media filters where fresh media is introduced into the airstream as needed to maintain essentially constant resistance and, consequently, constant average efficiency.

Electronic air cleaners require a power source and, if maintained properly by regular cleaning, have relatively constant pressure drop and efficiency. If they are not cleaned regularly, the accumulated dust can build up to the point that arcing can occur in the collection section. This may reduce collection efficiency as well as produce unwanted extraneous noise. Dust buildup in the ionizer section can also reduce efficiency.

Combination air cleaners combine the other types. For example, an electronic air cleaner may be used as an agglomerator with a fibrous media downstream to catch the agglomerated particles blown off the plates. Low-efficiency pads, throwaway panels and automatically renewable media roll filters, or low- to medium-efficiency pleated prefilters may be used upstream of a high-efficiency filter to extend the life of the better and more costly final filter. Charged media filters are also available that increase particle deposition on media fibers by an induced electrostatic field. With these filters, pressure loss increases as it does on a noncharged fibrous media filter. The benefits of combining different air cleaning processes vary.

Contaminant Control Applications

See Tables 12.2 and 12.3 for residential exhaust airflow requirements.

For information on laboratory applications, see Chapter 17 of the 2019 *ASHRAE Handbook—HVAC Applications*; also see *ASHRAE Laboratory Design Guide: Planning and Operation of Laboratory HVAC Systems*, Second Edition.

For cleanroom applications, see *ASHRAE Design Guide for Cleanrooms: Fundamentals, Systems, and Performance*; also see Chapter 19 of the 2019 *ASHRAE Handbook—HVAC Applications*.

Tables 2.6 to 2.9 provide data for hoods used in commercial kitchens.

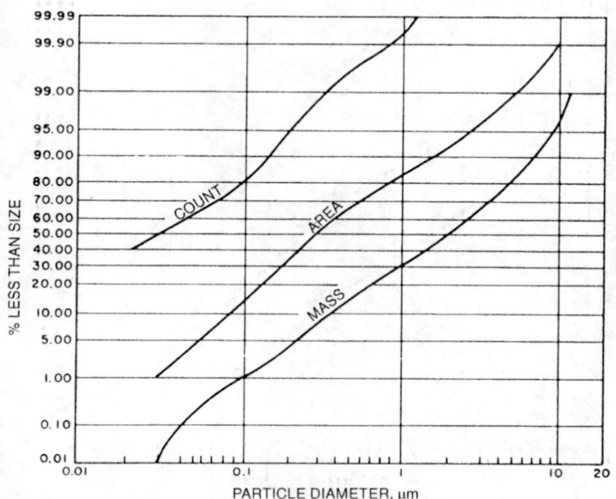

Count curve: Based on measurements by electron microscope.
Area curve: Calculated.
Mass curve: Solid section based on measurements by sedimentation.

Figure 2.1 Particle Size Distribution of Atmospheric Dust

Table 2.1 Air Filter Cross-Reference and Application Guidelines [2020S, Ch 29, Tbl 3]

Standard 52.2 MERV	Arrestance Value	Example Range of Contaminants Controlled	Example Applications	Sample Air Cleaner Type(s)
E-1 Range				
MERV 16	N/A	0.3 to 1.0 μm size range: bacteria, smoke (ETS), paint pigments, face powder, some virus, droplet nuclei, insecticide dusts, soldering fumes	Day surgery, general surgery, hospital general ventilation, turbo equipment, compressors, welding/soldering air cleaners, prefilters to HEPAs, LEED for existing (EB) and new (NC) commercial buildings, smoking lounges	Box-style wet-laid or lofted fiberglass, box-style synthetic media, minipleated synthetic or fiberglass paper, depths from 2 to 12 in. Pocket filters of fiberglass or synthetic media 12 to 36 in.
MERV 15	N/A			
MERV 14	N/A			
MERV 13	N/A			
E-2 Range				
MERV 12	N/A	1.0 to 3.0 μm size range: milled flour, lead dust, combustion soot, *Legionella*, coal dust, some bacteria, process grinding dust	Food processing facilities, air separation plants, commercial buildings, better residential, industrial air cleaning, prefiltration to higher-efficiency filters, schools, gymnasiums	Box-style wet-laid or lofted fiberglass, box-style synthetic media, minipleated synthetic or fiberglass paper, depths from 2 to 12 in. Pocket filters either rigid or flexible in synthetic or fiberglass, depths from 12 to 36 in.
MERV 11	N/A			
MERV 10	N/A			
MERV 9	N/A			
E-3 Range				
MERV 8	N/A	3.0 to 10 μm size range: pollens, earth-origin dust, mold spores, cement dust, powdered milk, snuff, hair spray mist	General HVAC filtration, industrial equipment filtration, commercial property, schools, prefilter to high-efficiency filters, paint booth intakes, electrical/phone equipment protection	Wide range of pleated media, ring panels, cubes, pockets in synthetic or fiberglass, disposable panels, depths from 1 to 24 in.
MERV 7	N/A			
MERV 6	N/A			
MERV 5	N/A			
MERV 4	>70%	Arrestance method	Protection from blowing large particle dirt and debris, industrial environment ventilation air	Inertial separators
MERV 3	>70%			
MERV 2	>65%			
MERV 1	<65%			

Note: MERV for non-HEPA/ULPA filters also includes test airflow rate, but it is not shown here because it is of no significance for the purposes of this table.
N/A = not applicable.

Table 2.2 NAAQS for the United States [2021F, Ch 11, Tbl 12]

Contaminant	Primary or Secondary Standard	Averaging Time	Level	Details
Carbon monoxide	Primary	1 h	35 ppm	Not to be exceeded more than once per year
		8 h	9 ppm	
Nitrogen dioxide	Primary	1 h	100 ppb	98th percentile, averaged over 3 years
	Primary/ secondary	1 yr	53 ppb	Annual mean
Ozone	Primary/ secondary	8 h	75 ppb	Annual fourth-highest daily maximum 8 h concentration, averaged over 3 years
Sulfur dioxide	Primary	1 h	75 ppb	99th percentile of 1 h daily maximum concentrations, averaged over 3 years
	Secondary	3 h	500 ppb	Not to be exceeded more than once per year
Particulate, $PM_{2.5}$[a]	Primary/ secondary	24 h	35 μg/m^3	98th percentile, averaged over 3 years
		1 yr	15 μg/m^3	Annual mean, averaged over 3 years
Particulate, PM_{10}[b]	Primary/ secondary	24 h	150 μg/m^3	Not to be exceeded more than once per year on average over 3 years
Lead (Pb) in particles	Primary/ secondary	3 mo	0.15 μg/m^3	Not to be exceeded

[a] $PM_{2.5}$ = particulates below 2.5 μm diameter.
[b] PM_{10} = particulates below 10 μm diameter.
ppb = parts per 10^9
Source: *National Ambient Air Quality Standards* (NAAQS), U.S. Environmental Protection Agency, Washington, DC, 2015.

Table 2.3 Sources and Indoor and Outdoor Concentrations of Selected Indoor Contaminants [2021F, Ch 11, Tbl 13]

Contaminant	Sources of Indoor Contaminants	Typical Indoor Concentration	Typical Outdoor Concentration	Locations
Carbon monoxide	Combustion equipment, engines, faulty heating systems	0.5 to 5 ppm[a] (without gas stoves) 5 to 15 ppm[a] (with gas stoves)	2 ppm[a]	Indoor ice rinks, homes, cars, vehicle repair shops, parking garages
$PM_{2.5}$	Stoves, fireplaces, cigarettes, condensation of volatiles, aerosol sprays, cooking	7 to 10 $\mu g/m^3$[a]	<10 $\mu g/m^3$[a]	Homes, offices, cars, public facilities, bars, restaurants
PM_{10}	Combustion, heating system, cooking	40 to 60 $\mu g/m^3$[a]	60 $\mu g/m^3$[a]	Homes, offices, transportation, restaurants
Organic vapors	Combustion, solvents, resin products, pesticides, aerosol sprays, cleaning products, building materials, paints	Different for each VOC[c] (2 to 5 times outdoor levels)	See 2021F, Ch 11, Tbl 11	Homes, restaurants, public facilities, offices, hospitals
Nitrogen dioxide	Combustion, gas stoves, water heaters, gas-fired dryers, cigarettes, engines	<8 ppb[a] (without combustion appliances) >15 ppb with combustion appliances)	15 ppb[a]	Homes, indoor ice rinks
Nitric oxide	Combustion, gas stoves, water heaters, gas-fired dryers, cigarettes, engines	—	Various	Homes, any building with combustion source
Sulfur dioxide	Heating system	20 $\mu g/m^3$[b]	<20 $\mu g/m^3$[b] 3 ppb[a]	Mechanical/furnace rooms
Formaldehyde	Insulation, product binders, pressed wood products, carpets	0.1 to 0.3 ppm[a]	NA	Homes, schools, offices
Radon and progeny	Building materials, groundwater, soil	1.3 pCi/L[a]	4 pCi/L[a]	Homes, schools
Carbon dioxide	Combustion appliances, humans, pets	600 to 1000 ppm[c]	300 to 500 ppm[c]	
Biological contaminants	Humans, pets, rodents, insects, plants, fungi, humidifiers, air conditioners	NA	NA (lower than indoor levels)	Homes, hospitals, schools, offices, public facilities
Ozone	Electric arcing, electronic air cleaners, copiers, printers	42 ppb[d]	70 ppb[a]	Airplanes, offices, homes

NA = not applicable
ppb = parts per 10^9

Sources:
[a]EPA (2011)
[b]NRC (1981)
[c]Seppänen et al. (1999) and ANSI/ASHRAE Standard 62.1, Appendix C
[d]Weschler (2000)

Table 2.4 Media Selection by Contaminant [2019A, Ch 47, Tbl 9]

Gaseous Contaminant	PIA	AC	AIC	BIC	Gaseous Contaminant	PIA	AC	AIC	BIC	Gaseous Contaminant	PIA	AC	AIC	BIC
Acetaldehyde	1	2			Dichlorofloromethane		1			Methyl formate	2	1		
Acetic acid (!)	1	2		2,1	R-114 (see note)		1			Methyl isobutyl ketone	2	1		
Acetic anhydride (!)	1,2	1		2	Diethylamine	2	1			Methyl sulfide	1			
Acetone (!)	1	2			Dimethylamine		1	2		Methyl vinyl ketone	2	1		
Acetylene	1				Dioctyl phthalate		1			Naphtha		1		
Acrolein	1	2			Dioxane	1	2			Naphthalene		1		
Acrylic acid (!)	1	1		2	Ethanol	1	2			Nicotine	1	2		
Allyl sulfide	1	2			Ethyl acetate	2	1			Nitric acid				1
Ammonia (NH_3)			1		Ethyl chloride (!)	1,2	2,1			Nitric oxide (NO)	1			2
Aniline	2	1			Ethylene (C_2H_4)	1				Nitrobenzene		1		
Arsine	1				Ethylene oxide	1	2			Nitrogen dioxide	1			2
Benzene		1			Ethyl ether	2	1			Nitromethane	1			
Borane (!)	1	2,2			Ethyl mercaptan (!)	1,1	2		2	Nitrous oxide				1
Bromine		1			Formaldehyde	1				Octane (!)	2	1,1		
1,3 Butadiene	1	2			Gasoline	1				Ozone (O_3) (!)	2	1,1		
Butane		1			General halocarbons		1			Perchloroethylene	2	1		
2-Butanone	1	2			General hydrocarbons	2	1			Peroxy acetyl nitrate (PAN)		1		
2-Butoxyethanol	2	1			General VOC	2	1			Phenol	2	1		
Butyl acetate (!)	1,2	2,1			Heptane		1			Phosgene	2	1		
Butyl alcohol	2	1			Hydrogen bromide		2		1	Phosphine	1			
Butyl mercaptan	2	1			Hydrogen chloride		2		1	Putrescine	1	2		
Butylene	2	1			Hydrogen cyanide	1				Pyridine (!)	1	1		

Table 2.4 Media Selection by Contaminant [2019A, Ch 47, Tbl 9] ***(Continued)***

Gaseous Contaminant	PIA	AC	AIC	BIC	Gaseous Contaminant	PIA	AC	AIC	BIC	Gaseous Contaminant	PIA	AC	AIC	BIC
Butyne	2	1			Hydrogen fluoride	1			1	Skatole	2	1		
Butyraldehyde	2	1			Hydrogen iodide	2				Silane	1			
Butyric acid		1		2	Hydrogen selenide					Stoddard solvent	1			
Cadaverine	2	1			Hydrogen sulfide	1			1	Stibine	1			
Camphor		1			Iodine		1			Styrene (!)	2	1,1		
Carbon dioxide (CO_2)	Carbon w/catalyst				Iodoform	2	1			Sulfur dioxide	1			1
Carbon disulfide	2	1			Isopropanol	2	1			Sulfur trioxide	1			1
Carbon monoxide (CO)	Carbon w/catalyst				Kerosene		1			Sulfuric acid		2		1
Carbon tetrachloride		1			Lactic acid		1			Toluene		1		
Chlorine (Cl_2)				1	Menthol	2	1			Triethylamine		2	1	
Chloroform		1			Mercury vapor		Impreg. AC			Trichlorethylene		1		
Creosote (!)	1,2	2,1			Methanol	2	1			1,1,1, trichloroethane (!)	1	2,1		
Cyclohexane		1			Methyl acrylate	2	1			R-11 (see below)		1		
Cyclohexanol	2	1			Methyl bromide (!)	2,1	1			Turpentine	2	1		
Cyclohexanone	2	1			Methyl butyl ketone (!)	1,2	2,1			Urea (!)	2	1,1		
Cyclohexene		1			Methyl cellosolve acetate	2	1			Uric acid (!)	1	1		2,2
Decane		1			Methylchloroform		1			Vinyl chloride		1		
Diborane	1				Methylcyclohexane		1			Xylene		1		
Dichlorobenzene		1			Methylene chloride		1							

1 = primary media selection for contaminant; 2 = secondary media selection.
PIA = permanganate-impregnated alumina; AC = activated carbon; AIC = acid-impregnated carbon; BIC = base-impregnated carbon.
R-114 is dichlorotetrafluoroethane; R-11 is trichlorofluoromethane.

Comments: Some contaminant molecules have isomers that, because they have different physical properties (boiling point, vapor pressures), require different treatment methods. For some contaminants, preferred treatment is ion exchange or another (nonlisted) impregnated carbon. For some contaminants, manufacturer recommendations differ. "!" is used to identify these cases.

Table 2.5 Example Generation of Gaseous Contaminants by Building Materials [2019A, Ch 47, Tbl 2]

Contaminant	CAS Number	Emission Factor Averages (ranges), $\mu g/(h \cdot m^2)$					
		Acoustic Ceiling Panels	Carpets	Fiberboards	Gypsum Boards	Paints on Gypsum Board	Particle Boards
4-Phenylcyclo-hexene (PCH)	4994-16-5		8.4 (n.d.-85)				
Acetaldehyde	75-07-0		2.8 (n.d.-37)	9.0 (n.d.-32)			28 (n.d.-55)
Acetic acid	64-19-7			8.4 (n.d.-26)			
Acetone	67-64-1	12 (n.d.-33)		35 (n.d.-67)	37 (n.d.-110)	35 (n.d.-120)	
Ethylene glycol	107-21-1			140 (n.d.-290)		19 (n.d.-190)	160 (140-200)
Formaldehyde	50-00-0	5.8 (n.d.-25)	3.6 (n.d.-41)	220 (n.d.-570)	6.8 (n.d.-19)		49 (n.d.-97)
Naphthalene	91-20-3		11 (n.d.-59)	3.0 (n.d.-8.2)			
n-Heptane	142-82-5			21 (n.d.-53)			
Nonanal	124-19-6	4.9 (1.7-11)	11 (n.d.-68)		10 (n.d.-28)	3.7 (n.d.-24)	
Toluene	108-88-3			19 (n.d.-46)			
TotalVOC (TVOC)*	N/A	32 (3.2-150)	1900 (270-9100)	400 (52-850)	15 (n.d.-61)	2500 (170-6200)	420 (240-510)

Table 2.5 Example Generation of Gaseous Contaminants by Building Materials [2019A, Ch 47, Tbl 2] ***(Continued)***

Contaminant	CAS Number	Emission Factor Averages (ranges), μg/(h·m²)					
		Plastic Laminates and Assemblies	Non-Rubber-Based Resilient Flooring	Rubber-Based Resilient Flooring	Tackable Wall Panels	Thermal Insulations	Wall Bases (Rubber-Based)
1,2,4-Trimethylbenzene	95-63-6			210 (n.d.-590)			
2-Butoxy-ethanol	111-76-2		2.7 (n.d.-24)	1.6 (n.d.-24)			
Acetaldehyde	75-07-0		11 (n.d.-49)				
Acetone	67-64-1	75 (4.8-150)	120 (n.d.-830)			12 (1.8-21)	220 (30-400)
Butyric acid	107-92-6		0.51 (n.d.-5.1)				
Dodecane	112-40-3			1.3 (n.d.-20)			
Ethylene glycol	107-21-1		38 (n.d.-210)				
Formaldehyde	50-00-0	13 (n.d.-29)	6.8 (n.d.-79)			5.9 (0.35-14)	32 (3.6-61)
Naphthalene	91-20-3		3.4 (n.d.-14)	5.6 (n.d.-28)	6.6 (6.6)		
n-Butanol	71-36-3						100 (n.d.-200)
Nonanal	124-19-6		5.7 (n.d.-19)	1.4 (n.d.-11)		1.8 (0.57-4)	
Octane	111-65-9						150 (n.d.-300)
Phenol	108-95-2	9.4 (4.4-19)	35 (n.d.-310)				340 (n.d.-680)
Toluene	108-88-3		5.1 (n.d.-12)				
Undecane	1120-21-4						140 (13-270)
TVOC*	N/A	160 (6.3-310)	680 (100-2100)	15000 (1500-100000)	270 (100-430)	7.5 (0.57-26)	7100 (1200-13000)

Source: CIWMB (2003).
n.d. = nondetectable N/A = not applicable
*TVOC concentrations calculated from total ion current (TIC) from GC/MS analysis by adding areas of integrated peaks with retention times greater than 5 min, subtracting from sum of area of internal standard chlorobenzene-d5, and using response factor of chlorobenzene-d5 as calibration.

Table 2.6 Type I Hood Requirements by Appliance Type [Std 154-2016, Tbl 1]

Appliance Description	Size	Type I Hoods[a] Light Duty	Medium Duty	Heavy Duty	Extra-Heavy Duty
Braising pan/tilting skillet, electric	All	•			
Oven, baking, electric and gas	All	•			
Oven, rotisserie, electric and gas	All	•			
Oven, combination, electric and gas	All	•			
Oven, convection, full-size, electric and gas	All	•			
Oven, convection, half-size, electric and gas (protein cooking)	All	•			
Oven, conveyor, electric	All	•			
Oven, deck, electric and gas	All	•			
Oven, duck, electric and gas	All	•			
Oven, revolving rack, electric and gas	All	•			
Oven, rapid cook, electric	All	•			
Oven, roasting, electric and gas	All	•			
Oven, rotisserie, electric and gas	All	•			
Oven, stone hearth, gas	All	•			
Range, cook-top, induction	All	•			
Range, discrete element, electric (with or without oven)	All	•			
Salamander, electric and gas	All	•			
Braising pan/tilting skillet, gas	All		•		
Broiler, chain conveyor, electric	All		•		
Broiler, electric, underfired	All		•		
Fryer, doughnut, electric and gas	All		•		
Fryer, kettle, electric and gas	All		•		
Fryer, open deep-fat, electric and gas	All		•		
Fryer, pressure, electric and gas	All		•		
Griddle, double-sided, electric and gas	All		•		
Griddle, flat, electric and gas	All		•		
Oven, conveyor, gas	All		•		
Range, open burner, gas (with or without oven)	All		•		
Range, hot top, electric and gas	All		•		
Smoker, electric and gas	All		•		
Broiler, chain conveyor, gas	All			•	
Broiler, electric and gas, over-fired (upright)	All			•	
Broiler, gas, underfired	All			•	
Grill, plancha, electric and gas	All			•	
Oven, tandoor, gas	All			•	
Range, wok, gas and electric	All			•	
Oven, stone hearth, wood-fired or wood for flavoring	All				•
Solid fuel cooking appliances combusting a solid fuel (such as wood, charcoal, or coal) to provide all or part of the heat for the cooking process[b]	All				•

[a] Where recirculating systems or recirculating hoods are used, the additional heat and moisture loads generated by such appliances shall be accounted for in the sensible and latent loads for the HVAC system.

[b] Solid-fuel flavoring cooking appliances shall comply with this table as if they do not combust solid fuel.

Table 2.7 Type II Hood Requirements by Appliance Description
[Std 154-2016, Tbl 2]

Appliance Description	Size	Hood Not Required[a]	Type II Hoods[b]	
			Light Duty	Medium Duty
Cabinet, holding, electric	All	•		
Cabinet, proofing, electric	All	•		
Cheese-melter, electric	All	•		
Coffee maker, electric	All	•		
Cooktop, induction, electric	All	•		
Dishwasher, door-type rack, hot water sanitizing, heat recovery and vapor reduction, electric	All	•		
Dishwasher, door-type rack, chemical sanitizing, heat recovery and vapor reduction, electric	All	•		
Dishwasher, door-type dump and fill, hot water sanitizing, electric	All	•		
Dishwasher, door-type dump and fill, chemical sanitizing, electric	All	•		
Dishwasher, pot and pan, hot water sanitizing, heat recovery and vapor reduction, electric	All	•		
Dishwasher, powered sink, electric	All	•		
Dishwasher, under-counter, chemical sanitizing, electric	All	•		
Dishwasher, under-counter, electric	All	•		
Dishwasher, undercounter, hot water sanitizing, heat recovery and vapor reduction, electric	All	•		
Drawer warmer, 2 drawer, electric	All	•		
Egg cooker, electric	All	•		
Espresso machine, electric	All	•		
Grill, panini, electric	All	•		
Hot dog cooker, electric	All	•		
Hot plate, countertop, electric	All	•		
Ovens, microwave, electric	All	•		
Popcorn machine, electric	All	•		
Rethermalizer, electric	All	•		
Rice cooker, electric	All	•		
Steam table, electric	All	•		
Steamers, bun, electric	All	•		
Steamer, compartment atmospheric, countertop, electric	All	•		
Steamer, compartment pressurized, countertop, electric	All	•		
Table, hot food, electric	All	•		
Toaster, electric	All	•		
Waffle iron, electric	All	•		
Kettle, steam jacketed, tabletop, electric, gas and direct steam	<20 gal		•	
Oven, convection, half-size, electric and gas (non-protein cooking)	All		•	

Table 2.7 Type II Hood Requirements by Appliance Description [Std 154-2016, Tbl 2] *(Continued)*

Appliance Description	Size	Hood Not Required[a]	Type II Hoods[b] Light Duty	Type II Hoods[b] Medium Duty
Pasta cooker, electric	All		•	
Rethermalizer, gas	All		•	
Rice cooker, gas	All		•	
Steamer, atmospheric, gas	All		•	
Steamer, pressurized, gas	All		•	
Steamer, atmospheric, floor-mounted, electric	All		•	
Steamer, pressurized, floor-mounted, electric	All		•	
Kettle, steam-jacketed floor mounted, electric, gas, and direct steam	<20 gal		•	
Dishwasher, conveyor rack, chemical sanitizing	All			•
Dishwasher, conveyor rack, hot water sanitizing	All			•
Dishwasher, door-type rack, chemical sanitizing	All			•
Dishwasher, door-type rack, hot water sanitizing	All			•
Dishwasher, pot and pan, hot water sanitizing	All			•
Pasta cooker, gas	All			•
Steam-jacketed kettle, floor mounted, electric and gas	≥20 gal			•

[a] Where hoods are not required, the additional heat and moisture loads generated by such appliances shall be accounted for in the sensible and latent loads for the HVAC system.

[b] Where recirculating systems or recirculating hoods are used, the additional heat and moisture loads generated by such appliances shall be accounted for in the sensible and latent loads for the HVAC system.

Table 2.8 Minimum Overhang Requirements for Type II Hoods [Std 154-2016, Tbl 3]

Type of Hood	End Overhang, in.	Front Overhang, in.	Rear Overhang, in.
Wall-mounted canopy	6	12	N/A
Single-island canopy	12	12	12
Double-island canopy	12	12	N/A
Eyebrow	N/A	12	N/A
Backshelf/proximity/pass-over	6	10 (setback)	N/A

N/A = Not Applicable

Table 2.9 Type II Hood Minimum Net Exhaust Airflow Rates [Std 154-2016, Tbl 4]

Type of Hood	Minimum Net Exhaust Flow Rate per Linear Hood Length, cfm/ft	
	Light Duty Equipment	Medium Duty Equipment
Wall-mounted canopy	200	300
Single island	400	500
Double island	250	250
Eyebrow	250	250
Backshelf (pass-over)	200	300

3. WATER

Table 3.1 Common Pump Terms, Symbols, and Formulas

Term	Symbol	Units	Formula
Velocity	v	ft/s	
Volume	V	ft^3	
Flow rate	Q_v	gpm	
Pressure	p	psi	
Density	ρ	lb/ft^3	
Acceleration of gravity	g	32.17 ft/s^2	
Speed	n	rpm	
Specific gravity	SG	—	$= \frac{\text{Mass of liquid}}{\text{Mass of water at 39°F}}$
Head	H	ft	$2.31\ p/SG$
Net positive suction head (NPSH)	H	ft	
Efficiency (percent)			
Pump	η_p		
Electric motor	η_m		
Variable speed drive	η_v		
Equipment (constant-speed pumps)	η_e		$\eta_e = \eta_p \eta_m / 100$
Equipment (variable-speed pumps)	η_e		$\eta_e = 10^{-4} \eta_p \eta_m \eta_v$
Utilization	η_u		
Q_D = design flow			
Q_A = actual flow			$\eta_u = 100 \frac{Q_D H_D}{Q_A H_A}$
H_D = design head			
H_A = actual head			
System Efficiency Index (decimal)			$SEI = 10^{-4} \eta_e \eta_u$
Output power (pump)	P_o	hp	$Q_v HSG/3960$
Shaft power	P_s	hp	$100 P_o / \eta_p$
Input power	P_i	kW	$74.6 P_s / \eta_m$

The theoretical power to circulate water in a hydronic system is the **water horsepower (whp)** and is calculated as follows:

$$\text{whp} = \frac{\dot{m}\Delta h}{33{,}000} \tag{3.1}$$

where

$\dot{m}$ = mass flow of fluid, lb/min
Δh = total head, ft of fluid
33,000 = units conversion, ft·lb/min per hp

At 68°F, water has a density of 62.3 lb/ft^3, and Equation 3.1 becomes

$$\text{whp} = \frac{Q\Delta h}{3960} \tag{3.2}$$

where

Q = fluid flow rate, gpm
3960 = units conversion, ft·gpm per hp

Pump efficiency is determined by comparing the output power to the input power:

$$\text{Efficiency} = \frac{\text{Output}}{\text{Input}} = \frac{\text{whp}}{\text{bhp}} \times 100\% \tag{3.3}$$

(3.4)

Table 3.2 Pump Affinity Laws [2020S, Ch 44, Tbl 1]

Function	Speed Change	Impeller Diameter Change
Flow	$Q_2 = Q_1\left(\frac{N_2}{N_1}\right)$	$Q_2 = Q_1\left(\frac{D_2}{D_1}\right)$
Head	$h_2 = h_1\left(\frac{N_2}{N_1}\right)^2$	$h_2 = h_1\left(\frac{D_2}{D_1}\right)^2$
Horsepower	$\text{bhp}_2 = \text{bhp}_1\left(\frac{N_2}{N_1}\right)^3$	$\text{bhp}_2 = \text{bhp}_1\left(\frac{D_2}{D_1}\right)^3$

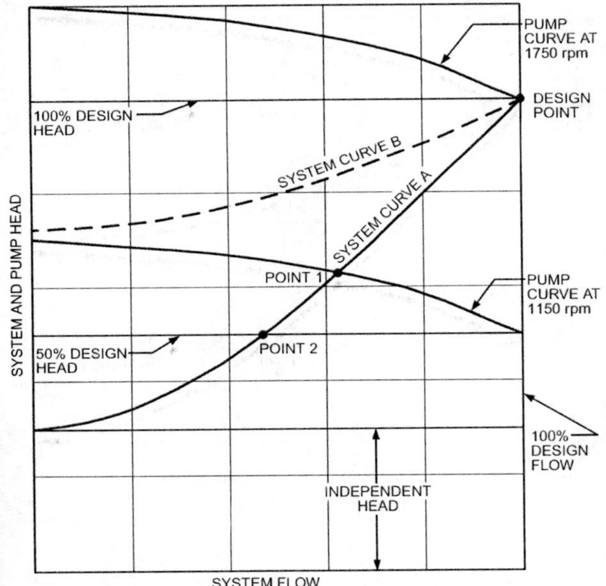

Figure 3.1 Example Application of Affinity Law [2020S, Ch 44, Fig 28]

If the hydronic system has a system head curve as shown in curve A, the pump at 1150 rpm will operate at point 1, not at point 2, as would be predicted by the affinity laws alone. If the hydronic system has a system head curve like curve B of Figure 3.1, the pump at 1150 rpm will run at shutoff head and deliver no water. This demonstrates that the affinity laws should be used to develop new pump head/capacity curves, but not to predict performance with a particular hydronic system unless its system head curve is known.

Net Positive Suction Characteristics

Particular attention must be given to the pressure and temperature of the water as it enters the pump, especially in condenser towers, steam condensate returns, and steam boiler feeds.

If the absolute pressure at the suction nozzle approaches the vapor pressure of the liquid, vapor pockets form in the impeller passages. The collapse of the vapor pockets (cavitation) is noisy and can be destructive to the pump impeller.

The pressure in excess of that required to prevent vapor pockets from forming is the net positive suction head required (NPSHR). NPSHR is a characteristic of a given pump and varies with pump speed and flow. It is determined by the manufacturer and is included on the pump performance curve.

NPSHR is particularly important when a pump is operating with hot liquids or is applied to a circuit having a suction lift. The vapor pressure increases with water temperature and reduces the net positive suction head available (NPSHA). Each pump has its NPSHR, and the installation has its NPSHA, which is the total useful energy above the vapor pressure at the pump inlet (see Figure 3.2).

$$\text{NPSHA} = h_p + h_z - h_{vpa} - h_f \tag{3.5}$$

where

h_p = absolute pressure on surface of liquid that enters pump, ft of head

h_z = static elevation of liquid above center line of pump (h_z is negative if liquid level is below pump center line), ft

h_{vpa} = absolute vapor pressure at pumping temperature, ft

h_f = friction and head losses in suction piping, ft

To determine the NPSHA in an existing installation, Equation 3.6 may be used (see Figure 3.2):

$$\text{NPSHA} = h_a + h_s + \frac{V^2}{2g} - h_{vpa} \tag{3.6}$$

where

h_a = atmospheric head for elevation of installation, ft

h_s = head at inlet flange corrected to center line of pump (h_s is negative if below atmospheric pressure), ft

$V^2/2g$ = velocity head at point of measurement of h_s, ft

For trouble-free design, the NPSHA must always be greater than the pump's NPSHR. In closed hot- and chilled-water systems where sufficient system fill pressure is exerted on the pump suction, NPSHR is normally not a factor.

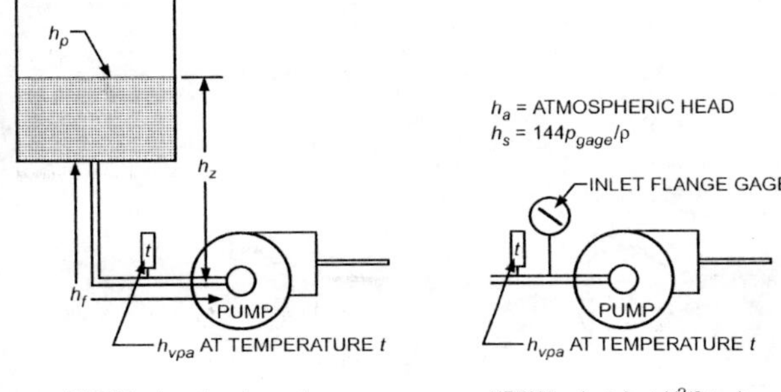

Figure 3.2 Net Positive Suction Head Available [2020S, Ch 44, Fig 33]

Water

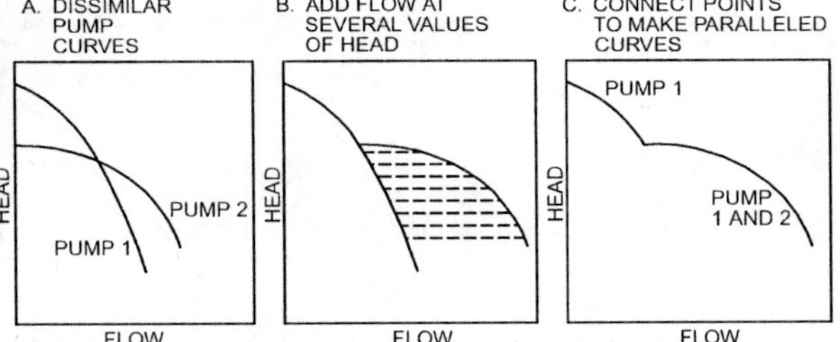

Figure 3.3 Construction of Curve for Dissimilar Parallel Pumps [2020S, Ch 44, Fig 38]

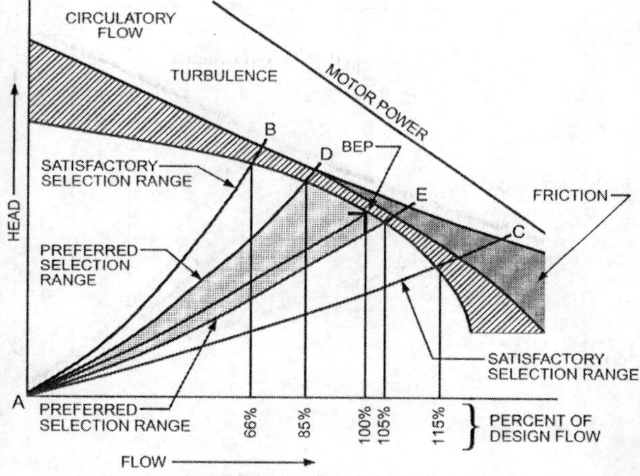

Figure 3.4 Pump Selection Regions [2020S, Ch 44, Fig 35]

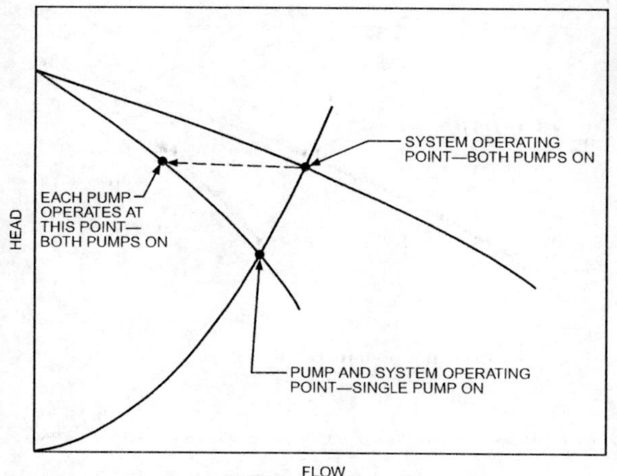

Figure 3.5 Operating Conditions for Parallel Operation [2020S, Ch 44, Fig 37]

Water

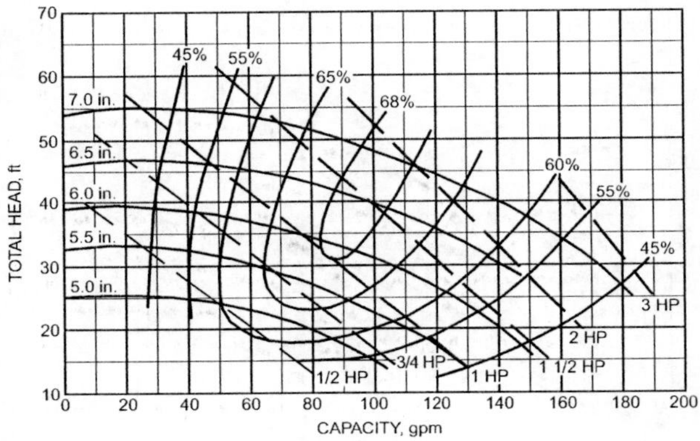

Figure 3.6 Typical Pump Performance Curves [2020S, Ch 44, Fig 13]

Table 3.3 Properties of Water, 212°F to 400°F [Adapted from 2020S, Ch 15, Tbl 1]

Temperature, °F	Absolute Pressure, psia*	Density, lb/ft³	Specific Heat, Btu/lb·°F
212	14.70	59.81	1.007
220	17.19	59.63	1.009
230	20.78	59.38	1.010
240	24.97	59.10	1.012
250	29.83	58.82	1.015
260	35.43	58.51	1.017
270	41.86	58.24	1.020
280	49.20	57.94	1.022
290	57.56	57.64	1.025
300	67.01	57.31	1.032
310	77.68	56.98	1.035
320	89.66	56.66	1.040
330	103.06	56.31	1.042
340	118.01	55.96	1.047
350	134.63	55.59	1.052
360	153.04	55.22	1.057
370	173.37	54.85	1.062
380	195.77	54.47	1.070
390	220.37	54.05	1.077
400	247.31	53.65	1.085

**Source*: *Thermodynamic Properties of Steam*, J.H. Keenan and F.G. Keyes, John Wiley & Sons, 1936.

Table 3.4 General Information on Water

Specific gravity of water is usually given as 1.0 at 60°F. However, for some purposes it is given as 1.0 at 39.2°F, the point of maximum density. Based on water at 39.2°F as 1.0, water at 60°F has a specific gravity of 0.999. Therefore, which base is selected makes no practical difference.

Viscosity of water varies as follows:

	32°F	50°F	60°F	70°F	80°F	100°F	120°F	140°F	160°F	180°F	212°F
Absolute viscosity, centipoises	1.70	1.31	1.12	.98	.86	.68	.56	.47	.40	.35	.28
Kinematic viscosity, centistokes	1.79	1.31	1.12	.98	.86	.69	.57	.45	.41	.36	.29

Table 3.5 Weight and Volume Equivalents

Convert from	Convert to								
	U.S. Gallon	Imperial Gallon	Cubic Inch	Cubic Foot	* Pound	* Cwt (U.S.)	* Ton (U.S.)	Litre	Cubic Metre
U.S. Gallon	1.	.8327	231.	.13368	8.345	.08345	.00418	3.785	.00378
Imperial Gallon	1.201	1.	22.741	.1605	10.02	.1002	.00502	4.546	.00455
Cubic Inch	.004329	.003607	1.	.000579	.036124	–	–	.0164	–
Cubic Foot	7.4805	6.229	1728.	1.	62.425	.6243	.03121	28.317	.0283
Pound[a]	.1198	.0998	27.68	.01602	1.	.01	.0005	.454	-
Cwt (U.S.)*	11.98	9.98	2765.	1.602	100.	1.	.05	45.36	.045
Ton (U.S.)*	239.6	199.6	–	32.04	2000.	20.0	1.	906.9	.907
Litre	.2642	.22	61.023	.0353	2.205	.022	.0011	1.	.001
Cubic Metre	264.2	220.	–	35.314	2204.5	22.045	1.102	1000.	1.

a. Volume—weight relationship taken for water at greatest density (39.2°F).

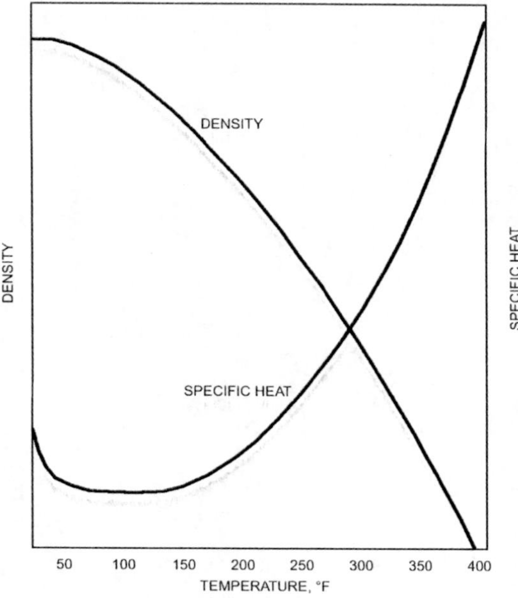

Figure 3.7 Density and Specific Heat of Water [2020S, Ch 15, Fig 3]

Table 3.6 Freezing Points for Solutions of Ethylene Glycol and Propylene Glycol

Glycol, % by mass	Ethylene Glycol °F	Propylene Glycol °F
10	26.2	26.1
15	22.2	22.9
20	17.9	19.2
25	12.7	14.7
30	6.7	9.2
40	–8.1	–6.0
50	–28.9	–28.3
60	–54.8	–59.9

Ethylene glycol solutions are less viscous than propylene glycol solutions at the same concentration. Less toxic propylene glycol is preferred for applications involving possible human contact.

Table 3.7 Volume of Vertical Cylindrical Tanks in Gallons per Foot of Depth

Diameter in ft	Diameter in in.	U.S. Gallons	Diameter in ft	Diameter in in.	U.S. Gallons	Diameter in ft	Diameter in in.	U.S. Gallons
1	0	5.875	3	6	71.97	6	0	211.5
1	2	7.997	3	8	78.99	6	6	248.2
1	4	10.44	3	10	86.33	7	0	287.9
1	6	13.22	4	0	94.00	7	6	330.5
1	8	16.32	4	2	102.0	8	0	376.0
1	10	19.75	4	4	110.3	8	6	424.5
2	0	23.50	4	6	119.0	9	0	475.9
2	2	27.58	4	8	127.9	9	6	530.2
2	4	31.99	4	10	137.3	10	0	587.5
2	6	36.72	5	0	146.9	10	6	647.7
2	8	41.78	5	2	156.8	11	0	710.9
2	10	47.16	5	4	167.1	11	6	777.0
3	0	52.88	5	6	177.7	12	0	846.0
3	2	58.92	5	8	188.7	12	6	918.0
3	4	65.28	5	10	199.9			

Table 3.8 Quantities for Various Depths of Vertical Cylindrical Tanks in Horizontal Position

% Depth Filled	% of Capacity	% Depth Filled	% of Capacity	% Depth Filled	% of Capacity	% Depth Filled	% of Capacity
1	.20	26	20.73	51	51.27	76	81.50
3	.90	28	23.00	53	53.81	78	83.68
5	1.87	30	25.31	55	56.34	80	85.77
7	3.07	32	27.66	57	58.86	82	87.76
9	4.45	34	30.03	59	61.36	84	89.68
11	5.98	36	32.44	61	63.86	86	91.50
13	7.64	38	34.90	63	66.34	88	93.20
15	9.40	40	37.36	65	68.81	90	94.80
17	11.27	42	39.89	67	71.16	92	96.26
19	13.23	44	42.40	69	73.52	94	97.55
21	15.26	46	44.92	71	75.93	96	98.66
23	17.40	48	47.45	73	78.14	98	99.50
25	19.61	50	50.00	75	80.39	100	100.0

Table 3.9 Volume of Water in Standard Pipe and Tube

Nominal Pipe Size, in.	Schedule No.	Standard Steel Pipe: Inside Diameter, in.	Standard Steel Pipe: Volume, gal/ft	Type *L* Copper Tube: Inside Diameter, in.	Type *L* Copper Tube: Volume, gal/ft
3/8	—	—	—	0.430	0.0075
1/2	40	0.622	0.0157	0.545	0.0121
5/8	—	—	—	0.666	0.0181
3/4	40	0.824	0.0277	0.785	0.0251
1	40	1.049	0.0449	1.025	0.0429
1 1/4	40	1.380	0.0779	1.265	0.0653
1 1/2	40	1.610	0.106	1.505	0.0924
2	40	2.067	0.174	1.985	0.161
2 1/2	40	2.469	0.249	2.465	0.248
3	40	3.068	0.384	2.945	0.354
3 1/2	40	3.548	0.514	3.425	0.479
4	40	4.026	0.661	3.905	0.622
5	40	5.047	1.04	4.875	0.970
6	40	6.065	1.50	5.845	1.39
8	30	8.071	2.66	7.725	2.43
10	30	10.136	4.19	9.625	3.78
12	30	12.090	5.96	11.565	5.46

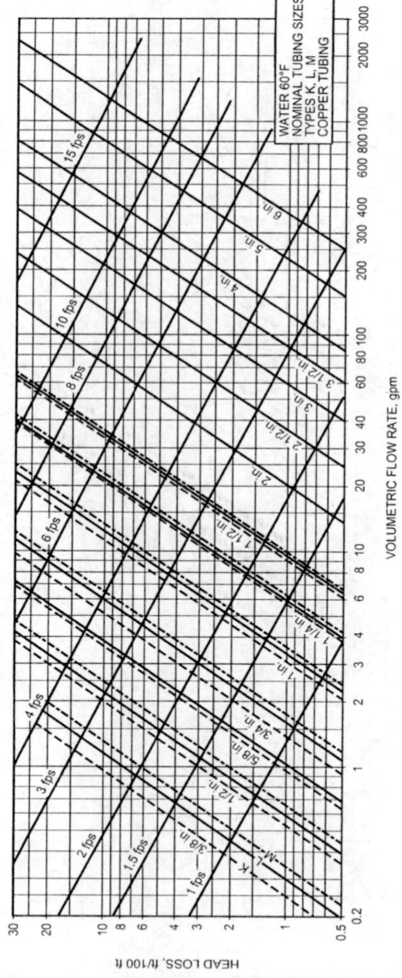

Figure 3.8 Friction Loss for Water in Copper Tubing (Types K, L, M)
[2021F, Ch 22, Fig 15]

Water

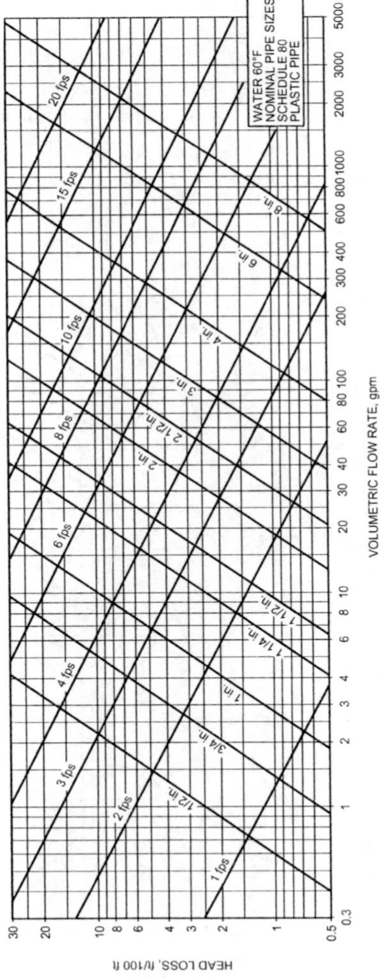

Figure 3.9 Friction Loss for Water in Plastic Pipe (Schedule 80)
[2021F, Ch 22, Fig 16]

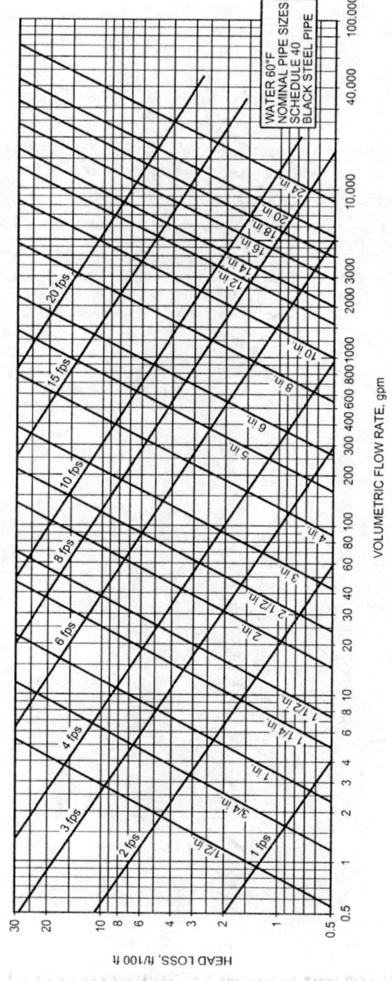

Figure 3.10 Friction Loss for Water in Commercial Steel Pipe (Schedule 40)
[2021F, Ch 22, Fig 14]

Valve and Fitting Losses

Valves and fittings cause pressure losses greater than those caused by the pipe alone. One formulation expresses losses as

$$\Delta p = K\left(\frac{\rho}{g_c}\right)\left(\frac{V^2}{2}\right) \quad \text{or} \quad \Delta h = K\frac{V^2}{2g} \tag{3.7}$$

where K = geometry- and size-dependent loss coefficient (see Tables 3.10 to 3.15).

ASHRAE research project RP-1193 found that, in general, PVC fitting geometry varied much more from one manufacturer to another than steel fittings did.

Calculating Pressure Losses

The most common engineering design flow loss calculation selects a pipe size for the desired total flow rate and available or allowable pressure drop.

Because formulation of fitting losses requires a known diameter, pipe size must be selected before calculating the detailed influence of fittings. A frequently used rule of thumb assumes that the design length of pipe is 50% to 100% longer than actual to account for fitting losses. After a pipe diameter has been selected on this basis, the influence of each fitting can be evaluated.

Table 3.10 *K* Factors: Threaded Pipe Fittings [2021F, Ch 22, Tbl 3]

Nominal Pipe Dia., in.	90° Standard Elbow	90° Long-Radius Elbow	45° Elbow	Return Bend	Tee-Line	Tee-Branch	Globe Valve	Gate Valve	Angle Valve	Swing Check Valve	Bell Mouth Inlet	Square Inlet	Projected Inlet
3/8	2.5	—	0.38	2.5	0.90	2.7	20	0.40	—	8.0	0.05	0.5	1.0
1/2	2.1	—	0.37	2.1	0.90	2.4	14	0.33	—	5.5	0.05	0.5	1.0
3/4	1.7	0.92	0.35	1.7	0.90	2.1	10	0.28	6.1	3.7	0.05	0.5	1.0
1	1.5	0.78	0.34	1.5	0.90	1.8	9	0.24	4.6	3.0	0.05	0.5	1.0
1 1/4	1.3	0.65	0.33	1.3	0.90	1.7	8.5	0.22	3.6	2.7	0.05	0.5	1.0
1 1/2	1.2	0.54	0.32	1.2	0.90	1.6	8	0.19	2.9	2.5	0.05	0.5	1.0
2	1.0	0.42	0.31	1.0	0.90	1.4	7	0.17	2.1	2.3	0.05	0.5	1.0
2 1/2	0.85	0.35	0.30	0.85	0.90	1.3	6.5	0.16	1.6	2.2	0.05	0.5	1.0
3	0.80	0.31	0.29	0.80	0.90	1.2	6	0.14	1.3	2.1	0.05	0.5	1.0
4	0.70	0.24	0.28	0.70	0.90	1.1	5.7	0.12	1.0	2.0	0.05	0.5	1.0

Source: Engineering Data Book (Hydraulic Institute 1990).

Table 3.11 *K* Factors: Flanged Welded Pipe Fittings [2021F, Ch 22, Tbl 4]

Nominal Pipe Dia., in.	90° Standard Elbow	90° Long-Radius Elbow	45° Long-Radius Elbow	Return Bend Standard	Return Bend Long-Radius	Tee-Line	Tee-Branch	Globe Valve	Gate Valve	Angle Valve	Swing Check Valve
1	0.43	0.41	0.22	0.43	0.43	0.26	1.0	13	—	4.8	2.0
1 1/4	0.41	0.37	0.22	0.41	0.38	0.25	0.95	12	—	3.7	2.0
1 1/2	0.40	0.35	0.21	0.40	0.35	0.23	0.90	10	—	3.0	2.0
2	0.38	0.30	0.20	0.38	0.30	0.20	0.84	9	0.34	2.5	2.0
2 1/2	0.35	0.28	0.19	0.35	0.27	0.18	0.79	8	0.27	2.3	2.0
3	0.34	0.25	0.18	0.34	0.25	0.17	0.76	7	0.22	2.2	2.0
4	0.31	0.22	0.18	0.31	0.22	0.15	0.70	6.5	0.16	2.1	2.0
6	0.29	0.18	0.17	0.29	0.18	0.12	0.62	6	0.10	2.1	2.0
8	0.27	0.16	0.17	0.27	0.15	0.10	0.58	5.7	0.08	2.1	2.0
10	0.25	0.14	0.16	0.25	0.14	0.09	0.53	5.7	0.06	2.1	2.0
12	0.24	0.13	0.16	0.24	0.13	0.08	0.50	5.7	0.05	2.1	2.0

Source: Engineering Data Book (Hydraulic Institute 1990).

Table 3.12 Summary of *K* Values for Steel Ells, Reducers, and Expansions
[Adapted from 2021F, Ch 22, Tbl 6]

	ASHRAE Research[a,b]		
	4 fps	8 fps	12 fps
2 in. S.R.[c] ell ($R/D = 1$) thread	0.60	0.68	0.736
4 in. S.R. ell ($R/D = 1$) weld	0.37	0.34	0.33
1 in. L.R. ell ($R/D = 1.5$) weld	—	—	—
2 in. L.R. ell ($R/D = 1.5$) weld	—	—	—
4 in. L.R. ell ($R/D = 1.5$) weld	0.26	0.24	0.23
6 in. L.R. ell ($R/D = 1.5$) weld	0.26	0.24	0.24
8 in. L.R. ell ($R/D = 1.5$) weld	0.22	0.20	0.19
10 in. L.R. ell ($R/D = 1.5$) weld	0.21	0.17	0.16
12 in. L.R. ell ($R/D = 1.5$) weld	0.17	0.17	0.17
16 in. L.R. ell ($R/D = 1.5$) weld	0.12	0.12	0.11
20 in. L.R. ell ($R/D = 1.5$) weld	0.12	0.10	0.10
24 in. L.R. ell ($R/D = 1.5$) weld	0.098	0.089	0.089
Reducer (2 by 1.5 in.) thread	0.53	0.28	0.20
(4 by 3 in.) weld	0.23	0.14	0.10
(6 by 4 in.) weld	0.62	0.54	0.53
(8 by 6 in.) weld	0.31	0.28	0.26
(10 by 8 in.) weld	0.16	0.14	0.14
(12 by 10 in.) weld	0.14	0.14	0.14
(16 by 12 in.) weld	0.17	0.16	0.17
(20 by 16 in.) weld	0.16	0.13	0.13
(24 by 20 in.) weld	0.053	0.053	0.055
Expansion (1.5 by 2 in.) thread	0.16	0.13	0.02
(3 by 4 in.) weld	0.11	0.11	0.11
(4 by 6 in.) weld	0.28	0.28	0.29
(6 by 8 in.) weld	0.15	0.12	0.11
(8 by 10 in.) weld	0.11	0.09	0.08
(10 by 12 in.) weld	0.11	0.11	0.11
(12 by 16 in.) weld	0.073	0.076	0.073
(16 by 20 in.) weld	0.024	0.021	0.022
(20 by 24 in.) weld	0.020	0.023	0.020

Source: Rahmeyer (2003a).
[b]Rahmeyer (1999a, 2002a).
[c] S.R.—short radius or regular ell; L.R.—long-radius ell.

Water

Table 3.13 Summary of *K* Factors for Pipe Tees [2021F, Ch 22, Tbl 7]

		ASHRAE Research[a,b]		
		4 fps	8 fps	12 fps
2 in. thread tee,	100% branch	0.93	—	—
	100% line (flow-through)	0.19	—	—
	100% mix	1.19	—	
4 in.weld tee,	100% branch	—	0.57	—
	100% line (flow-through)	—	0.06	—
	100% mix	—	0.49	—
6 in.weld tee,	100% branch	—	0.56	—
	100% line (flow-through)	—	0.12	—
	100% mix	—	0.88	—
8 in.weld tee,	100% branch	—	0.53	—
	100% line (flow-through)	—	0.08	—
	100% mix	—	0.70	—
10 in.weld tee,	100% branch	—	0.52	—
	100% line (flow-through)	—	0.06	—
	100% mix	—	0.77	—
12 in.weld tee,	100% branch	0.70	0.63	0.62
	100% line (flow-through)	0.062	0.091	0.096
	100% mix	0.88	0.72	0.72
16 in.weld tee,	100% branch	0.54	0.55	0.54
	100% line (flow-through)	0.032	0.028	0.028
	100% mix	0.74	0.74	0.76

[a]Rahmeyer (1999b, 2002b).
[b]Ding et al. (2005).

Table 3.14 Test Summary for Loss Coefficients *K* and Equivalent Loss Lengths [2021F, Ch 22, Tbl 8]

Schedule 80 PVC Fitting		*K*	*L*, ft
Injected molded elbow,	2 in.	0.91 to 1.00	8.4 to 9.2
	4 in.	0.86 to 0.91	18.3 to 19.3
	6 in.	0.76 to 0.91	26.2 to 31.3
	8 in.	0.68 to 0.87	32.9 to 42.1
8 in. fabricated elbow, Type I, components		0.40 to 0.42	19.4 to 20.3
Type II, mitered		0.073 to 0.76	35.3 to 36.8
6 by 4 in. injected molded reducer		0.12 to 0.59	4.1 to 20.3
Bushing type		0.49 to 0.59	16.9 to 20.3
8 by 6 in. injected molded reducer		0.13 to 0.63	6.3 to 30.5
Bushing type		0.48 to 0.68	23.2 to 32.9
Gradual reducer type		0.21	10.2
4 by 6 in. injected molded expansion		0.069 to 1.19	1.5 to 25.3
Bushing type		0.069 to 1.14	1.5 to 24.2
6 by 8 in. injected molded expansion		0.95 to 0.96	32.7 to 33.0
Bushing type		0.94 to 0.95	32.4 to 32.7
Gradual reducer type		0.99	34.1

Table 3.15 Test Summary for Loss Coefficients *K* of PVC Tees [2021F, Ch 22, Tbl 9]

Branching		
Schedule 80 PVC Fitting	K_{1-2}	K_{1-3}
2 in. injection molded branching tee, 100% line flow	0.13 to 0.26	—
50/50 flow	0 to 0.12	0.74 to 1.02
100% branch flow	—	0.98 to 1.39
4 in. injection molded branching tee, 100% line flow	0.07 to 0.22	—
50/50 flow	0.03 to 0.13	0.74 to 0.82
100% branch flow	—	0.97 to 1.12
6 in. injection molded branching tee, 100% line flow	0.01 to 0.14	—
50/50 flow	0.06 to 0.11	0.70 to 0.84
100% branch flow	—	0.95 to 1.15
6 in. fabricated branching tee, 100% line flow	0.21 to 0.22	—
50/50 flow	0.04 to 0.09	1.29 to 1.40
100% branch flow	—	1.74 to 1.88
8 in. injection molded branching tee, 100% line flow	0.04 to 0.09	—
50/50 flow	0.04 to 0.07	0.64 to 0.75
100% branch flow	—	0.85 to 0.96
8 in. fabricated branching tee, 100% line flow	0.09 to 0.16	—
50/50 flow	0.08 to 0.13	1.07 to 1.16
100% branch flow	—	1.40 to 1.62
Mixing		
PVC Fitting	K_{1-2}	K_{3-2}
2 in. injection molded mixing tee, 100% line flow	0.12 to 0.25	—
50/50 flow	1.22 to 1.19	0.89 to 1.88
100% mix flow	—	0.89 to 1.54
4 in. injection molded mixing tee, 100% line flow	0.07 to 0.18	—
50/50 flow	1.19 to 1.88	0.98 to 1.88
100% mix flow	—	0.88 to 1.02
6 in. injection molded mixing tee, 100% line flow	0.06 to 0.14	—
50/50 flow	1.26 to 1.80	1.02 to 1.60
100% mix flow	—	0.90 to 1.07
6 in. fabricated mixing tee, 100% line flow	0.19 to 0.21	—
50/50 flow	2.94 to 3.32	2.57 to 3.17
100% mix flow	—	1.72 to 1.98
8 in. injection molded mixing tee, 100% line flow	0.04 to 0.09	—
50/50 flow	1.10 to 1.60	0.96 to 1.32
100% mix flow	—	0.81 to 0.93
8 in. fabricated mixing tee, 100% line flow	0.13 to 0.70	—
50/50 flow	2.36 to 10.62	2.02 to 2.67
100% mix flow	—	1.34 to 1.53

Coefficients based on average velocity of 8 fps. Range of values varies with fitting manufacturers. Line or straight flow is Q_2/Q_1 = 100%. Branch flow is Q_2/Q_1 = 0%.

4. STEAM

Table 4.1 Properties of Saturated Steam

Pressure p	Temperature t, °F	Specific Volume V_g, cu ft/lb	Enthalpy, Btu/lb Saturated Water h_f	Evaporation h_{fg}	Saturated Steam h_g
0.25 in. Hg	40.34	2423.7	8.28	1071.1	1079.4
0.50	58.80	1256.4	26.86	1060.6	1087.5
1.00	79.03	652.3	47.05	1049.2	1096.3
2.00	101.14	339.2	69.10	1036.6	1105.7
2 psia	126.08	173.7	93.99	1022.2	1116.2
3	141.48	118.7	109.37	1013.2	1122.6
4	152.97	90.63	120.86	1006.4	1127.3
5	162.24	73.52	130.13	1001.0	1131.1
6	170.06	61.98	137.94	996.2	1164.2
7	176.85	53.64	144.76	992.1	1136.9
8	182.86	47.34	150.79	988.5	1139.3
9	188.28	42.40	156.22	985.2	1141.4
10	193.21	38.42	161.17	982.1	1143.3
12	201.96	32.40	169.96	976.6	1146.6
14	209.56	28.04	177.61	971.9	1149.5
14.696	212.00	26.80	180.07	970.3	1150.4
20	227.96	20.09	196.16	960.1	1156.3
30	250.33	13.75	218.82	945.3	1164.1
40	267.25	10.50	236.03	933.7	1169.7
50	281.01	8.515	250.09	924.0	1174.1
60	292.71	7.175	262.09	915.5	1177.6
70	302.92	6.206	272.61	907.9	1180.6
80	312.03	5.472	282.02	901.1	1183.1
90	320.27	4.896	290.56	894.7	1185.3
100	327.81	4.432	298.40	888.8	1187.2
120	341.25	3.728	312.44	877.9	1190.4
140	353.02	3.220	324.82	868.2	1193.0
160	363.53	2.834	335.93	859.2	1195.1
180	373.06	2.532	346.03	850.8	1196.9
200	381.79	2.228	355.36	843.0	1198.4

Sources:

1. Keenan, J., and F. Keyes. 1936. *Thermodynamic Properties of Steam*. John Wiley and Sons, New York.
2. Holladay, W., and C. Otterholm. 1985. *Numbers*. Altadena, CA.

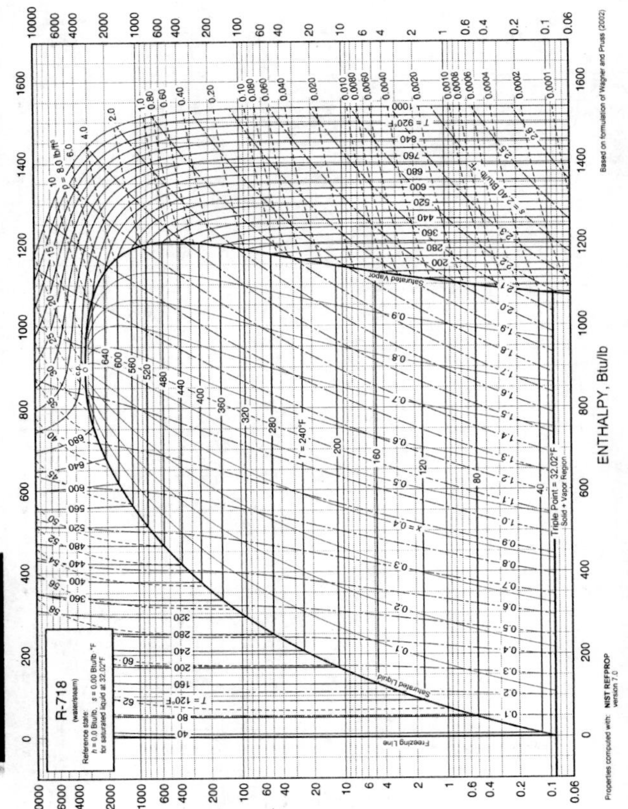

Figure 4.1 Pressure-Enthalpy Diagram for Refrigerant 718 (Water/Steam)
[2021F, Ch 30, Fig 20]

Table 4.2 Flow Rate of Steam in Schedule 40 Pipe [2021F, Ch 22, Tbl 32]

Nominal Pipe Size, in.	Pressure Drop per 100 ft of Length: 1/16 psi (1 oz/in^2) Sat. Press., psig		1/8 psi (2 oz/in^2) Sat. Press., psig		1/4 psi (4 oz/in^2) Sat. Press., psig		1/2 psi (8 oz/in^2) Sat. Press., psig		3/4 psi (12 oz/in^2) Sat. Press., psig		1 psi Sat. Press., psig		2 psi Sat. Press., psig	
	3.5	12	3.5	12	3.5	12	3.5	12	3.5	12	3.5	12	3.5	12
3/4	9	11	14	16	20	24	29	35	36	43	42	50	60	73
1	17	21	26	31	37	46	54	66	68	82	81	95	114	137
1-1/4	36	45	53	66	78	96	111	138	140	170	162	200	232	280
1-1/2	56	70	84	100	120	147	174	210	218	260	246	304	360	430
2	108	134	162	194	234	285	336	410	420	510	480	590	710	850
2-1/2	174	215	258	310	378	460	540	660	680	820	780	950	1,150	1,370
3	318	380	465	550	660	810	960	1,160	1,190	1,430	1,380	1,670	1,950	2,400
3-1/2	462	550	670	800	990	1,218	1,410	1,700	1,740	2,100	2,000	2,420	2,950	3,450
4	640	800	950	1,160	1,410	1,690	1,980	2,400	2,450	3,000	2,880	3,460	4,200	4,900
5	1,200	1,430	1,680	2,100	2,440	3,000	3,570	4,250	4,380	5,250	5,100	6,100	7,500	8,600
6	1,920	2,300	2,820	3,350	3,960	4,850	5,700	6,800	7,000	8,600	8,400	10,000	11,900	14,200
8	3,900	4,800	5,570	7,000	8,100	10,000	11,400	14,300	14,500	17,700	16,500	20,500	24,000	29,500
10	7,200	8,800	10,200	12,600	15,000	18,200	21,000	26,000	26,200	32,000	30,000	37,000	42,700	52,000
12	11,400	13,700	16,500	19,500	23,400	28,400	33,000	40,000	41,000	49,500	48,000	57,500	67,800	81,000

Notes:

1. Flow rate is in lb/h at initial saturation pressures of 3.5 and 12 psig. Flow is based on Moody friction factor, where the flow of condensate does not inhibit the flow of steam.
2. The flow rates at 3.5 psig cover saturated pressure from 1 to 6 psig, and the rates at 12 psig cover saturated pressure from 8 to 16 psig with an error not exceeding 8%.
3. The steam velocities corresponding to the flow rates given in this table can be found from Figures 18 and 20 of Chapter 22 of the 2021 *ASHRAE Handbook—Fundamentals*.

Table 4.3 Medium-Pressure Steam Pipe Capacities (30 psig)—Pounds Per Hour

Pipe Size, in.	Pressure Drop per 100 ft 1/8 psi	1/4 psi	1/2 psi	3/4 psi	1 psi	2 psi
Supply Mains and Risers 25–35 psig—Max Error 8%						
3/4	15	22	31	38	45	63
1	31	46	63	77	89	125
1 1/4	69	100	141	172	199	281
1 1/2	107	154	219	267	309	437
2	217	313	444	543	627	886
2 1/2	358	516	730	924	1,033	1,460
3	651	940	1,330	1,628	1,880	2,660
3 1/2	979	1,414	2,000	2,447	2,825	4,000
4	1,386	2,000	2,830	3,464	4,000	5,660
5	2,560	3,642	5,225	6,402	7,390	10,460
6	4,210	6,030	8,590	10,240	12,140	17,180
8	8,750	12,640	17,860	21,865	25,250	35,100
10	16,250	23,450	33,200	40,625	46,900	66,350
12	25,640	36,930	52,320	64,050	74,000	104,500
Return Mains and Risers 0–4 psig—Max Return Pressure						
3/4	115	170	245	308	365	
1	230	340	490	615	730	
1 1/4	485	710	1,025	1,285	1,530	
1 1/2	790	1,155	1,670	2,100	2,500	
2	1,575	2,355	3,400	4,300	5,050	
2 1/2	2,650	3,900	5,600	7,100	8,400	
3	4,850	7,100	10,250	12,850	15,300	
3 1/2	7,200	10,550	15,250	19,150	22,750	
4	10,200	15,000	21,600	27,000	32,250	
5	19,000	27,750	40,250	55,500	60,000	
6	31,000	45,500	65,500	83,000	98,000	

Table 4.4 High-Pressure Steam Pipe Capacities (150 psig)—Pounds Per Hour

Pipe Size, in.	Pressure Drop per 100 ft 1/8 psi	1/4 psi	1/2 psi	3/4 psi	1 psi	2 psi	5 psi	6 psi
Supply Mains and Risers 130–180 psig—Max Error 8%								
3/4	29	41	58	82	116	184	300	420
1	58	82	117	165	233	369	550	790
1 1/4	130	185	262	370	523	827	1,230	1,720
1 1/2	203	287	407	575	813	1,230	1,730	2,600
2	412	583	825	1,167	1,650	2,000	3,410	4,820
2 1/2	683	959	1,359	1,920	2,430	3,300	5,200	7,600
3	1,237	1,750	2,476	3,500	4,210	6,000	9,400	13,500
3 1/2	1,855	2,626	3,715	5,250	6,020	8,500	13,100	20,000
4	2,625	3,718	5,260	7,430	8,400	12,300	19,200	28,000
5	4,858	6,875	9,725	13,750	15,000	21,200	33,100	47,500
6	7,960	11,275	15,950	22,550	25,200	36,500	56,500	80,000
8	16,590	23,475	33,200	46,950	50,000	70,200	120,000	170,000
10	30,820	43,430	61,700	77,250	90,000	130,000	210,000	300,000
12	48,600	68,750	97,250	123,000	155,000	200,000	320,000	470,000
Return Mains and Risers 1–20 psig—Max Return Pressure								
3/4	156	232	360	465	560	890		
1	313	462	690	910	1,120	1,780		
1 1/4	650	960	1,500	1,950	2,330	3,700		
1 1/2	1,070	1,580	2,460	3,160	3,800	6,100		
2	2,160	3,300	4,950	6,400	7,700	12,300		
2 1/2	3,600	5,350	8,200	10,700	12,800	20,400		
3	6,500	9,600	15,000	19,500	23,300	37,200		
3 1/2	9,600	14,400	22,300	28,700	34,500	55,000		
4	13,700	20,500	31,600	40,500	49,200	78,500		
5	25,600	38,100	58,500	76,000	91,500	146,000		
6	42,000	62,500	96,000	125,000	150,000	238,000		

Table 4.5 Steam Pipe Capacities for Low-Pressure Systems [2021F, Ch 22, Tbl 33]

Nominal Pipe Size, in.	Capacity, lb/h				
	Two-Pipe System		One-Pipe Systems		
	Condensate Flowing Against Steam		Supply Risers Upfeed	Radiator Valves and Vertical Connections	Radiator and Riser Runouts
	Vertical	Horizontal			
A	B[a]	C[b]	D[c]	E	F[b]
3/4	8	7	6	—	7
1	14	14	11	7	7
1 1/4	31	27	20	16	16
1 1/2	48	42	38	23	16
2	97	93	72	42	23
2 1/2	159	132	116	—	42
3	282	200	200	—	65
3 1/2	387	288	286	—	119
4	511	425	380	—	186
5	1,050	788	—	—	278
6	1,800	1,400	—	—	545
8	3,750	3,000	—	—	—
10	7,000	5,700	—	—	—
12	11,500	9,500	—	—	—
16	22,000	19,000	—	—	—

Notes:
1. For one- or two-pipe systems in which condensate flows against steam flow.
2. Steam at average pressure of 1 psig used as basis of calculating capacities.

[a] Do not use column B for pressure drops of less than 1/16 psi per 100 ft of equivalent run. Use Figure 18 or Table 31 of Chapter 22 of 2021 *ASHRAE Handbook—Fundamentals* instead.

[b] Pitch of horizontal runouts to risers and radiators should be not less than 0.5 in/ft. Where this pitch cannot be obtained, runouts over 8 ft in length should be one pipe size larger than that called for in this table.

[c] Do not use column D for pressure drops of less than 1/24 psi per 100 ft of equivalent run except on sizes 3 in. and over. Use Figure 18 or Table 31 of Chapter 22 of 2021 *ASHRAE Handbook—Fundamentals* instead.

Table 4.6 Return Main and Riser Capacities for Low-Pressure Steam Systems—Pounds per Hour [2021F, Ch 22, Tbl 34]

	Pipe Size, In.	Pressure Drop per 100 ft																	
		1/32 psi (1/2 oz)			1/24 psi (2/3 oz)			1/6 psi (1 oz)			1/8 psi (2 oz)			1/4 psi (4 oz)			1/2 psi (8 oz)		
		Wet	Dry	Vac.	Wet	Dry	Vac.	Wet	Dry	Vac.	Wet	Dry	Vac.	Wet	Dry	Vac.	Wet	Dry	Vac.
Return Main	3/4	–	-	-	-	-	42	-	-	100	-	-	142	-	-	200	-	-	283
	1	125	62	-	145	71	143	175	80	175	250	103	249	350	115	350	-	-	494
	1 1/4	213	130	-	248	149	244	300	168	300	425	217	426	600	241	600	-	-	848
	1 1/2	338	206	-	393	236	388	475	265	475	675	340	674	950	378	950	-	-	1,340
	2	700	470	-	810	535	815	1,000	575	1,000	1,400	740	1,420	2,000	825	2,000	-	-	2,830
	2 1/2	1,180	760	-	1,580	868	1,360	1,680	950	1,680	2,350	1,230	2,380	3,350	1,360	3,350	-	-	4,730
	3	1,880	1,460	-	2,130	1,560	2,180	2,680	1,750	2,680	3,750	2,250	3,800	5,350	2,500	5,350	-	-	7,560
	3 1/2	2,750	1,970	-	3,300	2,200	3,250	4,000	2,500	4,000	5,500	3,230	5,680	8,000	3,580	8,000	-	-	11,300
	4	3,880	2,930	-	4,580	3,350	4,500	5,500	3,750	5,500	7,750	4,830	7,810	11,000	5,380	11,000	-	-	15,500
	5	-	-	-	-	-	7,880	-	-	9,680	-	-	13,700	-	-	19,400	-	-	27,300
	6	-	-	-	-	-	12,600	-	-	15,500	-	-	22,000	-	-	31,000	-	-	43,800
Riser	3/4	-	48	-	-	48	143	-	48	175	-	48	249	-	48	350	-	-	494
	1	-	113	-	-	113	244	-	113	300	-	113	426	-	113	600	-	-	848
	1 1/4	-	248	-	-	248	388	-	248	475	-	248	674	-	248	950	-	-	1,340
	1 1/2	-	375	-	-	375	815	-	375	1,000	-	375	1,420	-	375	2,000	-	-	2,830
	2	-	750	-	-	750	1,360	-	750	1,680	-	750	2,380	-	750	3,350	-	-	4,730
	2 1/2	-	-	-	-	-	2,180	-	-	2,680	-	-	3,800	-	-	5,350	-	-	7,560
	3	-	-	-	-	-	3,250	-	-	4,000	-	-	5,680	-	-	8,000	-	-	11,300
	3 1/2	-	-	-	-	-	4,480	-	-	5,500	-	-	7,810	-	-	11,000	-	-	15,500
	4	-	-	-	-	-	7,880	-	-	9,680	-	-	13,700	-	-	19,400	-	-	27,300
	5	-	-	-	-	-	12,600	-	-	15,500	-	-	22,000	-	-	31,000	-	-	43,800

5. PIPING

Table 5.1 Common Applications of Pipe, Fittings, and Valves for Heating and Air Conditioning [2021F, Ch 22, Tbl 1]

Application	Size, in.	Material	Weight	Joint Type	Fitting Material	Class (When Applicable)	System[g] Temp., °F	Maximum Pressure at Temperature,[a,b] psi
Chilled water	≤ 2	Steel Type F (CW)	Schedule 40	Thread	Cast iron	125	250	125
	2.5 to 12	Steel A or B, Type E (ERW)	Schedule 40	Weld	Wrought steel	Standard	250	400
				Flange	Wrought steel	150	250	250
					Cast iron	125	250	175
					Cast iron	250	250	400
		Copper, hard or soft	Type K or L	Solder Flared (soft) Rolled groove (2 to 8 in.) Press-connect (0.5 to 4 in.) Push connect (0.5 to 2 in.) Mechanical formed	Wrought or cast Cu		100	370 Type K soft 635 Type K hard 250 Type L soft 435 Type L hard
				Braze Weld	Wrought or cast Cu		100	250 Type L soft 370 Type K soft
		Copper, hard	Type M	Solder Rolled groove (2 to 8 in.) Press-connect (0.5 to 4 in.) Push connect (0.5 to 2 in.) Mechanical formed	Wrought or cast Cu		100	395 Type M hard
				Braze Weld	Wrought or cast Cu		100	230 Type M soft
	0.375 to 1.0	PEX (barrier)	SDR-9	Crimp Clamp Expansion Compression Push fit Proprietary	Bronze Brass Copper Engineered plastic		73	145

Table 5.1 **Common Applications of Pipe, Fittings, and Valves for Heating and Air Conditioning** [2021F, Ch 22, Tbl 1] ***(Continued)***

Application	Size, in.	Material	Weight	Joint Type	Fitting Material	Class (When Applicable)	System[g] Temp., °F	Maximum Pressure at Temperature,[a,b] psi
Chilled water (cont'd)	0.5 to 6	PE	Schedule 40,[f] 80, SDR	Thermal fusion, compression	PE		120 (140) limit for some applications)	Varies with pipe wall thickness, grade, schedule, size. Check manufacturer's documentation for design ratings 30 to110 at 130°F
Heating and recirculating	2 and smaller	Steel Type F (CW)	Schedule 40	Thread	Cast iron	125	250	125
	0.25 to 12	Steel B Type E (ERW)	Schedule 40	Weld	Wrought steel	Standard	250	400
				Flange	Wrought steel	150	250	250
					Cast iron	125	250	125
					Cast iron	250	250	400
		Copper, hard or soft	Type K or L	Solder Braze Flared (soft) Rolled groove (2 to 8 in.) Press-connect (0.5 to 4 in.) Push connect (0.5 to 2 in.) Mechanical formed	Wrought or cast Cu		200	300 Type K soft 635 Type K hard 205 Type L soft 435 Type L hard
				Braze Weld	Wrought or cast Cu		200	300 Type K soft 205 Type L soft
	0.25 to 12	Copper, hard	Type M	Solder Rolled groove (2 to 8 in.) Press-connect (0.5 to 4 in.) Push connect (0.5 to 2 in.) Mechanical formed	Wrought or cast Cu		200	395 Type M hard
				Braze Weld	Wrought or cast Cu		200	200 Type M soft

Table 5.1 Common Applications of Pipe, Fittings, and Valves for Heating and Air Conditioning [2021F, Ch 22, Tbl 1] ***(Continued)***

Application	Size, in.	Material	Weight	Joint Type	Fitting Material	Class (When Applicable)	System[g] Temp., °F	Maximum Pressure at Temperature,[a,b] psi
Heating and recirculating (cont'd)	0.375 to 1.0	PEX (barrier)	SDR-9	Crimp	Bronze		200	79
				Clamp	Brass			
				Expansion	Copper			
				Compression	Engineered plastic			
				Push fit				
				Proprietary				
Steam and condensate	2 and smaller	Steel Type F (CW) or S	Schedule 40[d]	Thread	Cast iron	125		90
				Thread	Malleable iron	150		90
				Socket	Forged steel	3000		90
		Steel B Type E (ERW) or S	Schedule 40[d]	Thread	Cast iron	125		100
				Thread	Malleable iron	150		125
				Socket	Forged steel	3000		400
		Steel B Type E (ERW) or S	Schedule 80	Thread	Cast iron	250		200
				Socket				
				Thread	Malleable iron	300		250
				Socket	Forged steel	3000		400
	2 to 12	Steel B Type E (ERW) or S	Schedule 40	Weld	Wrought steel	Standard		250
				Flange	Wrought steel	150		200
					Cast iron	125		100
		Steel B Type E (ERW) or S	Schedule 80	Weld	Wrought steel	XS		700
				Flange	Wrought steel	300		500
					Cast iron	250		200

Table 5.1 Common Applications of Pipe, Fittings, and Valves for Heating and Air Conditioning [2021F, Ch 22, Tbl 1] ***(Continued)***

Application	Size, in.	Material	Weight	Joint Type	Fitting Material	Class (When Applicable)	System[g] Temp., °F	Maximum Pressure at Temperature,[a,b] psi
Ground-source heat pump	0.25 to 2	Copper, hard or soft	Type L or ACR	Flared or brazed	Wrought or cast Cu		200	205 Type L soft, 435 Type L hard, 240 ACR soft, 500 ACR hard
	0.375 to 1.0	PEX (barrier)	SDR-9	Crimp Clamp Expansion Compression Push fit Proprietary	Bronze Brass Copper Engineered plastic		180	100
Refrigerant	0.375 to 4.125	Steel B Type E (ERW)	Schedule 40	Weld			Wrought steel	
		Copper, hard	Type L or ACR	Braze	Wrought or forged Cu		200	435 Type L hard, 240 ACR soft
Natural gas and LP	0.25 to 12	Copper, hard or soft	Type K or L	Solder Rolled groove (2 to 8 in.) Press-connect (0.5 to 4 in.) Push connect (0.5 to 2 in.) Mechanically formed	Wrought or cast Cu		100	370 Type K soft 635 Type K hard 250 Type L soft 435 Type L hard
				Braze Weld	Wrought or cast Cu		100	370 Type K soft 250 Type L soft
	0.375 to 4.125	Copper, hard	ACR	Solder	Wrought or cast Cu		100	500 Type ACR hard
				Braze	Wrought or cast Cu		100	290 Type ACR Soft

Table 5.1 Common Applications of Pipe, Fittings, and Valves for Heating and Air Conditioning [2021F, Ch 22, Tbl 1] *(Continued)*

Application	Size, in.	Material	Weight	Joint Type	Fitting Material	Class (When Applicable)	System[g] Temp., °F	Maximum Pressure at Temperature,[a,b] psi
Natural gas and LP (cont'd)	0.375 to 1.0	PEX	SDR-9	Crimp Clamp Expansion Compression Push fit Proprietary	Bronze Brass Copper Engineered plastic		73	145
	0.5 to 6	PE	Schedule 40, 80, SDR	Thermal fusion, compression	PE		120 (140) limit for some applications)	Depends on pipe, grade, schedule, size. Generally 30 to 110 at 130°F
	0.5 to 6	HDPE	SDR	Thermal fusion, compression	HDPE		120	Depends on pipe, grade, schedule, size. Generally 64 for SDR 11 at 120°F
Fuel oil, above-ground	2 to 12	Black Steel, B Type E (ERW) or S (seamless)	Schedule 40	Thread or weld	Black malleable iron Wrought steel weld Forged steel flanges	150 150		
	0.25 to 12	Copper, hard or soft	Type K or L	Solder Flared (soft) Rolled groove (2 to 8 in.) Press-connect (0.5 to 4 in.) Push connect (0.5 to 2 in.) Mechanical formed	Wrought or cast Cu		100	300 Type K soft 635 Type K hard 250 Type L soft 435 Type L hard
				Braze or weld	Wrought or cast Cu		100	300 Type K soft, 250 Type L soft

Table 5.1 Common Applications of Pipe, Fittings, and Valves for Heating and Air Conditioning [2021F, Ch 22, Tbl 1] ***(Continued)***

Application	Size, in.	Material	Weight	Joint Type	Fitting Material	Class (When Applicable)	System[g] Temp., °F	Maximum Pressure at Temperature,[a,b] psi
Fuel oil, above-ground (cont'd)	0.25 to 12 (cont'd)	Copper, hard	Type M	Solder	Wrought or cast Cu		100	395 Type M hard
				Braze Rolled groove (2 to 8 in.) Press-connect (0.5 to 4 in.) Push connect (0.5 to 2 in.) Mechanical formed				
	0.25 to 12	ABS	Schedule 40,[f] 80, SDR	Solvent weld, thread, flange	ABS		160 limit	Depends on pipe class: approximately 50 at 160°F
	0.5 to 6	HDPE	SDR-9	Thermal fusion, compression	HDPE		120	Depends on pipe, grade, schedule, size. Generally 64 for SDR 11 at 120°F
Compressed air	≤2.5 and smaller	Black steel	Schedule 40	Thread	Black malleable iron	150	350	
	>2.5	Black steel	Schedule 40	Flange or weld	Black malleable iron	150	350	
	0.375 to 4.125	Copper, hard	ACR	Solder Flared (soft) Mechanical formed	Wrought or cast Cu		200	240 ACR soft 500 ACR hard
				Braze			200	240 ACR hard
	0.5 to 4	ABS HDPE	Schedule 40 Schedule 40, 80, SDR	Solvent weld	ABS HDPE		73	185
	0.375 to 1.0	PEX	SDR-9					

Table 5.1 Common Applications of Pipe, Fittings, and Valves for Heating and Air Conditioning [2021F, Ch 22, Tbl 1] ***(Continued)***

Application	Size, in.	Material	Weight	Joint Type	Fitting Material	Class (When Applicable)	System[g] Temp., °F	Maximum Pressure at Temperature,[a,b] psi
Potable water, inside building	0.25 to 12	Steel, galvanized	Schedule 40	Thread	Galv. cast iron	150	100	125
					Galv. cast iron	150	100	150
		Copper, hard or soft	Type K or L	Solder[c] Flared (soft) Rolled groove (2 to 8 in.) Press-connect (0.5 to 4 in.) Push connect (0.5 to 2 in.) Mechanical formed	Wrought or cast Cu		100	370 Type K soft 635 Type K hard 250 Type L soft 435 Type L hard
				Braze Weld	Wrought or cast Cu		100	370 Type K soft 250 Type L soft
	0.25 to 12	Copper, hard	Type M	Solder[c] Rolled groove (2 to 8 in.) Press-connect (0.5 to 4 in.) Push connect (0.5 to 2 in.) Mechanical formed	Wrought or cast Cu		100	395 Type M hard
				Braze Weld	Wrought or cast Cu		100	230 Type M soft
	0.5 to 8	CPVC	Schedule 40,[f] 80		CPVC		210 Limit, 200 operating	
	0.375 to 1.0	PEX	SDR-9	Crimp Clamp Expansion Compression Push fit Proprietary	Bronze Brass Copper Engineered plastic		100	145

Table 5.1 Common Applications of Pipe, Fittings, and Valves for Heating and Air Conditioning [2021F, Ch 22, Tbl 1] ***(Continued)***

Application	Size, in.	Material	Weight	Joint Type	Fitting Material	Class (When Applicable)	System[g] Temp., °F	Maximum Pressure at Temperature,[a,b] psi
Potable water, inside building (cont'd)	0.5 to 6	PE	Schedule 40,[f] 80, SDR	Thermal fusion, compression	PE		120 (140 limit for some applications)	Depends on pipe, grade, schedule, size generally 30 to 110 at 130°F
	0.5 to 6	PP	Schedule 40,[f] 80, SDR	Thermal fusion, flange, Thread[e]	PP		180	50
Water services, underground	Through 6	Ductile iron	Class 50	Mechanical joint	Cast iron		75	250
	0.25 to 12	Copper, hard or soft	Type K or L	Solder[c] Flared (soft) Rolled groove (2 to 8 in.) Press-connect (0.5 to 4 in.) Push connect (0.5 to 2 in.) Mechanical formed	Wrought or cast Cu		100	370 Type K soft 635 Type K hard 250 Type L soft 435 Type L hard
				Braze Weld	Wrought or cast Cu		100	370 Type K soft 250 Type L soft
				Flange	Bronze		100	
	0.25 to 12	Copper, hard	Type M	Solder[c] Rolled groove (2 to 8 in.) Press-connect (0.5 to 4 in.) Push connect (0.5 to 2 in.) Mechanical formed	Wrought or cast Cu		100	395 Type K hard
				Braze Weld	Wrought or cast Cu		100	230 Type M soft

Table 5.1 Common Applications of Pipe, Fittings, and Valves for Heating and Air Conditioning [2021F, Ch 22, Tbl 1] ***(Continued)***

Application	Size, in.	Material	Weight	Joint Type	Fitting Material	Class (When Applicable)	System[g] Temp., °F	Maximum Pressure at Temperature,[a,b] psi
Water services, underground (cont'd)	0.375 to 1.0	PEX	SDR-9	Crimp Clamp Expansion Compression Push fit Proprietary	Bronze Brass Copper Engineered plastic		73	145
	0.25 to 20	PVC	Schedule 40, 80, 120, SDR	Solvent weld, thread,[f] thermal weld	PVC		150 limit, 140 operating	79 to 105, depending on schedule and size
Drainage, waste, and vent (DWV)	1.25 to 8	Copper, hard	DWV	Solder	Wrought or cast Cu		100	250 DWV hard
	1.25 to 12	ABS	Schedule DWV, 40,[f] 80, SDR	Solvent weld, thread, flange	ABS		160 limit	Depends on pipe class: approximately 50 at 160°F
	1.25 to 20	PV	Schedule 40,[f] 80, 120, SDR	Solvent weld, thread, thermal weld	PVC		150 limit, 140 operating	79 to 105, depending on schedule and size

[a]Maximum allowable working pressures have been derated in this table. Higher system pressures can be used for lower temperatures and smaller pipe sizes. Pipe, fittings, joints, and valves must all be considered.
[b]Temperature and pressure relationships can vary based on pipe material composition, size, class, and schedule.
[c]Lead- and antimony-based solders are prohibited for potable water systems. Brazing should be used.
[d]Piping codes typically require thicker-walled pipe for threaded joints to maintain corrosion allowance and pressure ratings.
[e]All plumbing codes require both hot and cold water piping to have a 100 psi at 180°F rating.
[f]Threads are not recommended on Schedule 40 plastic pipe.
[g]Designer should confirm that all materials are suitably rated for intended operation.

Table 5.2 Properties of Pipe Materials[a] [2021F, Ch22, Tbl 18]

Material			Tensile Strength, psi	Hydrostatic[b] Design Stress, psi (at 73°F)		Upper Temperature Limit, °F		HDS[b] Upper Limit, psi	Specific Gravity[c]	Impact Strength, ft·lb/in (at 73°F)	Modulus of Elasticity, psi (at 73°F)	Coefficient of Expansion, in/10[6] in·°F	Thermal Conductivity, Btu·in/h·ft²·°F	Relative Pipe Cost[d]
Designation	Type and Grade	Cell No.	(at 73°F)	Mfr.	ASME B31	Mfr.	ASME B31							
Metals														
Copper	L	Drawn – hard	36,000		9,000		400	8,200	8.90		17,000,000	9.4	232	2.2
Steel	A53 B	ERW	60,000	12,800			800	9,200	7.80	30	27,500,000	6.31	26	1.0
Stainless steel	304	Drawn or Welded	73,200				350		7.90		28,000,000	9.6	8	2.0
Thermoplastics														
PVC 1120	T I,G1	12454-B	7,500	2,000	2,000	140	150	440	1.40	0.8	420,000	30.0	1.1	0.6
PVC 1200	T I,G2	12454-C			2,000		150				410,000	35.0		
PVC 2120	T II,G1	14333-D			2,000		150					30.0		
CPVC 4120	T IV,G1	23447-B	8,000	2,000	2,000	210	210	320	1.55	1.5	423,000	35.0	0.95	0.8
PE 2306	Gr. P23				630		140				90,000	80.0		
PE 3306	Gr. P34				630		160				130,000	70.0		
PE 3406	Gr. P33				630		180				150,000	60.0		
HDPE 3408	Gr. P34	355434-C	5,000	1,600	800	140	180	800	0.96	12	110,000	120.0	2.7	1.1
PP			5,000	705		212	210		0.91	1.3	120,000	60.0	1.3	2.9
ABS	Acrylonitrile copolymer	6-3-3	5,500			176			1.06	8.5	240,000	56.0	1.7	3.4
ABS 1210	T I,G2	5-2-2		1,000		180	640		250,000	55.0				
ABS 1316	T I,G3	3-5-5		1,600		180	1,000		340,000	40.0				
ABS 2112	T II,G1	4-4-5		1,250		180	800			40.0				
PVDF			7,000	1,275		280	275	306	1.78	3.8	125,000	79.0	0.8	2.6

Table 5.2 Properties of Pipe Materials[a] [2021F, Ch22, Tbl 18] *(Continued)*

Material			Tensile Strength, psi	Hydrostatic[b] Design Stress, psi (at 73°F)		Upper Temperature Limit, °F		HDS[b] Upper Limit, psi	Specific Gravity[c]	Impact Strength, ft·lb/in (at 73°F)	Modulus of Elasticity, psi (at 73°F)	Coefficient of Expansion, in/10⁶ in·°F	Thermal Conductivity, Btu·in/h·ft²·°F	Relative Pipe Cost[d]
Designation	Type and Grade	Cell No.	(at 73°F)	Mfr.	ASME B31	Mfr.	ASME B31							
Thermosetting														
Epoxy-glass	RTRP-11AF		44,000	8,000		300	7,000				1,000,000	9 to 13	2.9	1.5
PEX	A,B,C[e]		3,200	630	200	180	79		0.94		75,000	90.0	3.2	0.7
Polyester-glass	RTRP-12EF		44,000	9,000	200	200	5,000				1,000,000	9 to 11	1.3	1.5

[a]Properties listed are for specific materials listed; each plastic has other formulations. Consult the manufacturer of the system chosen. These values are for comparative purposes.
[b]Hydrostatic design stress (HDS) is equivalent to allowable design stress
[c]Relative to water at 62.4 lb/ft^3.
[d]Based on cost for 2 in. pipe only, without factoring in fittings, joints, hangers, and labor.
[e]A, B, and C are the three manufacturing processes of PEX pipe. The classifications are not related to a ranking system.

Table 5.3 Steel Pipe Data [2021F, Ch 22, Tbl 16]

Nominal Size, in.	Pipe OD, in.	Schedule Number or Weight[a]	Wall Thickness t, in.	Inside Diameter d, in.	Surface Area		Cross Section		Weight		Working Pressure[c] ASTM A53 B to 400°F		
					Outside, ft^2/ft	Inside, ft^2/ft	Metal Area, in^2	Flow Area, in^2	Pipe, lb/ft	Water, lb/ft	Mfr. Process	Joint Type[b]	psig
1/4	0.540	40 ST	0.088	0.364	0.141	0.095	0.125	0.104	0.424	0.045	CW	T	188
		80 XS	0.119	0.302	0.141	0.079	0.157	0.072	0.535	0.031	CW	T	871
3/8	0.675	40 ST	0.091	0.493	0.177	0.129	0.167	0.191	0.567	0.083	CW	T	203
		80 XS	0.126	0.423	0.177	0.111	0.217	0.141	0.738	0.061	CW	T	820
1/2	0.840	40 ST	0.109	0.622	0.220	0.163	0.250	0.304	0.850	0.131	CW	T	214
		80 XS	0.147	0.546	0.220	0.143	0.320	0.234	1.087	0.101	CW	T	753
3/4	1.050	40 ST	0.113	0.824	0.275	0.216	0.333	0.533	1.13	0.231	CW	T	217
		80 XS	0.154	0.742	0.275	0.194	0.433	0.432	1.47	0.187	CW	T	681
1	1.315	40 ST	0.133	1.049	0.344	0.275	0.494	0.864	1.68	0.374	CW	T	226
		80 XS	0.179	0.957	0.344	0.251	0.639	0.719	2.17	0.311	CW	T	642
1 1/4	1.660	40 ST	0.140	1.380	0.435	0.361	0.669	1.50	2.27	0.647	CW	T	229
		80 XS	0.191	1.278	0.435	0.335	0.881	1.28	2.99	0.555	CW	T	594
1 1/2	1.900	40 ST	0.145	1.610	0.497	0.421	0.799	2.04	2.72	0.881	CW	T	231
		80 XS	0.200	1.500	0.497	0.393	1.068	1.77	3.63	0.765	CW	T	576
2	2.375	40 ST	0.154	2.067	0.622	0.541	1.07	3.36	3.65	1.45	CW	T	230
		80 XS	0.218	1.939	0.622	0.508	1.48	2.95	5.02	1.28	CW	T	551
2 1/2	2.875	40 ST	0.203	2.469	0.753	0.646	1.70	4.79	5.79	2.07	CW	W	533
		80 XS	0.276	2.323	0.753	0.608	2.25	4.24	7.66	1.83	CW	W	835
3	3.500	40 ST	0.216	3.068	0.916	0.803	2.23	7.39	7.57	3.20	CW	W	482
		80 XS	0.300	2.900	0.916	0.759	3.02	6.60	10.25	2.86	CW	W	767

Table 5.3 Steel Pipe Data [2021F, Ch 22, Tbl 16] *(Continued)*

Nominal Size, in.	Pipe OD, in.	Schedule Number or Weight[a]	Wall Thickness t, in.	Inside Diameter d, in.	Surface Area		Cross Section		Weight		Working Pressure[c] ASTM A53 B to 400°F		
					Outside, ft^2/ft	Inside, ft^2/ft	Metal Area, in^2	Flow Area, in^2	Pipe, lb/ft	Water, lb/ft	Mfr. Process	Joint Type[b]	psig
4	4.500	40 ST	0.237	4.026	1.178	1.054	3.17	12.73	10.78	5.51	CW	W	430
		80 XS	0.337	3.826	1.178	1.002	4.41	11.50	14.97	4.98	CW	W	695
6	6.625	40 ST	0.280	6.065	1.734	1.588	5.58	28.89	18.96	12.50	ERW	W	696
		80 XS	0.432	5.761	1.734	1.508	8.40	26.07	28.55	11.28	ERW	W	1209
8	8.625	30	0.277	8.071	2.258	2.113	7.26	51.16	24.68	22.14	ERW	W	526
		40 ST	0.322	7.981	2.258	2.089	8.40	50.03	28.53	21.65	ERW	W	643
		80 XS	0.500	7.625	2.258	1.996	12.76	45.66	43.35	19.76	ERW	W	1106
10	10.75	30	0.307	10.136	2.814	2.654	10.07	80.69	34.21	34.92	ERW	W	485
		40 ST	0.365	10.020	2.814	2.623	11.91	78.85	40.45	34.12	ERW	W	606
		XS	0.500	9.750	2.814	2.552	16.10	74.66	54.69	32.31	ERW	W	887
		80	0.593	9.564	2.814	2.504	18.92	71.84	64.28	31.09	ERW	W	1081
12	12.75	30	0.330	12.090	3.338	3.165	12.88	114.8	43.74	49.68	ERW	W	449
		ST	0.375	12.000	3.338	3.141	14.58	113.1	49.52	48.94	ERW	W	528
		40	0.406	11.938	3.338	3.125	15.74	111.9	53.48	48.44	ERW	W	583
		XS	0.500	11.750	3.338	3.076	19.24	108.4	65.37	46.92	ERW	W	748
		80	0.687	11.376	3.338	2.978	26.03	101.6	88.44	43.98	ERW	W	1076
14	14.00	30 ST	0.375	13.250	3.665	3.469	16.05	137.9	54.53	59.67	ERW	W	481
		40	0.437	13.126	3.665	3.436	18.62	135.3	63.25	58.56	ERW	W	580
		XS	0.500	13.000	3.665	3.403	21.21	132.7	72.04	57.44	ERW	W	681
		80	0.750	12.500	3.665	3.272	31.22	122.7	106.05	53.11	ERW	W	1081

Table 5.3 Steel Pipe Data [2021F, Ch 22, Tbl 16] ***(Continued)***

Nominal Size, in.	Pipe OD, in.	Schedule Number or Weight[a]	Wall Thickness t, in.	Inside Diameter d, in.	Surface Area		Cross Section		Weight		Working Pressure[c] ASTM A53 B to 400°F		
					Outside, ft^2/ft	Inside, ft^2/ft	Metal Area, in^2	Flow Area, in^2	Pipe, lb/ft	Water, lb/ft	Mfr. Process	Joint Type[b]	psig
16	16.00	30 ST	0.375	15.250	4.189	3.992	18.41	182.6	62.53	79.04	ERW	W	421
		40 XS	0.500	15.000	4.189	3.927	24.35	176.7	82.71	76.47	ERW	W	596
18	18.00	ST	0.375	17.250	4.712	4.516	20.76	233.7	70.54	101.13	ERW	W	374
		30	0.437	17.126	4.712	4.483	24.11	230.3	81.91	99.68	ERW	W	451
		XS	0.500	17.000	4.712	4.450	27.49	227.0	93.38	98.22	ERW	W	530
		40	0.562	16.876	4.712	4.418	30.79	223.7	104.59	96.80	ERW	W	607
20	20.00	20 ST	0.375	19.250	5.236	5.039	23.12	291.0	78.54	125.94	ERW	W	337
		30 XS	0.500	19.000	5.236	4.974	30.63	283.5	104.05	122.69	ERW	W	477
		40	0.593	18.814	5.236	4.925	36.15	278.0	122.82	120.30	ERW	W	581

[a] Numbers are schedule numbers per ASME Standard B36.10M; ST = Standard Weight; XS = Extra Strong.
[b] T = Thread; W = Weld
[c] Working pressures were calculated per ASME B31.9 using furnace butt-weld (continuous weld, CW) pipe through 4 in. and electric resistance weld (ERW) thereafter. The allowance A has been taken as
(1) 12.5% of t for mill tolerance on pipe wall thickness, *plus*
(2) An arbitrary corrosion allowance of 0.025 in. for pipe sizes through NPS 2 and 0.065 in. from NPS 2 1/2 through 20, *plus*
(3) A thread cutting allowance for sizes through NPS 2.
Because the pipe wall thickness of threaded standard pipe is so small after deducting allowance A, the mechanical strength of the pipe is impaired. It is good practice to limit standard weight threaded pipe pressure to 90 psig for steam and 125 psig for water.

Table 5.4 Copper Tube Data [2021F, Ch 22, Tbl 17]

Nominal Diameter, in.	Type	Wall Thickness t, in.	Diameter		Surface Area		Cross Section		Weight		Working Pressure[a,b,c] ASTM B88 to 250°F	
			Outside D, in.	Inside d, in.	Outside, ft^2/ft	Inside, ft^2/ft	Metal Area, in^2	Flow Area, in^2	Tube, lb/ft	Water, lb/ft	Annealed, psig	Drawn, psig
1/4	K	0.035	0.375	0.305	0.098	0.080	0.037	0.073	0.145	0.032	851	1596
	L	0.030	0.375	0.315	0.098	0.082	0.033	0.078	0.126	0.034	730	1368
3/8	K	0.049	0.500	0.402	0.131	0.105	0.069	0.127	0.269	0.055	894	1676
	L	0.035	0.500	0.430	0.131	0.113	0.051	0.145	0.198	0.063	638	1197
	M	0.025	0.500	0.450	0.131	0.118	0.037	0.159	0.145	0.069	456	855
1/2	K	0.049	0.625	0.527	0.164	0.138	0.089	0.218	0.344	0.094	715	1341
	L	0.040	0.625	0.545	0.164	0.143	0.074	0.233	0.285	0.101	584	1094
	M	0.028	0.625	0.569	0.164	0.149	0.053	0.254	0.203	0.110	409	766
5/8	K	0.049	0.750	0.652	0.196	0.171	0.108	0.334	0.418	0.144	596	1117
	L	0.042	0.750	0.666	0.196	0.174	0.093	0.348	0.362	0.151	511	958
3/4	K	0.065	0.875	0.745	0.229	0.195	0.165	0.436	0.641	0.189	677	1270
	L	0.045	0.875	0.785	0.229	0.206	0.117	0.484	0.455	0.209	469	879
	M	0.032	0.875	0.811	0.229	0.212	0.085	0.517	0.328	0.224	334	625
1	K	0.065	1.125	0.995	0.295	0.260	0.216	0.778	0.839	0.336	527	988
	L	0.050	1.125	1.025	0.295	0.268	0.169	0.825	0.654	0.357	405	760
	M	0.035	1.125	1.055	0.295	0.276	0.120	0.874	0.464	0.378	284	532
1 1/4	K	0.065	1.375	1.245	0.360	0.326	0.268	1.217	1.037	0.527	431	808
	L	0.055	1.375	1.265	0.360	0.331	0.228	1.257	0.884	0.544	365	684
	M	0.042	1.375	1.291	0.360	0.338	0.176	1.309	0.682	0.566	279	522
	DWV	0.040	1.375	1.295	0.360	0.339	0.168	1.317	0.650	0.570	265	497

Table 5.4 Copper Tube Data [2021F, Ch 22, Tbl 17] ***(Continued)***

Nominal Diameter, in.	Type	Wall Thickness *t*, in.	Diameter		Surface Area		Cross Section		Weight		Working Pressure[a,b,c] ASTM B88 to 250°F	
			Outside *D*, in.	Inside *d*, in.	Outside, ft^2/ft	Inside, ft^2/ft	Metal Area, in^2	Flow Area, in^2	Tube, lb/ft	Water, lb/ft	Annealed, psig	Drawn, psig
1 1/2	K	0.072	1.625	1.481	0.425	0.388	0.351	1.723	1.361	0.745	404	758
	L	0.060	1.625	1.505	0.425	0.394	0.295	1.779	1.143	0.770	337	631
	M	0.049	1.625	1.527	0.425	0.400	0.243	1.831	0.940	0.792	275	516
	DWV	0.042	1.625	1.541	0.425	0.403	0.209	1.865	0.809	0.807	236	442
2	K	0.083	2.125	1.959	0.556	0.513	0.532	3.014	2.063	1.304	356	668
	L	0.070	2.125	1.985	0.556	0.520	0.452	3.095	1.751	1.339	300	573
	M	0.058	2.125	2.009	0.556	0.526	0.377	3.170	1.459	1.372	249	467
	DWV	0.042	2.125	2.041	0.556	0.534	0.275	3.272	1.065	1.416	180	338
2 1/2	K	0.095	2.625	2.435	0.687	0.637	0.755	4.657	2.926	2.015	330	619
	L	0.080	2.625	2.465	0.687	0.645	0.640	4.772	2.479	2.065	278	521
	M	0.065	2.625	2.495	0.687	0.653	0.523	4.889	2.026	2.116	226	423
3	K	0.109	3.125	2.907	0.818	0.761	1.033	6.637	4.002	2.872	318	596
	L	0.090	3.125	2.945	0.818	0.771	0.858	6.812	3.325	2.947	263	492
	M	0.072	3.125	2.981	0.818	0.780	0.691	6.979	2.676	3.020	210	394
	DWV	0.045	3.125	3.035	0.818	0.795	0.435	7.234	1.687	3.130	131	246
3 1/2	K	0.120	3.625	3.385	0.949	0.886	1.321	8.999	5.120	3.894	302	566
	L	0.100	3.625	3.425	0.949	0.897	1.107	9.213	4.291	3.987	252	472
	M	0.083	3.625	3.459	0.949	0.906	0.924	9.397	3.579	4.066	209	392
4	K	0.134	4.125	3.857	1.080	1.010	1.680	11.684	6.510	5.056	296	555
	L	0.110	4.125	3.905	1.080	1.022	1.387	11.977	5.377	5.182	243	456
	M	0.095	4.125	3.935	1.080	1.030	1.203	12.161	4.661	5.262	210	394
	DWV	0.058	4.125	4.009	1.080	1.050	0.741	12.623	2.872	5.462	128	240

Table 5.4 Copper Tube Data [2021F, Ch 22, Tbl 17] ***(Continued)***

Nominal Diameter, in.	Type	Wall Thickness t, in.	Diameter		Surface Area		Cross Section		Weight		Working Pressure[a,b,c] ASTM B88 to 250°F	
			Outside D, in.	Inside d, in.	Outside, ft^2/ft	Inside, ft^2/ft	Metal Area, in^2	Flow Area, in^2	Tube, lb/ft	Water, lb/ft	Annealed, psig	Drawn, psig
5	K	0.160	5.125	4.805	1.342	1.258	2.496	18.133	9.671	7.846	285	534
	L	0.125	5.125	4.875	1.342	1.276	1.963	18.665	7.609	8.077	222	417
	M	0.109	5.125	4.907	1.342	1.285	1.718	18.911	6.656	8.183	194	364
	DWV	0.072	5.125	4.981	1.342	1.304	1.143	19.486	4.429	8.432	128	240
6	K	0.192	6.125	5.741	1.603	1.503	3.579	25.886	13.867	11.201	286	536
	L	0.140	6.125	5.845	1.603	1.530	2.632	26.832	10.200	11.610	208	391
	M	0.122	6.125	5.881	1.603	1.540	2.301	27.164	8.916	11.754	182	341
	DWV	0.083	6.125	5.959	1.603	1.560	1.575	27.889	6.105	12.068	124	232
8	K	0.271	8.125	7.583	2.127	1.985	6.687	45.162	25.911	19.542	304	570
	L	0.200	8.125	7.725	2.127	2.022	4.979	46.869	19.295	20.280	224	421
	M	0.170	8.125	7.785	2.127	2.038	4.249	47.600	16.463	20.597	191	358
	DWV	0.109	8.125	7.907	2.127	2.070	2.745	49.104	10.637	21.247	122	229
10	K	0.338	10.125	9.449	2.651	2.474	10.392	70.123	40.271	30.342	304	571
	L	0.250	10.125	9.625	2.651	2.520	7.756	72.760	30.054	31.483	225	422
	M	0.212	10.125	9.701	2.651	2.540	6.602	73.913	25.584	31.982	191	358
12	K	0.405	12.125	11.315	3.174	2.962	14.912	100.554	57.784	43.510	305	571
	L	0.280	12.125	11.565	3.174	3.028	10.419	105.046	40.375	45.454	211	395
	M	0.254	12.125	11.617	3.174	3.041	9.473	105.993	36.706	45.863	191	358

[a]When using soldered or brazed fittings, the joint determines the limiting pressure.

[b]Working pressures were calculated using ASME Standard B31.9 allowable stresses. A 5% mill tolerance has been used on the wall thickness. Higher tube ratings can be calculated using the allowable stress for lower temperatures.

[c]If soldered or brazed fittings are used on hard drawn tubing, use the annealed ratings. Full-tube allowable pressures can be used with suitably rated flare or compression-type fittings.

Table 5.5 Thermal Expansion of Metal Pipe [2021F, Ch 22, Tbl 13]

	Saturated Steam Pressure, psig	Temperature, °F	Linear Thermal Expansion, in/100 ft		
			Carbon Steel	Type 304 Stainless Steel	Copper
		–30	–0.19	–0.30	–0.32
		–20	–0.12	–0.20	–0.21
		–10	–0.06	–0.10	–0.11
		0	0	0	0
		10	0.08	0.11	0.12
		20	0.15	0.22	0.24
Vacuum	–14.6	32	0.24	0.36	0.37
Vacuum	–14.6	40	0.30	0.45	0.45
Vacuum	–14.5	50	0.38	0.56	0.57
Vacuum	–14.4	60	0.46	0.67	0.68
Vacuum	–14.3	70	0.53	0.78	0.79
Vacuum	–14.2	80	0.61	0.90	0.90
Vacuum	–14.0	90	0.68	1.01	1.02
Vacuum	–13.7	100	0.76	1.12	1.13
Vacuum	–13.0	120	0.91	1.35	1.37
Vacuum	–11.8	140	1.06	1.57	1.59
Vacuum	–10.0	160	1.22	1.79	1.80
Vacuum	–7.2	180	1.37	2.02	2.05
Vacuum	–3.2	200	1.52	2.24	2.30
	0	212	1.62	2.38	2.43
	2.5	220	1.69	2.48	2.52
	10.3	240	1.85	2.71	2.76
	20.7	260	2.02	2.94	2.99
	34.6	280	2.18	3.17	3.22
	52.3	300	2.35	3.40	3.46
	75.0	320	2.53	3.64	3.70
	103.3	340	2.70	3.88	3.94
	138.3	360	2.88	4.11	4.18
	181.1	380	3.05	4.35	4.42
	232.6	400	3.23	4.59	4.87
	666.1	500	4.15	5.80	5.91
	1528	600	5.13	7.03	7.18
	3079	700	6.16	8.29	8.47
		800	7.23	9.59	9.79
		900	8.34	10.91	11.16
		1000	9.42	12.27	12.54

Table 5.6 Suggested Hanger Spacing and Rod Size for Straight Horizontal Runs [2021F, Ch 22, Tbl 11]

NPS, in.	Hanger Spacing, ft			Rod Size, in.
	Standard Steel Pipe*		Copper Tube	
	Water	Steam	Water	
1/2	7	8	5	1/4
3/4	7	9	5	1/4
1	7	9	6	1/4
1 1/2	9	12	8	3/8
2	10	13	8	3/8
2 1/2	11	14	9	3/8
3	12	15	10	3/8
4	14	17	12	1/2
6	17	21	14	1/2
8	19	24	16	5/8
10	20	26	18	3/4
12	23	30	19	7/8
14	25	32		1
16	27	35		1
18	28	37		1 1/4
20	30	39		1 1/4

Source: Adapted from MSS Standard SP-69

*Spacing does not apply where span calculations are made or where concentrated loads are placed between supports such as flanges, valves, specialties, etc.

Table 5.7 Capacities of ASTM A36 Steel Threaded Rods [2021F, Ch 22, Tbl 10]

Rod Diameter, in.	Root Area of Coarse Thread, in^2	Maximum Load,* lb
1/4	0.027	240
3/8	0.068	610
1/2	0.126	1130
5/8	0.202	1810
3/4	0.302	2710
7/8	0.419	3770
1	0.552	4960
1 1/4	0.889	8000

*Based on an allowable stress of 12,000 psi reduced by 25% using the root area in accordance with ASME Standard B31.1 and MSS Standard SP-58.

6. SERVICE WATER HEATING

Water heating energy use is second only to space conditioning in most residential buildings, and is also significant in many commercial and industrial settings. In some climates and applications, water heating is the largest energy use in a building. Moreover, quick availability of adequate amounts of hot water is an important factor in user satisfaction. Both water and energy waste can be significant in poorly designed service water-heating systems: from over- or undersizing pipes and equipment, from poor building layout, and from poor system design and operating strategies. Good service water-heating system design and operating practices can often reduce first costs as well as operating costs.

System Elements

A service water-heating system has (1) one or more heat energy sources, (2) heat transfer equipment, (3) a distribution system, and (4) terminal hot-water usage devices.

Heat energy sources may be (1) fuel combustion; (2) electrical conversion; (3) solar energy; (4) geothermal, air, or other environmental energy; and/or (5) recovered waste heat from sources such as flue gases, ventilation and air-conditioning systems, refrigeration cycles, and process waste discharge.

Heat transfer equipment is direct, indirect, or a combination of the two. For direct equipment, heat is derived from combustion of fuel or direct conversion of electrical energy into heat and is applied within the water-heating equipment. For indirect heat transfer equipment, heat energy is developed from remote heat sources (e.g., boilers; solar energy collection; air, geothermal, or other environmental source; cogeneration; refrigeration; waste heat) and is then transferred to the water in a separate piece of equipment. Storage tanks may be part of or associated with either type of heat transfer equipment.

Distribution systems transport hot water produced by water-heating equipment to terminal hot-water usage devices. Water consumed must be replenished from the building water service main. For locations where constant supply temperatures are desired, circulation piping or a means of heat maintenance must be provided.

End-use fixtures are plumbing faucets, accessories, and equipment requiring hot water that may have periods of irregular flow, constant flow, and no flow. These patterns and their related water usage vary with different buildings, process applications, and personal preferences. Examples of end-use accessories are prerinse spray valves, faucet aerators, showerheads, washdown sprayers, and hose bibbs. Examples of end-use equipment are dishwashers, clothes washers, and pressure washers.

Legionellosis (Legionnaires' Disease)

Legionnaires' disease (a form of severe pneumonia) is caused by inhaling aerosolized water droplets containing the bacteria *Legionella pneumophila*. Susceptibility to Legionnaire's disease varies among individuals. People with compromised immune systems (e.g., organ transplant patients or others on immunosuppressant drugs, AIDS patients, smokers, elderly, those with other chronic health conditions or injuries) are at greater risk of contracting the disease at lower exposure levels.

Most water supplied to buildings contains some *Legionella* bacteria (and/or other microorganisms), often at levels too low to detect. The concern is that organism colonies can grow (amplify) within the building hot- and cold-water systems under certain conditions. At high *Legionella* concentrations, a hazard may exist. Some examples of conditions potentially conducive to *Legionella* growth are temperatures within a certain range (warm, not too hot or cold), locations of flow stagnation (e.g., pipe dead legs, low flow velocities, other flow stagnation points, intermittent or seasonal use), and inadequate oxidant residual levels. For more specific water system design guidance, refer to ANSI/ASHRAE Standard 188 and ASHRAE Guideline 12.

Hot-Water Load

Methods for sizing storage water heaters vary. Those using recovery versus storage curves are based on extensive research. All methods provide adequate hot water if the designer allows for unusual conditions. To serve a hot-water load adequately, the needs of both the peak energy withdrawal rate and total integrated energy delivery for end uses must be met. Meeting these needs can be done either by providing a heating rate large enough to meet the peak energy withdrawal rate of the system (and modulating that heating input for smaller loads), or by providing a lower heating rate combined with storage (from which the peak rates can be satisfied). Lower costs are usually achieved by using at least some storage. A variety of different heating rate/storage volume combinations can be used to meet the needs of a given water-heating load profile.

Load Diversity

The greatest difficulty in designing water-heating systems comes from uncertainty about design hot-water loads, especially for buildings not yet built. Although it is fairly simple to test maximum flow rates of various hot-water fixtures and appliances, actual flow rates and durations are user-dependent. Moreover, the timing of different hot-water use events varies from day to day, with some overlap, but almost never will all fixtures be used simultaneously. As the number of hot-water-using fixtures and appliances grows, the percent of those fixtures used simultaneously decreases.

Some of the hot-water load information here is based on limited-scale field testing combined with statistical analysis to estimate load demand or **diversity** factors (percent of total possible load that is ever actually used at one time) versus number of end use points, number of people, etc. Much of the work to provide these diversity factors dates from the 1930s to the 1960s; it remains, however, the best information currently available (with a few exceptions, as noted). Of greatest concern is the fact that most of the data from those early studies were for fixtures that used water at much higher flow rates than modern energy-efficient fixtures (e.g., low-flow shower heads and sink aerators, energy-efficient washing machines and dishwashers). Using the older load diversity information usually results in a water-heating system that adequately serves the loads, but often results in substantial oversizing. Oversizing can be a deterrent to using modern high-efficiency water-heating equipment, which may have higher first cost per unit of capacity than less efficient equipment.

Table 6.1 Typical Residential Use of Hot Water [2019A, Ch 51, Tbl 3]

Use	High Flow, Gallons/Task	Low Flow (Water Savers Used), Gallons/Task	Ultralow Flow, Gallons/Task
Food preparation	5	3	3
Hand dish washing	4	4	3
Automatic dishwasher	15	15	3 to 10
Clothes washer	32	21	5 to 15
Shower or bath	20	15	10 to 15
Face and hand washing	4	2	1 to 2

Table 6.2 HUD-FHA Minimum Water Heater Capacities for One- and Two-Family Living Units [2019A, Ch 51, Tbl 4]

Number of Baths	1 to 1.5			2 to 2.5				3 to 3.5			
Number of Bedrooms	**1**	**2**	**3**	**2**	**3**	**4**	**5**	**3**	**4**	**5**	**6**
Gas[a]											
Storage, gal	20	30	30	30	40	40	50	40	50	50	50
1000 Btu/h input	27	36	36	36	36	38	47	38	38	47	50
1 h draw, gal	43	60	60	60	70	72	90	72	82	90	92
Recovery, gph	23	30	30	30	30	32	40	32	32	40	42
Electric[a]											
Storage, gal	20	30	40	40	50	50	66	50	66	66	80
kW input	2.5	3.5	4.5	4.5	5.5	5.5	5.5	5.5	5.5	5.5	5.5
1 h draw, gal	30	44	58	58	72	72	88	72	88	88	102
Recovery, gph	10	14	18	18	22	22	22	22	22	22	22
Oil[a]											
Storage, gal	30	30	30	30	30	30	30	30	30	30	30
1000 Btu/h input	70	70	70	70	70	70	70	70	70	70	70
1 h draw, gal	89	89	89	89	89	89	89	89	89	89	89
Recovery, gph	59	59	59	59	59	59	59	59	59	59	59
Tank-Type Indirect[b,c]											
I-W-H-rated draw, gal in 3 h, 100°F rise		40	40		66	66[e]	66	66	66	66	66
Manufacturer-rated draw, gal in 3 h, 100°F rise		49	49		75	75[e]	75	75	75	75	75
Tank capacity, gal		66	66		66	66[e]	82	66	82	82	82
Tankless-Type Indirect[c,d]											
I-W-H-rated draw, gpm, 100°F rise		2.75	2.75		3.25	3.25[e]	3.75	3.25	3.75	3.75	3.75
Manufacturer-rated draw, gal in 5 min, 100°F rise		15	15		25	25[e]	35	25	35	35	35

Note: Applies to tank-type water heaters only.

[a] Storage capacity, input, and recovery requirements indicated are typical and may vary with manufacturer. Any combination of requirements to produce stated 1 h draw is satisfactory.

[b] Boiler-connected water heater capacities (180°F boiler water, internal or external connection).

[c] Heater capacities and inputs are minimum allowable. Variations in tank size are permitted when recovery is based on 4 gph/kW at 100°F rise for electrical, AGA recovery ratings for gas, and IBR ratings for steam and hot-water heaters.

[d] Boiler-connected heater capacities (200°F boiler water, internal or external connection).

[e] Also for 1 to 1.5 baths and 4 bedrooms for indirect water heaters.

Table 6.3 Overall (OVL) and Peak Average Hot-Water Use [2019A, Ch 51, Tbl 5]

Group	Average Hot-Water Use, gal							
	Hourly		Daily		Weekly		Monthly	
	OVL	Peak	OVL	Peak	OVL	Peak	OVL	Peak
All families	2.6	4.6	62.4	67.1	436	495	1897	2034
"Typical" families	2.6	5.8	63.1	66.6	442	528	1921	2078

Table 6.4 Hot-Water Demands and Use for Various Types of Buildings* [2019A, Ch 51, Tbl 6]

Type of Building	Maximum Hourly	Maximum Daily	Average Daily
Men's dormitories	3.8 gal/student	22.0 gal/student	13.1 gal/student
Women's dormitories	5.0 gal/student	26.5 gal/student	12.3 gal/student
Motels: Number of units[a]			
20 or less	6.0 gal/unit	35.0 gal/unit	20.0 gal/unit
60	5.0 gal/unit	25.0 gal/unit	14.0 gal/unit
100 or more	4.0 gal/unit	15.0 gal/unit	10.0 gal/unit
Nursing homes	4.5 gal/bed	30.0 gal/bed	18.4 gal/bed
Office buildings	0.4 gal/person	2.0 gal/person	1.0 gal/person
Food service establishments			
Type A: Full-meal restaurants and cafeterias	1.5 gal/max meals/h	11.0 gal/max meals/day	2.4 gal/average meals/day[b]
Type B: Drive-ins, grills, luncheonettes, sandwich, and snack shops	0.7 gal/max meals/h	6.0 gal/max meals/day	0.7 gal/average meals/day[b]
Apartment houses: Number of apartments			
20 or less	12.0 gal/apartment	80.0 gal/apartment	42.0 gal/apartment
50	10.0 gal/apartment	73.0 gal/apartment	40.0 gal/apartment
75	8.5 gal/apartment	66.0 gal/apartment	38.0 gal/apartment
100	7.0 gal/apartment	60.0 gal/apartment	37.0 gal/apartment
200 or more	5.0 gal/apartment	50.0 gal/apartment	35.0 gal/apartment
Elementary schools	0.6 gal/student	1.5 gal/student	0.6 gal/student[b]
Junior and senior high schools	1.0 gal/student	3.6 gal/student	1.8 gal/student[b]

*Data predate modern low-flow fixtures and appliances.
[a]Interpolate for intermediate values. [b]Per day of operation.

Table 6.5 Hot-Water Demand per Fixture for Various Types of Buildings [2019A, Ch 51, Tbl 10]
(Gallons of water per hour per fixture, calculated at a final temperature of 140°F)

	Apartment House	Club	Gymnasium	Hospital	Hotel	Industrial Plant	Office Building	Private Residence	School	YMCA
1. Basin, private lavatory	2	2	2	2	2	2	2	2	2	2
2. Basin, public lavatory	4	6	8	6	8	12	6	—	15	8
3. Bathtub[c]	20	20	30	20	20	—	—	20	—	30
4. Dishwasher[a]	15	50-150	—	50-150	50-200	20-100	—	15	20-100	20-100
5. Foot basin	3	3	12	3	3	12	—	3	3	12
6. Kitchen sink	10	20	—	20	30	20	20	10	20	20
7. Laundry, stationary tub	20	28	—	28	28	—	—	20	—	28
8. Pantry sink	5	10	—	10	10	—	10	5	10	10
9. Shower	30	150	225	75	75	225	30	30	225	225
10. Service sink	20	20	—	20	30	20	20	15	20	20
11. Hydrotherapeutic shower				400						
12. Hubbard bath				600						
13. Leg bath				100						
14. Arm bath				35						
15. Sitz bath				30						
16. Continuous-flow bath				165						
17. Circular wash sink				20	20	30	20		30	
18. Semicircular wash sink				10	10	15	10		15	
19. DEMAND FACTOR	0.30	0.30	0.40	0.25	0.25	0.40	0.30	0.30	0.40	0.40
20. STORAGE CAPACITY FACTOR[b]	1.25	0.90	1.00	0.60	0.80	1.00	2.00	0.70	1.00	1.00

Note: Data sources predate low-flow fixtures and appliances.
[a]Dishwasher requirements should be taken from this table or from manufacturers' data for model to be used, if known.
[b]Ratio of storage tank capacity to probable maximum demand/h. Storage capacity may be reduced where unlimited supply of steam is available from central street steam system or large boiler plant.
[c]Whirlpool baths require specific consideration based on capacity. They are not included in the bathtub category.

Table 6.6 Hot-Water Demand in Fixture Units (140°F Water) [2019A, Ch 51, Tbl 16]

	Apartments	Club	Gymnasium	Hospital	Hotels and Dormitories	Industrial Plant	Office Building	School	YMCA
Basin, private lavatory	0.75	0.75	0.75	0.75	0.75	0.75	0.75	0.75	0.75
Basin, public lavatory	—	1	1	1	1	1	1	1	1
Bathtub	1.5	1.5	—	1.5	1.5	—	—	—	—
Dishwasher*	1.5	Five fixture units per 250 seating capacity							
Therapeutic bath	—	—	—	5	—	—	—	—	—
Kitchen sink	0.75	1.5	—	3	1.5	3	—	0.75	3
Pantry sink	—	2.5	—	2.5	2.5	—	—	2.5	2.5
Service sink	1.5	2.5	—	2.5	2.5	2.5	2.5	2.5	2.5
Shower	1.5	1.5	1.5	1.5	1.5	3.5	—	1.5	1.5
Circular wash fountain	—	2.5	2.5	2.5	—	4	—	2.5	2.5
Semicircular wash fountain	—	1.5	1.5	1.5	—	3	—	1.5	1.5

Note: Data predate modern low-flow fixtures and appliances.

* Fixture unit: A number, on an arbitrarily chosen scale, that expresses the load-producing effects on the system of different kinds of fixtures.

Table 6.7 Tankless Water Heater Output Heat Rates, Btu/h*
[2019A, Ch 51, Tbl 15]

Flow Rate, gpm	Temperature Rise						
	10°F	25°F	50°F	55°F	75°F	77°F	100°F
0.1	504	1,260	2,520	2,772	3,780	3,881	5,040
0.5	2,520	6,300	12,600	13,860	18,900	19,404	25,200
1.0	5,040	12,600	25,200	27,720	37,800	38,808	50,400
1.5	7,560	18,900	37,800	41,580	56,700	58,212	75,600
2.0	10,080	25,200	50,400	55,440	75,600	77,616	100,800
2.5	12,600	31,500	63,000	69,300	94,500	97,020	126,000
3.0	15,120	37,800	75,600	83,160	113,400	116,424	151,200
3.5	17,640	44,100	88,200	97,020	132,300	135,828	176,400
4.0	20,160	50,400	100,800	110,880	151,200	155,232	201,600
4.5	22,680	56,700	113,400	124,740	170,100	174,636	226,800
5.0	25,200	63,000	126,000	138,600	189,000	194,040	252,000
6.0	30,240	75,600	151,200	166,320	226,800	232,848	302,400
7.0	35,280	88,200	176,400	194,040	264,600	271,656	352,800
8.0	40,320	100,800	201,600	221,760	302,400	310,464	403,200
9.0	45,360	113,400	226,800	249,480	340,200	349,272	453,600
10.0	50,400	126,000	252,000	277,200	378,000	388,080	504,000

*Divide table values by input efficiency to determine required heat input rate.

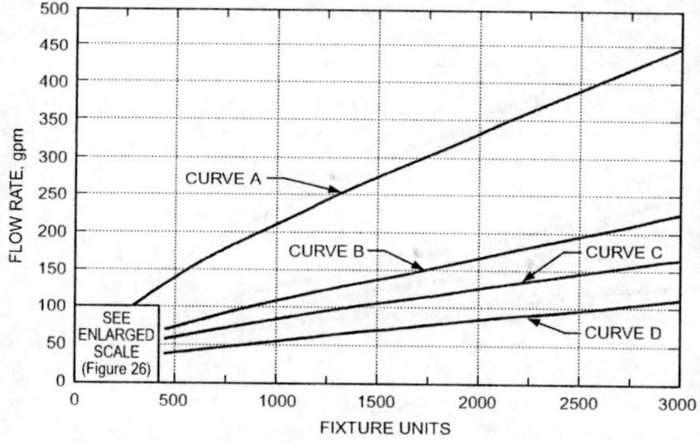

FLOW RATE, gpm
500
450
400
350
300
250
200
150
100
50
0
CURVE A
CURVE B
CURVE C
CURVE D
SEE ENLARGED SCALE (Figure 26)
0
500
1000
1500
2000
2500
3000
FIXTURE UNITS
CURVE A: RESTAURANTS
CURVE B: HOSPITALS, NURSING HOMES, NURSES' RESIDENCES, DORMITORIES, HOTELS, AND MOTELS
CURVE C: APARTMENTS AND HOUSES
CURVE D: OFFICE BUILDINGS, ELEMENTARY AND HIGH SCHOOLS

Figure 6.1 Modified Hunter Curve for Calculating Hot-Water Flow Rate [2019A, Ch 51, Fig 27]
(Data Predate Modern Low-Flow Fixtures and Appliances)

FLOW RATE, gpm
100
90
80
70
60
50
40
30
20
10
0
CURVE A
CURVE B
CURVE C
CURVE D
0
50
100
150
200
250
300
350
400
FIXTURE UNITS
CURVE A: RESTAURANTS
CURVE B: HOSPITALS, NURSING HOMES, NURSES' RESIDENCES, DORMITORIES, HOTELS, AND MOTELS
CURVE C: APARTMENTS AND HOUSES
CURVE D: OFFICE BUILDINGS, ELEMENTARY AND HIGH SCHOOLS

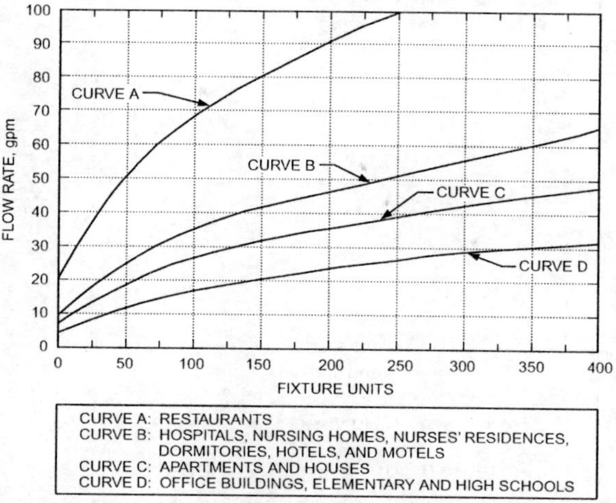

Figure 6.2 Enlarged Section of Modified Hunter Curve [2019A, Ch 51, Fig 28]
(Data Predate Modern Low-Flow Fixtures and Appliances)

Temperature Requirement

Typical temperature requirements for some services are shown in Table 6.8. A 140°F water temperature minimizes flue gas condensation in the equipment.

Table 6.8 Representative Hot-Water Temperatures [2019A, Ch 51, Tbl 19]

Use	Temperature, °F
Lavatory	
Hand washing	105
Shaving	115
Showers and tubs	110
Therapeutic baths	95
Commercial or institutional laundry, based on fabric	up to 180
Residential dish washing and laundry	140
Surgical scrubbing	110
Commercial spray-type dish washing[a]	
Single- or multiple-tank hood or rack type	
Wash	150 minimum
Final rinse	180 to 195
Single-tank conveyor type	
Wash	160 minimum
Final rinse	180 to 195
Single-tank rack or door type	
Single-temperature wash and rinse	165 minimum
Chemical sanitizing types[b]	140
Multiple-tank conveyor type	
Wash	150 minimum
Pumped rinse	160 minimum
Final rinse	180 to 195
Chemical sanitizing glass washer	
Wash	140
Rinse	75 minimum

[a]As required by NSF.
[b]See manufacturer for actual temperature required.

Other Safety Concerns

Regulatory agencies differ as to the selection of protective devices and methods of installation. It is therefore essential to check and comply with the manufacturer's instructions and the applicable local codes. In the absence of such instructions and codes, the following recommendations may be used as a guide:

- Water expands when it is heated. Although the water-heating system is initially under service pressure, the pressure rises rapidly if backflow is prevented by devices such as a check valve, pressure-reducing valve, or backflow preventer in the cold-water line or by temporarily shutting off the cold-water valve. When backflow is prevented, the pressure rise during heating may cause the safety relief valve to weep to relieve the pressure. However, if the safety relief valve is inadequate, inoperative, or missing, pressure rise may rupture the tank or cause other damage. Systems having this potential problem must be protected by a properly sized expansion tank located on the cold-water line downstream of and as close as practical to the device preventing backflow.
- Temperature-limiting devices (energy cutoff/high limit) prevent water temperatures from exceeding 210°F by stopping the flow of fuel or energy. These devices should be listed and labeled by a recognized certifying agency.
- Safety relief valves open when pressure exceeds the valve setting. These valves are typically applied to water-heating and hot-water supply boilers. The set pressure should not exceed the maximum allowable working pressure of the boiler. The heat input pressure steam rating (in Btu/h) should equal or exceed the maximum out-put rating for the boiler. The valves should comply with current applicable standards or the ASME *Boiler and Pressure Vessel Code.*
- Temperature and pressure safety relief valves also open if the water temperature reaches 210°F. These valves are typically applied to water heaters and hot-water storage tanks. The heat input temperature/steam rating (in Btu/h) should equal or exceed the heat input rating of the water heater. Combination temperature- and pressure-relief valves should be installed with the temperature-sensitive element located in the top 6 in. of the tank (i.e., where the water is hottest).
- To reduce scald hazards, discharge temperature at fixtures accessible to the occupant should not exceed 120°F. Thermostatically controlled mixing valves can be used to blend hot and cold water to maintain safe service hot-water temperatures.
- A relief valve should be installed in any part of the system containing a heat input device that can be isolated by valves. The heat input device may be solar water-heating panels, desuperheater water heaters, heat recovery devices, or similar equipment.

7. REFRIGERATION CYCLES

Refrigeration cycles transfer thermal energy from a region of low temperature T_R to one of higher temperature. Usually the higher-temperature heat sink is the ambient air or cooling water, at temperature T_0, the temperature of the surroundings.

The first and second laws of thermodynamics can be applied to individual components to determine mass and energy balances and the irreversibility of the components. This procedure is illustrated in later sections in this chapter.

Performance of a refrigeration cycle is usually described by a **coefficient of performance (COP)**, defined as the benefit of the cycle (amount of heat removed) divided by the required energy input to operate the cycle:

$$\text{COP} \equiv \frac{\text{Useful refrigerating effect}}{\text{Net energy supplied from external sources}} \tag{7.1}$$

For a mechanical vapor compression system, the net energy supplied is usually in the form of work, mechanical or electrical, and may include work to the compressor and fans or pumps. Thus,

$$\text{COP} = \frac{Q_{evap}}{W_{net}} \tag{7.2}$$

In an absorption refrigeration cycle, the net energy supplied is usually in the form of heat into the generator and work into the pumps and fans, or

$$\text{COP} = \frac{Q_{evap}}{Q_{gen} + W_{net}} \tag{7.3}$$

In many cases, work supplied to an absorption system is very small compared to the amount of heat supplied to the generator, so the work term is often neglected.

Applying the second law to an entire refrigeration cycle shows that a completely reversible cycle operating under the same conditions has the maximum possible COP. Departure of the actual cycle from an ideal reversible cycle is given by the **refrigerating efficiency**:

$$\eta_R = \frac{\text{COP}}{(\text{COP})_{rev}} \tag{7.4}$$

Theoretical Refrigeration Cycle

$$\text{COP} = \frac{{}_4Q_1}{{}_1W_2} = \frac{h_1 - h_4}{h_2 - h_1} \tag{7.5}$$

where

Heat into evaporator ${}_4Q_1 = m(h_1 - h_4)$, Btu/min

Work of compression ${}_1W_2 = m(h_2 - h_1)$ with s = constant, Btu/min

Heat out to condenser ${}_2Q_3 = m(h_2 - h_3)$, Btu/min

Expansion by throttling flow $h_3 = h_4$

m = refrigerant flow rate, lb/min

h = enthalpy, Btu/lb

s = entropy, Btu/lb·°R

Theoretical Compressor Displacement

$$D = m\, v_1 \text{ ft}^3/\text{min} \tag{7.6}$$

where v_1 = specific volume at suction, ft³/lb.

For a given cycle, capacity in tons of refrigeration:

$$m = \frac{(\text{tons})(200 \text{ Btu/min} - \text{ton})}{h_1 - h_4} \tag{7.7}$$

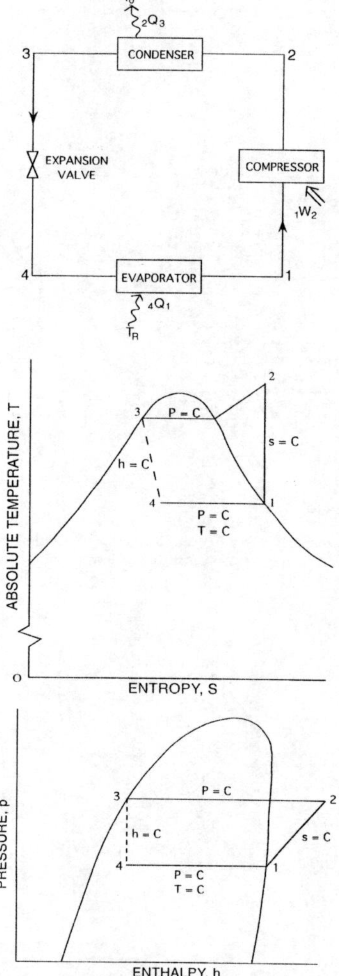

Figure 7.1 Theoretical Single-Stage Vapor Compression Refrigeration Cycle
[2021F, Ch 2, Fig 8]

Actual Refrigeration Systems. Actual systems operating steadily differ from the ideal cycles considered in the previous sections in many respects. Pressure drops occur everywhere in the system except in the compression process. Heat transfers between the refrigerant and its environment in all components.

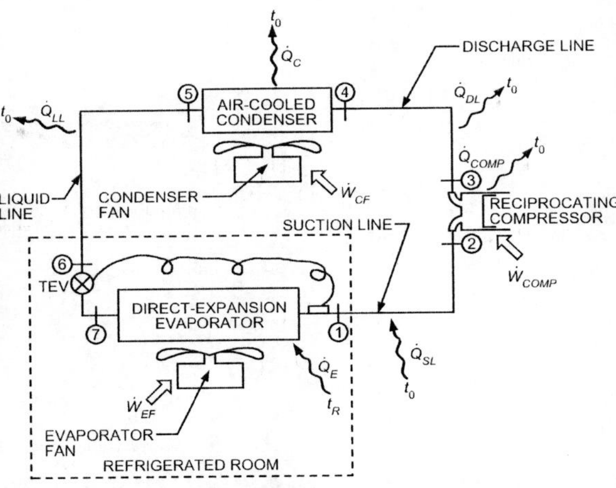

Figure 7.2 Schematic of Real, Direct-Expansion, Single-Stage Mechanical Vapor-Compression Refrigeration System [2021F, Ch 2, Fig 14]

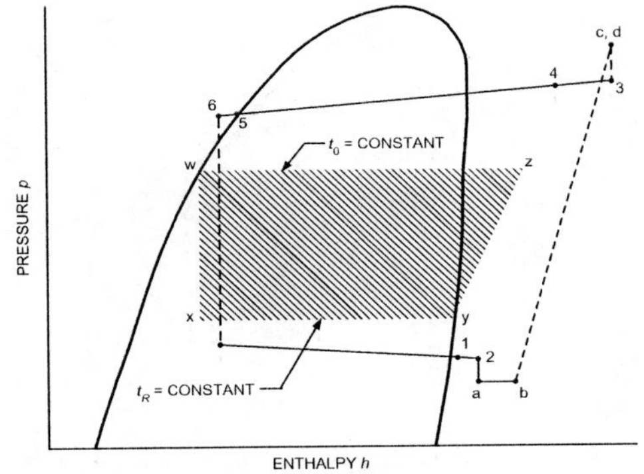

Figure 7.3 Pressure-Enthalpy Diagram of Actual System and Theoretical Single-Stage System Operating Between Same Inlet Air Temperatures t_R and t_0 [2021F, Ch 2, Fig 15]

8. REFRIGERANTS

Table 8.1 Physical Properties of Selected Refrigerants[a] [2021F, Ch 29, Tbl 5]

Refrigerant									
No.	Chemical Name or Composition (% by Mass)	Chemical Formula	Molecular Mass	Boiling Pt.[f] (NBP) at 14.696 psia, °F	Freezing Point, °F	Critical Temp., °F	Critical Pressure, psi	Critical Density, lb/ft^3	Refractive Index of Liquid[b,c]
728	Nitrogen	N_2	28.013	−320.44	−346	−232.528	492.5	19.56	1.205 (83 K) 589.3 nm
729	Air	—	28.959	−317.65	—	−221.062	549.6	20.97	—
740	Argon	Ar	39.948	−302.53	−308.812	−188.428	705.3	33.44	1.233 (84 K) 589.3 nm
732	Oxygen	O_2	31.999	−297.328	−361.822	−181.426	731.4	27.23	1.221 (92 K) 589.3 nm
50	Methane	CH_4	16.043	−258.664	−296.428	−116.6548	667.1	10.15	—
14	Tetrafluoromethane	CF_4	88.005	−198.49	−298.498	−50.152	543.9	39.06	—
170	Ethane	C_2H_6	30.07	−127.4764	−297.01	89.924	706.6	12.87	—
508A	R-23/116 (39/61)	—	100.1	−125.73	—	50.346	529.5	35.43	—
508B	R-23/116 (46/54)	—	95.394	−125.68	—	52.170	547.0	35.49	—
23	Trifluoromethane	CHF_3	70.014	−115.6324	−247.234	79.0574	700.8	32.87	—
13	Chlorotrifluoromethane	$CClF_3$	104.46	−114.664	−294.07	83.93	562.6	36.39	1.146 (25)[2]
744	Carbon dioxide	CO_2	44.01	−109.12[d]	−69.8044[e]	87.7604	1070.0	29.19	1.195 (15)
504	R-32/115 (48.2/51.8)	—	79.249	−72.23	—	143.85	642.3	31.51	—
32	Difluoromethane	CH_2F_2	52.024	−60.9718	−214.258	172.589	838.6	26.47	—
410A	R-32/125 (50/50)	—	72.585	−60.5974	—	160.4444	711.1	28.69	—
125	Pentafluoroethane	C_2HF_5	120.02	−54.562	−149.134	150.8414	524.7	35.81	—

Table 8.1 Physical Properties of Selected Refrigerants[a] [2021F, Ch 29, Tbl 5] (*Continued*)

Refrigerant									
No.	Chemical Name or Composition (% by Mass)	Chemical Formula	Molecular Mass	Boiling Pt.[f] (NBP) at 14.696 psia, °F	Freezing Point, °F	Critical Temp., °F	Critical Pressure, psi	Critical Density, lb/ft^3	Refractive Index of Liquid[b,c]
1270	Propylene	C_3H_6	42.08	–53.716	–301.35	195.91	660.6	14.36	1.3640 (–50)[1]
143a	Trifluoroethane	CH_3CF_3	84.041	–53.0338	–169.258	162.8726	545.5	26.91	—
507A	R-125/143a (50/50)	—	98.859	–52.1338	—	159.1106	537.4	30.64	—
404A	R-125/143a/134a (44/52/4)	—	97.604	–51.1996	—	161.6828	540.8	30.37	—
502	R-22/115 (48.8/51.2)	—	111.63	–49.3132	—	178.71	582.6	35.50	—
407C	R-32/125/134a (23/25/52)	—	86.204	–46.5286	—	186.8612	671.5	30.23	—
290	Propane	C_3H_8	44.096	–43.805	–305.72	206.13	616.58	13.76	1.3397 (–42)
22	Chlorodifluoromethane	$CHClF_2$	86.468	–41.458	–251.356	205.061	723.7	32.70	1.234 (25)[2]
115	Chloropentafluoroethane	$CClF_2CF_3$	154.47	–38.65	–146.92	175.91	453.8	38.38	1.221 (25)[2]
500	R-12/152a (73.8/26.2)	—	99.303	–28.4854	—	215.762	604.6	30.91	—
717	Ammonia	NH_3	17.03	–27.9886	–107.779	270.05	1643.7	14.05[d]	1.325 (16.5)
12	Dichlorodifluoromethane	CCl_2F_2	120.91	–21.5536	–250.69	233.546	599.9	35.27	1.288 (25)[2]
1234yf	2,3,3,3-tetrafluoroprop-1-ene	$CF_3CF{=}CH_2$	114.04	–21.01		202.46	490.55	29.668	
134a	Tetrafluoroethane	CF_3CH_2F	102.03	–14.9332	–153.94	213.908	588.8	31.96	—
152a	Difluoroethane	CHF_2CH_3	66.051	–11.2414	–181.462	235.868	655.1	22.97	—
1234ze (E)	Trans-1,3,3,3- tetrafluoropropene	$CF_3CH{=}CHF$	114.04	–2.11		228.87	527.29	30.542	
124	Chlorotetrafluoroethane	$CHClFCF_3$	136.48	10.4666	–326.47	252.104	525.7	34.96	—
600a	Isobutane	C_4H_{10}	58.122	10.852	–254.96	274.39	526.34	14.08	1.3514 (–25)[1]

Table 8.1 Physical Properties of Selected Refrigerants[a] [2021F, Ch 29, Tbl 5] (*Continued*)

Refrigerant									
No.	Chemical Name or Composition (% by Mass)	Chemical Formula	Molecular Mass	Boiling Pt.[f] (NBP) at 14.696 psia, °F	Freezing Point, °F	Critical Temp., °F	Critical Pressure, psi	Critical Density, lb/ft^3	Refractive Index of Liquid[b,c]
142b	Chlorodifluoroethane	$CClF_2CH_3$	100.5	15.53	–202.774	278.798	590.3	27.84	—
C318	Octafluorocyclobutane	C_4F_8	200.03	21.245	–39.64	239.414	402.8	38.70	
600	Butane	C_4H_{10}	58.122	31.118	–216.86	305.564	550.6	14.23	1.3562 (–15)[1]
1336mzz (Z)	Cis-1,1,1,4,4,4-hexafluoro-2-butene	$CF_3CH{=}CHCF_3$	164.1	33.4	—	340.3	421.0	31.506	—
114	Dichlorotetrafluoroethane	$CClF_2CClF_2$	170.92	38.4548	–134.54	294.224	472.4	36.21	1.294 (25)
1233zd (E)	Trans-1-chloro-3,3,3-trifluoro-1-propene	$CF_3CH{=}CHCl$	130.5	64.6	—	330.1	519.2	30.030	—
11	Trichlorofluoromethane	CCl_3F	137.37	74.6744	–166.846	388.328	639.3	34.59	1.362 (25)[2]
123	Dichlorotrifluoroethane	$CHCl_2CF_3$	152.93	82.08	–160.87	362.624	531.1	34.34	—
141b	Dichlorofluoroethane	CCl_2FCH_3	116.95	89.69	–154.25	399.83	610.9	28.63	—
113	Trichlorotrifluoroethane	CCl_2FCClF_2	187.38	117.653	–33.196	417.308	492.0	34.96	1.357 (25)[2]
718[3]	Water	H_2O	18.015	211.9532	32.018	705.11	3200.1	20.10	—

Notes:
[a] Data from NIST (2010) REFPROP v. 9.0.
[b] Temperature of measurement (°C, unless kelvin is noted) shown in parentheses. Data from CRC (1987), unless otherwise noted.
[c] For the sodium D line.
[d] Sublimes.
[e] At 76.4 psi.
[f] Bubble point used for blends

References:
[1] Kirk and Othmer (1956).
[2] *Bulletin* B-32A (DuPont).
[3] *Handbook of Chemistry* (1967).

Ozone-depleting substances, including CFCs and HCFCs, are to be phased out of production under the Montreal Protocol. In the United States, production and importation of CFCs were banned completely in 1996. HCFCs are being phased down, with complete phaseout set for 2030.

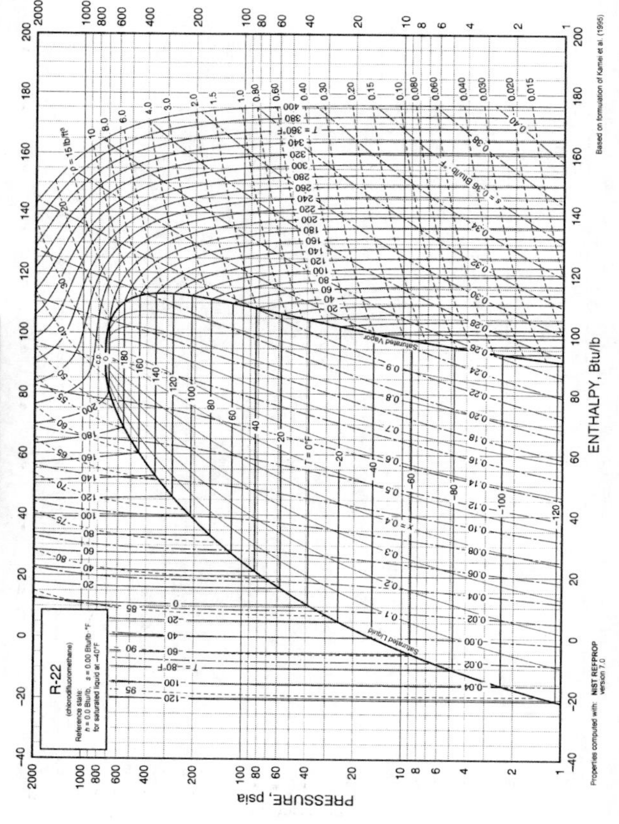

Figure 8.1 Pressure-Enthalpy Diagram for Refrigerant 22
[2021F, Ch 30, Fig 2]

Table 8.2 R-22 (Chlorodifluoromethane)
Properties of Saturated Liquid and Saturated Vapor [2021F, Ch 30, Tbl R-22]

Temp.,* °F	Pressure, psia	Density, lb/ft³ Liquid	Volume, ft³/lb Vapor	Enthalpy, Btu/lb Liquid	Enthalpy, Btu/lb Vapor	Entropy, Btu/lb·°F Liquid	Entropy, Btu/lb·°F Vapor
−150	0.263	98.28	146.06	−28.119	87.566	−0.07757	0.29600
−140	0.436	97.36	90.759	−25.583	88.729	−0.06951	0.28808
−130	0.698	96.44	58.384	−23.046	89.899	−0.06170	0.28090
−120	1.082	95.52	38.745	−20.509	91.074	−0.05412	0.27439
−110	1.629	94.59	26.444	−17.970	92.252	−0.04675	0.26846
−100	2.388	93.66	18.511	−15.427	93.430	−0.03959	0.26307
−95	2.865	93.19	15.623	−14.154	94.018	−0.03608	0.26055
−90	3.417	92.71	13.258	−12.880	94.605	−0.03261	0.25815
−85	4.053	92.24	11.309	−11.604	95.191	−0.02918	0.25585
−80	4.782	91.76	9.6939	−10.326	95.775	−0.02580	0.25366
−75	5.615	91.28	8.3487	−9.046	96.357	−0.02245	0.25155
−70	6.561	90.79	7.2222	−7.763	96.937	−0.01915	0.24954
−65	7.631	90.31	6.2744	−6.477	97.514	−0.01587	0.24761
−60	8.836	89.82	5.4730	−5.189	98.087	−0.01264	0.24577
−55	10.190	89.33	4.7924	−3.897	98.657	−0.00943	0.24400
−50	11.703	88.83	4.2119	−2.602	99.224	−0.00626	0.24230
−45	13.390	88.33	3.7147	−1.303	99.786	−0.00311	0.24067
−41.46[b]	14.696	87.97	3.4054	−0.381	100.181	−0.00091	0.23955
−40	15.262	87.82	3.2872	0.000	100.343	0.00000	0.23910
−35	17.336	87.32	2.9181	1.308	100.896	0.00309	0.23759
−30	19.624	86.80	2.5984	2.620	101.443	0.00615	0.23615
−25	22.142	86.29	2.3204	3.937	101.984	0.00918	0.23475
−20	24.906	85.76	2.0778	5.260	102.519	0.01220	0.23341
−15	27.929	85.24	1.8656	6.588	103.048	0.01519	0.23211
−10	31.230	84.71	1.6792	7.923	103.570	0.01815	0.23086
−5	34.824	84.17	1.5150	9.263	104.085	0.02110	0.22965
0	38.728	83.63	1.3701	10.610	104.591	0.02403	0.22848
5	42.960	83.08	1.2417	11.964	105.090	0.02694	0.22735
10	47.536	82.52	1.1276	13.325	105.580	0.02983	0.22625
15	52.475	81.96	1.0261	14.694	106.061	0.03270	0.22519
20	57.795	81.39	0.9354	16.070	106.532	0.03556	0.22415
25	63.514	80.82	0.8543	17.455	106.994	0.03841	0.22315
30	69.651	80.24	0.7815	18.848	107.445	0.04124	0.22217
35	76.225	79.65	0.7161	20.250	107.884	0.04406	0.22121
40	83.255	79.05	0.6572	21.662	108.313	0.04686	0.22028
45	90.761	78.44	0.6040	23.083	108.729	0.04966	0.21936
50	98.763	77.83	0.5558	24.514	109.132	0.05244	0.21847
55	107.28	77.20	0.5122	25.956	109.521	0.05522	0.21758
60	116.33	76.57	0.4725	27.409	109.897	0.05798	0.21672
65	125.94	75.92	0.4364	28.874	110.257	0.06074	0.21586
70	136.13	75.27	0.4035	30.350	110.602	0.06350	0.21501
75	146.92	74.60	0.3734	31.839	110.929	0.06625	0.21417
80	158.33	73.92	0.3459	33.342	111.239	0.06899	0.21333
85	170.38	73.23	0.3207	34.859	111.530	0.07173	0.21250
90	183.09	72.52	0.2975	36.391	111.801	0.07447	0.21166
95	196.50	71.80	0.2762	37.938	112.050	0.07721	0.21083
100	210.61	71.06	0.2566	39.502	112.276	0.07996	0.20998
105	225.46	70.30	0.2385	41.084	112.478	0.08270	0.20913
110	241.06	69.52	0.2217	42.686	112.653	0.08545	0.20827
115	257.45	68.72	0.2062	44.308	112.799	0.08821	0.20739
120	274.65	67.90	0.1918	45.952	112.914	0.09098	0.20649
125	292.69	67.05	0.1785	47.621	112.996	0.09376	0.20557
130	311.58	66.18	0.1660	49.316	113.040	0.09656	0.20462
135	331.37	65.27	0.1544	51.041	113.043	0.09937	0.20364
140	352.08	64.32	0.1435	52.798	113.000	0.10222	0.20261
145	373.74	63.34	0.1334	54.591	112.907	0.10509	0.20153
150	396.38	62.31	0.1238	56.425	112.756	0.10800	0.20040
155	420.04	61.22	0.1149	58.305	112.539	0.11096	0.19919
160	444.75	60.07	0.1064	60.240	112.247	0.11397	0.19790
165	470.56	58.84	0.0984	62.237	111.866	0.11705	0.19650
170	497.50	57.53	0.0907	64.309	111.378	0.12022	0.19497
175	525.62	56.10	0.0834	66.474	110.760	0.12350	0.19328
180	554.98	54.52	0.0764	68.757	109.976	0.12693	0.19136
185	585.63	52.74	0.0695	71.196	108.972	0.13056	0.18916
190	617.64	50.67	0.0626	73.859	107.654	0.13450	0.18651
195	651.12	48.14	0.0556	76.875	105.835	0.13893	0.18316
200	686.20	44.68	0.0479	80.593	103.010	0.14437	0.17835
205.06[c]	723.74	32.70	0.0306	91.208	91.208	0.16012	0.16012

*Temperatures on ITS-90 scale [b]Normal boiling point [c]Critical point

Table 8.3 Superheated Vapor Thermodynamic Properties of R-22

Temp., °F	Pressure = 30 psia Sat. Temp. = –11.85°F			Pressure = 60 psia Sat. Temp. = 21.94°F		
	V	*h*	*s*	*V*	*h*	*s*
–10	1.760	103.92	0.2325			
30	1.943	109.92	0.2453	0.9271	108.35	0.2271
60	2.078	114.55	0.2545	1.001	113.17	0.2367
100	2.255	120.92	0.2663	1.096	119.74	0.2488
150	2.473	129.17	0.2804	1.212	128.19	0.2633
Temp., °F	**Pressure = 75 psia Sat. Temp. = 34.06°F**			**Pressure = 90 psia Sat. Temp. = 44.47°F**		
	V	*h*	*s*	*V*	*h*	*s*
30	0.7851	107.81	0.2229			
60	0.7847	112.45	0.2306	0.6401	111.69	0.2253
100	0.8639	119.13	0.2429	0.7088	118.50	0.2379
150	0.9591	127.69	0.2576	0.7906	127.18	0.2528
Temp., °F	**Pressure = 135 psia Sat. Temp. = 69.39°F**			**Pressure = 180 psia Sat. Temp. = 88.72°F**		
	V	*h*	*s*	*V*	*h*	*s*
100	0.4492	116.50	0.2260	0.3177	114.29	0.2164
150	0.5092	125.59	0.2416	0.3678	123.90	0.2329
200	0.5655	134.79	0.2561	0.4132	133.45	0.2479
250	0.6193	144.20	0.2698	0.4558	143.10	0.2620
300	0.6713	153.84	0.2829	0.4965	152.93	0.2754
Temp., °F	**Pressure = 200 psia Sat. Temp. = 96.17°F**			**Pressure = 220 psia Sat. Temp. = 103.09°F**		
	V	*h*	*s*	*V*	*h*	*s*
100	0.2776	113.22	0.2126			
150	0.3251	123.11	0.2295	0.2900	122.30	0.2263
200	0.3674	132.83	0.2448	0.3299	132.20	0.2419
250	0.4067	142.60	0.2591	0.3666	142.09	0.2564
300	0.4441	152.52	0.2726	0.4012	152.10	0.2700
Temp., °F	**Pressure = 240 psia Sat. Temp. = 109.57°F**			**Pressure = 260 psia Sat. Temp. = 115.66°F**		
	V	*h*	*s*	*V*	*h*	*s*
150	0.2606	121.45	0.2232	0.2356	120.58	0.2203
200	0.2985	131.56	0.2392	0.2720	130.90	0.2366
250	0.3330	141.58	0.2538	0.3046	141.06	0.2514
300	0.3654	151.69	0.2676	0.3351	151.27	0.2653

V = vapor volume, ft^3/lb
h = enthalpy, Btu/lb
s = entropy, Btu/lb·°F

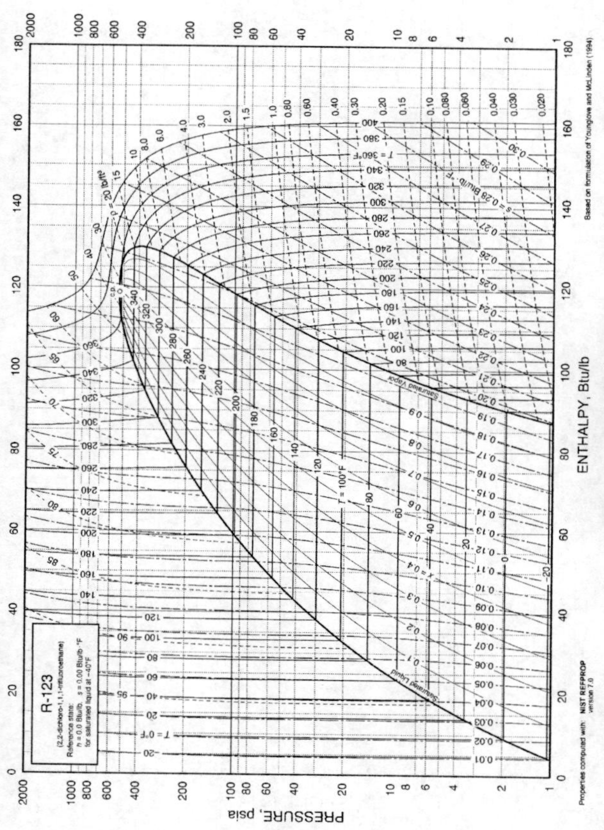

Figure 8.2 Pressure-Enthalpy Diagram for Refrigerant 123
[2021F, Ch 30, Fig 5]

Table 8.4 R-123 (2,2-Dichloro-1,1,1-Trifluoroethane) Properties of Saturated Liquid and Saturated Vapor [2021F, Ch 30, Tbl R-123]

Temp.,* °F	Pressure, psia	Density, lb/ft³ Liquid	Volume, ft³/lb Vapor	Enthalpy, Btu/lb Liquid	Enthalpy, Btu/lb Vapor	Entropy, Btu/lb·°F Liquid	Entropy, Btu/lb·°F Vapor	c_p/c_v Vapor
−140	0.003	108.90	7431.6	−22.241	71.783	−0.06050	0.23363	1.1237
−130	0.006	108.12	3871.0	−20.033	72.974	−0.05370	0.22843	1.1212
−120	0.011	107.35	2111.6	−17.826	74.187	−0.04710	0.22379	1.1187
−110	0.020	106.57	1201.0	−15.619	75.421	−0.04070	0.21966	1.1165
−100	0.036	105.80	709.46	−13.410	76.676	−0.03447	0.21600	1.1144
−90	0.060	105.03	433.83	−11.195	77.950	−0.02840	0.21275	1.1124
−80	0.097	104.26	273.77	−8.975	79.244	−0.02247	0.20989	1.1106
−70	0.154	103.48	177.81	−6.746	80.556	−0.01668	0.20737	1.1090
−60	0.236	102.70	118.57	−4.509	81.885	−0.01101	0.20516	1.1075
−50	0.354	101.92	80.999	−2.260	83.231	−0.00545	0.20323	1.1061
−40	0.519	101.13	56.576	0.000	84.592	0.00000	0.20157	1.1050
−30	0.744	100.34	40.333	2.272	85.967	0.00535	0.20014	1.1040
−20	1.046	99.54	29.299	4.558	87.355	0.01061	0.19892	1.1032
−10	1.445	98.73	21.655	6.857	88.754	0.01578	0.19790	1.1026
0	1.963	97.92	16.264	9.170	90.163	0.02086	0.19706	1.1022
5	2.274	97.51	14.174	10.332	90.871	0.02337	0.19670	1.1021
10	2.625	97.10	12.396	11.498	91.582	0.02587	0.19638	1.1020
15	3.019	96.69	10.878	12.667	92.294	0.02834	0.19609	1.1020
20	3.460	96.28	9.5779	13.840	93.008	0.03080	0.19585	1.1020
25	3.952	95.86	8.4595	15.017	93.723	0.03324	0.19563	1.1021
30	4.499	95.44	7.4943	16.198	94.440	0.03566	0.19544	1.1023
35	5.106	95.02	6.6586	17.382	95.158	0.03806	0.19529	1.1025
40	5.778	94.60	5.9327	18.570	95.877	0.04045	0.19517	1.1028
45	6.519	94.17	5.3002	19.762	96.597	0.04282	0.19507	1.1031
50	7.334	93.74	4.7474	20.958	97.317	0.04518	0.19500	1.1035
55	8.229	93.31	4.2629	22.158	98.038	0.04752	0.19495	1.1040
60	9.208	92.88	3.8371	23.362	98.760	0.04984	0.19493	1.1046
65	10.278	92.44	3.4617	24.570	99.481	0.05215	0.19493	1.1052
70	11.445	92.01	3.1301	25.782	100.203	0.05444	0.19495	1.1059
75	12.713	91.56	2.8362	26.998	100.924	0.05673	0.19499	1.1067
80	14.090	91.12	2.5753	28.218	101.645	0.05899	0.19505	1.1075
82.08[b]	14.696	90.94	2.4753	28.728	101.945	0.05993	0.19508	1.1079
85	15.580	90.67	2.3429	29.443	102.365	0.06124	0.19513	1.1085
90	17.192	90.22	2.1356	30.671	103.085	0.06348	0.19522	1.1095
95	18.931	89.77	1.9503	31.904	103.804	0.06571	0.19534	1.1106
100	20.804	89.31	1.7841	33.141	104.521	0.06792	0.19546	1.1119
105	22.819	88.85	1.6349	34.383	105.238	0.07012	0.19560	1.1132
110	24.980	88.39	1.5006	35.628	105.953	0.07231	0.19576	1.1146
115	27.297	87.92	1.3795	36.879	106.666	0.07449	0.19593	1.1162
120	29.776	87.45	1.2701	38.134	107.377	0.07665	0.19611	1.1178
125	32.425	86.98	1.1710	39.393	108.086	0.07881	0.19630	1.1196
130	35.251	86.50	1.0812	40.657	108.792	0.08095	0.19650	1.1215
135	38.261	86.01	0.9996	41.926	109.497	0.08308	0.19671	1.1236
140	41.464	85.52	0.9253	43.200	110.198	0.08520	0.19693	1.1258
145	44.868	85.03	0.8577	44.479	110.896	0.08732	0.19716	1.1281
150	48.479	84.53	0.7959	45.763	111.591	0.08942	0.19739	1.1306
160	56.360	83.52	0.6876	48.347	112.970	0.09359	0.19788	1.1362
170	65.173	82.49	0.5965	50.953	114.333	0.09773	0.19839	1.1426
180	74.986	81.43	0.5195	53.583	115.678	0.10184	0.19892	1.1499
190	85.868	80.34	0.4539	56.237	117.001	0.10592	0.19945	1.1583
200	97.892	79.23	0.3979	58.918	118.300	0.10997	0.19999	1.1681
210	111.13	78.08	0.3497	61.627	119.572	0.11400	0.20053	1.1793
220	125.66	76.89	0.3080	64.367	120.813	0.11801	0.20106	1.1925
230	141.56	75.66	0.2719	67.141	122.019	0.12201	0.20158	1.2079
240	158.91	74.38	0.2404	69.952	123.184	0.12599	0.20207	1.2262
250	177.80	73.04	0.2128	72.805	124.303	0.12997	0.20254	1.2482
260	198.31	71.64	0.1885	75.704	125.367	0.13396	0.20296	1.2749
270	220.53	70.16	0.1670	78.655	126.368	0.13795	0.20334	1.3079
280	244.58	68.60	0.1479	81.666	127.294	0.14196	0.20365	1.3496
290	270.54	66.92	0.1309	84.749	128.128	0.14600	0.20387	1.4035
300	298.53	65.11	0.1155	87.916	128.851	0.15010	0.20398	1.4755
310	328.69	63.12	0.1016	91.188	129.431	0.15426	0.20395	1.5762
320	361.16	60.91	0.0889	94.594	129.822	0.15853	0.20372	1.7258
330	396.11	58.37	0.0770	98.186	129.950	0.16297	0.20320	1.9693
340	433.76	55.33	0.0658	102.059	129.670	0.16769	0.20222	2.4318
350	474.41	51.32	0.0544	106.459	128.628	0.17298	0.20036	3.6383
360	518.66	43.97	0.0403	112.667	125.064	0.18039	0.19551	14.6330
362.63[c]	531.10	34.34	0.0291	118.800	118.800	0.18779	0.18779	∞

*Temperatures on ITS-90 scale   [b]Normal boiling point   [c]Critical point

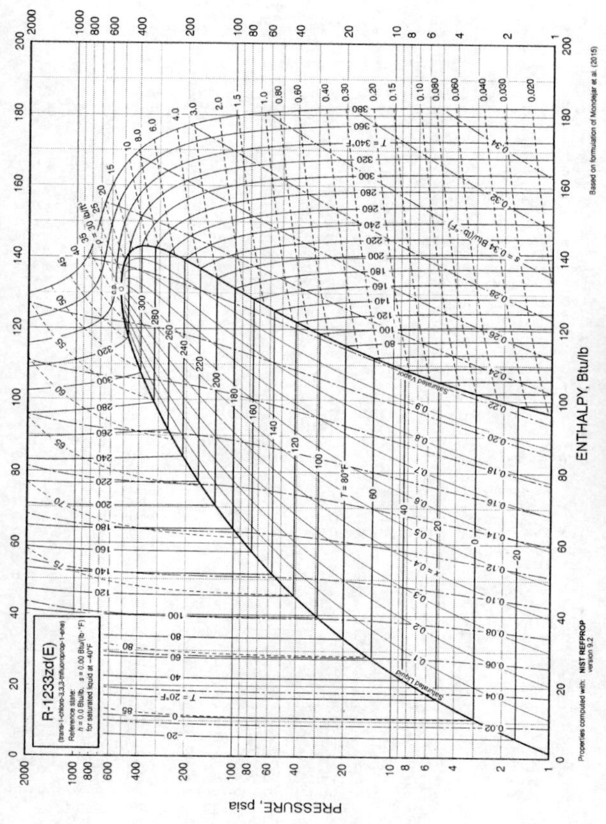

Figure 8.3 Pressure-Enthalpy Diagram for Refrigerant 1233zd(E)
[2021F, Ch 30, Fig 12]

Table 8.5 Refrigerant 1233zd(E) (trans-1-chloro-3,3,3-trifluoroprop-1-ene) Properties of Saturated Liquid and Saturated Vapor [2021F, Ch 30, Tbl R-1233zd(E)]

Temp., °F	Pressure, psia	Density, lb/ft³	Volume, ft³/lb	Enthalpy, Btu/lb		Entropy, Btu/lb·°F		Specific Heat, c_p Btu/lb·°F		c_p / c_v
		Liquid	Vapor	Liquid	Vapor	Liquid	Vapor	Liquid	Vapor	Vapor
−60	0.387	89.41	84.710	−5.327	92.383	−0.01300	0.23147	0.2646	0.1573	1.1086
−50	0.572	88.68	58.669	−2.673	93.947	−0.00644	0.22940	0.2663	0.1603	1.1069
−40	0.827	87.94	41.517	−0.000	95.532	−0.00000	0.22764	0.2681	0.1632	1.1054
−30	1.171	87.20	29.964	2.690	97.137	0.00633	0.22614	0.2699	0.1661	1.1043
−20	1.628	86.46	22.022	5.398	98.758	0.01256	0.22490	0.2717	0.1689	1.1034
−15	1.906	86.09	18.999	6.759	99.575	0.01564	0.22437	0.2726	0.1704	1.1030
−10	2.223	85.71	16.457	8.125	100.394	0.01869	0.22388	0.2735	0.1718	1.1028
−5	2.581	85.33	14.310	9.495	101.217	0.02172	0.22345	0.2744	0.1732	1.1026
0	2.986	84.96	12.488	10.870	102.043	0.02472	0.22307	0.2753	0.1746	1.1025
5	3.441	84.57	10.937	12.249	102.871	0.02771	0.22273	0.2762	0.1760	1.1024
10	3.952	84.19	9.6112	13.634	103.701	0.03067	0.22244	0.2772	0.1774	1.1024
15	4.522	83.81	8.4736	15.022	104.533	0.03361	0.22218	0.2781	0.1789	1.1026
20	5.157	83.42	7.4939	16.416	105.367	0.03652	0.22197	0.2791	0.1803	1.1027
25	5.862	83.03	6.6474	17.815	106.202	0.03942	0.22179	0.2800	0.1817	1.1030
30	6.643	82.64	5.9135	19.218	107.038	0.04230	0.22164	0.2810	0.1832	1.1034
35	7.505	82.25	5.2752	20.626	107.874	0.04516	0.22153	0.2819	0.1846	1.1038
40	8.455	81.85	4.7183	22.040	108.711	0.04799	0.22145	0.2829	0.1861	1.1043
45	9.498	81.45	4.2310	23.458	109.549	0.05081	0.22140	0.2839	0.1876	1.1050
50	10.641	81.05	3.8033	24.881	110.386	0.05362	0.22138	0.2849	0.1891	1.1057
55	11.890	80.65	3.4269	26.310	111.223	0.05640	0.22138	0.2859	0.1907	1.1065
60	13.252	80.24	3.0947	27.744	112.059	0.05917	0.22141	0.2870	0.1922	1.1074
64.87[b]	14.696	79.84	2.8079	29.146	112.873	0.06185	0.22146	0.2880	0.1937	1.1083
65	14.735	79.83	2.8008	29.183	112.894	0.06191	0.22147	0.2880	0.1938	1.1084
70	16.345	79.42	2.5402	30.627	113.728	0.06465	0.22154	0.2891	0.1954	1.1095
75	18.090	79.00	2.3084	32.077	114.561	0.06736	0.22164	0.2902	0.1970	1.1107
80	19.977	78.58	2.1018	33.532	115.392	0.07007	0.22175	0.2913	0.1987	1.1120
85	22.013	78.16	1.9172	34.993	116.222	0.07275	0.22188	0.2924	0.2004	1.1135
90	24.208	77.73	1.7519	36.460	117.049	0.07542	0.22204	0.2935	0.2021	1.1150
95	26.569	77.30	1.6037	37.933	117.874	0.07808	0.22220	0.2947	0.2038	1.1167
100	29.104	76.86	1.4703	39.412	118.696	0.08072	0.22239	0.2959	0.2056	1.1186
105	31.821	76.42	1.3502	40.896	119.515	0.08335	0.22258	0.2971	0.2075	1.1205
110	34.730	75.98	1.2418	42.387	120.331	0.08597	0.22279	0.2984	0.2093	1.1226
115	37.838	75.53	1.1437	43.885	121.144	0.08857	0.22301	0.2997	0.2113	1.1249
120	41.155	75.08	1.0548	45.389	121.953	0.09116	0.22325	0.3010	0.2132	1.1274
125	44.690	74.62	0.9741	46.900	122.758	0.09374	0.22349	0.3024	0.2152	1.1300
130	48.452	74.16	0.9007	48.417	123.558	0.09631	0.22374	0.3038	0.2173	1.1328
135	52.449	73.69	0.8339	49.942	124.354	0.09887	0.22400	0.3052	0.2194	1.1358
140	56.693	73.21	0.7729	51.474	125.145	0.10142	0.22427	0.3067	0.2216	1.1391
145	61.191	72.73	0.7171	53.014	125.931	0.10396	0.22455	0.3083	0.2239	1.1426
150	65.955	72.25	0.6661	54.561	126.711	0.10649	0.22483	0.3099	0.2262	1.1463
155	70.993	71.75	0.6193	56.117	127.485	0.10900	0.22511	0.3116	0.2286	1.1503
160	76.316	71.25	0.5763	57.680	128.253	0.11152	0.22540	0.3133	0.2311	1.1546
165	81.934	70.75	0.5368	59.253	129.013	0.11402	0.22570	0.3151	0.2337	1.1593
170	87.858	70.23	0.5004	60.834	129.767	0.11652	0.22599	0.3170	0.2364	1.1643
175	94.098	69.71	0.4669	62.424	130.512	0.11901	0.22629	0.3190	0.2392	1.1697
180	100.66	69.17	0.4359	64.024	131.249	0.12149	0.22658	0.3211	0.2421	1.1755
185	107.57	68.63	0.4072	65.634	131.977	0.12397	0.22688	0.3233	0.2451	1.1819
190	114.82	68.08	0.3807	67.254	132.695	0.12644	0.22717	0.3256	0.2483	1.1887
195	122.43	67.52	0.3561	68.886	133.403	0.12891	0.22746	0.3280	0.2517	1.1962
200	130.42	66.95	0.3333	70.528	134.099	0.13138	0.22774	0.3306	0.2552	1.2043
210	147.55	65.77	0.2923	73.850	135.455	0.13630	0.22829	0.3363	0.2629	1.2230
220	166.31	64.54	0.2567	77.225	136.754	0.14123	0.22881	0.3427	0.2717	1.2456
230	186.81	63.24	0.2256	80.660	137.988	0.14615	0.22928	0.3503	0.2818	1.2733
240	209.15	61.87	0.1983	84.161	139.142	0.15110	0.22968	0.3591	0.2938	1.3079
250	233.46	60.42	0.1742	87.741	140.202	0.15608	0.23000	0.3698	0.3084	1.3522
260	259.84	58.86	0.1528	91.410	141.147	0.16110	0.23021	0.3831	0.3267	1.4103
270	288.46	57.17	0.1337	95.189	141.946	0.16618	0.23026	0.4002	0.3506	1.4894
280	319.45	55.31	0.1165	99.102	142.560	0.17137	0.23012	0.4231	0.3835	1.6020
290	352.98	53.22	0.1009	103.188	142.927	0.17670	0.22971	0.4563	0.4319	1.7731
300	389.27	50.82	0.0864	107.515	142.944	0.18227	0.22890	0.5093	0.5111	2.0591
310	428.56	47.89	0.0727	112.212	142.420	0.18822	0.22746	0.6110	0.6642	2.6221
320	471.16	43.95	0.0590	117.623	140.880	0.19498	0.22481	0.896	1.086	4.191
330	517.63	36.02	0.0415	125.873	135.691	0.20521	0.21765	5.598	7.067	26.548
331.61[c]	525.57	29.98	0.0334	130.891	130.891	0.21150	0.21150	∞	∞	∞

[b]Normal boiling point

[c]Critical point

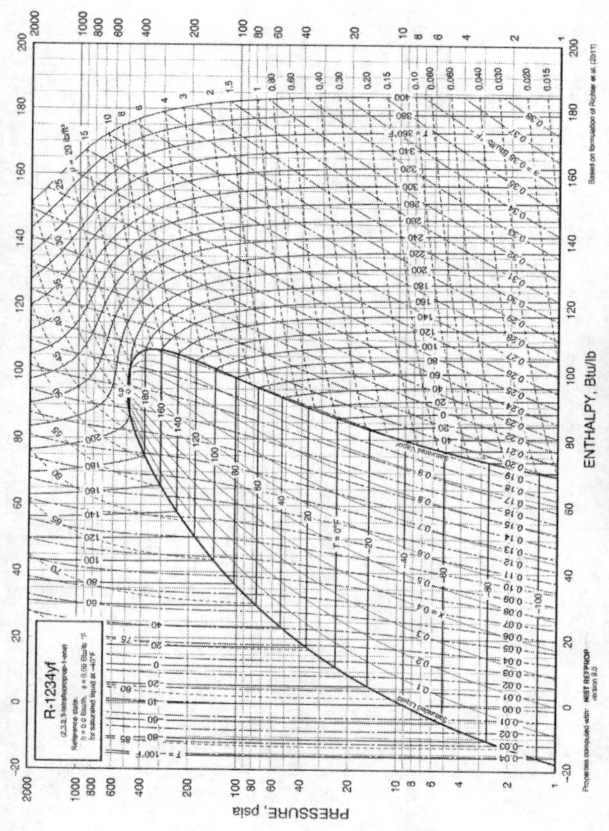

Figure 8.4 Pressure-Enthalpy Diagram for Refrigerant 1234yf
[2021F, Ch 30, Fig 13]

Table 8.6 Refrigerant 1234yf (2,3,3,3-tetrafluoroprop-1-ene) Properties of Saturated Liquid and Saturated Vapor [2021F, Ch 30, Tbl R-1234yf]

Temp., °F	Pressure, psia	Density, lb/ft³	Volume, ft³/lb	Enthalpy, Btu/lb		Entropy, Btu/lb·°F		Specific Heat, c_p Btu/lb·°F		c_p / c_v
		Liquid	Vapor	Liquid	Vapor	Liquid	Vapor	Liquid	Vapor	Vapor
−60	5.111	82.49	7.1955	−5.458	76.593	−0.01330	0.19200	0.2688	0.1776	1.1241
−55	5.932	82.03	6.2622	−4.109	77.395	−0.00995	0.19146	0.2707	0.1796	1.1243
−50	6.855	81.58	5.4710	−2.749	78.198	−0.00662	0.19097	0.2727	0.1817	1.1247
−45	7.889	81.11	4.7974	−1.380	79.002	−0.00330	0.19055	0.2746	0.1838	1.1252
−40	9.046	80.65	4.2215	−0.000	79.808	−0.00000	0.19017	0.2766	0.1859	1.1258
−35	10.333	80.18	3.7271	1.390	80.614	0.00328	0.18984	0.2787	0.1880	1.1265
−30	11.761	79.71	3.3012	2.790	81.420	0.00655	0.18956	0.2807	0.1903	1.1274
−25	13.341	79.23	2.9329	4.200	82.226	0.00981	0.18932	0.2828	0.1925	1.1285
−21.07[b]	14.696	78.85	2.6781	5.315	82.859	0.01236	0.18916	0.2844	0.1943	1.1294
−20	15.084	78.75	2.6132	5.621	83.032	0.01305	0.18912	0.2848	0.1948	1.1297
−15	17.001	78.26	2.3349	7.053	83.837	0.01628	0.18896	0.2870	0.1971	1.1310
−10	19.104	77.77	2.0917	8.495	84.641	0.01949	0.18883	0.2891	0.1995	1.1325
−5	21.404	77.28	1.8786	9.948	85.444	0.02269	0.18874	0.2912	0.2019	1.1342
0	23.914	76.78	1.6913	11.412	86.244	0.02588	0.18868	0.2934	0.2043	1.1361
5	26.647	76.27	1.5262	12.887	87.043	0.02906	0.18865	0.2956	0.2068	1.1381
10	29.615	75.76	1.3802	14.374	87.839	0.03223	0.18865	0.2979	0.2094	1.1404
15	32.831	75.24	1.2508	15.871	88.632	0.03538	0.18867	0.3001	0.2120	1.1429
20	36.309	74.72	1.1357	17.381	89.422	0.03853	0.18872	0.3024	0.2147	1.1457
25	40.062	74.19	1.0332	18.902	90.208	0.04166	0.18878	0.3048	0.2174	1.1486
30	44.105	73.65	0.9416	20.434	90.989	0.04479	0.18887	0.3072	0.2202	1.1519
35	48.451	73.11	0.8596	21.979	91.765	0.04790	0.18898	0.3096	0.2231	1.1555
40	53.116	72.55	0.7860	23.536	92.536	0.05101	0.18910	0.3121	0.2261	1.1594
45	58.113	71.99	0.7198	25.106	93.301	0.05411	0.18924	0.3147	0.2291	1.1637
50	63.459	71.42	0.6601	26.688	94.059	0.05720	0.18939	0.3173	0.2323	1.1685
55	69.167	70.84	0.6062	28.283	94.810	0.06029	0.18955	0.3199	0.2355	1.1736
60	75.255	70.25	0.5573	29.891	95.552	0.06337	0.18972	0.3227	0.2389	1.1793
65	81.737	69.65	0.5130	31.513	96.285	0.06644	0.18989	0.3255	0.2425	1.1856
70	88.629	69.04	0.4728	33.149	97.008	0.06951	0.19007	0.3285	0.2462	1.1926
75	95.949	68.42	0.4361	34.799	97.720	0.07257	0.19025	0.3315	0.2501	1.2002
80	103.71	67.78	0.4027	36.463	98.420	0.07563	0.19044	0.3346	0.2543	1.2087
85	111.94	67.14	0.3721	38.142	99.106	0.07869	0.19062	0.3379	0.2587	1.2181
90	120.64	66.47	0.3441	39.837	99.779	0.08174	0.19079	0.3413	0.2635	1.2286
95	129.84	65.80	0.3185	41.548	100.435	0.08479	0.19096	0.3450	0.2686	1.2402
100	139.55	65.10	0.2949	43.275	101.075	0.08784	0.19112	0.3488	0.2742	1.2533
105	149.80	64.39	0.2732	45.021	101.696	0.09090	0.19126	0.3530	0.2802	1.2679
110	160.60	63.66	0.2532	46.784	102.296	0.09395	0.19140	0.3574	0.2867	1.2843
115	171.97	62.92	0.2347	48.568	102.874	0.09701	0.19151	0.3623	0.2940	1.3028
120	183.93	62.14	0.2176	50.373	103.428	0.10008	0.19160	0.3676	0.3019	1.3239
125	196.51	61.35	0.2017	52.201	103.955	0.10315	0.19167	0.3735	0.3107	1.3479
130	209.72	60.52	0.1870	54.054	104.452	0.10624	0.19171	0.3801	0.3206	1.3756
135	223.59	59.66	0.1733	55.935	104.916	0.10934	0.19171	0.3875	0.3318	1.4077
140	238.13	58.77	0.1606	57.845	105.342	0.11246	0.19167	0.3959	0.3446	1.4453
145	253.39	57.83	0.1487	59.789	105.726	0.11561	0.19158	0.4055	0.3594	1.4898
150	269.37	56.84	0.1375	61.769	106.061	0.11879	0.19144	0.4167	0.3767	1.5432
155	286.11	55.80	0.1270	63.792	106.340	0.12200	0.19122	0.4300	0.3974	1.6082
160	303.64	54.68	0.1172	65.861	106.554	0.12526	0.19093	0.4459	0.4227	1.6891
165	321.99	53.49	0.1078	67.986	106.690	0.12857	0.19053	0.4655	0.4544	1.7922
170	341.19	52.21	0.0990	70.175	106.731	0.13196	0.19001	0.4906	0.4956	1.9275
175	361.28	50.80	0.0905	72.445	106.653	0.13543	0.18933	0.5241	0.5513	2.1127
180	382.32	49.24	0.0823	74.816	106.421	0.13903	0.18844	0.5717	0.6314	2.3809
185	404.35	47.47	0.0743	77.328	105.976	0.14281	0.18725	0.6458	0.7571	2.8031
190	427.45	45.39	0.0662	80.050	105.213	0.14688	0.18561	0.7788	0.9837	3.5641
195	451.72	42.73	0.0578	83.145	103.888	0.15147	0.18315	1.094	1.517	5.344
200	477.33	38.53	0.0475	87.241	101.103	0.15752	0.17853	2.821	4.285	14.439
202.46[c]	490.55	29.69	0.0337	93.995	93.995	0.16763	0.16763	∞	∞	∞

[b]Normal boiling point [c]Critical point

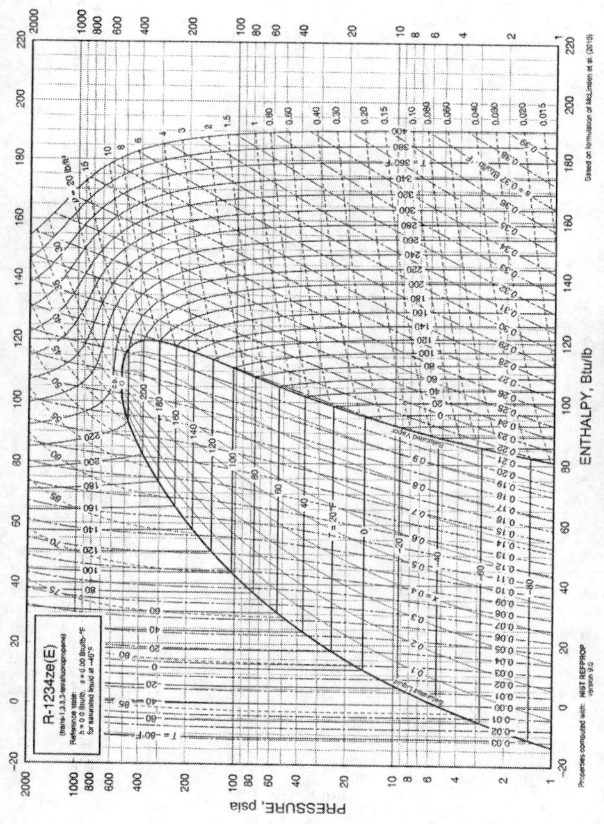

Figure 8.5 Pressure-Enthalpy Diagram for Refrigerant 1234ze(E)
[2021F, Ch 30, Fig 14]

Table 8.7 Refrigerant 1234ze(E) (Trans-1,3,3,3-tetrafluoropropene) Properties of Saturated Liquid and Saturated Vapor [2021F, Ch 30, Tbl R-1234ze(E)]

Temp., °F	Pressure, psia	Density, lb/ft³	Volume, ft³/lb	Enthalpy, Btu/lb		Entropy, Btu/lb·°F		Specific Heat, c_p Btu/lb·°F		c_p / c_v
		Liquid	Vapor	Liquid	Vapor	Liquid	Vapor	Liquid	Vapor	Vapor
−60	2.839	86.03	13.083	−5.955	85.763	−0.01452	0.21496	0.2962	0.1797	1.1146
−55	3.347	85.59	11.219	−4.472	86.613	−0.01084	0.21425	0.2968	0.1812	1.1145
−50	3.926	85.14	9.6638	−2.985	87.465	−0.00719	0.21360	0.2976	0.1827	1.1146
−45	4.584	84.70	8.3603	−1.494	88.319	−0.00358	0.21301	0.2983	0.1843	1.1148
−40	5.330	84.25	7.2623	−0.000	89.172	−0.00000	0.21248	0.2991	0.1858	1.1150
−35	6.170	83.80	6.3334	1.499	90.027	0.00355	0.21201	0.2999	0.1873	1.1154
−30	7.113	83.34	5.5439	3.002	90.881	0.00706	0.21159	0.3008	0.1889	1.1159
−25	8.170	82.88	4.8703	4.509	91.735	0.01054	0.21121	0.3017	0.1905	1.1165
−20	9.347	82.42	4.2931	6.022	92.588	0.01400	0.21088	0.3027	0.1921	1.1172
−15	10.657	81.96	3.7966	7.539	93.440	0.01742	0.21060	0.3037	0.1938	1.1181
−10	12.107	81.50	3.3680	9.062	94.290	0.02082	0.21035	0.3047	0.1955	1.1191
−5	13.710	81.03	2.9967	10.590	95.138	0.02419	0.21015	0.3058	0.1972	1.1202
−2.15[b]	14.696	80.76	2.8072	11.463	95.621	0.02610	0.21004	0.3064	0.1982	1.1209
0	15.476	80.55	2.6738	12.123	95.985	0.02754	0.20997	0.3069	0.1989	1.1214
5	17.416	80.07	2.3922	13.663	96.828	0.03086	0.20983	0.3081	0.2007	1.1228
10	19.542	79.59	2.1458	15.208	97.669	0.03415	0.20973	0.3093	0.2026	1.1244
15	21.865	79.11	1.9295	16.760	98.506	0.03743	0.20965	0.3105	0.2044	1.1261
20	24.398	78.62	1.7391	18.318	99.339	0.04068	0.20959	0.3118	0.2064	1.1280
25	27.153	78.12	1.5710	19.883	100.168	0.04391	0.20956	0.3131	0.2083	1.1301
30	30.143	77.62	1.4221	21.455	100.993	0.04713	0.20956	0.3145	0.2104	1.1324
35	33.382	77.11	1.2900	23.034	101.812	0.05032	0.20957	0.3160	0.2125	1.1349
40	36.882	76.60	1.1725	24.620	102.627	0.05349	0.20961	0.3175	0.2146	1.1376
45	40.658	76.09	1.0676	26.215	103.435	0.05665	0.20966	0.3191	0.2169	1.1405
50	44.723	75.56	0.9738	27.817	104.237	0.05979	0.20973	0.3208	0.2192	1.1437
55	49.093	75.03	0.8897	29.428	105.032	0.06291	0.20981	0.3225	0.2216	1.1472
60	53.780	74.49	0.8141	31.048	105.820	0.06602	0.20991	0.3243	0.2240	1.1510
65	58.802	73.95	0.7461	32.677	106.600	0.06912	0.21001	0.3262	0.2266	1.1551
70	64.172	73.40	0.6848	34.315	107.371	0.07220	0.21013	0.3282	0.2293	1.1596
75	69.905	72.84	0.6293	35.964	108.134	0.07527	0.21025	0.3303	0.2321	1.1645
80	76.019	72.27	0.5790	37.623	108.887	0.07833	0.21038	0.3325	0.2350	1.1698
85	82.528	71.69	0.5334	39.293	109.630	0.08138	0.21052	0.3348	0.2380	1.1757
90	89.450	71.10	0.4919	40.974	110.362	0.08442	0.21066	0.3373	0.2412	1.1820
95	96.800	70.50	0.4541	42.668	111.081	0.08745	0.21079	0.3399	0.2446	1.1889
100	104.60	69.89	0.4196	44.374	111.789	0.09048	0.21093	0.3426	0.2481	1.1966
105	112.85	69.26	0.3881	46.093	112.482	0.09350	0.21107	0.3455	0.2519	1.2049
110	121.59	68.63	0.3592	47.826	113.161	0.09651	0.21120	0.3486	0.2559	1.2142
115	130.83	67.97	0.3327	49.573	113.823	0.09952	0.21132	0.3519	0.2602	1.2245
120	140.58	67.31	0.3084	51.336	114.469	0.10253	0.21144	0.3554	0.2648	1.2359
125	150.87	66.62	0.2860	53.115	115.095	0.10554	0.21154	0.3592	0.2697	1.2486
130	161.72	65.92	0.2653	54.911	115.701	0.10854	0.21164	0.3632	0.2752	1.2629
135	173.14	65.20	0.2462	56.726	116.285	0.11155	0.21171	0.3676	0.2811	1.2789
140	185.15	64.46	0.2286	58.560	116.845	0.11457	0.21176	0.3724	0.2877	1.2971
145	197.78	63.69	0.2122	60.414	117.379	0.11759	0.21179	0.3777	0.2950	1.3176
150	211.04	62.90	0.1971	62.291	117.884	0.12061	0.21180	0.3835	0.3032	1.3412
155	224.97	62.08	0.1829	64.192	118.357	0.12365	0.21177	0.3899	0.3124	1.3682
160	239.58	61.22	0.1698	66.120	118.794	0.12670	0.21171	0.3972	0.3229	1.3994
165	254.89	60.33	0.1575	68.076	119.193	0.12977	0.21160	0.4054	0.3350	1.4360
170	270.94	59.40	0.1461	70.065	119.548	0.13287	0.21145	0.4148	0.3490	1.4791
175	287.74	58.43	0.1353	72.090	119.853	0.13598	0.21124	0.4258	0.3655	1.5307
180	305.33	57.40	0.1252	74.156	120.101	0.13914	0.21096	0.4387	0.3852	1.5934
185	323.74	56.30	0.1157	76.268	120.282	0.14233	0.21061	0.4544	0.4092	1.6709
190	343.00	55.14	0.1067	78.436	120.384	0.14558	0.21015	0.4737	0.4392	1.7689
195	363.15	53.88	0.0981	80.669	120.391	0.14890	0.20958	0.4983	0.4779	1.8967
200	384.22	52.51	0.0899	82.982	120.281	0.15231	0.20885	0.5309	0.5297	2.0694
205	406.27	50.99	0.0820	85.398	120.019	0.15584	0.20793	0.5764	0.6031	2.3154
210	429.35	49.28	0.0743	87.952	119.554	0.15954	0.20673	0.6450	0.7152	2.6920
215	453.52	47.28	0.0666	90.703	118.794	0.16350	0.20513	0.7613	0.9082	3.3385
220	478.88	44.79	0.0587	93.782	117.552	0.16789	0.20287	1.007	1.319	4.702
225	505.55	41.25	0.0497	97.579	115.267	0.17329	0.19912	1.893	2.784	9.484
228.85[c]	527.20	30.54	0.0327	106.210	106.210	0.18569	0.18569	∞	∞	∞

[b]Normal boiling point

[c]Critical point

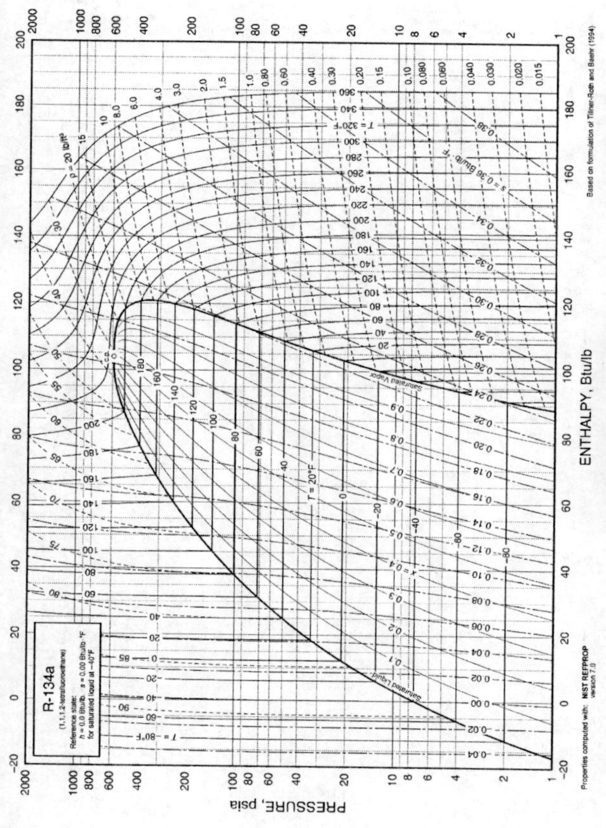

Refrigerants

Figure 8.6 Pressure-Enthalpy Diagram for Refrigerant 134a
[2021F, Ch 30, Fig 8]

Table 8.8 R-134a (1,1,1,2-Tetrafluoroethane)
Properties of Saturated Liquid and Saturated Vapor [2021F, Ch 30, Tbl R-134a]

Temp.,* °F	Pressure, psia	Density, lb/ft³ Liquid	Volume, ft³/lb Vapor	Enthalpy, Btu/lb Liquid	Enthalpy, Btu/lb Vapor	Entropy, Btu/lb·°F Liquid	Entropy, Btu/lb·°F Vapor	Specific Heat c_p, Btu/lb·°F Liquid	Specific Heat c_p, Btu/lb·°F Vapor	c_p/c_v Vapor
−153.94[a]	0.057	99.33	568.59	−32.992	80.362	−0.09154	0.27923	0.2829	0.1399	1.1637
−150	0.072	98.97	452.12	−31.878	80.907	−0.08791	0.27629	0.2830	0.1411	1.1623
−140	0.129	98.05	260.63	−29.046	82.304	−0.07891	0.26941	0.2834	0.1443	1.1589
−130	0.221	97.13	156.50	−26.208	83.725	−0.07017	0.26329	0.2842	0.1475	1.1559
−120	0.365	96.20	97.481	−23.360	85.168	−0.06166	0.25784	0.2853	0.1508	1.1532
−110	0.583	95.27	62.763	−20.500	86.629	−0.05337	0.25300	0.2866	0.1540	1.1509
−100	0.903	94.33	41.637	−17.626	88.107	−0.04527	0.24871	0.2881	0.1573	1.1490
−90	1.359	93.38	28.381	−14.736	89.599	−0.03734	0.24490	0.2898	0.1607	1.1475
−80	1.993	92.42	19.825	−11.829	91.103	−0.02959	0.24152	0.2916	0.1641	1.1465
−75	2.392	91.94	16.711	−10.368	91.858	−0.02577	0.23998	0.2925	0.1658	1.1462
−70	2.854	91.46	14.161	−8.903	92.614	−0.02198	0.23854	0.2935	0.1676	1.1460
−65	3.389	90.97	12.060	−7.432	93.372	−0.01824	0.23718	0.2945	0.1694	1.1459
−60	4.002	90.49	10.321	−5.957	94.131	−0.01452	0.23590	0.2955	0.1713	1.1460
−55	4.703	90.00	8.8733	−4.476	94.890	−0.01085	0.23470	0.2965	0.1731	1.1462
−50	5.501	89.50	7.6621	−2.989	95.650	−0.00720	0.23358	0.2976	0.1751	1.1466
−45	6.406	89.00	6.6438	−1.498	96.409	−0.00358	0.23252	0.2987	0.1770	1.1471
−40	7.427	88.50	5.7839	0.000	97.167	0.00000	0.23153	0.2999	0.1790	1.1478
−35	8.576	88.00	5.0544	1.503	97.924	0.00356	0.23060	0.3010	0.1811	1.1486
−30	9.862	87.49	4.4330	3.013	98.679	0.00708	0.22973	0.3022	0.1832	1.1496
−25	11.299	86.98	3.9014	4.529	99.433	0.01058	0.22892	0.3035	0.1853	1.1508
−20	12.898	86.47	3.4449	6.051	100.184	0.01406	0.22816	0.3047	0.1875	1.1521
−15	14.671	85.95	3.0514	7.580	100.932	0.01751	0.22744	0.3060	0.1898	1.1537
−14.93[b]	14.696	85.94	3.0465	7.600	100.942	0.01755	0.22743	0.3061	0.1898	1.1537
−10	16.632	85.43	2.7109	9.115	101.677	0.02093	0.22678	0.3074	0.1921	1.1554
−5	18.794	84.90	2.4154	10.657	102.419	0.02433	0.22615	0.3088	0.1945	1.1573
0	21.171	84.37	2.1579	12.207	103.156	0.02771	0.22557	0.3102	0.1969	1.1595
5	23.777	83.83	1.9330	13.764	103.889	0.03107	0.22502	0.3117	0.1995	1.1619
10	26.628	83.29	1.7357	15.328	104.617	0.03440	0.22451	0.3132	0.2021	1.1645
15	29.739	82.74	1.5623	16.901	105.339	0.03772	0.22403	0.3147	0.2047	1.1674
20	33.124	82.19	1.4094	18.481	106.056	0.04101	0.22359	0.3164	0.2075	1.1705
25	36.800	81.63	1.2742	20.070	106.767	0.04429	0.22317	0.3181	0.2103	1.1740
30	40.784	81.06	1.1543	21.667	107.471	0.04755	0.22278	0.3198	0.2132	1.1777
35	45.092	80.49	1.0478	23.274	108.167	0.05079	0.22241	0.3216	0.2163	1.1818
40	49.741	79.90	0.9528	24.890	108.856	0.05402	0.22207	0.3235	0.2194	1.1862
45	54.749	79.32	0.8680	26.515	109.537	0.05724	0.22174	0.3255	0.2226	1.1910
50	60.134	78.72	0.7920	28.150	110.209	0.06044	0.22144	0.3275	0.2260	1.1961
55	65.913	78.11	0.7238	29.796	110.871	0.06362	0.22115	0.3297	0.2294	1.2018
60	72.105	77.50	0.6625	31.452	111.524	0.06680	0.22088	0.3319	0.2331	1.2079
65	78.729	76.87	0.6072	33.120	112.165	0.06996	0.22062	0.3343	0.2368	1.2145
70	85.805	76.24	0.5572	34.799	112.796	0.07311	0.22037	0.3368	0.2408	1.2217
75	93.351	75.59	0.5120	36.491	113.414	0.07626	0.22013	0.3394	0.2449	1.2296
80	101.39	74.94	0.4710	38.195	114.019	0.07939	0.21989	0.3422	0.2492	1.2382
85	109.93	74.27	0.4338	39.913	114.610	0.08252	0.21966	0.3451	0.2537	1.2475
90	119.01	73.58	0.3999	41.645	115.186	0.08565	0.21944	0.3482	0.2585	1.2578
95	128.65	72.88	0.3690	43.392	115.746	0.08877	0.21921	0.3515	0.2636	1.2690
100	138.85	72.17	0.3407	45.155	116.289	0.09188	0.21898	0.3551	0.2690	1.2813
105	149.65	71.44	0.3148	46.934	116.813	0.09500	0.21875	0.3589	0.2747	1.2950
110	161.07	70.69	0.2911	48.731	117.317	0.09811	0.21851	0.3630	0.2809	1.3101
115	173.14	69.93	0.2693	50.546	117.799	0.10123	0.21826	0.3675	0.2875	1.3268
120	185.86	69.14	0.2493	52.382	118.258	0.10435	0.21800	0.3723	0.2948	1.3456
125	199.28	68.32	0.2308	54.239	118.690	0.10748	0.21772	0.3775	0.3026	1.3666
130	213.41	67.49	0.2137	56.119	119.095	0.11062	0.21742	0.3833	0.3112	1.3903
135	228.28	66.62	0.1980	58.023	119.468	0.11376	0.21709	0.3897	0.3208	1.4173
140	243.92	65.73	0.1833	59.954	119.807	0.11692	0.21673	0.3968	0.3315	1.4481
145	260.36	64.80	0.1697	61.915	120.108	0.12010	0.21634	0.4048	0.3435	1.4837
150	277.61	63.83	0.1571	63.908	120.366	0.12330	0.21591	0.4138	0.3571	1.5250
155	295.73	62.82	0.1453	65.936	120.576	0.12653	0.21542	0.4242	0.3729	1.5738
160	314.73	61.76	0.1343	68.005	120.731	0.12979	0.21488	0.4362	0.3914	1.6318
165	334.65	60.65	0.1239	70.118	120.823	0.13309	0.21426	0.4504	0.4133	1.7022
170	355.53	59.47	0.1142	72.283	120.842	0.13644	0.21356	0.4675	0.4400	1.7889
175	377.41	58.21	0.1051	74.509	120.773	0.13985	0.21274	0.4887	0.4733	1.8984
180	400.34	56.86	0.0964	76.807	120.598	0.14334	0.21180	0.5156	0.5159	2.0405
185	424.36	55.38	0.0881	79.193	120.294	0.14693	0.21069	0.5512	0.5729	2.2321
190	449.52	53.76	0.0801	81.692	119.822	0.15066	0.20935	0.6012	0.6532	2.5041
195	475.91	51.91	0.0724	84.343	119.123	0.15459	0.20771	0.6768	0.7751	2.9192
200	503.59	49.76	0.0647	87.214	118.097	0.15880	0.20562	0.8062	0.9835	3.6309
205	532.68	47.08	0.0567	90.454	116.526	0.16353	0.20275	1.0830	1.4250	5.1360
210	563.35	43.20	0.0477	94.530	113.746	0.16945	0.19814	2.1130	3.0080	10.5120
213.91[c]	588.75	31.96	0.0313	103.894	103.894	0.18320	0.18320	∞	∞	∞

*Temperatures on ITS-90 scale [a]Triple point [b]Normal boiling point [c]Critical point

Table 8.9 Superheated Vapor Thermodynamic Properties of R-134a

Temp, °F	Pressure = 15 psia Sat. temp. = –14.25°F			Pressure = 30 psia Sat. temp. = 15.39°F		
	V	*h*	*s*	*V*	*h*	*s*
0	3.118	103.35	0.2324			
20	3.268	107.07	0.2403	1.584	106.18	0.2255
40	3.417	110.88	0.2481	1.663	110.06	0.2335
60	3.565	114.79	0.2558	1.741	114.03	0.2413
80	3.712	118.79	0.2633	1.818	118.08	0.2489
100	3.858	122.87	0.2708	1.895	122.22	0.2564
120	4.004	127.05	0.2781	1.971	126.44	0.2638
140	4.149	131.31	0.2853	2.046	130.75	0.2711
Temp, °F	**Pressure = 45 psia Sat. temp. = 34.94°F**			**Pressure = 60 psia Sat. temp. = 49.94°F**		
	V	*h*	*s*	*V*	*h*	*s*
40	1.077	109.20	0.2243			
60	1.132	113.24	0.2323	0.8269	112.41	0.2255
80	1.187	117.36	0.2400	0.8699	116.60	0.2334
100	1.240	121.55	0.2477	0.9120	120.86	0.2412
120	1.293	125.82	0.2552	0.9533	125.18	0.2488
140	1.345	130.17	0.2625	0.9940	129.58	0.2562
Temp, °F	**Pressure = 150 psia Sat. temp. = 105.14°F**			**Pressure = 200 psia Sat. temp. = 125.19°F**		
	V	*h*	*s*	*V*	*h*	*s*
125	0.3433	122.06	0.2274			
150	0.3692	128.08	0.2375	0.2596	125.69	0.2289
175	0.3937	134.13	0.2472	0.2807	132.07	0.2391
200	0.4171	140.23	0.2566	0.3003	138.42	0.2489
225	0.4397	146.41	0.2658	0.3189	144.80	0.2584
250	0.4616	152.66	0.2748	0.3366	151.23	0.2676
Temp, °F	**Pressure = 250 psia Sat. temp. = 141.79°F**			**Pressure = 300 psia Sat. temp. = 156.07°F**		
	V	*h*	*s*	*V*	*h*	*s*
150	0.1920	122.93	0.2210			
175	0.2118	129.79	0.2320	0.1646	127.20	0.2252
200	0.2295	136.47	0.2423	0.1817	134.35	0.2362
225	0.2460	143.10	0.2522	0.1969	141.29	0.2466
250	0.2614	149.73	0.2617	0.2110	148.15	0.2564
275	0.2761	156.37	0.2709	0.2242	154.99	0.2659
300	0.2902	163.07	0.2798	0.2367	161.84	0.2750

V = vapor volume, ft^3/lb
h = enthalpy, Btu/lb
s = entropy, Btu/lb·°F

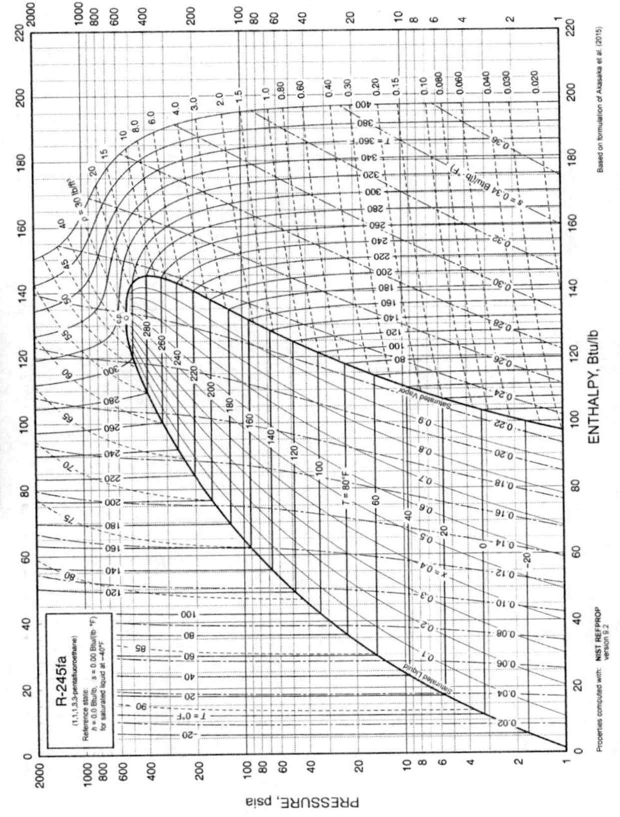

Figure 8.7 Pressure-Enthalpy Diagram for Refrigerant 245fa
[2021F, Ch 30, Fig 11]

Table 8.10 Refrigerant 245fa (1,1,1,3,3-Pentafluoropropane) Properties of Saturated Liquid and Saturated Vapor [2021F, Ch 30, Tbl R-245fa]

Temp., °F	Pressure, psia	Density, lb/ft³	Volume, ft³/lb	Enthalpy, Btu/lb		Entropy, Btu/lb·°F		Specific Heat c_p, Btu/lb·°F		c_p/c_v
		Liquid	Vapor	Liquid	Vapor	Liquid	Vapor	Liquid	Vapor	Vapor
−50	0.578	94.55	56.518	−2.840	94.771	−0.00685	0.23142	0.2830	0.1734	1.0958
−45	0.702	94.14	47.084	−1.422	95.622	−0.00341	0.23062	0.2840	0.1748	1.0953
−40	0.847	93.74	39.436	−0.000	96.478	−0.00000	0.22989	0.2849	0.1763	1.0949
−35	1.018	93.32	33.201	1.427	97.337	0.00338	0.22923	0.2859	0.1778	1.0945
−30	1.216	92.91	28.090	2.859	98.201	0.00673	0.22863	0.2869	0.1792	1.0942
−25	1.446	92.50	23.879	4.296	99.069	0.01006	0.22809	0.2879	0.1807	1.0939
−20	1.711	92.08	20.391	5.739	99.940	0.01335	0.22761	0.2889	0.1822	1.0937
−15	2.015	91.67	17.489	7.186	100.815	0.01663	0.22718	0.2900	0.1837	1.0936
−10	2.363	91.25	15.062	8.640	101.692	0.01987	0.22681	0.2911	0.1853	1.0935
−5	2.759	90.83	13.024	10.099	102.573	0.02310	0.22649	0.2923	0.1868	1.0934
0	3.208	90.40	11.305	11.563	103.456	0.02630	0.22621	0.2934	0.1884	1.0935
5	3.717	89.98	9.8498	13.034	104.342	0.02948	0.22598	0.2946	0.1900	1.0936
10	4.289	89.55	8.6119	14.511	105.230	0.03264	0.22579	0.2958	0.1916	1.0937
15	4.931	89.12	7.5553	15.994	106.120	0.03578	0.22565	0.2971	0.1933	1.0940
20	5.650	88.69	6.6500	17.483	107.011	0.03890	0.22554	0.2983	0.1949	1.0943
25	6.452	88.26	5.8715	18.979	107.904	0.04199	0.22547	0.2996	0.1966	1.0947
30	7.343	87.82	5.1998	20.481	108.798	0.04507	0.22544	0.3009	0.1983	1.0951
35	8.332	87.38	4.6183	21.990	109.694	0.04814	0.22543	0.3023	0.2001	1.0957
40	9.424	86.94	4.1132	23.506	110.590	0.05118	0.22546	0.3037	0.2018	1.0963
45	10.629	86.49	3.6731	25.029	111.486	0.05421	0.22552	0.3051	0.2036	1.0970
50	11.954	86.04	3.2885	26.560	112.383	0.05722	0.22561	0.3065	0.2055	1.0978
55	13.407	85.59	2.9515	28.097	113.280	0.06022	0.22573	0.3079	0.2073	1.0987
59.09[b]	14.696	85.22	2.7065	29.359	114.013	0.06265	0.22584	0.3092	0.2089	1.0995
60	14.997	85.13	2.6552	29.642	114.176	0.06320	0.22587	0.3094	0.2092	1.0997
65	16.733	84.67	2.3941	31.195	115.072	0.06616	0.22603	0.3109	0.2112	1.1008
70	18.624	84.21	2.1634	32.755	115.968	0.06911	0.22622	0.3125	0.2131	1.1021
75	20.679	83.75	1.9590	34.323	116.862	0.07205	0.22643	0.3140	0.2151	1.1034
80	22.909	83.27	1.7775	35.899	117.755	0.07498	0.22666	0.3156	0.2172	1.1048
85	25.322	82.80	1.6159	37.483	118.646	0.07789	0.22690	0.3173	0.2193	1.1064
90	27.930	82.32	1.4717	39.076	119.536	0.08079	0.22717	0.3189	0.2214	1.1082
95	30.742	81.84	1.3427	40.677	120.423	0.08368	0.22745	0.3206	0.2236	1.1100
100	33.769	81.35	1.2271	42.287	121.308	0.08655	0.22775	0.3224	0.2258	1.1120
105	37.022	80.85	1.1233	43.905	122.190	0.08942	0.22806	0.3241	0.2281	1.1142
110	40.513	80.35	1.0299	45.533	123.069	0.09228	0.22838	0.3260	0.2304	1.1166
115	44.251	79.85	0.9456	47.169	123.945	0.09512	0.22872	0.3278	0.2328	1.1192
120	48.249	79.33	0.8695	48.815	124.816	0.09796	0.22907	0.3297	0.2353	1.1219
125	52.518	78.82	0.8005	50.471	125.684	0.10078	0.22943	0.3317	0.2378	1.1249
130	57.071	78.29	0.7380	52.137	126.546	0.10360	0.22979	0.3337	0.2405	1.1282
135	61.918	77.76	0.6812	53.812	127.404	0.10641	0.23016	0.3358	0.2431	1.1317
140	67.074	77.22	0.6295	55.498	128.255	0.10922	0.23054	0.3379	0.2459	1.1355
145	72.550	76.67	0.5824	57.195	129.101	0.11201	0.23093	0.3401	0.2488	1.1396
150	78.358	76.12	0.5393	58.902	129.939	0.11480	0.23132	0.3424	0.2518	1.1440
155	84.512	75.55	0.5000	60.621	130.771	0.11758	0.23171	0.3447	0.2549	1.1489
160	91.025	74.98	0.4639	62.351	131.594	0.12036	0.23210	0.3472	0.2581	1.1542
165	97.911	74.39	0.4308	64.093	132.409	0.12313	0.23250	0.3497	0.2615	1.1599
170	105.18	73.80	0.4003	65.847	133.214	0.12590	0.23289	0.3524	0.2650	1.1662
175	112.85	73.19	0.3723	67.614	134.009	0.12867	0.23328	0.3551	0.2688	1.1731
180	120.94	72.58	0.3465	69.395	134.793	0.13143	0.23367	0.3580	0.2727	1.1806
185	129.45	71.95	0.3227	71.189	135.565	0.13419	0.23405	0.3611	0.2768	1.1889
190	138.41	71.30	0.3007	72.997	136.324	0.13695	0.23442	0.3643	0.2812	1.1981
195	147.82	70.64	0.2803	74.820	137.068	0.13970	0.23479	0.3677	0.2859	1.2082
200	157.71	69.97	0.2614	76.659	137.797	0.14246	0.23514	0.3713	0.2910	1.2194
205	168.08	69.28	0.2438	78.514	138.508	0.14522	0.23548	0.3752	0.2964	1.2320
210	178.96	68.57	0.2275	80.386	139.200	0.14798	0.23581	0.3794	0.3023	1.2460
215	190.36	67.84	0.2123	82.277	139.872	0.15075	0.23612	0.3838	0.3087	1.2617
220	202.30	67.08	0.1981	84.187	140.521	0.15352	0.23641	0.3887	0.3157	1.2795
225	214.80	66.31	0.1849	86.117	141.145	0.15630	0.23667	0.3940	0.3234	1.2998
230	227.87	65.50	0.1725	88.070	141.742	0.15909	0.23691	0.3998	0.3320	1.3229
235	241.53	64.67	0.1609	90.047	142.307	0.16189	0.23712	0.4062	0.3417	1.3496
240	255.81	63.80	0.1500	92.049	142.837	0.16470	0.23729	0.4134	0.3526	1.3806
245	270.72	62.90	0.1398	94.080	143.329	0.16753	0.23742	0.4215	0.3652	1.4169
250	286.28	61.96	0.1301	96.141	143.777	0.17038	0.23751	0.4307	0.3798	1.4599
260	319.47	59.92	0.1124	100.372	144.514	0.17616	0.23750	0.4540	0.4174	1.5741
270	355.57	57.63	0.0964	104.780	144.980	0.18209	0.23718	0.4874	0.4735	1.7498
280	394.83	54.97	0.0818	109.431	145.063	0.18824	0.23641	0.5410	0.5663	2.0476
290	437.52	51.72	0.0680	114.455	144.549	0.19479	0.23493	0.6449	0.7492	2.6453
300	484.03	47.29	0.0543	120.218	142.886	0.20219	0.23203	0.962	1.292	4.439
308.95[c]	529.53	32.43	0.0308	132.508	132.508	0.21798	0.21798	∞	∞	∞

*Temperatures on ITS-90 scale

[b]Normal boiling point

[c]Critical point

Refrigerants

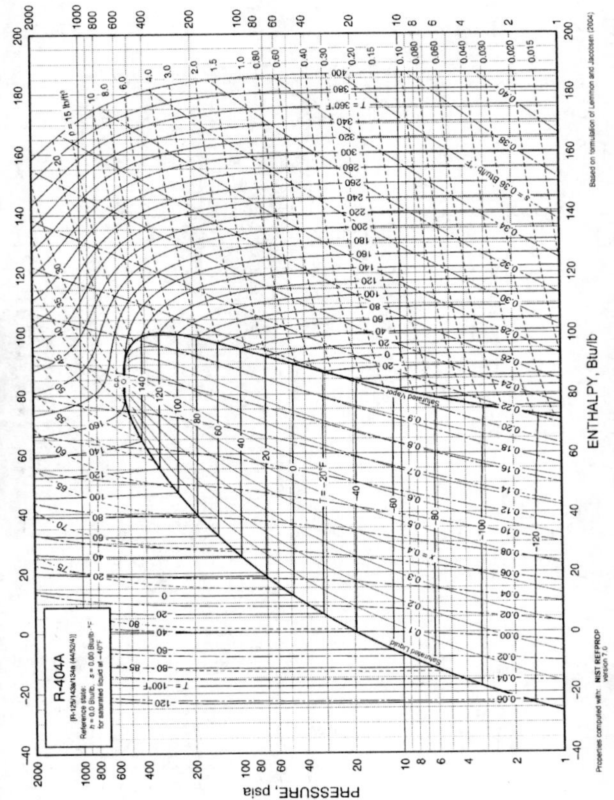

Figure 8.8 Pressure-Enthalpy Diagram for Refrigerant 404A
[2021F, Ch 30, Fig 15]

Table 8.11 R-404A [R-125/143a/134a (44/52/4)]
Properties of Liquid on Bubble Line and Vapor on Dew Line [2021F, Ch 30, Tbl R-404A]

Pressure, psia	Temperature,* °F		Density, lb/ft³	Volume, ft³/lb	Enthalpy, Btu/lb		Entropy, Btu/lb·°F	
	Bubble	Dew	Liquid	Vapor	Liquid	Vapor	Liquid	Vapor
1	−129.56	−127.50	89.61	36.2311	−26.33	71.76	−0.07039	0.22616
1.5	−120.05	−118.11	88.64	24.7754	−23.56	73.11	−0.06215	0.22201
2	−112.90	−111.03	87.92	18.9245	−21.49	74.14	−0.05611	0.21920
2.5	−107.10	−105.29	87.33	15.3578	−19.81	74.98	−0.05129	0.21710
3	−102.18	−100.42	86.83	12.9493	−18.38	75.69	−0.04727	0.21544
4	−94.08	−92.40	86.01	9.8941	−16.02	76.86	−0.04076	0.21292
5	−87.49	−85.87	85.33	8.0300	−14.10	77.82	−0.03555	0.21106
6	−81.89	−80.32	84.76	6.7705	−12.46	78.64	−0.03119	0.20960
7	−77.00	−75.46	84.25	5.8607	−11.02	79.35	−0.02742	0.20841
8	−72.64	−71.14	83.80	5.1716	−9.74	79.98	−0.02409	0.20741
10	−65.08	−63.64	83.01	4.1954	−7.51	81.07	−0.01839	0.20581
12	−58.65	−57.25	82.34	3.5353	−5.60	82.00	−0.01360	0.20457
14	−53.01	−51.65	81.74	3.0582	−3.91	82.81	−0.00944	0.20357
14.7[b]	−51.20	−49.85	81.55	2.9217	−3.37	83.07	−0.00812	0.20326
16	−47.98	−46.65	81.20	2.6968	−2.41	83.53	−0.00577	0.20273
18	−43.42	−42.11	80.71	2.4132	−1.03	84.18	−0.00246	0.20203
20	−39.24	−37.96	80.26	2.1845	0.23	84.78	0.00055	0.20141
22	−35.37	−34.11	79.83	1.9960	1.40	85.32	0.00332	0.20088
24	−31.77	−30.53	79.44	1.8379	2.50	85.83	0.00588	0.20041
26	−28.39	−27.17	79.06	1.7033	3.53	86.30	0.00827	0.19998
28	−25.21	−24.01	78.71	1.5873	4.51	86.75	0.01051	0.19960
30	−22.20	−21.02	78.37	1.4863	5.44	87.16	0.01263	0.19925
32	−19.34	−18.17	78.05	1.3974	6.32	87.56	0.01463	0.19894
34	−16.62	−15.46	77.74	1.3187	7.16	87.93	0.01653	0.19864
36	−14.01	−12.87	77.44	1.2484	7.97	88.29	0.01834	0.19838
38	−11.52	−10.39	77.15	1.1852	8.75	88.62	0.02007	0.19813
40	−9.12	−8.01	76.87	1.1281	9.50	88.95	0.02172	0.19790
42	−6.81	−5.71	76.60	1.0763	10.22	89.26	0.02331	0.19768
44	−4.59	−3.50	76.34	1.0290	10.92	89.56	0.02484	0.19748
46	−2.44	−1.36	76.09	0.9857	11.60	89.84	0.02632	0.19729
48	−0.36	0.71	75.84	0.9459	12.25	90.12	0.02774	0.19711
50	1.65	2.71	75.60	0.9091	12.89	90.38	0.02911	0.19694
55	6.43	7.47	75.03	0.8285	14.41	91.01	0.03237	0.19655
60	10.89	11.90	74.48	0.7609	15.84	91.58	0.03539	0.19621
65	15.07	16.07	73.97	0.7033	17.19	92.11	0.03822	0.19590
70	19.02	20.00	73.47	0.6537	18.47	92.61	0.04088	0.19562
75	22.76	23.72	72.99	0.6104	19.69	93.07	0.04339	0.19537
80	26.32	27.27	72.54	0.5724	20.86	93.50	0.04578	0.19514
85	29.71	30.64	72.09	0.5387	21.98	93.91	0.04804	0.19492
90	32.96	33.88	71.67	0.5085	23.05	94.30	0.05021	0.19471
95	36.07	36.98	71.25	0.4815	24.09	94.66	0.05229	0.19452
100	39.07	39.96	70.84	0.4570	25.10	95.00	0.05428	0.19434
110	44.73	45.60	70.06	0.4145	27.01	95.64	0.05804	0.19400
120	50.02	50.86	69.32	0.3789	28.82	96.21	0.06155	0.19368
130	54.99	55.81	68.60	0.3485	30.53	96.73	0.06485	0.19338
140	59.68	60.48	67.90	0.3222	32.16	97.20	0.06795	0.19309
150	64.13	64.91	67.23	0.2994	33.73	97.62	0.07090	0.19281
160	68.36	69.13	66.57	0.2793	35.23	98.01	0.07371	0.19253
170	72.40	73.15	65.93	0.2614	36.68	98.37	0.07639	0.19226
180	76.26	76.99	65.30	0.2454	38.08	98.69	0.07896	0.19198
190	79.97	80.68	64.68	0.2311	39.44	98.98	0.08143	0.19170
200	83.53	84.23	64.07	0.2181	40.76	99.25	0.08381	0.19143
220	90.27	90.94	62.87	0.1955	43.29	99.70	0.08833	0.19085
240	96.57	97.21	61.70	0.1764	45.70	100.05	0.09259	0.19026
260	102.48	103.09	60.53	0.1601	48.02	100.32	0.09663	0.18962
280	108.06	108.64	59.37	0.1460	50.25	100.51	0.10047	0.18895
300	113.34	113.90	58.20	0.1336	52.42	100.61	0.10417	0.18823
320	118.36	118.89	57.03	0.1226	54.54	100.64	0.10773	0.18745
340	123.14	123.65	55.83	0.1127	56.61	100.58	0.11118	0.18660
360	127.71	128.19	54.61	0.1038	58.65	100.43	0.11456	0.18566
380	132.09	132.54	53.35	0.0956	60.67	100.20	0.11787	0.18464
400	136.28	136.71	52.03	0.0881	62.68	99.85	0.12114	0.18349
450	146.07	146.42	48.36	0.0713	67.80	98.42	0.12934	0.17987
500	154.97	155.22	43.51	0.0556	73.49	95.51	0.13833	0.17416
548.24[c]	162.50	162.50	35.84	0.0279	80.85	80.85	0.14987	0.14987

*Temperatures on ITS-90 scale [b]Bubble and dew points at one standard atmosphere [c]Critical point

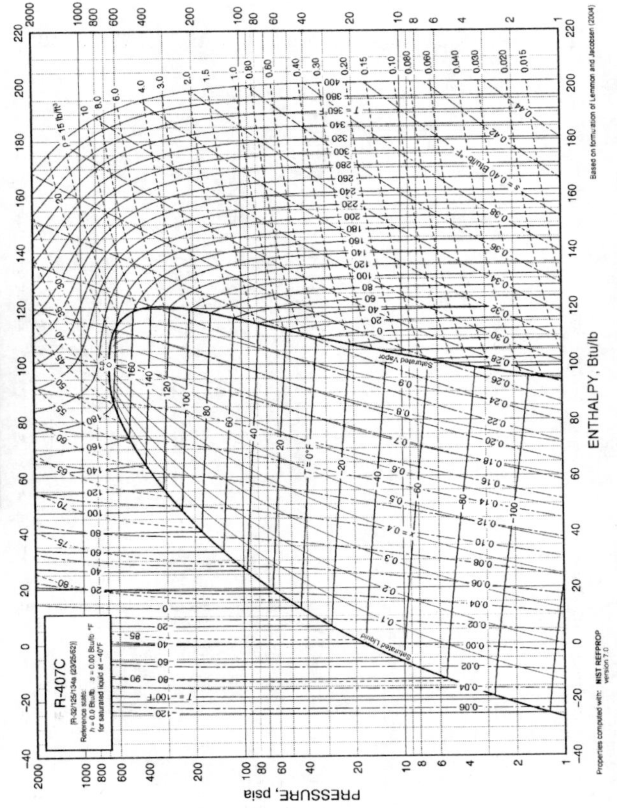

Figure 8.9 Pressure-Enthalpy Diagram for Refrigerant 407C
[2021F, Ch 30, Fig 16]

Table 8.12 R-407C [R-32/125/134a (23/25/52)]
Properties of Liquid on Bubble Line and Vapor on Dew Line [2021F, Ch 30, Tbl R-407C]

Pressure, psia	Temp.,* °F Bubble	Temp.,* °F Dew	Density, lb/ft³ Liquid	Volume, ft³/lb Vapor	Enthalpy, Btu/lb Liquid	Enthalpy, Btu/lb Vapor	Entropy, Btu/lb·°F Liquid	Entropy, Btu/lb·°F Vapor	Specific Heat c_p, Btu/lb·°F Liquid	Specific Heat c_p, Btu/lb·°F Vapor	c_p/c_v Vapor
1	−125.19	−111.30	94.24	43.0887	−26.34	93.96	−0.07002	0.28254	0.3065	0.1568	1.183
1.5	−115.58	−101.85	93.28	29.4430	−23.40	95.34	−0.06135	0.27716	0.3063	0.1600	1.182
2	−108.36	−94.75	92.55	22.4776	−21.18	96.37	−0.05499	0.27346	0.3063	0.1624	1.181
2.5	−102.52	−88.99	91.97	18.2333	−19.39	97.21	−0.04994	0.27066	0.3065	0.1644	1.181
3	−97.57	−84.12	91.47	15.3685	−17.87	97.92	−0.04572	0.26841	0.3068	0.1662	1.181
4	−89.43	−76.11	90.64	11.7361	−15.37	99.09	−0.03889	0.26495	0.3074	0.1693	1.181
5	−82.81	−69.61	89.97	9.5211	−13.34	100.03	−0.03345	0.26234	0.3081	0.1719	1.182
6	−77.20	−64.09	89.40	8.0252	−11.60	100.83	−0.02889	0.26025	0.3087	0.1742	1.182
7	−72.30	−59.27	88.89	6.9450	−10.09	101.52	−0.02496	0.25852	0.3094	0.1762	1.183
8	−67.94	−54.97	88.44	6.1272	−8.74	102.13	−0.02149	0.25705	0.3100	0.1781	1.184
10	−60.38	−47.55	87.66	4.9690	−6.39	103.19	−0.01556	0.25464	0.3112	0.1814	1.186
12	−53.96	−41.23	86.98	4.1864	−4.38	104.08	−0.01059	0.25272	0.3123	0.1844	1.188
14	−48.34	−35.71	86.39	3.6210	−2.62	104.85	−0.00629	0.25114	0.3133	0.1871	1.189
14.7[b]	−46.53	−33.93	86.19	3.4593	−2.06	105.10	−0.00492	0.25065	0.3137	0.1880	1.190
16	−43.32	−30.78	85.85	3.1928	−1.05	105.54	−0.00249	0.24979	0.3143	0.1896	1.191
18	−38.77	−26.31	85.36	2.8570	0.39	106.15	0.00092	0.24863	0.3153	0.1919	1.193
20	−34.61	−22.23	84.91	2.5862	1.70	106.71	0.00402	0.24760	0.3162	0.1941	1.195
22	−30.76	−18.45	84.50	2.3632	2.92	107.22	0.00687	0.24668	0.3172	0.1961	1.197
24	−27.18	−14.93	84.10	2.1761	4.06	107.70	0.00950	0.24586	0.3180	0.1981	1.199
26	−23.83	−11.64	83.73	2.0169	5.13	108.14	0.01196	0.24510	0.3189	0.1999	1.201
28	−20.66	−8.54	83.38	1.8798	6.15	108.55	0.01426	0.24442	0.3197	0.2017	1.203
30	−17.67	−5.60	83.05	1.7603	7.10	108.93	0.01643	0.24378	0.3205	0.2034	1.205
32	−14.84	−2.82	82.73	1.6553	8.02	109.30	0.01848	0.24319	0.3213	0.2051	1.207
34	−12.13	−0.17	82.43	1.5622	8.89	109.64	0.02042	0.24265	0.3221	0.2067	1.209
36	−9.55	2.37	82.14	1.4791	9.72	109.97	0.02227	0.24213	0.3229	0.2083	1.211
38	−7.07	4.79	81.85	1.4045	10.53	110.28	0.02404	0.24165	0.3236	0.2098	1.213
40	−4.70	7.12	81.58	1.3371	11.30	110.58	0.02573	0.24120	0.3244	0.2113	1.215
42	−2.41	9.37	81.32	1.2759	12.04	110.86	0.02735	0.24077	0.3251	0.2127	1.217
44	−0.20	11.53	81.06	1.2201	12.76	111.13	0.02891	0.24036	0.3258	0.2141	1.219
46	1.93	13.61	80.82	1.1690	13.46	111.39	0.03041	0.23998	0.3265	0.2155	1.221
48	3.98	15.63	80.58	1.1220	14.13	111.64	0.03186	0.23961	0.3272	0.2169	1.223
50	5.98	17.58	80.34	1.0786	14.79	111.88	0.03326	0.23926	0.3279	0.2182	1.225
55	10.71	22.21	79.78	0.9835	16.34	112.44	0.03656	0.23844	0.3296	0.2214	1.230
60	15.13	26.53	79.25	0.9037	17.81	112.96	0.03963	0.23771	0.3313	0.2246	1.235
65	19.27	30.58	78.75	0.8359	19.19	113.44	0.04250	0.23703	0.3329	0.2276	1.240
70	23.18	34.40	78.27	0.7774	20.49	113.88	0.04519	0.23641	0.3346	0.2305	1.245
75	26.88	38.02	77.82	0.7264	21.74	114.29	0.04773	0.23584	0.3362	0.2333	1.250
80	30.39	41.46	77.38	0.6816	22.92	114.67	0.05014	0.23530	0.3378	0.2361	1.255
85	33.75	44.73	76.95	0.6419	24.06	115.03	0.05243	0.23480	0.3393	0.2389	1.260
90	36.96	47.87	76.54	0.6064	25.16	115.37	0.05462	0.23432	0.3409	0.2416	1.266
95	40.04	50.87	76.15	0.5746	26.21	115.68	0.05671	0.23387	0.3424	0.2442	1.271
100	43.00	53.75	75.76	0.5458	27.23	115.98	0.05871	0.23344	0.3440	0.2468	1.276
110	48.60	59.21	75.02	0.4959	29.16	116.53	0.06250	0.23265	0.3471	0.2520	1.287
120	53.83	64.30	74.32	0.4540	30.99	117.03	0.06602	0.23191	0.3502	0.2570	1.298
130	58.75	69.08	73.64	0.4183	32.72	117.47	0.06932	0.23122	0.3533	0.2621	1.310
140	63.39	73.59	72.99	0.3875	34.36	117.88	0.07244	0.23058	0.3564	0.2671	1.321
150	67.79	77.86	72.37	0.3607	35.94	118.24	0.07538	0.22997	0.3596	0.2721	1.334
160	71.98	81.92	71.76	0.3372	37.45	118.57	0.07818	0.22938	0.3628	0.2772	1.346
170	75.97	85.79	71.17	0.3163	38.90	118.87	0.08086	0.22882	0.3660	0.2824	1.359
180	79.80	89.49	70.59	0.2976	40.30	119.15	0.08341	0.22828	0.3693	0.2876	1.373
190	83.47	93.04	70.02	0.2808	41.66	119.39	0.08587	0.22776	0.3727	0.2929	1.387
200	87.00	96.45	69.47	0.2656	42.97	119.61	0.08823	0.22725	0.3761	0.2983	1.401
220	93.69	102.90	68.40	0.2393	45.49	119.99	0.09271	0.22625	0.3832	0.3095	1.432
240	99.94	108.92	67.35	0.2171	47.88	120.29	0.09691	0.22529	0.3907	0.3213	1.466
260	105.82	114.56	66.33	0.1982	50.17	120.52	0.10088	0.22434	0.3986	0.3338	1.502
280	111.37	119.88	65.33	0.1819	52.36	120.68	0.10464	0.22340	0.4070	0.3473	1.542
300	116.64	124.91	64.34	0.1676	54.48	120.78	0.10824	0.22246	0.4161	0.3618	1.586
320	121.66	129.69	63.37	0.1550	56.53	120.82	0.11168	0.22152	0.4260	0.3777	1.635
340	126.45	134.24	62.39	0.1438	58.53	120.80	0.11500	0.22056	0.4368	0.3951	1.689
360	131.03	138.58	61.42	0.1337	60.47	120.73	0.11821	0.21958	0.4487	0.4143	1.750
380	135.43	142.73	60.44	0.1246	62.38	120.61	0.12132	0.21857	0.4620	0.4358	1.819
400	139.66	146.71	59.46	0.1163	64.25	120.42	0.12435	0.21753	0.4769	0.4600	1.897
450	149.59	155.98	56.92	0.0984	68.84	119.71	0.13167	0.21473	0.5248	0.5373	2.151
500	158.73	164.41	54.21	0.0835	73.37	118.56	0.13879	0.21152	0.5982	0.6546	2.541
550	167.22	172.09	51.15	0.0706	78.00	116.83	0.14595	0.20765	0.7284	0.8572	3.217
600	175.17	179.07	47.39	0.0586	83.04	114.18	0.15363	0.20253	1.0271	1.2973	4.683
650	182.79	185.22	41.60	0.0457	89.56	109.19	0.16351	0.19401	2.4146	3.0022	10.265
673.36[c]	186.94	186.94	31.59	0.0317	99.99	99.99	0.17797	0.17797	—	—	—

*Temperatures on ITS-90 scale [b]Bubble and dew points at one standard atmosphere [c]Critical point

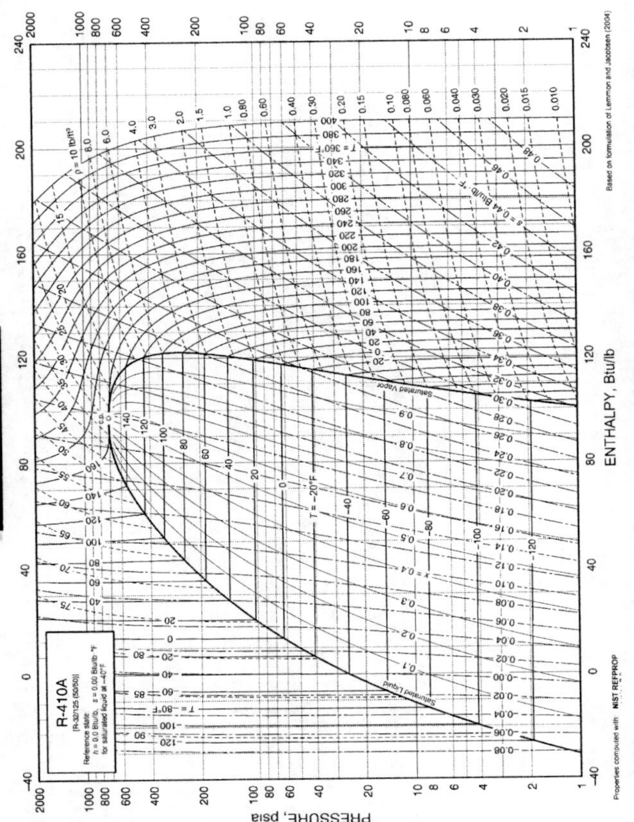

Figure 8.10 Pressure-Enthalpy Diagram for Refrigerant 410A
[2021F, Ch 30, Fig 17]

Table 8.13 R-410A [R-32/125 (50/50)]
Properties of Liquid on Bubble Line and Vapor on Dew Line [2021F, Ch 30, Tbl R-410A]

Pressure,	Temp.,* °F		Density, lb/ft³	Volume, ft³/lb	Enthalpy, Btu/lb		Entropy, Btu/lb·°F		Specific Heat c_p, Btu/lb·°F		c_p/c_v
psia	Bubble	Dew	Liquid	Vapor	Liquid	Vapor	Liquid	Vapor	Liquid	Vapor	Vapor
1	−135.16	−134.98	92.02	47.6458	−30.90	100.62	−0.08330	0.32188	0.3215	0.1568	1.228
1.5	−126.03	−125.87	91.10	32.5774	−27.97	101.90	−0.07439	0.31477	0.3212	0.1600	1.227
2	−119.18	−119.02	90.41	24.8810	−25.76	102.86	−0.06786	0.30981	0.3213	0.1626	1.227
2.5	−113.63	−113.48	89.84	20.1891	−23.98	103.63	−0.06267	0.30602	0.3214	0.1648	1.228
3	−108.94	−108.78	89.36	17.0211	−22.47	104.27	−0.05834	0.30296	0.3216	0.1668	1.228
4	−101.22	−101.07	88.57	13.0027	−19.98	105.33	−0.05133	0.29820	0.3221	0.1703	1.229
5	−94.94	−94.80	87.92	10.5514	−17.96	106.18	−0.04574	0.29455	0.3226	0.1733	1.230
6	−89.63	−89.48	87.36	8.8953	−16.24	106.89	−0.04107	0.29162	0.3231	0.1760	1.232
7	−84.98	−84.84	86.87	7.6992	−14.74	107.50	−0.03704	0.28916	0.3236	0.1785	1.233
8	−80.85	−80.71	86.44	6.7935	−13.40	108.05	−0.03349	0.28705	0.3241	0.1807	1.234
10	−73.70	−73.56	85.67	5.5105	−11.08	108.97	−0.02743	0.28356	0.3251	0.1848	1.237
12	−67.62	−67.48	85.02	4.6434	−9.10	109.75	−0.02235	0.28075	0.3261	0.1884	1.240
14	−62.31	−62.16	84.44	4.0168	−7.36	110.42	−0.01795	0.27840	0.3270	0.1917	1.243
14.70[b]	−60.60	−60.46	84.26	3.8375	−6.80	110.63	−0.01655	0.27766	0.3274	0.1928	1.244
16	−57.56	−57.42	83.93	3.5423	−5.80	111.01	−0.01407	0.27638	0.3279	0.1947	1.245
18	−53.27	−53.13	83.45	3.1699	−4.39	111.54	−0.01059	0.27461	0.3288	0.1975	1.248
20	−49.34	−49.19	83.02	2.8698	−3.09	112.01	−0.00743	0.27305	0.3297	0.2002	1.251
22	−45.70	−45.56	82.61	2.6225	−1.89	112.45	−0.00452	0.27164	0.3305	0.2027	1.254
24	−42.32	−42.18	82.23	2.4151	−0.77	112.85	−0.00184	0.27036	0.3313	0.2050	1.256
26	−39.15	−39.01	81.87	2.2386	0.28	113.22	0.00067	0.26919	0.3321	0.2073	1.259
28	−36.17	−36.02	81.54	2.0865	1.27	113.56	0.00301	0.26811	0.3329	0.2094	1.261
30	−33.35	−33.20	81.21	1.9540	2.22	113.88	0.00522	0.26711	0.3337	0.2115	1.264
32	−30.68	−30.53	80.90	1.8375	3.11	114.19	0.00730	0.26617	0.3345	0.2135	1.267
34	−28.13	−27.98	80.61	1.7343	3.97	114.47	0.00928	0.26530	0.3352	0.2154	1.269
36	−25.69	−25.54	80.33	1.6422	4.79	114.74	0.01116	0.26448	0.3360	0.2173	1.272
38	−23.36	−23.20	80.05	1.5594	5.57	115.00	0.01296	0.26371	0.3367	0.2191	1.274
40	−21.12	−20.96	79.79	1.4847	6.33	115.24	0.01467	0.26297	0.3374	0.2208	1.277
42	−18.96	−18.81	79.54	1.4168	7.06	115.47	0.01632	0.26228	0.3382	0.2226	1.279
44	−16.89	−16.73	79.29	1.3549	7.76	115.69	0.01791	0.26162	0.3389	0.2242	1.282
46	−14.88	−14.73	79.05	1.2982	8.45	115.90	0.01943	0.26098	0.3396	0.2259	1.284
48	−12.94	−12.79	78.82	1.2460	9.11	116.10	0.02090	0.26038	0.3403	0.2275	1.287
50	−11.07	−10.91	78.59	1.1979	9.75	116.30	0.02232	0.25980	0.3410	0.2290	1.289
55	−6.62	−6.45	78.05	1.0925	11.27	116.75	0.02568	0.25845	0.3427	0.2328	1.295
60	−2.46	−2.30	77.54	1.0040	12.70	117.16	0.02880	0.25722	0.3445	0.2365	1.301
65	1.43	1.60	77.06	0.9287	14.05	117.53	0.03171	0.25610	0.3462	0.2400	1.308
70	5.10	5.27	76.60	0.8638	15.33	117.88	0.03444	0.25505	0.3478	0.2434	1.314
75	8.58	8.75	76.15	0.8073	16.54	118.20	0.03702	0.25408	0.3495	0.2467	1.320
80	11.88	12.06	75.73	0.7576	17.70	118.49	0.03946	0.25316	0.3512	0.2499	1.326
85	15.03	15.21	75.32	0.7135	18.81	118.77	0.04178	0.25231	0.3528	0.2531	1.333
90	18.05	18.22	74.93	0.6742	19.88	119.02	0.04400	0.25149	0.3545	0.2562	1.339
95	20.93	21.11	74.54	0.6389	20.91	119.26	0.04611	0.25072	0.3561	0.2592	1.345
100	23.71	23.89	74.17	0.6070	21.90	119.48	0.04815	0.24999	0.3578	0.2622	1.352
110	28.96	29.14	73.46	0.5515	23.79	119.89	0.05198	0.24862	0.3611	0.2681	1.365
120	33.86	34.05	72.78	0.5051	25.57	120.24	0.05555	0.24736	0.3644	0.2738	1.378
130	38.46	38.65	72.13	0.4655	27.25	120.56	0.05890	0.24618	0.3678	0.2795	1.392
140	42.80	42.99	71.51	0.4314	28.85	120.83	0.06205	0.24508	0.3712	0.2852	1.406
150	46.91	47.11	70.90	0.4016	30.38	121.08	0.06503	0.24403	0.3746	0.2908	1.420
160	50.82	51.02	70.32	0.3755	31.85	121.29	0.06787	0.24304	0.3781	0.2965	1.435
170	54.56	54.76	69.75	0.3523	33.27	121.48	0.07057	0.24210	0.3816	0.3022	1.451
180	58.13	58.33	69.20	0.3316	34.63	121.65	0.07316	0.24119	0.3851	0.3080	1.467
190	61.55	61.76	68.66	0.3130	35.95	121.79	0.07565	0.24031	0.3888	0.3139	1.483
200	64.84	65.05	68.13	0.2962	37.22	121.91	0.07804	0.23946	0.3925	0.3200	1.500
220	71.07	71.28	67.10	0.2669	39.67	122.09	0.08258	0.23783	0.4001	0.3325	1.537
240	76.89	77.10	66.11	0.2424	41.99	122.20	0.08683	0.23628	0.4081	0.3457	1.576
260	82.35	82.57	65.14	0.2215	44.21	122.25	0.09084	0.23478	0.4165	0.3599	1.619
280	87.51	87.73	64.19	0.2034	46.34	122.24	0.09464	0.23333	0.4255	0.3751	1.665
300	92.40	92.61	63.26	0.1876	48.40	122.18	0.09827	0.23190	0.4350	0.3915	1.716
320	97.04	97.26	62.34	0.1736	50.38	122.07	0.10175	0.23049	0.4452	0.4094	1.772
340	101.48	101.69	61.42	0.1613	52.31	121.91	0.10509	0.22909	0.4564	0.4290	1.833
360	105.71	105.93	60.52	0.1501	54.19	121.70	0.10832	0.22769	0.4685	0.4507	1.901
380	109.78	109.99	59.61	0.1401	56.03	121.44	0.11145	0.22629	0.4820	0.4747	1.977
400	113.68	113.89	58.70	0.1310	57.83	121.13	0.11450	0.22488	0.4971	0.5016	2.063
450	122.82	123.01	56.39	0.1114	62.23	120.14	0.12182	0.22124	0.5443	0.5857	2.333
500	131.19	131.38	53.97	0.0952	66.54	118.80	0.12888	0.21732	0.6143	0.7083	2.728
550	138.93	139.09	51.32	0.0814	70.89	117.02	0.13590	0.21295	0.7303	0.9059	3.367
600	146.12	146.25	48.24	0.0690	75.47	114.59	0.14320	0.20777	0.9603	1.2829	4.579
692.78[c]	158.40	158.40	34.18	0.0293	90.97	90.97	0.16781	0.16781	—	—	—

*Temperatures on ITS-90 scale [b]Bubble and dew points at one standard atmosphere [c]Critical point

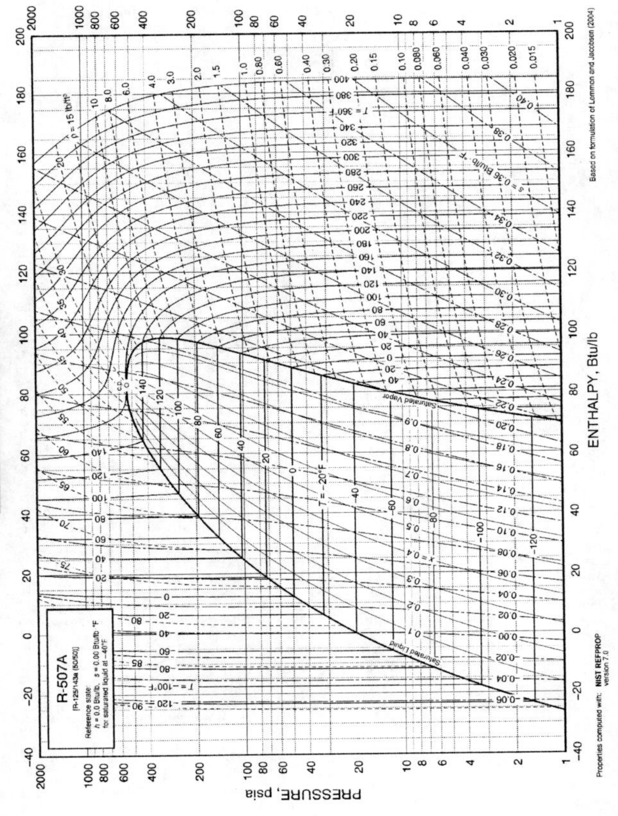

Figure 8.11 Pressure-Enthalpy Diagram for Refrigerant 507A
[2021F, Ch 30, Fig 18]

Table 8.14 R-507A [R-125/143a (50/50)]
Properties of Saturated Liquid and Saturated Vapor [2021F, Ch 30, Tbl R-507A]

Temp.,* °F	Pressure,** psia	Density, lb/ft³ Liquid	Volume, ft³/lb Vapor	Enthalpy, Btu/lb Liquid	Enthalpy, Btu/lb Vapor	Entropy, Btu/lb·°F Liquid	Entropy, Btu/lb·°F Vapor	Specific Heat c_p, Btu/lb·°F Liquid	Specific Heat c_p, Btu/lb·°F Vapor	c_p/c_v Vapor
−150	0.386	92.41	86.952	−32.027	67.009	−0.08831	0.23154	0.2919	0.1470	1.1650
−145	0.497	91.88	68.522	−30.571	67.711	−0.08365	0.22872	0.2904	0.1487	1.1637
−140	0.634	91.36	54.501	−29.121	68.416	−0.07908	0.22607	0.2893	0.1504	1.1626
−135	0.801	90.84	43.729	−27.677	69.126	−0.07460	0.22358	0.2885	0.1522	1.1616
−130	1.004	90.32	35.377	−26.235	69.838	−0.07019	0.22125	0.2879	0.1540	1.1607
−125	1.249	89.80	28.844	−24.796	70.554	−0.06586	0.21906	0.2876	0.1558	1.1599
−120	1.541	89.29	23.692	−23.359	71.272	−0.06160	0.21701	0.2874	0.1576	1.1593
−115	1.887	88.77	19.596	−21.921	71.993	−0.05740	0.21509	0.2874	0.1595	1.1588
−110	2.295	88.26	16.315	−20.484	72.716	−0.05326	0.21328	0.2875	0.1614	1.1584
−105	2.773	87.75	13.669	−19.045	73.440	−0.04918	0.21159	0.2878	0.1633	1.1581
−100	3.329	87.23	11.521	−17.604	74.166	−0.04515	0.21001	0.2882	0.1652	1.1580
−95	3.974	86.72	9.7644	−16.161	74.892	−0.04117	0.20852	0.2887	0.1672	1.1581
−90	4.715	86.20	8.3201	−14.716	75.619	−0.03723	0.20713	0.2893	0.1692	1.1583
−85	5.566	85.68	7.1254	−13.266	76.346	−0.03335	0.20583	0.2900	0.1712	1.1586
−80	6.535	85.16	6.1316	−11.813	77.073	−0.02950	0.20462	0.2908	0.1733	1.1592
−75	7.636	84.64	5.3004	−10.356	77.800	−0.02569	0.20348	0.2917	0.1754	1.1599
−70	8.879	84.11	4.6018	−8.894	78.525	−0.02192	0.20242	0.2926	0.1776	1.1607
−65	10.280	83.58	4.0116	−7.427	79.248	−0.01819	0.20143	0.2937	0.1798	1.1618
−60	11.849	83.05	3.5108	−5.954	79.970	−0.01449	0.20050	0.2948	0.1821	1.1631
−55	13.603	82.51	3.0839	−4.475	80.690	−0.01082	0.19963	0.2960	0.1844	1.1646
−52.13[b]	14.696	82.20	2.8676	−3.625	81.101	−0.00873	0.19916	0.2967	0.1858	1.1655
−50	15.554	81.97	2.7184	−2.990	81.406	−0.00719	0.19882	0.2972	0.1868	1.1663
−45	17.719	81.43	2.4043	−1.499	82.119	−0.00358	0.19807	0.2985	0.1893	1.1682
−40	20.112	80.88	2.1331	0.000	82.829	0.00000	0.19737	0.30000	0.1918	1.1704
−35	22.750	80.33	1.8983	1.506	83.534	0.00355	0.19671	0.3014	0.1944	1.1728
−30	25.649	79.77	1.6941	3.020	84.235	0.00708	0.19610	0.3030	0.1971	1.1755
−25	28.827	79.20	1.5160	4.541	84.931	0.01058	0.19553	0.3046	0.1998	1.1785
−20	32.300	78.63	1.3601	6.071	85.621	0.01407	0.19500	0.3063	0.2026	1.1818
−15	36.086	78.05	1.2231	7.610	86.304	0.01753	0.19450	0.3081	0.2056	1.1854
−10	40.203	77.46	1.1025	9.158	86.981	0.02097	0.19404	0.3100	0.2086	1.1894
−5	44.671	76.87	0.9960	10.716	87.651	0.02439	0.19360	0.3119	0.2117	1.1938
0	49.508	76.27	0.9016	12.284	88.313	0.02779	0.19319	0.3140	0.2149	1.1986
5	54.733	75.66	0.8177	13.862	88.966	0.03118	0.19281	0.3161	0.2183	1.2038
10	60.367	75.04	0.7430	15.452	89.610	0.03455	0.19245	0.3184	0.2218	1.2095
15	66.429	74.41	0.6763	17.052	90.245	0.03791	0.19211	0.3208	0.2254	1.2157
20	72.941	73.77	0.6165	18.665	90.868	0.04126	0.19179	0.3233	0.2291	1.2226
25	79.923	73.12	0.5629	20.290	91.480	0.04459	0.19148	0.3260	0.2330	1.2301
30	87.396	72.45	0.5146	21.929	92.079	0.04791	0.19118	0.3288	0.2371	1.2384
35	95.384	71.78	0.4711	23.581	92.664	0.05123	0.19089	0.3318	0.2414	1.2476
40	103.91	71.09	0.4318	25.249	93.234	0.05454	0.19061	0.3350	0.2460	1.2577
45	112.99	70.38	0.3962	26.931	93.788	0.05784	0.19032	0.3384	0.2508	1.2690
50	122.65	69.66	0.3638	28.630	94.324	0.06114	0.19004	0.3421	0.2560	1.2816
55	132.92	68.92	0.3344	30.346	94.840	0.06444	0.18976	0.3460	0.2616	1.2956
60	143.82	68.16	0.3076	32.080	95.336	0.06773	0.18946	0.3503	0.2676	1.3113
65	155.38	67.39	0.2832	33.834	95.808	0.07103	0.18916	0.3549	0.2742	1.3289
70	167.62	66.58	0.2608	35.609	96.255	0.07434	0.18884	0.3599	0.2814	1.3488
75	180.56	65.76	0.2403	37.406	96.675	0.07764	0.18850	0.3654	0.2894	1.3713
80	194.24	64.90	0.2214	39.228	97.065	0.08096	0.18814	0.3715	0.2983	1.3970
85	208.68	64.02	0.2041	41.076	97.421	0.08429	0.18775	0.3783	0.3083	1.4265
90	223.92	63.10	0.1880	42.952	97.740	0.08764	0.18732	0.3858	0.3196	1.4606
95	239.97	62.14	0.1732	44.860	98.019	0.09101	0.18686	0.3944	0.3325	1.5003
100	256.88	61.14	0.1595	46.803	98.251	0.09441	0.18634	0.4043	0.3475	1.5471
105	274.68	60.09	0.1468	48.784	98.431	0.09784	0.18576	0.4157	0.3650	1.6029
110	293.40	58.99	0.1349	50.809	98.551	0.10130	0.18511	0.4291	0.3858	1.6706
115	313.08	57.82	0.1238	52.885	98.600	0.10482	0.18438	0.4453	0.4112	1.7541
120	333.77	56.57	0.1134	55.018	98.568	0.10840	0.18354	0.4652	0.4427	1.8597
125	355.50	55.22	0.1036	57.221	98.435	0.11206	0.18256	0.4904	0.4833	1.9972
130	378.33	53.76	0.0943	59.509	98.177	0.11583	0.18141	0.5237	0.5375	2.1831
135	402.31	52.15	0.0855	61.903	97.759	0.11973	0.18003	0.5700	0.6142	2.4480
140	427.52	50.32	0.0769	64.439	97.125	0.12382	0.17833	0.6399	0.7313	2.8546
145	454.04	48.19	0.0684	67.182	96.173	0.12821	0.17616	0.7590	0.9326	3.5556
150	481.99	45.55	0.0597	70.265	94.697	0.13311	0.17318	1.0130	1.3606	5.0420
155	511.55	41.76	0.0499	74.107	92.081	0.13918	0.16842	1.9550	2.8693	10.2379
159.12[c]	537.40	30.64	0.0326	83.010	83.010	0.15339	0.15339	∞	∞	∞

*Temperatures on ITS-90 scale
**Small deviations from azeotropic behavior occur at some conditions; tabulated pressures are average of bubble and dew-point pressures

[b]Normal boiling point
[c]Critical point

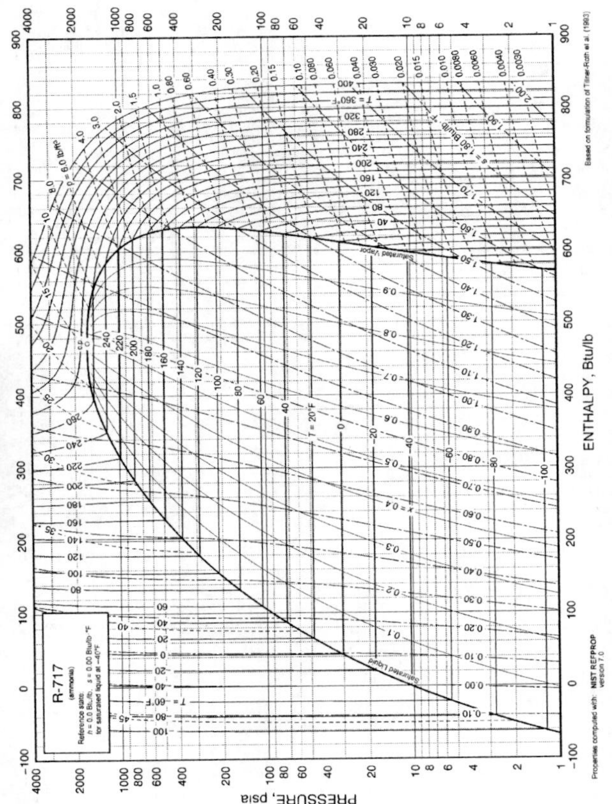

Figure 8.12 Pressure-Enthalpy Diagram for Refrigerant 717 (Ammonia)
[2021F, Ch 30, Fig 19]

Table 8.15 R-717 (Ammonia)
Properties of Saturated Liquid and Saturated Vapor [2021F, Ch 30, Tbl R-717]

Temp.,* °F	Pressure, psia	Density, lb/ft³ Liquid	Volume, ft³/lb Vapor	Enthalpy, Btu/lb Liquid	Enthalpy, Btu/lb Vapor	Entropy, Btu/lb·°F Liquid	Entropy, Btu/lb·°F Vapor	Specific Heat c_p, Btu/lb·°F Liquid	Specific Heat c_p, Btu/lb·°F Vapor	c_p/c_v Vapor
−107.78[a]	0.883	45.75	249.92	−69.830	568.765	−0.18124	1.63351	1.0044	0.4930	1.3252
−100	1.237	45.47	182.19	−61.994	572.260	−0.15922	1.60421	1.0100	0.4959	1.3262
−90	1.864	45.09	124.12	−51.854	576.688	−0.13142	1.56886	1.0176	0.5003	1.3278
−80	2.739	44.71	86.546	−41.637	581.035	−0.10416	1.53587	1.0254	0.5056	1.3296
−70	3.937	44.31	61.647	−31.341	585.288	−0.07741	1.50503	1.0331	0.5118	1.3319
−60	5.544	43.91	44.774	−20.969	589.439	−0.05114	1.47614	1.0406	0.5190	1.3346
−50	7.659	43.50	33.105	−10.521	593.476	−0.02534	1.44900	1.0478	0.5271	1.3379
−40	10.398	43.08	24.881	0.000	597.387	0.00000	1.42347	1.0549	0.5364	1.3419
−30	13.890	42.66	18.983	10.592	601.162	0.02491	1.39938	1.0617	0.5467	1.3465
−27.99[b]	14.696	42.57	18.007	12.732	601.904	0.02987	1.39470	1.0631	0.5490	1.3475
−25	15.962	42.45	16.668	15.914	602.995	0.03720	1.38784	1.0651	0.5524	1.3491
−20	18.279	42.23	14.684	21.253	604.789	0.04939	1.37660	1.0684	0.5583	1.3520
−15	20.858	42.01	12.976	26.609	606.544	0.06148	1.36567	1.0716	0.5646	1.3550
−10	23.723	41.79	11.502	31.982	608.257	0.07347	1.35502	1.0749	0.5711	1.3584
−5	26.895	41.57	10.226	37.372	609.928	0.08536	1.34463	1.0782	0.5781	1.3619
0	30.397	41.34	9.1159	42.779	611.554	0.09715	1.33450	1.0814	0.5853	1.3657
5	34.253	41.12	8.1483	48.203	613.135	0.10885	1.32462	1.0847	0.5929	1.3698
10	38.487	40.89	7.3020	53.644	614.669	0.12045	1.31496	1.0880	0.6009	1.3742
15	43.126	40.66	6.5597	59.103	616.154	0.13197	1.30552	1.0914	0.6092	1.3789
20	48.194	40.43	5.9067	64.579	617.590	0.14340	1.29629	1.0948	0.6179	1.3840
25	53.720	40.20	5.3307	70.072	618.974	0.15474	1.28726	1.0983	0.6271	1.3894
30	59.730	39.96	4.8213	75.585	620.305	0.16599	1.27842	1.1019	0.6366	1.3951
35	66.255	39.72	4.3695	81.116	621.582	0.17717	1.26975	1.1056	0.6465	1.4012
40	73.322	39.48	3.9680	86.666	622.803	0.18827	1.26125	1.1094	0.6569	1.4078
45	80.962	39.24	3.6102	92.237	623.967	0.19929	1.25291	1.1134	0.6678	1.4147
50	89.205	38.99	3.2906	97.828	625.072	0.21024	1.24472	1.1175	0.6791	1.4222
55	98.083	38.75	3.0045	103.441	626.115	0.22111	1.23667	1.1218	0.6909	1.4301
60	107.63	38.50	2.7479	109.076	627.097	0.23192	1.22875	1.126	0.703	1.438
65	117.87	38.25	2.5172	114.734	628.013	0.24266	1.22095	1.131	0.716	1.447
70	128.85	37.99	2.3094	120.417	628.864	0.25334	1.21327	1.136	0.730	1.457
75	140.59	37.73	2.1217	126.126	629.647	0.26396	1.20570	1.141	0.744	1.467
80	153.13	37.47	1.9521	131.861	630.359	0.27452	1.19823	1.147	0.758	1.478
85	166.51	37.21	1.7983	137.624	630.999	0.28503	1.19085	1.153	0.774	1.490
90	180.76	36.94	1.6588	143.417	631.564	0.29549	1.18356	1.159	0.790	1.502
95	195.91	36.67	1.5319	149.241	632.052	0.30590	1.17634	1.166	0.807	1.515
100	212.01	36.40	1.4163	155.098	632.460	0.31626	1.16920	1.173	0.824	1.529
105	229.09	36.12	1.3108	160.990	632.785	0.32659	1.16211	1.180	0.843	1.544
110	247.19	35.83	1.2144	166.919	633.025	0.33688	1.15508	1.188	0.862	1.561
115	266.34	35.55	1.1262	172.887	633.175	0.34713	1.14809	1.197	0.883	1.578
120	286.60	35.26	1.0452	178.896	633.232	0.35736	1.14115	1.206	0.905	1.597
125	307.98	34.96	0.9710	184.949	633.193	0.36757	1.13423	1.216	0.928	1.617
130	330.54	34.66	0.9026	191.049	633.053	0.37775	1.12733	1.227	0.952	1.638
135	354.32	34.35	0.8397	197.199	632.807	0.38792	1.12044	1.239	0.978	1.662
140	379.36	34.04	0.7817	203.403	632.451	0.39808	1.11356	1.251	1.006	1.687
145	405.70	33.72	0.7280	209.663	631.978	0.40824	1.10666	1.265	1.035	1.715
150	433.38	33.39	0.6785	215.984	631.383	0.41840	1.09975	1.280	1.067	1.745
155	462.45	33.06	0.6325	222.370	630.659	0.42857	1.09281	1.296	1.101	1.778
160	492.95	32.72	0.5899	228.827	629.798	0.43875	1.08582	1.313	1.138	1.813
165	524.94	32.37	0.5504	235.359	628.791	0.44896	1.07878	1.333	1.178	1.853
170	558.45	32.01	0.5136	241.973	627.630	0.45919	1.07167	1.354	1.222	1.896
175	593.53	31.64	0.4793	248.675	626.302	0.46947	1.06447	1.377	1.270	1.944
180	630.24	31.26	0.4473	255.472	624.797	0.47980	1.05717	1.403	1.322	1.998
185	668.63	30.87	0.4174	262.374	623.100	0.49019	1.04974	1.432	1.381	2.058
190	708.74	30.47	0.3895	269.390	621.195	0.50066	1.04217	1.465	1.446	2.126
195	750.64	30.05	0.3633	276.530	619.064	0.51121	1.03443	1.502	1.519	2.203
200	794.38	29.62	0.3387	283.809	616.686	0.52188	1.02649	1.543	1.602	2.290
205	840.03	29.17	0.3156	291.240	614.035	0.53267	1.01831	1.591	1.697	2.392
210	887.64	28.70	0.2938	298.842	611.081	0.54360	1.00986	1.646	1.806	2.509
215	937.28	28.21	0.2733	306.637	607.788	0.55472	1.00109	1.711	1.935	2.648
220	989.03	27.69	0.2538	314.651	604.112	0.56605	0.99193	1.788	2.088	2.814
225	1042.96	27.15	0.2354	322.918	599.996	0.57763	0.98232	1.882	2.272	3.015
230	1099.14	26.57	0.2178	331.483	595.371	0.58953	0.97216	1.999	2.501	3.265
235	1157.69	25.95	0.2010	340.404	590.142	0.60182	0.96133	2.148	2.790	3.582
240	1218.68	25.28	0.1849	349.766	584.183	0.61462	0.94966	2.346	3.171	4.000
245	1282.24	24.55	0.1693	359.695	577.309	0.62809	0.93690	2.624	3.693	4.575
250	1348.49	23.72	0.1540	370.391	569.240	0.64249	0.92269	3.047	4.460	5.420
260	1489.71	21.60	0.1233	395.943	547.139	0.67662	0.88671	5.273	8.106	9.439
270.05[c]	1643.71	14.05	0.0712	473.253	473.253	0.78093	0.78093	∞	∞	∞

*Temperatures on ITS-90 scale [a]Triple point [b]Normal boiling point [c]Critical point

Refrigerants

Table 8.16 Comparative Refrigerant Performance per Ton of Refrigeration [2021F, Ch 29, Tbl 8]

No.	Refrigerant: Chemical Name or Composition (% by mass)	Evaporator Pressure, psia	Condenser Pressure, psia	Compression Ratio	Net Refrigerating Effect, Btu/lb	Refrigerant Circulated, lb/min	Liquid Circulated, gal/min	Specific Volume of Suction Gas, ft^3/lb	Compressor Displacement, ft^3/min	Power Consumption, hp	Coefficient of Performance	Compressor Discharge Temp., °F
Evaporator −25°F/Condenser 86°F												
744	Carbon dioxide	195.7	1046.2	5.35	56.8	3.52	0.711	0.457	1.61	2.779	1.698	196.3
170	Ethane	146.8	675.1	4.6	66.0	3.03	1.314	0.878	2.66	2.805	1.681	136.2
1270	Propylene	28.8	189.3	6.57	115.7	1.73	0.416	3.63	6.28	1.637	2.88	120.3
507A	R-125/143a (50/50)	28.8	211.7	7.34	43.5	4.60	0.54	1.52	6.98	1.833	2.573	100.6
404A	R-125/143a/134a (44/52/4)	27.6	206.1	7.46	45.1	4.44	0.521	1.61	7.13	1.817	2.595	102.1
502	R-22/115 (48.8/51.2)	26.5	189.2	7.14	42.1	4.76	0.48	1.48	7.06	1.722	2.739	106.3
22	Chlorodifluoromethane	22.1	172.9	7.81	66.8	3.00	0.307	2.32	6.95	1.589	2.967	149.8
717	Ammonia	16.0	169.3	10.61	463.9	0.43	0.087	16.7	7.19	1.569	3.007	285.6
Evaporator 20°F/Condenser 86°F												
744	Carbon dioxide	421.9	1046.2	2.48	55.7	3.59	0.726	0.203	0.73	1.342	3.514	142.3
170	Ethane	293.6	675.1	2.3	70.1	2.85	1.238	0.421	1.20	1.314	3.588	115.8
32	Difluoromethane	94.7	279.6	2.95	111.2	1.80	0.229	0.902	1.62	0.797	5.924	139.4
410A	R-32/125 (50/50)	93.2	273.6	2.94	73.5	2.72	0.316	0.651	1.77	0.815	5.78	115.8
507A	R-125/143a (50/50)	72.9	211.7	2.9	49.4	4.05	0.476	0.616	2.50	0.848	5.564	93.5
404A	R-125/143a/134a (44/52/4)	70.5	206.1	2.92	51.1	3.92	0.46	0.649	2.54	0.842	5.598	94.3
1270	Propylene	69.1	189.3	2.74	126.6	1.58	0.381	1.58	2.50	0.79	5.975	102.8
502	R-22/115 (48.8/51.2)	66.3	189.2	2.86	47.1	4.25	0.429	0.619	2.63	0.813	5.799	95.8
22	Chlorodifluoromethane	57.8	172.9	2.99	71.3	2.80	0.287	0.935	2.62	0.772	6.105	118.0
407C	R-32/125/134a (23/25/52)	57.5	183.7	3.19	71.9	2.78	0.296	0.942	2.62	0.795	5.93	111.0
290	Propane	55.8	156.5	2.8	124.1	1.61	0.399	1.89	3.05	0.787	5.987	94.8
717	Ammonia	48.2	169.3	3.51	478.5	0.42	0.084	5.91	2.47	0.754	6.254	179.8
1234yf	2,3,3,3-tetrafluoropropene*	36.3	113.6	3.13	51.8	3.86	0.43	1.15	4.44	0.809	5.835	86.0
134a	Tetrafluoroethane	33.1	111.7	3.37	65.8	3.04	0.307	1.41	4.28	0.778	6.063	94.7
1234ze(E)	Trans-1,3,3,3-tetrafluoropropene*	24.4	83.9	3.44	60.0	3.33	0.349	1.74	5.81	0.782	6.03	86.0
600a	Isobutane*	17.9	58.7	3.29	119.5	1.67	0.368	4.78	7.99	0.764	6.171	86.0

Table 8.16 Comparative Refrigerant Performance per Ton of Refrigeration [2021F, Ch 29, Tbl 8] ***(Continued)***

Refrigerant No.	Chemical Name or Composition (% by mass)	Evaporator Pressure, psia	Condenser Pressure, psia	Compression Ratio	Net Refrigerating Effect, Btu/lb	Refrigerant Circulated, lb/min	Liquid Circulated, gal/min	Specific Volume of Suction Gas, ft^3/lb	Compressor Displacement, ft^3/min	Power Consumption, hp	Coefficient of Performance	Compressor Discharge Temp., °F
Evaporator 45°F/Condenser 86°F												
32	Difluoromethane	147.7	279.6	1.89	112.2	1.78	0.223	0.577	1.03	0.445	10.602	116.4
410A	R-32/125 (50/50)	145.0	273.6	1.89	75.2	2.66	0.308	0.416	1.11	0.455	10.379	103.7
502	R-22/115 (48.8/51.2)	102.0	189.2	1.85	49.6	4.03	0.407	0.404	1.63	0.451	10.474	91.8
407C	R-32/125/134a (23/25/52)	92.8	183.7	1.98	74.7	2.68	0.284	0.588	1.57	0.443	10.655	102.7
22	Chlorodifluoromethane	90.8	172.9	1.9	73.5	2.72	0.279	0.604	1.64	0.433	10.885	104.5
290	Propane	85.3	156.5	1.84	130.7	1.53	0.379	1.26	1.92	0.439	10.743	90.7
717	Ammonia	81.0	169.3	2.09	484.9	0.41	0.083	3.61	1.49	0.421	11.186	137.4
500	R-12/152a (73.8/26.2)	66.5	127.6	1.92	64.7	3.09	0.331	0.725	2.24	0.432	10.925	94.2
1234yf	2,3,3,3-tetrafluoropropene*	58.1	113.6	1.96	55.5	3.61	0.402	0.726	2.62	0.444	10.623	86.0
12	Dichlorodifluoromethane	56.3	107.9	1.92	54.6	3.67	0.34	0.719	2.64	0.429	11.004	91.6
134a	Tetrafluoroethane	54.7	111.7	2.04	69.2	2.89	0.292	0.868	2.51	0.433	10.903	90.6
1234ze(E)	Trans-1,3,3,3-tetrafluoropropene*	40.6	83.9	2.06	64.1	3.12	0.327	1.07	3.34	0.433	10.899	86.0
600a	Isobutane*	29.2	58.7	2.01	127.4	1.57	0.345	3.01	4.72	0.425	11.084	86.0
600	Butane*	19.5	41.1	2.11	140.5	1.42	0.301	4.57	6.50	0.42	11.226	86.0
123	Dichlorotrifluoroethane	6.5	15.9	2.44	66.9	2.99	0.246	5.3	15.85	0.414	11.397	86.0
113	Trichlorotrifluoroethane*	3.1	7.9	2.57	59.2	3.38	0.26	9.41	31.81	0.413	11.409	86.0

*Superheat required

Source: Data from NIST CYCLE_D 4.0, zero subcool, zero superheat unless noted, no line losses, 100% efficiencies, average temperatures.

Table 8.17 Suction, Discharge, and Liquid Line Capacities in Tons for Refrigerant 22 (Single- or High-Stage Applications)
[2018R, Ch 1, Tbl 3]

Line Size		Suction Lines ($\Delta t = 2°F$)					Discharge Lines ($\Delta t = 1°F$, $\Delta p = 3.05$ psi)		Line Size		Liquid Lines	
		Saturated Suction Temperature, °F									See notes a and b	
Type L Copper, OD		–40	–20	0	20	40	Saturated Suction Temperature, °F		Type L Copper, OD		Vel. = 100 fpm	$\Delta t = 1°F$
		Corresponding Δp, psi/100 ft										
		0.79	1.15	1.6	2.22	2.91	–40	40				$\Delta p = 3.05$
1/2		—	—	—	0.40	0.6	0.75	0.85	1/2		2.3	3.6
5/8		—	0.32	0.51	0.76	1.1	1.4	1.6	5/8		3.7	6.7
7/8		0.52	0.86	1.3	2.0	2.9	3.7	4.2	7/8		7.8	18.2
1 1/8		1.1	1.7	2.7	4.0	5.8	7.5	8.5	1 1/8		13.2	37.0
1 3/8		1.9	3.1	4.7	7.0	10.1	13.1	14.8	1 3/8		20.2	64.7
1 5/8		3.0	4.8	7.5	11.1	16.0	20.7	23.4	1 5/8		28.5	102.5
2 1/8		6.2	10.0	15.6	23.1	33.1	42.8	48.5	2 1/8		49.6	213.0
2 5/8		10.9	17.8	27.5	40.8	58.3	75.4	85.4	2 5/8		76.5	376.9
3 1/8		17.5	28.4	44.0	65.0	92.9	120.2	136.2	3 1/8		109.2	601.5
3 5/8		26.0	42.3	65.4	96.6	137.8	178.4	202.1	3 5/8		147.8	895.7
4 1/8		36.8	59.6	92.2	136.3	194.3	251.1	284.4	4 1/8		192.1	1263.2
Steel									Steel			
IPS	SCH								IPS	SCH		
1/2	40	—	0.38	0.58	0.85	1.2	1.5	1.7	1/2	80	3.8	5.7
3/4	40	0.50	0.8	1.2	1.8	2.5	3.3	3.7	3/4	80	6.9	12.8
1	40	0.95	1.5	2.3	3.4	4.8	6.1	6.9	1	80	11.5	25.2
1 1/4	40	2.0	3.2	4.8	7.0	9.9	12.6	14.3	1 1/4	80	20.6	54.1
1 1/2	40	3.0	4.7	7.2	10.5	14.8	19.0	21.5	1 1/2	80	28.3	82.6
2	40	5.7	9.1	13.9	20.2	28.5	36.6	41.4	2	40	53.8	192.0

Table 8.17 Suction, Discharge, and Liquid Line Capacities in Tons for Refrigerant 22 (Single- or High-Stage Applications) [2018R, Ch 1, Tbl 3] ***(Continued)***

Line Size		Suction Lines ($\Delta t = 2°F$)					Discharge Lines ($\Delta t = 1°F$, $\Delta p = 3.05$ psi)		Line Size		Liquid Lines	
		Saturated Suction Temperature, °F					Saturated Suction Temperature, °F				See notes a and b	
		−40	−20	0	20	40	−40	40			Vel. = 100 fpm	$\Delta t = 1°F$
		Corresponding Δp, psi/100 ft										
		0.79	1.15	1.6	2.22	2.91						$\Delta p = 3.05$
Steel									Steel			
IPS	SCH								IPS	SCH		
2 1/2	40	9.2	14.6	22.1	32.2	45.4	58.1	65.9	2 1/2	40	76.7	305.8
3	40	16.2	25.7	39.0	56.8	80.1	102.8	116.4	3	40	118.5	540.3
4	40	33.1	52.5	79.5	115.9	163.2	209.5	237.3	4	40	204.2	1101.2

Notes:

1. Table capacities are in tons of refrigeration.

   Δp = pressure drop from line friction, psi per 100 ft of equivalent line length

   Δt = corresponding change in saturation temperature, °F per 100 ft

2. Line capacity for other saturation temperatures Δt and equivalent lengths L_e

$$\text{Line capacity} = \text{Table capacity}\left(\frac{\text{Table } L_e}{\text{Actual } L_e} \times \frac{\text{Actual } \Delta t}{\text{Table } \Delta t}\right)^{0.55}$$

3. Saturation temperature Δt for other capacities and equivalent lengths L_e

$$\Delta t = \text{Table } \Delta t \left(\frac{\text{Actual } L_e}{\text{Table } L_e}\right)\left(\frac{\text{Actual capacity}}{\text{Table capacity}}\right)^{1.8}$$

4. Values based on 105°F condensing temperature. Multiply table capacities by the following factors for other condensing temperatures.

Condensing Temperature, °F	Suction Line	Discharge Line
80	1.11	0.79
90	1.07	0.88
100	1.03	0.95
110	0.97	1.04
120	0.90	1.10
130	0.86	1.18
140	0.80	1.26

[a] Sizing shown is recommended where any gas generated in receiver must return up condensate line to condenser without restricting condensate flow. Water-cooled condensers, where receiver ambient temperature may be higher than refrigerant condensing temperature, fall into this category.

[b] Line pressure drop Δp is conservative; if subcooling is substantial or line is short, a smaller size line may be used. Applications with very little subcooling or very long lines may require a larger line.

c System working pressures may exceed calculated allowable pressure in some listed type L annealed copper tubes at certain saturated condensing temperatures. Review maximum working pressure allowances for the pipe material used before selecting pipe sizes to ensure the pipe is properly rated for system working and design pressures.

Table 8.18 Suction, Discharge, and Liquid Line Capacities in Tons for Refrigerant 134a (Single- or High-Stage Applications)
[2018R, Ch 1, Tbl 5]

Line Size		Suction Lines (Δt = 2°F)					Discharge Lines (Δt = 1°F, Δp = 2.2 psi/100 ft)			Line Size		Liquid Lines See notes a and b	
		Saturated Suction Temperature, °F					Saturated Suction Temperature, °F						
Type L Copper, OD		0	10	20	30	40				Type L Copper, OD		Velocity = 100 fpm	Δt = 1°F
		Corresponding Δp, psi/100 ft											
		1.00	1.19	1.41	1.66	1.93	0	20	40				Δp = 2.2
1/2		0.14	0.18	0.23	0.29	0.35	0.54	0.57	0.59	1/2		2.13	2.79
5/8		0.27	0.34	0.43	0.54	0.66	1.01	1.07	1.12	5/8		3.42	5.27
7/8		0.71	0.91	1.14	1.42	1.75	2.67	2.81	2.94	7/8		7.09	14.00
1 1/8		1.45	1.84	2.32	2.88	3.54	5.40	5.68	5.95	1 1/8		12.10	28.40
1 3/8		2.53	3.22	4.04	5.02	6.17	9.42	9.91	10.40	1 3/8		18.40	50.00
1 5/8		4.02	5.10	6.39	7.94	9.77	14.90	15.70	16.40	1 5/8		26.10	78.60
2 1/8		8.34	10.60	13.30	16.50	20.20	30.80	32.40	34.00	2 1/8		45.30	163.00
2 5/8		14.80	18.80	23.50	29.10	35.80	54.40	57.20	59.90	2 5/8		69.90	290.00
3 1/8		23.70	30.00	37.50	46.40	57.10	86.70	91.20	95.50	3 1/8		100.00	462.00
3 5/8		35.10	44.60	55.80	69.10	84.80	129.00	135.00	142.00	3 5/8		135.00	688.00
4 1/8		49.60	62.90	78.70	97.40	119.43	181.00	191.00	200.00	4 1/8		175.00	971.00
Steel										Steel			
IPS	SCH									IPS	SCH		
1/2	80	0.22	0.28	0.35	0.43	0.53	0.79	0.84	0.88	1/2	80	3.43	4.38
3/4	80	0.51	0.64	0.79	0.98	1.19	1.79	1.88	1.97	3/4	80	6.34	9.91
1	80	1.00	1.25	1.56	1.92	2.33	3.51	3.69	3.86	1	80	10.50	19.50
1 1/4	40	2.62	3.30	4.09	5.03	6.12	9.20	9.68	10.10	1 1/4	80	18.80	41.80

Table 8.18 Suction, Discharge, and Liquid Line Capacities in Tons for Refrigerant 134a (Single- or High-Stage Applications) [2018R, Ch 1, Tbl 5] *(Continued)*

Line Size		Suction Lines ($\Delta t = 2°F$)					Discharge Lines ($\Delta t = 1°F$, $\Delta p = 2.2$ psi/100 ft)			Line Size		Liquid Lines (See notes a and b)	
		Saturated Suction Temperature, °F					Saturated Suction Temperature, °F					Velocity = 100 fpm	$\Delta t = 1°F$
		0	10	20	30	40							
		Corresponding Δp, psi/100 ft											
		1.00	1.19	1.41	1.66	1.93	0	20	40				$\Delta p = 2.2$
Steel										Steel			
IPS	SCH									IPS	SCH		
1 1/2	40	3.94	4.95	6.14	7.54	9.18	13.80	14.50	15.20	1 1/2	80	25.90	63.70
2	40	7.60	9.56	11.90	14.60	17.70	26.60	28.00	29.30	2	40	49.20	148.00
2 1/2	40	12.10	15.20	18.90	23.10	28.20	42.40	44.60	46.70	2 1/2	40	70.10	236.00
3	40	21.40	26.90	33.40	41.00	49.80	75.00	78.80	82.50	3	40	108.00	419.00
4	40	43.80	54.90	68.00	83.50	101.60	153.00	160.00	168.00	4	40	187.00	853.00

Notes:

1. Table capacities are in tons of refrigeration.

   Δp = pressure drop from line friction, psi per 100 ft of equivalent line length

   Δt = corresponding change in saturation temperature, °F per 100 ft

2. Line capacity for other saturation temperatures Δt and equivalent lengths L_e

   $$\text{Line capacity} = \text{Table capacity}\left(\frac{\text{Table } L_e}{\text{Actual } L_e} \times \frac{\text{Actual } \Delta t}{\text{Table } \Delta t}\right)^{0.55}$$

3. Saturation temperature Δt for other capacities and equivalent lengths L_e

   $$\Delta t = \text{Table } \Delta t\left(\frac{\text{Actual } L_e}{\text{Table } L_e}\right)\left(\frac{\text{Actual capacity}}{\text{Table capacity}}\right)^{1.8}$$

4. Values based on 105°F condensing temperature. Multiply table capacities by the following factors for other condensing temperatures.

Condensing Temperature, °F	Suction Line	Discharge Line
80	1.158	0.804
90	1.095	0.882
100	1.032	0.961
110	0.968	1.026
120	0.902	1.078
130	0.834	1.156

[a] Sizing shown is recommended where any gas generated in receiver must return up condensate line to the condenser without restricting condensate flow. Water-cooled condensers, where receiver ambient temperature may be higher than refrigerant condensing temperature, fall into this category.

[b] Line pressure drop Δp is conservative; if subcooling is substantial or line is short, a smaller size line may be used. Applications with very little subcooling or very long lines may require a larger line.

[c] System working pressures may exceed calculated allowable pressure in some listed type L annealed copper tubes at certain saturated condensing temperatures. Review maximum working pressure allowances for the pipe material used before selecting pipe sizes to ensure the pipe is properly rated for system working and design pressures.

Table 8.19 Suction, Discharge, and Liquid Line Capacities in Tons for Refrigerant 404A (Single- or High-Stage Applications)
[2018R, Ch 1, Tbl 6]

Line Size	Suction Lines ($\Delta t = 2°F$)						Discharge Lines ($\Delta t = 1°F$, $\Delta p = 3.55$ psi)[c]						Liquid Lines[a,c]		
	Saturated Suction Temperature, °F						Saturated Suction Temperature, °F								
Type L Copper, OD	–60	–40	–20	0	20	40	–60	–40	–20	0	20	40	Velocity = 100 fpm	$\Delta t = 1°F$ Drop	$\Delta t = 5°F$ Drop
	Corresponding Δp, psi/100 ft						Corresponding Δp, psi/100 ft								
	0.64	0.97	1.41	1.96	2.62	3.44	3.55	3.55	3.55	3.55	3.55	3.55		$\Delta p = 3.6$	$\Delta p = 17.4$
1/2	0.05	0.09	0.15	0.24	0.36	0.53	0.56	0.61	0.65	0.70	0.75	0.79	1.3	2.6	6.09
5/8	0.09	0.16	0.28	0.44	0.68	1.00	1.04	1.14	1.23	1.31	1.40	1.48	2.1	4.9	11.39
3/4	0.15	0.28	0.47	0.76	1.15	1.70	1.77	1.93	2.09	2.23	2.38	2.51	3.1	8.1	18.87
7/8	0.24	0.43	0.73	1.17	1.78	2.63	2.73	2.98	3.22	3.44	3.66	3.87	4.4	12.8	29.81
1 1/8	0.49	0.88	1.49	2.37	3.61	5.31	5.52	6.01	6.49	6.96	7.40	7.81	7.5	25.9	60.17
1 3/8	0.86	1.54	2.59	4.13	6.28	9.23	9.60	10.46	11.29	12.10	12.87	13.58	11.4	45.2	104.41
1 5/8	1.36	2.44	4.10	6.53	9.92	14.57	15.14	16.49	17.80	19.07	20.28	21.41	16.1	71.4	164.68
2 1/8	2.83	5.07	8.52	13.53	20.51	30.06	31.29	34.08	36.80	39.43	41.93	44.26	28.0	147.9	339.46
2 5/8	5.03	8.97	15.07	23.88	36.16	52.96	55.04	59.95	64.74	69.36	73.76	77.85	43.2	261.2	597.42
3 1/8	8.05	14.34	24.02	38.05	57.56	84.33	87.66	95.48	103.11	110.47	117.48	124.00	61.7	416.2	950.09
3 5/8	11.98	21.31	35.73	56.53	85.39	125.18	129.88	141.46	152.76	163.67	174.05	183.71	83.5	618.4	1407.96
4 1/8	16.93	30.09	50.32	79.66	120.39	176.20	182.83	199.13	215.05	230.40	245.01	258.61	108.5	871.6	1982.40

Table 8.19 Suction, Discharge, and Liquid Line Capacities in Tons for Refrigerant 404A (Single- or High-Stage Applications) [2018R, Ch 1, Tbl 6] ***(Continued)***

Line Size		Suction Lines ($\Delta t = 2°F$)						Discharge Lines ($\Delta t = 1°F$, $\Delta p = 3.55$ psi)[c]						Liquid Lines[a,c]		
		Saturated Suction Temperature, °F						Saturated Suction Temperature, °F								
		−60	−40	−20	0	20	40	−60	−40	−20	0	20	40	Velocity = 100 fpm	$\Delta t = 1°F$ Drop	$\Delta t = 5°F$ Drop
		Corresponding Δp, psi/100 ft						Corresponding Δp, psi/100 ft								
		0.64	0.97	1.41	1.96	2.62	3.44	3.55	3.55	3.55	3.55	3.55	3.55		$\Delta p = 3.6$	$\Delta p = 17.4$
Steel																
IPS	SCH															
3/8	80	0.04	0.07	0.11	0.18	0.27	0.39	0.40	0.44	0.47	0.51	0.54	0.57	1.3	1.9	4.3
1/2	80	0.08	0.14	0.22	0.35	0.53	0.76	0.79	0.86	0.93	0.99	1.06	1.12	2.1	3.8	8.5
3/4	80	0.18	0.31	0.51	0.79	1.18	1.71	1.78	1.93	2.09	2.24	2.38	2.51	3.9	8.6	19.2
1	80	0.35	0.60	0.99	1.55	2.32	3.36	3.48	3.79	4.09	4.38	4.66	4.92	6.5	16.9	37.5
1 1/4	80	0.75	1.30	2.13	3.33	4.97	7.20	7.45	8.12	8.77	9.39	9.99	10.54	11.6	36.3	80.3
1 1/2	80	1.14	1.98	3.26	5.08	7.57	10.96	11.35	12.37	13.35	14.31	15.21	16.06	16.0	55.3	122.3
2	40	2.65	4.61	7.55	11.78	17.57	25.45	26.36	28.71	31.01	33.22	35.33	37.29	30.4	128.4	283.5
2 1/2	40	4.23	7.34	12.04	18.74	27.94	40.49	41.93	45.67	49.32	52.84	56.19	59.31	43.3	204.7	450.9
3	40	7.48	12.98	21.26	33.11	49.37	71.55	74.10	80.71	87.16	93.38	99.31	104.82	66.9	361.6	796.8
4	40	15.30	26.47	43.34	67.50	100.66	145.57	150.75	164.20	177.32	189.98	202.03	213.24	115.3	735.6	1623.0
5	40	27.58	47.78	78.24	121.87	181.32	262.52	272.21	296.49	320.19	343.04	364.80	385.05	181.1	1328.2	2927.2
6	40	44.58	77.26	126.52	197.09	293.24	424.04	439.72	478.94	517.21	554.13	589.28	621.99	261.7	2148.0	4728.3
8	40	91.40	158.09	258.81	402.66	599.91	867.50	898.42	978.56	1056.75	1132.18	1203.99	1270.82	453.2	4394.4	9674.1
10	40	165.52	286.19	468.14	728.40	1083.73	1569.40	1625.34	1770.31	1911.78	2048.23	2178.15	2299.05	714.4	7938.5	17,477.4
12	ID[b]	264.36	457.37	748.94	1163.62	1733.87	2507.30	2600.54	2832.50	3058.84	3277.16	3485.04	3678.47	1024.6	12,681.8	27,963.7
14	30	342.81	592.13	968.21	1506.59	2244.98	3246.34	3362.07	3661.96	3954.59	4236.83	4505.59	4755.67	1249.2	16,419.6	36,152.5
16	30	493.87	852.84	1395.24	2171.13	3230.27	4678.48	4845.26	5277.44	5699.16	6105.92	6493.24	6853.65	1654.7	23,662.2	52,101.2

Table 8.19 Suction, Discharge, and Liquid Line Capacities in Tons for Refrigerant 404A (Single- or High-Stage Applications) [2018R, Ch 1, Tbl 6] *(Continued)*

[a] Sizing shown is recommended where any gas generated in receiver must return up condensate line to condenser without restricting condensate flow. Water-cooled condensers, where receiver ambient temperature may be higher than refrigerant condensing temperature, fall into this category.

[b] Pipe inside diameter is same as nominal pipe size.

[c] System working pressures may exceed calculated allowable pressure in some listed type L annealed copper tubes at certain saturated condensing temperatures. Review maximum working pressure allowances for the pipe material used before selecting pipe sizes to ensure the pipe is properly rated for system working and design pressures.

Notes:

1. Table capacities are in tons of refrigeration.
   Δp = pressure drop from line friction, psi per 100 ft of equivalent line length
   Δt = corresponding change in saturation temperature, °F per 100 ft
2. Line capacity for other saturation temperatures Δt and equivalent lengths L_e

$$\text{Line capacity} = \text{Table capacity}\left(\frac{\text{Table } L_e}{\text{Actual } L_e} \times \frac{\text{Actual } \Delta t}{\text{Table } \Delta t}\right)^{0.55}$$

3. Saturation temperature Δt for other capacities and equivalent lengths L_e

$$\Delta t = \text{Table } \Delta t \left(\frac{\text{Actual } L_e}{\text{Table } L_e}\right)\left(\frac{\text{Actual capacity}}{\text{Table capacity}}\right)^{1.8}$$

4. Tons based on standard refrigerant cycle of 105°F liquid and saturated evaporator outlet temperature. Liquid tons based on 20°F evaporator temperature.
5. Thermophysical properties and viscosity data based on calculations from NIST REFPROP program Version 6.01.
6. For brazed Type L copper tubing larger than 1 1/8 in. OD for discharge or liquid service, see Safety Requirements section.
7. Values based on 105°F condensing temperature. Multiply table capacities by the following factors for other condensing temperatures.

Cond. Temp., °F	Suction Line	Discharge Line
80	1.246	0.870
90	1.150	0.922
100	1.051	0.974
110	0.948	1.009
120	0.840	1.026
130	0.723	1.043

Table 8.20 Suction, Discharge, and Liquid Line Capacities in Tons for Refrigerant 407C (Single- or High-Stage Applications)
[2018R, Ch 1, Tbl 9]

Line Size	Suction Lines ($\Delta t = 2°F$)						Discharge Lines ($\Delta t = 1°F$, $\Delta p = 3.3$ psi)[c]						Liquid Lines[a,c]		
	Saturated Suction Temperature, °F						Saturated Suction Temperature, °F								
Type L Copper, OD	−60	−40	−20	0	20	40	−60	−40	−20	0	20	40	Velocity = 100 fpm	$\Delta t = 1°F$ Drop	$\Delta t = 5°F$ Drop
	Corresponding Δp, psi/100 ft						Corresponding Δp, psi/100 ft								
	0.435	0.7	1.06	1.55	2.16	2.92	3.3	3.3	3.3	3.3	3.3	3.3		$\Delta p = 3.5$	$\Delta p = 16.9$
1/2	0.04	0.08	0.14	0.23	0.36	0.54	0.71	0.75	0.78	0.82	0.86	0.89	2.1	3.8	8.90
5/8	0.08	0.15	0.26	0.43	0.68	1.02	1.33	1.40	1.47	1.54	1.61	1.67	3.4	7.1	16.68
3/4	0.14	0.26	0.45	0.74	1.16	1.74	2.26	2.38	2.50	2.62	2.73	2.84	4.9	11.8	27.66
7/8	0.21	0.40	0.70	1.15	1.79	2.68	3.48	3.67	3.86	4.05	4.22	4.38	6.9	18.7	43.73
1 1/8	0.44	0.82	1.42	2.33	3.63	5.42	7.05	7.43	7.82	8.19	8.53	8.86	11.8	37.9	88.21
1 3/8	0.77	1.43	2.48	4.07	6.33	9.45	12.25	12.92	13.59	14.23	14.83	15.40	18.0	66.2	153.45
1 5/8	1.23	2.27	3.93	6.44	10.00	14.93	19.33	20.39	21.44	22.46	23.40	24.30	25.5	104.7	241.93
2 1/8	2.56	4.74	8.18	13.37	20.72	30.90	39.99	42.17	44.35	46.45	48.40	50.27	44.4	217.1	499.23
2 5/8	4.55	8.42	14.49	23.64	36.62	54.50	70.56	74.41	78.25	81.96	85.40	88.70	68.5	383.7	879.85
3 1/8	7.30	13.47	23.15	37.76	58.34	86.88	112.34	118.47	124.59	130.50	135.97	141.22	97.7	611.3	1401.50
3 5/8	10.90	20.08	34.44	56.15	86.64	128.89	166.39	175.47	184.54	193.29	201.39	209.17	132.2	907.9	2076.59
4 1/8	15.42	28.37	48.62	79.21	122.10	181.34	234.63	247.42	260.22	272.56	283.98	294.95	171.8	1281.5	2923.40

Table 8.20 Suction, Discharge, and Liquid Line Capacities in Tons for Refrigerant 407C (Single- or High-Stage Applications) [2018R, Ch 1, Tbl 9] ***(Continued)***

Line Size		Suction Lines (Δt = 2°F)						Discharge Lines (Δt = 1°F, Δp = 3.3 psi)[c]						Liquid Lines[a,c]		
		Saturated Suction Temperature, °F						Saturated Suction Temperature, °F								
		−60	−40	−20	0	20	40	−60	−40	−20	0	20	40	Velocity = 100 fpm	Δt = 1°F Drop	Δt = 5°F Drop
		Corresponding Δp, psi/100 ft						Corresponding Δp, psi/100 ft								
		0.435	0.7	1.06	1.55	2.16	2.92	3.3	3.3	3.3	3.3	3.3	3.3		Δp = 3.5	Δp = 16.9
Steel																
IPS	SCH															
3/8	80	0.04	0.07	0.11	0.18	0.27	0.40	0.52	0.55	0.57	0.60	0.63	0.65	2.0	2.9	6.4
1/2	80	0.07	0.13	0.22	0.35	0.54	0.79	1.02	1.07	1.13	1.18	1.23	1.28	3.4	5.7	12.6
3/4	80	0.16	0.30	0.50	0.80	1.22	1.79	2.29	2.42	2.54	2.66	2.78	2.88	6.2	12.8	28.4
1	80	0.32	0.58	0.98	1.57	2.38	3.50	4.50	4.74	4.99	5.22	5.44	5.65	10.3	25.1	55.6
1 1/4	80	0.69	1.25	2.10	3.37	5.12	7.50	9.63	10.15	10.68	11.18	11.65	12.10	18.4	53.7	118.9
1 1/2	80	1.06	1.91	3.21	5.13	7.79	11.44	14.66	15.46	16.26	17.03	17.74	18.43	25.4	82.0	181.1
2	40	2.49	4.46	7.47	11.93	18.13	26.57	34.04	35.89	37.75	39.54	41.20	42.79	48.1	190.3	420.6
2 1/2	40	3.97	7.11	11.90	19.01	28.83	42.25	54.25	57.21	60.16	63.02	65.66	68.19	68.6	303.2	669.0
3	40	7.04	12.59	21.05	33.59	50.94	74.66	95.76	100.99	106.21	111.24	115.90	120.38	106.0	535.7	1182.3
4	40	14.38	25.70	42.97	68.47	103.84	152.24	195.04	205.68	216.31	226.57	236.06	245.18	182.6	1092.0	2405.3
5	40	26.00	46.36	77.55	123.61	187.25	274.21	351.31	370.46	389.62	408.09	425.19	441.61	286.8	1969.0	4343.2
6	40	42.13	75.15	125.49	199.88	302.82	443.47	568.16	599.14	630.12	659.99	687.65	714.21	414.5	3184.3	7015.7
8	40	86.32	153.84	256.66	408.86	619.47	907.26	1162.36	1225.74	1289.12	1350.24	1406.83	1461.15	717.7	6514.5	14,334.3
10	40	156.54	278.57	464.86	739.58	1120.60	1638.95	2102.83	2217.49	2332.15	2442.72	2545.10	2643.38	1131.3	11,784.6	25,932.3
12	ID[b]	250.23	445.65	742.54	1183.19	1790.17	2622.17	3359.45	3542.64	3725.82	3902.46	4066.02	4223.03	1622.5	18,826.0	41,491.5
14	30	324.38	576.93	961.33	1529.58	2317.81	3395.13	4349.77	4586.95	4824.14	5052.85	5264.62	5467.92	1978.2	24,374.8	53,641.7
16	30	468.29	831.27	1385.24	2204.17	3340.17	4885.19	6258.81	6600.09	6941.37	7270.46	7575.17	7867.69	2620.4	35,126.4	77,305.8

Table 8.20 Suction, Discharge, and Liquid Line Capacities in Tons for Refrigerant 407C (Single- or High-Stage Applications) [2018R, Ch 1, Tbl 9] *(Continued)*

[a]Sizing shown is recommended where any gas generated in receiver must return up condensate line to condenser without restricting condensate flow. Water-cooled condensers, where receiver ambient temperature may be higher than refrigerant condensing temperature, fall into this category.

[b]Pipe inside diameter is same as nominal pipe size.

[c]System working pressures may exceed calculated allowable pressure in some listed type L annealed copper tubes at certain saturated condensing temperatures. Review maximum working pressure allowances for the pipe material used before selecting pipe sizes to ensure the pipe is properly rated for system working and design pressures.

Notes:

1. Table capacities are in tons of refrigeration.

   Δp = pressure drop from line friction, psi per 100 ft of equivalent line length

   Δt = corresponding change in saturation temperature, °F per 100 ft

2. Line capacity for other saturation temperatures Δt and equivalent lengths L_e

   $$\text{Line capacity} = \text{Table capacity}\left(\frac{\text{Table } L_e}{\text{Actual } L_e} \times \frac{\text{Actual } \Delta t}{\text{Table } \Delta t}\right)^{0.55}$$

3. Saturation temperature Δt for other capacities and equivalent lengths L_e

   $$\Delta t = \text{Table } \Delta t \left(\frac{\text{Actual } L_e}{\text{Table } L_e}\right)\left(\frac{\text{Actual capacity}}{\text{Table capacity}}\right)^{1.8}$$

4. Tons based on standard refrigerant cycle of 105°F liquid and saturated evaporator outlet temperature. Liquid tons based on 20°F evaporator temperature.
5. Thermophysical properties and viscosity data based on calculations from NIST REFPROP program Version 6.01.
6. For brazed Type L copper tubing larger than 2 1/8 in. OD for discharge or liquid service, see Safety Requirements section.
7. Values based on 105°F condensing temperature. Multiply table capacities by the following factors for other condensing temperatures.

Cond. Temp., °F	Suction Line	Discharge Line
80	1.163	0.787
90	1.099	0.872
100	1.033	0.957
110	0.966	1.036
120	0.896	1.109
130	0.824	1.182

Table 8.21 Suction, Discharge, and Liquid Line Capacities in Tons for Refrigerant 410A (Single- or High-Stage Applications)
[2018R, Ch 1, Tbl 8]

Line Size	Suction Lines ($\Delta t = 2°F$)						Discharge Lines ($\Delta t = 1°F$, $\Delta p = 4.75$ psi)[c]						Liquid Lines[a,c]		
	Saturated Suction Temperature, °F						Saturated Suction Temperature, °F								
Type L Copper, OD	–60	–40	–20	0	20	40	–60	–40	–20	0	20	40	Velocity = 100 fpm	$\Delta t = 1°F$ Drop	$\Delta t = 5°F$ Drop
	Corresponding Δp, psi/100 ft						Corresponding Δp, psi/100 ft								
	0.84	**1.27**	**1.85**	**2.57**	**3.46**	**4.5**	**4.75**	**4.75**	**4.75**	**4.75**	**4.75**	**4.75**		$\Delta p = 4.75$	$\Delta p = 23.3$
1/2	0.10	0.17	0.27	0.42	0.62	0.89	1.13	1.17	1.22	1.26	1.30	1.33	2.0	4.6	10.81
5/8	0.18	0.31	0.51	0.79	1.17	1.67	2.11	2.20	2.29	2.36	2.43	2.49	3.2	8.6	20.24
3/4	0.31	0.53	0.87	1.35	2.00	2.84	3.59	3.74	3.88	4.02	4.14	4.23	4.7	14.3	33.53
7/8	0.48	0.83	1.35	2.08	3.08	4.39	5.53	5.76	5.99	6.19	6.38	6.52	6.7	22.6	52.92
1 1/8	0.98	1.69	2.74	4.22	6.23	8.86	11.16	11.64	12.09	12.50	12.88	13.17	11.4	45.8	106.59
1 3/8	1.72	2.95	4.78	7.34	10.85	15.41	19.39	20.21	21.00	21.72	22.37	22.88	17.4	79.7	185.04
1 5/8	2.73	4.67	7.56	11.61	17.14	24.28	30.63	31.92	33.16	34.30	35.33	36.14	24.6	125.9	291.48
2 1/8	5.69	9.71	15.71	24.05	35.45	50.19	63.20	65.88	68.44	70.78	72.90	74.57	42.8	260.7	601.13
2 5/8	10.09	17.17	27.74	42.45	62.53	88.43	111.20	115.90	120.41	124.53	128.25	131.20	66.0	459.7	1056.39
3 1/8	16.15	27.44	44.24	67.77	99.53	140.83	177.12	184.62	191.80	198.36	204.29	208.98	94.2	733.0	1680.52
3 5/8	24.06	40.84	65.81	100.50	147.66	208.65									
4 1/8	33.98	57.58	92.66	141.61	208.22	293.70									

Table 8.21 Suction, Discharge, and Liquid Line Capacities in Tons for Refrigerant 410A (Single- or High-Stage Applications) [2018R, Ch 1, Tbl 8] *(Continued)*

Line Size		Suction Lines ($\Delta t = 2°F$)						Discharge Lines ($\Delta t = 1°F$, $\Delta p = 4.75$ psi)[c]						Liquid Lines[a,c]		
		Saturated Suction Temperature, °F						Saturated Suction Temperature, °F								
		−60	−40	−20	0	20	40	−60	−40	−20	0	20	40	Velocity = 100 fpm	$\Delta t = 1°F$ Drop	$\Delta t = 5°F$ Drop
		Corresponding Δp, psi/100 ft						Corresponding Δp, psi/100 ft								
		0.84	1.27	1.85	2.57	3.46	4.5	4.75	4.75	4.75	4.75	4.75	4.75		$\Delta p = 4.75$	$\Delta p = 23.3$
Steel																
IPS	SCH															
3/8	80	0.08	0.13	0.21	0.32	0.46	0.65	0.81	0.84	0.88	0.91	0.93	0.95	1.9	3.4	7.6
1/2	80	0.16	0.26	0.41	0.62	0.91	1.27	1.59	1.66	1.73	1.78	1.84	1.88	3.2	6.7	15.0
3/4	80	0.35	0.59	0.93	1.41	2.04	2.86	3.59	3.74	3.88	4.02	4.14	4.23	6.0	15.1	33.6
1	80	0.69	1.15	1.83	2.75	4.00	5.59	7.02	7.32	7.60	7.86	8.10	8.28	10.0	29.5	65.8
1 1/4	80	1.49	2.48	3.92	5.90	8.58	12.00	15.03	15.67	16.28	16.83	17.34	17.74	17.7	63.3	140.9
1 1/2	80	2.28	3.79	5.98	9.01	13.06	18.27	22.89	23.86	24.79	25.64	26.41	27.01	24.4	96.6	214.7
2	40	5.30	8.80	13.89	20.91	30.32	42.43	53.16	55.41	57.57	59.54	61.32	62.73	46.4	224.2	498.0
2 1/2	40	8.46	14.02	22.13	33.29	48.23	67.48	84.56	88.14	91.57	94.70	97.53	99.77	66.2	356.5	793.0
3	40	14.98	24.81	39.10	58.81	85.22	119.26	149.44	155.76	161.82	167.36	172.37	176.32	102.2	630.0	1398.4
4	40	30.58	50.56	79.68	119.77	173.76	242.63	304.02	316.88	329.21	340.47	350.66	358.70	176.1	1284.6	2851.7
5	40	55.19	91.27	143.84	216.23	312.97	437.56	548.97	572.20	594.46	614.79	633.19	647.71	276.5	2313.7	5137.0
6	40	89.34	147.57	232.61	349.71	506.16	707.69	886.76	924.29	960.25	993.09	1022.80	1046.26	399.6	3741.9	8308.9
8	40	182.90	301.82	475.80	715.45	1035.51	1445.92	1811.80	1888.48	1961.96	2029.05	2089.76	2137.68	692.0	7655.3	16,977.6
10	40	331.22	546.64	860.67	1292.44	1870.67	2615.83	3277.74	3416.46	3549.40	3670.77	3780.59	3867.29	1090.7	13,829.2	30,716.4
12	ID[b]	529.89	873.19	1376.89	2064.68	2992.85	4185.32	5244.38	5466.33	5679.03	5873.23	6048.94	6187.65	1564.3	22,125.4	49,074.9
14	30	685.86	1130.48	1779.99	2673.23	3875.08	5410.92	6780.14	7067.08	7342.06	7593.13	7820.29	7999.63	1907.2	28,647.5	63,445.8
16	30	988.28	1628.96	2569.05	3852.37	5575.79	7797.98	9771.20	10,184.73	10,581.02	10,942.85	11,270.23	11,528.68	2526.4	41,220.5	91,435.1

Table 8.21 Suction, Discharge, and Liquid Line Capacities in Tons for Refrigerant 410A (Single- or High-Stage Applications) [2018R, Ch 1, Tbl 8] *(Continued)*

[a] Sizing shown is recommended where any gas generated in receiver must return up condensate line to condenser without restricting condensate flow. Water-cooled condensers, where receiver ambient temperature may be higher than refrigerant condensing temperature, fall into this category.

[b] Pipe inside diameter is same as nominal pipe size.

[c] System working pressures may exceed calculated allowable pressure in some listed type L annealed copper tubes at certain saturated condensing temperatures. Review maximum working pressure allowances for the pipe material used before selecting pipe sizes to ensure the pipe is properly rated for system working and design pressures.

Notes:

1. Table capacities are in tons of refrigeration.

   Δp = pressure drop from line friction, psi per 100 ft of equivalent line length

   Δt = corresponding change in saturation temperature, °F per 100 ft

2. Line capacity for other saturation temperatures Δt and equivalent lengths L_e

$$\text{Line capacity} = \text{Table capacity}\left(\frac{\text{Table } L_e}{\text{Actual } L_e} \times \frac{\text{Actual } \Delta t}{\text{Table } \Delta t}\right)^{0.55}$$

3. Saturation temperature Δt for other capacities and equivalent lengths L_e

$$\Delta t = \text{Table } \Delta t \left(\frac{\text{Actual } L_e}{\text{Table } L_e}\right)\left(\frac{\text{Actual capacity}}{\text{Table capacity}}\right)^{1.8}$$

4. Tons based on standard refrigerant cycle of 105°F liquid and saturated evaporator outlet temperature. Liquid tons based on 20°F evaporator temperature.
5. Thermophysical properties and viscosity data based on calculations from NIST REFPROP program Version 6.01.
6. For brazed Type L copper tubing larger than 5/8 in. OD for discharge or liquid service, see Safety Requirements section.
7. Values based on 105°F condensing temperature. Multiply table capacities by the following factors for other condensing temperatures.

Cond. Temp., °F	Suction Line	Discharge Line
80	1.170	0.815
90	1.104	0.889
100	1.035	0.963
110	0.964	1.032
120	0.889	1.096
130	0.808	1.160

Table 8.22 Suction, Discharge, and Liquid Line Capacities in Tons for Refrigerant 507A (Single- or High-Stage Applications)

[2018R, Ch 1, Tbl 7]

Line Size	Suction Lines ($\Delta t = 2°F$)						Discharge Lines ($\Delta t = 1°F$, $\Delta p = 3.65$ psi)[c]						Liquid Lines[a,c]		
	Saturated Suction Temperature, °F						Saturated Suction Temperature, °F								
Type L Copper, OD	–60	–40	–20	0	20	40	–60	–40	–20	0	20	40	Velocity = 100 fpm	$\Delta t = 1°F$ Drop	$\Delta t = 5°F$ Drop
	Corresponding Δp, psi/100 ft						Corresponding Δp, psi/100 ft								
	0.67	1.01	1.46	2.02	2.71	3.6	3.65	3.65	3.65	3.65	3.65	3.65		$\Delta p = 3.65$	$\Delta p = 17.8$
1/2	0.05	0.09	0.15	0.24	0.37	0.55	0.55	0.60	0.65	0.70	0.75	0.79	1.3	2.5	5.96
5/8	0.09	0.17	0.28	0.45	0.69	1.02	1.04	1.13	1.22	1.31	1.40	1.48	2.0	4.7	11.13
3/4	0.16	0.28	0.48	0.77	1.17	1.74	1.76	1.92	2.08	2.24	2.38	2.52	3.0	7.9	18.45
7/8	0.25	0.44	0.74	1.18	1.81	2.68	2.72	2.97	3.22	3.45	3.68	3.89	4.2	12.5	29.14
1 1/8	0.50	0.90	1.51	2.40	3.66	5.41	5.48	5.99	6.49	6.96	7.41	7.84	7.2	25.2	58.74
1 3/8	0.88	1.57	2.63	4.18	6.35	9.41	9.54	10.42	11.28	12.11	12.90	13.63	11.0	44.0	102.09
1 5/8	1.39	2.48	4.17	6.61	10.04	14.84	15.04	16.43	17.79	19.09	20.34	21.50	15.6	69.5	161.04
2 1/8	2.91	5.17	8.65	13.70	20.76	30.66	31.03	33.90	36.70	39.40	41.96	44.36	27.1	144.0	331.97
2 5/8	5.15	9.14	15.27	24.19	36.62	54.04	54.69	59.74	64.68	69.43	73.96	78.18	41.8	254.3	584.28
3 1/8	8.24	14.61	24.40	38.55	58.29	85.90	86.95	94.98	102.84	110.39	117.58	124.29	59.6	405.2	929.27
3 5/8	12.27	21.75	36.22	57.15	86.47	127.52									
4 1/8	17.34	30.66	51.13	80.55	121.93	179.33									

Table 8.22 Suction, Discharge, and Liquid Line Capacities in Tons for Refrigerant 507A (Single- or High-Stage Applications) [2018R, Ch 1, Tbl 7] *(Continued)*

Line Size		Suction Lines ($\Delta t = 2$°F)						Discharge Lines ($\Delta t = 1$°F, $\Delta p = 3.65$ psi)[c]						Liquid Lines[a,c]		
		Saturated Suction Temperature, °F						Saturated Suction Temperature, °F								
		–60	–40	–20	0	20	40	–60	–40	–20	0	20	40	Velocity = 100 fpm	$\Delta t = 1$°F Drop	$\Delta t = 5$°F Drop
		Corresponding Δp, psi/100 ft						Corresponding Δp, psi/100 ft								
		0.67	1.01	1.46	2.02	2.71	3.6	3.65	3.65	3.65	3.65	3.65	3.65		$\Delta p = 3.65$	$\Delta p = 17.8$
Steel																
IPS	SCH															
3/8	80	0.04	0.07	0.12	0.18	0.27	0.39	0.40	0.43	0.47	0.51	0.54	0.57	1.2	1.9	4.2
1/2	80	0.08	0.14	0.23	0.35	0.53	0.77	0.78	0.86	0.93	0.99	1.06	1.12	2.1	3.7	8.3
3/4	80	0.18	0.31	0.51	0.80	1.20	1.74	1.76	1.93	2.09	2.24	2.39	2.52	3.8	8.4	18.7
1	80	0.35	0.61	1.01	1.57	2.34	3.41	3.45	3.77	4.08	4.38	4.67	4.94	6.3	16.4	36.6
1 1/4	80	0.76	1.32	2.16	3.36	5.02	7.32	7.39	8.08	8.74	9.39	10.00	10.57	11.2	35.2	78.4
1 1/2	80	1.16	2.01	3.29	5.12	7.65	11.15	11.26	12.30	13.32	14.30	15.23	16.10	15.5	53.8	119.4
2	40	2.70	4.68	7.65	11.89	17.76	25.88	26.15	28.56	30.93	33.20	35.36	37.38	29.4	124.8	276.7
2 1/2	40	4.31	7.45	12.18	18.93	28.24	41.17	41.59	45.43	49.19	52.80	56.24	59.45	41.9	198.9	440.6
3	40	7.63	13.19	21.54	33.45	49.90	72.75	73.50	80.29	86.93	93.32	99.39	105.06	64.6	351.5	777.9
4	40	15.57	26.88	43.92	68.12	101.75	148.00	149.53	163.33	176.85	189.84	202.20	213.74	111.4	714.9	1586.3
5	40	28.10	48.52	79.19	122.99	183.27	266.91	270.00	294.93	319.34	342.79	365.11	385.94	174.9	1290.8	2857.5
6	40	45.48	78.45	128.06	198.91	296.40	431.69	436.14	476.41	515.85	553.73	589.78	623.44	252.8	2087.5	4622.0
8	40	93.13	160.66	261.94	406.93	606.38	882.01	891.10	973.39	1053.96	1131.36	1205.02	1273.79	437.7	4270.8	9443.9
10	40	168.64	290.60	473.82	735.12	1095.44	1595.65	1612.10	1760.97	1906.72	2046.75	2180.00	2304.41	690.0	7715.1	17,086.7
12	ID[b]	269.75	464.87	758.01	1174.36	1752.56	2553.03	2579.36	2817.55	3050.75	3274.79	3488.00	3687.06	989.6	12,324.9	27,298.3
14	30	349.22	601.87	979.92	1520.49	2269.19	3300.65	3334.69	3642.64	3944.13	4233.77	4509.42	4766.76	1206.5	15,957.5	35,292.2
16	30	503.20	866.37	1414.32	2191.17	3265.09	4756.74	4805.79	5249.60	5684.09	6101.51	6498.76	6869.63	1598.2	22,996.2	50,861.5

Table 8.22 Suction, Discharge, and Liquid Line Capacities in Tons for Refrigerant 507A (Single- or High-Stage Applications) [2018R, Ch 1, Tbl 7] *(Continued)*

[a]Sizing shown is recommended where any gas generated in receiver must return up condensate line to condenser without restricting condensate flow. Water-cooled condensers, where receiver ambient temperature may be higher than refrigerant condensing temperature, fall into this category.

[b]Pipe inside diameter is same as nominal pipe size.

[c]System working pressures may exceed calculated allowable pressure in some listed type L annealed copper tubes at certain saturated condensing temperatures. Review maximum working pressure allowances for the pipe material used before selecting pipe sizes to ensure the pipe is properly rated for system working and design pressures.

Notes:

1. Table capacities are in tons of refrigeration.

   Δp = pressure drop from line friction, psi per 100 ft of equivalent line length

   Δt = corresponding change in saturation temperature, °F per 100 ft

2. Line capacity for other saturation temperatures Δt and equivalent lengths L_e

$$\text{Line capacity} = \text{Table capacity}\left(\frac{\text{Table } L_e}{\text{Actual } L_e} \times \frac{\text{Actual } \Delta t}{\text{Table } \Delta t}\right)^{0.55}$$

3. Saturation temperature Δt for other capacities and equivalent lengths L_e

$$\Delta t = \text{Table } \Delta t \left(\frac{\text{Actual } L_e}{\text{Table } L_e}\right)\left(\frac{\text{Actual capacity}}{\text{Table capacity}}\right)^{1.8}$$

4. Tons based on standard refrigerant cycle of 105°F liquid and saturated evaporator outlet temperature. Liquid tons based on 20°F evaporator temperature.
5. Thermophysical properties and viscosity data based on calculations from NIST REFPROP program Version 6.01.
6. For brazed Type L copper tubing larger than 1 1/8 in. OD for discharge or liquid service, see Safety Requirements section.
7. Values based on 105°F condensing temperature. Multiply table capacities by the following factors for other condensing temperatures.

Cond. Temp., °F	Suction Line	Discharge Line
80	1.267	0.873
90	1.163	0.924
100	1.055	0.975
110	0.944	1.005
120	0.826	1.014
130	0.701	1.024

Table 8.23 Suction, Discharge, and Liquid Line Capacities in Tons for Ammonia (Single- or High-Stage Applications) [2018R, Ch 2, Tbl 2]

Steel Line Size		Suction Lines ($\Delta t = 1°F$), Saturated Suction Temperature, °F					Discharge Lines	Steel Line Size		Liquid Lines	
IPS	SCH	−40 $\Delta p = 0.31$	−20 $\Delta p = 0.49$	0 $\Delta p = 0.73$	20 $\Delta p = 1.06$	40 $\Delta p = 1.46$	$\Delta t = 1°F$ $\Delta p = 2.95$	IPS	SCH	Velocity = 100 fpm	$\Delta p = 2.0$ psi $\Delta t = 0.7°F$
3/8	80	—	—	—	—	—	—	3/8	80	8.6	12.1
1/2	80	—	—	—	—	—	3.1	1/2	80	14.2	24.0
3/4	80	—	—	—	2.6	3.8	7.1	3/4	80	26.3	54.2
1	80	—	2.1	3.4	5.2	7.6	13.9	1	80	43.8	106.4
1 1/4	40	3.2	5.6	8.9	13.6	19.9	36.5	1 1/4	80	78.1	228.6
1 1/2	40	4.9	8.4	13.4	20.5	29.9	54.8	1 1/2	80	107.5	349.2
2	40	9.5	16.2	26.0	39.6	57.8	105.7	2	40	204.2	811.4
2 1/2	40	15.3	25.9	41.5	63.2	92.1	168.5	2 1/2	40	291.1	1292.6
3	40	27.1	46.1	73.5	111.9	163.0	297.6	3	40	449.6	2287.8
4	40	55.7	94.2	150.1	228.7	333.0	606.2	4	40	774.7	4662.1
5	40	101.1	170.4	271.1	412.4	600.9	1095.2	5	40	—	—
6	40	164.0	276.4	439.2	667.5	971.6	1771.2	6	40	—	—
8	40	337.2	566.8	901.1	1366.6	1989.4	3623.0	8	40	—	—
10	40	611.6	1027.2	1634.3	2474.5	3598.0	—	10	40	—	—
12	ID*	981.6	1644.5	2612.4	3963.5	5764.6	—	12	ID*	—	—

Notes:

1. Table capacities are in tons of refrigeration.

   Δp = pressure drop due to line friction, psi per 100 ft of equivalent line length

   Δt = corresponding change in saturation temperature, °F per 100 ft

2. Line capacity for other saturation temperatures Δt and equivalent lengths L_e

$$\text{Line capacity} = \text{Table capacity}\left(\frac{\text{Table } L_e}{\text{Actual } L_e} \times \frac{\text{Actual } \Delta t}{\text{Table } \Delta t}\right)^{0.55}$$

3. Saturation temperature Δt for other capacities and equivalent lengths L_e

$$\Delta t = \text{Table } \Delta t \left(\frac{\text{Actual } L_e}{\text{Table } L_e}\right)\left(\frac{\text{Actual capacity}}{\text{Table capacity}}\right)^{1.8}$$

4. Values based on 90°F condensing temperature. Multiply table capacities by the following factors for other condensing temperatures:

Condensing Temperature, °F	Suction Lines	Discharge Lines
70	1.05	0.78
80	1.02	0.89
90	1.00	1.00
100	0.98	1.11

5. Discharge and liquid line capacities based on 20°F suction. Evaporator temperature is 0°F. The capacity is affected less than 3% when applied from −40 to +40°F extremes.

* The inside diameter of the pipe is the same as the nominal pipe size.

Table 8.24 Liquid Ammonia Line Capacities (Capacity in Tons of Refrigeration, Except as Noted) [2018R, Ch 2, Tbl 3]

Nominal Size, in.	Pumped Liquid Overfeed Ratio			High-Pressure Liquid at 3 psi[a]	Hot-Gas Defrost[a]	Equalizer High Side[b]	Thermosiphon Lubricant Cooling Lines Gravity Flow,[c] 1000 Btu/h		
	3:1	4:1	5:1				Supply	Return	Vent
1/2	10	7.5	6	30	—	—	—	—	—
3/4	22	16.5	13	69	9-15	50	—	—	—
1	43	32.5	26	134	16-27	100	—	—	—
1 1/4	93.5	70	56	286	28-38	150	—	—	—
1 1/2	146	110	87.5	439	39-64	225	200	120	203
2	334	250	200	1016	65-107	300	470	300	362
2 1/2	533	400	320	1616	108-152	500	850	530	638
3	768	576	461	2886	153-246	1000	1312	870	1102
4	1365	1024	819	—	247-411	2000	2261	1410	2000
5	—	—	—	—	—	—	3550	2214	3624
6	—	—	—	—	—	—	5130	3200	6378
8	—	—	—	—	—	—	8874	5533	11596

Source: Wile (1977).

[a] Rating for hot-gas branch lines under 100 ft with minimum inlet pressure of 105 psig, defrost pressure of 70 psig, and –20°F evaporators designed for a 10°F temperature differential.

[b] Line sizes based on experience using total system evaporator tons.

[c] From Frick Co. (2004). Values for line sizes above 4 in. are extrapolated.

Table 8.25 Minimum Refrigeration Capacity in Tons for Oil Entrainment up Suction Risers (Type L Copper Tubing)
[2018R, Ch 1, Tbl 20]

Refrigerant	Saturated Suction Temp., °F	Suction Gas Temp., °F	Pipe OD, in. 1/2	5/8	3/4	7/8	1 1/8	1 3/8	1 5/8	2 1/8	2 5/8	3 1/8	3 5/8	4 1/8
			Area, in^2											
			0.146	0.233	0.348	0.484	0.825	1.256	1.780	3.094	4.770	6.812	9.213	11.970
22	−40.0	−30.0	0.067	0.119	0.197	0.298	0.580	0.981	1.52	3.03	5.20	8.12	11.8	16.4
		−10.0	0.065	0.117	0.194	0.292	0.570	0.963	1.49	2.97	5.11	7.97	11.6	16.1
		10.0	0.066	0.118	0.195	0.295	0.575	0.972	1.50	3.00	5.15	8.04	11.7	16.3
	−20.0	−10.0	0.087	0.156	0.258	0.389	0.758	1.28	1.98	3.96	6.80	10.6	15.5	21.5
		10.0	0.085	0.153	0.253	0.362	0.744	1.26	1.95	3.88	6.67	10.4	15.2	21.1
		30.0	0.086	0.154	0.254	0.383	0.747	1.26	1.95	3.90	6.69	10.4	15.2	21.1
	0.0	10.0	0.111	0.199	0.328	0.496	0.986	1.63	2.53	5.04	8.66	13.5	19.7	27.4
		30.0	0.108	0.194	0.320	0.484	0.942	1.59	2.46	4.92	8.45	13.2	19.2	26.7
		50.0	0.109	0.195	0.322	0.486	0.946	1.60	2.47	4.94	8.48	13.2	19.3	26.8
	20.0	30.0	0.136	0.244	0.403	0.608	1.18	2.00	3.10	6.18	10.6	16.6	24.2	33.5
		50.0	0.135	0.242	0.399	0.603	1.17	1.99	3.07	6.13	10.5	16.4	24.0	33.3
		70.0	0.135	0.242	0.400	0.605	1.18	1.99	3.08	6.15	10.6	16.5	24.0	33.3
	40.0	50.0	0.167	0.300	0.495	0.748	1.46	2.46	3.81	7.60	13.1	20.4	29.7	41.3
		70.0	0.165	0.296	0.488	0.737	1.44	2.43	3.75	7.49	12.9	20.1	29.3	40.7
		90.0	0.165	0.296	0.488	0.738	1.44	2.43	3.76	7.50	12.9	20.1	29.3	40.7

Table 8.25 Minimum Refrigeration Capacity in Tons for Oil Entrainment up Suction Risers (Type L Copper Tubing)
[2018R, Ch 1, Tbl 20] ***(Continued)***

Refrig-erant	Saturated Suction Temp., °F	Suction Gas Temp., °F	Pipe OD, in.											
			1/2	5/8	3/4	7/8	1 1/8	1 3/8	1 5/8	2 1/8	2 5/8	3 1/8	3 5/8	4 1/8
			Area, in^2											
			0.146	**0.233**	**0.348**	**0.484**	**0.825**	**1.256**	**1.780**	**3.094**	**4.770**	**6.812**	**9.213**	**11.970**
134a	0.0	10.0	0.089	0.161	0.259	0.400	0.78	1.32	2.03	4.06	7.0	10.9	15.9	22.1
		30.0	0.075	0.135	0.218	0.336	0.66	1.11	1.71	3.42	5.9	9.2	13.4	18.5
		50.0	0.072	0.130	0.209	0.323	0.63	1.07	1.64	3.28	5.6	8.8	12.8	17.8
	10.0	20.0	0.101	0.182	0.294	0.453	0.88	1.49	2.31	4.61	7.9	12.4	18.0	25.0
		40.0	0.084	0.152	0.246	0.379	0.74	1.25	1.93	3.86	6.6	10.3	15.1	20.9
		60.0	0.081	0.147	0.237	0.366	0.71	1.21	1.87	3.73	6.4	10.0	14.6	20.2
	20.0	30.0	0.113	0.205	0.331	0.510	0.99	1.68	2.60	5.19	8.9	13.9	20.3	28.2
		50.0	0.095	0.172	0.277	0.427	0.83	1.41	2.17	4.34	7.5	11.6	17.0	23.6
		70.0	0.092	0.166	0.268	0.413	0.81	1.36	2.10	4.20	7.2	11.3	16.4	22.8
	30.0	40.0	0.115	0.207	0.335	0.517	1.01	1.70	2.63	5.25	9.0	14.1	20.5	28.5
		60.0	0.107	0.193	0.311	0.480	0.94	1.58	2.44	4.88	8.4	13.1	19.1	26.5
		80.0	0.103	0.187	0.301	0.465	0.91	1.53	2.37	4.72	8.1	12.7	18.5	25.6
	40.0	50.0	0.128	0.232	0.374	0.577	1.12	1.90	2.94	5.87	10.1	15.7	22.9	31.8
		70.0	0.117	0.212	0.342	0.528	1.03	1.74	2.69	5.37	9.2	14.4	21.0	29.1
		90.0	0.114	0.206	0.332	0.512	1.00	1.69	2.61	5.21	8.9	14.0	20.4	28.3

Notes:
1. Refrigeration capacity in tons is based on 90°F liquid temperature and superheat as indicated by listed temperature. For other liquid line temperatures, use correction factors in table at right.
2. Values computed using ISO 32 mineral oil for R-22. R-134a computed using ISO 32 ester-based oil.

Refrigerant	Liquid Temperature, °F								
	50	**60**	**70**	**80**	**100**	**110**	**120**	**130**	**140**
22	1.17	1.14	1.10	1.06	0.98	0.94	0.89	0.85	0.80
134a	1.26	1.20	1.13	1.07	0.94	0.87	0.80	0.74	0.67

Table 8.26 Minimum Refrigeration Capacity in Tons for Oil Entrainment up Hot-Gas Risers (Type L Copper Tubing)
[2018R, Ch 1, Tbl 19]

Refrigerant	Saturated Temp., °F	Discharge Gas Temp., °F	Pipe OD, in.											
			1/2	5/8	3/4	7/8	1 1/8	1 3/8	1 5/8	2 1/8	2 5/8	3 1/8	3 5/8	4 1/8
			Area, in^2											
			0.146	0.233	0.348	0.484	0.825	1.256	1.780	3.094	4.770	6.812	9.213	11.970
22	80.0	110.0	0.235	0.421	0.695	1.05	2.03	3.46	5.35	10.7	18.3	28.6	41.8	57.9
		140.0	0.223	0.399	0.659	0.996	1.94	3.28	5.07	10.1	17.4	27.1	39.6	54.9
		170.0	0.215	0.385	0.635	0.960	1.87	3.16	4.89	9.76	16.8	26.2	38.2	52.9
	90.0	120.0	0.242	0.433	0.716	1.06	2.11	3.56	5.50	11.0	18.9	29.5	43.0	59.6
		150.0	0.226	0.406	0.671	1.01	1.97	3.34	5.16	10.3	17.7	27.6	40.3	55.9
		180.0	0.216	0.387	0.540	0.956	1.88	3.18	4.92	9.82	16.9	26.3	38.4	53.3
	100.0	130.0	0.247	0.442	0.730	1.10	2.15	3.83	5.62	11.2	19.3	30.1	43.9	60.8
		160.0	0.231	0.414	0.884	1.03	2.01	3.40	5.26	10.5	18.0	28.2	41.1	57.0
		190.0	0.220	0.394	0.650	0.982	1.91	3.24	3.00	9.96	17.2	26.8	39.1	54.2
	110.0	140.0	0.251	0.451	0.744	1.12	2.19	3.70	5.73	11.4	19.6	30.6	44.7	62.0
		170.0	0.235	0.421	0.693	1.05	2.05	3.46	3.35	10.7	18.3	28.6	41.8	57.9
		200.0	0.222	0.399	0.658	0.994	1.94	3.28	5.06	10.1	17.4	27.1	39.5	54.8
	120.0	150.0	0.257	0.460	0.760	1.15	2.24	3.78	5.85	11.7	20.0	31.3	45.7	63.3
		180.0	0.239	0.428	0.707	1.07	2.08	3.51	5.44	10.8	18.6	29.1	42.4	58.9
		210.0	0.225	0.404	0.666	1.01	1.96	3.31	5.12	10.2	17.6	27.4	40.0	55.5

Table 8.26 Minimum Refrigeration Capacity in Tons for Oil Entrainment up Hot-Gas Risers (Type L Copper Tubing) [2018R, Ch 1, Tbl 19] ***(Continued)***

Refrigerant	Saturated Temp., °F	Discharge Gas Temp., °F	Pipe OD, in.											
			1/2	5/8	3/4	7/8	1 1/8	1 3/8	1 5/8	2 1/8	2 5/8	3 1/8	3 5/8	4 1/8
			Area, in^2											
			0.146	**0.233**	**0.348**	**0.484**	**0.825**	**1.256**	**1.780**	**3.094**	**4.770**	**6.812**	**9.213**	**11.970**
134a	80.0	110.0	0.199	0.360	0.581	0.897	1.75	2.96	4.56	9.12	15.7	24.4	35.7	49.5
		140.0	0.183	0.331	0.535	0.825	1.61	2.72	4.20	8.39	14.4	22.5	32.8	45.6
		170.0	0.176	0.318	0.512	0.791	1.54	2.61	4.02	8.04	13.8	21.6	31.4	43.6
	90.0	120.0	0.201	0.364	0.587	0.906	1.76	2.99	4.61	9.21	15.8	24.7	36.0	50.0
		150.0	0.184	0.333	0.538	0.830	1.62	2.74	4.22	8.44	14.5	22.6	33.0	45.8
		180.0	0.177	0.320	0.516	0.796	1.55	2.62	4.05	8.09	13.9	21.7	31.6	43.9
	100.0	130.0	0.206	0.372	0.600	0.926	1.80	3.05	4.71	9.42	16.2	25.2	36.8	51.1
		160.0	0.188	0.340	0.549	0.848	1.65	2.79	4.31	8.62	14.8	23.1	33.7	46.8
		190.0	0.180	0.326	0.526	0.811	1.58	2.67	4.13	8.25	14.2	22.1	32.2	44.8
	110.0	140.0	0.209	0.378	0.610	0.942	1.83	3.10	4.79	9.57	16.5	25.7	37.4	52.0
		170.0	0.191	0.346	0.558	0.861	1.68	2.84	4.38	8.76	15.0	23.5	34.2	47.5
		200.0	0.183	0.331	0.534	0.824	1.61	2.72	4.19	8.38	14.4	22.5	32.8	45.5
	120.0	150.0	0.212	0.383	0.618	0.953	1.86	3.14	4.85	9.69	16.7	26.0	37.9	52.6
		180.0	0.194	0.351	0.566	0.873	1.70	2.88	4.44	8.88	15.3	23.8	34.7	48.2
		210.0	0.184	0.334	0.538	0.830	1.62	2.74	4.23	8.44	14.5	22.6	33.0	45.8

Notes:
1. Refrigeration capacity in tons based on saturated suction temperature of 20°F with 15°F superheat at indicated saturated condensing temperature with 15°F subcooling. For other saturated suction temperatures with 15°F superheat, use correction factors in the table at right.
2. Table computed using ISO 32 mineral oil for R-22, and ISO 32 ester-based oil for R-134a.

Refrigerant	Saturated Suction Temperature, °F			
	−40	**−20**	**0**	**+40**
22	0.92	0.95	0.97	1.02
134a	—	—	0.96	1.04

Lubricants In Refrigerant Systems

Oil in refrigerant compressors lubricates, acts as coolant, and seals the suction from the discharge side. Oil mixes well with hydrocarbon refrigerants at higher temperatures; miscibility is reduced as temperature lowers. Oil leaves the compressor and dissolves into the refrigerant in the condenser, and passes through the liquid line to the evaporator where it separates. In higher temperature systems, it returns by gravity or is dragged by the returning vapor. Low temperature halocarbon systems need an oil separator at the compressor discharge. Oil return up vertical piping requires significant refrigerant velocity. Lubricants are generally not miscible with ammonia and separate easily out of the liquid. Oil separators at the discharge of compressors are essential. Oil must be periodically or continuously removed and returned to the compressor.

There is no ideal lubricant. For halocarbon refrigerants, there are mineral lubricants, both naphthenic and paraffinic, and synthetic lubricants, ester and glycol. Viscosity grades required vary with the temperature and the solubility of the refrigerant in the lubricant. Additives are used to enhance lubricant properties or impact new characteristics. They may be polar compounds, polymers, or compounds containing active elements such as sulfur or phosphorus. Lubricants should be dry; normally almost all hydrocarbon lubricants have a moisture content of about 30 ppm. Synthetic lubricants polyalkylene glycols (PAGs) are used commonly in automobile R-134a systems; polyalphaolefins (PAOs) are mainly used an immiscible oil in ammonia systems; polyol esters are used with HFC refrigerants in all types of compressors. Low pour point is essential for oils in ammonia systems.

When retrofitting to a new refrigerant, follow the recommendations of the equipment manufacturer on the lubricants that are suitable for use.

Mixing lubricants can cause serious problems; to extend equipment life, it is important to use lubricants approved or specified by the system or compressor manufacturer.

Table 8.27 Secondary Coolant Performance Comparisons [2018R, Ch 13, Tbl 1]

Secondary Coolant	Concentration (by Weight), %	Freeze Point, °F	gpm/ton[a]	Pressure Drop,[b] psi	Heat Transfer Coefficient[c] h_i, Btu/h·ft²·°F
Propylene glycol	39	−5.1	2.56	2.91	205
Ethylene glycol	38	−6.9	2.76	2.38	406
Methanol	26	−5.3	2.61	2.05	473
Sodium chloride	23	−5.1	2.56	2.30	558
Calcium chloride	22	−7.8	2.79	2.42	566
Aqua ammonia	14	−7.0	2.48	2.44	541
Trichloroethylene	100	−123	7.44	2.11	432
d-Limonene	100	−142	6.47	1.48	321
Methylene chloride	100	−142	6.39	1.86	58
R-11	100	−168	7.61	2.08	428

[a]Based on inlet secondary coolant temperature at pump of 25°F.

[b]Based on one length of 16 ft tube with 1.06 in. ID and use of Moody Chart (1944) for an average velocity of 7 fps. Input/output losses equal one Vel. $H_D(V^2\rho/2g)$ for 7 fps velocity. Evaluations are at a bulk temperature of 20°F and a temperature range of 10°F.

[c]Based on curve fit equation for Kern's (1950) adaptation of Sieder and Tate's (1936) heat transfer equation using 16 ft tube for $L/D = 181$ and film temperature of 5°F lower than average bulk temperature with 7 fps velocity.

Table 8.28 Relative Pumping Energy Required* [2018R, Ch 13, Tbl 3]

Secondary Coolant	Energy Factor
Aqua ammonia	1.000
Methanol	1.078
Propylene glycol	1.142
Ethylene glycol	1.250
Sodium chloride	1.295
Calcium chloride	1.447
d-Limonene	2.406
Methylene chloride	3.735
Trichloroethylene	4.787
R-11	5.022

*Based on same pump pressure, refrigeration load, 20°F average temperature, 10°F range, and freezing point (for water-based secondary coolants) 20 to 23°F below lowest secondary coolant temperature.

9. REFRIGERANT SAFETY

(For more guidance, see ANSI/ASHRAE Standard 15, *Safety Standard for Refrigeration Systems*, and ANSI/ASHRAE Standard 34, *Designation and Safety Classification of Refrigerants*)

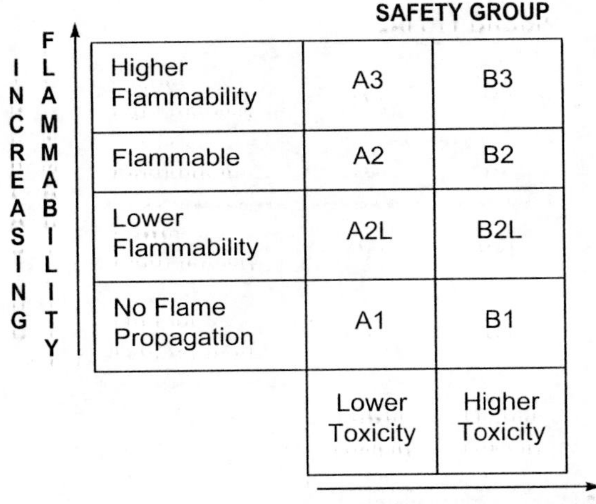

Figure 9.1 Refrigerant Safety Group Classification [Std 34-2019, Fig 6-1]

Refrigerant Safety

Table 9.1 **Refrigerant Data and Safety Classifications** [Std 34-2019, Tbl 4-1]

Refrigerant No.	Chemical Name[a,b]	Chemical Formula[a]	OEL[f], ppm v/v	Safety Group	RCL[c] (ppm v/v)	RCL[c] (lb/Mcf)	RCL[c] (g/m^3)	Highly Toxic or Toxic[d] Under Code Classification
Methane Series								
11	trichlorofluoromethane	CCl_3F	1000	A1	1100	0.39	6.2	Neither
12	dichlorodifluoromethane	CCl_2F_2	1000	A1	18,000	5.6	90	Neither
12B1	bromochlorodifluoromethane	$CBrClF_2$						Neither
13	chlorotrifluoromethane	$CClF_3$	1000	A1				Neither
13B1	bromotrifluoromethane	$CBrF_3$	1000	A1				Neither
14[e]	tetrafluoromethane (carbon tetrafluoride)	CF_4	1000	A1	110,000	25	400	Neither
21	dichlorofluoromethane	$CHCl_2F$		B1				Toxic
22	chlorodifluoromethane	$CHClF_2$	1000	A1	59,000	13	210	Neither
23	trifluoromethane	CHF_3	1000	A1	41,000	7.3	120	Neither
30	dichloromethane (methylene chloride)	CH_2Cl_2		B1				Neither
31	chlorofluoromethane	CH_2ClF						Neither
32	difluoromethane (methylene fluoride)	CH_2F_2	1000	A2L	36,000	4.8	77	Neither
40	chloromethane (methyl chloride)	CH_3Cl		B2				Toxic
41	fluoromethane (methyl fluoride)	CH_3F						Neither
50	methane	CH_4	1000	A3				Neither
Ethane Series								
113	1,1,2-trichloro-1,2,2-trifluoroethane	CCl_2FCClF_2	1000	A1	2600	1.2	20	Neither
114	1,2-dichloro-1,1,2,2-tetrafluoroethane	$CClF_2CClF_2$	1000	A1	20,000	8.7	140	Neither
115[g]	chloropentafluoroethane	$CClF_2CF_3$	1000	A1	120,000	47	760	Neither
116[e]	hexafluoroethane	CF_3CF_3	1000	A1	97,000	34	550	Neither
123	2,2-dichloro-1,1,1-trifluoroethane	$CHCl_2CF_3$	50	B1	9100	3.5	57	Neither

Table 9.1 Refrigerant Data and Safety Classifications [Std 34-2019, Tbl 4-1] ***(Continued)***

Refrigerant No.	Chemical Name[a,b]	Chemical Formula[a]	OEL[f], ppm v/v	Safety Group	RCL[c] (ppm v/v)	RCL[c] (lb/Mcf)	RCL[c] (g/m^3)	Highly Toxic or Toxic[d] Under Code Classification
124	2-chloro-1,1,1,2-tetrafluoroethane	$CHClFCF_3$	1000	A1	10,000	3.5	56	Neither
125[e]	pentafluoroethane	CHF_2CF_3	1000	A1	75,000	23	370	Neither
134a	1,1,1,2-tetrafluoroethane	CH_2FCF_3	1000	A1	50,000	13	210	Neither
141b	1,1-dichloro-1-fluoroethane	CH_3CCl_2F	500		2600	0.78	12	Neither
142b	1-chloro-1,1-difluoroethane	CH_3CClF_2	1000	A2	20,000	5.1	83	Neither
143a	1,1,1-trifluoroethane	CH_3CF_3	1000	A2L	21,000	4.5	70	Neither
152a	1,1-difluoroethane	CH_3CHF_2	1000	A2	12,000	2.0	32	Neither
170	ethane	CH_3CH_3	1000	A3	7000	0.54	8.7	Neither
Ethers								
E170	methoxymethane (dimethyl ether)	CH_3OCH_3	1000	A3	8500	1.0	16	Neither
Propane								
218[e]	octafluoropropane	$CF_3CF_2CF_3$	1000	A1	90,000	43	690	Neither
227ea[e]	1,1,1,2,3,3,3-heptafluoropropane	CF_3CHFCF_3	1000	A1	84,000	36	580	Neither
236fa	1,1,1,3,3,3-hexafluoropropane	$CF_3CH_2CF_3$	1000	A1	55,000	21	340	Neither
245fa	1,1,1,3,3-pentafluoropropane	$CHF_2CH_2CF_3$	300	B1	34,000	12	190	Neither
290	propane	$CH_3CH_2CH_3$	1000	A3	5300	0.56	9.5	Neither
Cyclic Organic Compounds								
C318	octafluorocyclobutane	$-(CF_2)_4-$	1000	A1	80,000	41	660	Neither
Miscellaneous Organic Compounds								
hydrocarbons								
600	butane	$CH_3CH_2CH_2CH_3$	1000	A3	1000	0.15	2.4	Neither
600a	2-methylpropane (isobutane)	$CH(CH_3)_2CH_3$	1000	A3	4000	0.59	9.6	Neither

Table 9.1 Refrigerant Data and Safety Classifications [Std 34-2019, Tbl 4-1] ***(Continued)***

Refrigerant No.	Chemical Name[a,b]	Chemical Formula[a]	OEL[f], ppm v/v	Safety Group	RCL[c] (ppm v/v)	RCL[c] (lb/Mcf)	RCL[c] (g/m^3)	Highly Toxic or Toxic[d] Under Code Classification
601	pentane	$CH_3CH_2CH_2CH_2CH_3$	600	A3	1000	0.18	2.9	Neither
601a	2-methylbutane (isopentane)	$(CH_3)_2CHCH_2CH_3$	600	A3	1000	0.18	2.9	Neither
oxygen compounds								
610	ethoxyethane (ethyl ether)	$CH_3CH_2OCH_2CH_3$	400					Neither
611	methyl formate	$HCOOCH_3$	100	B2				Neither
sulfur compounds								
620	(Reserved for future assignment)							
Nitrogen Compounds								
630	methanamine (methyl amine)	CH_3NH_2						Toxic
631	ethanamine (ethyl amine)	$CH_3CH_2(NH_2)$						Neither
Inorganic Compounds								
702	hydrogen	H_2		A3				Neither
704	helium	He		A1				Neither
717	ammonia	NH_3	25	B2L	320	0.014	0.22	Neither
718	water	H_2O		A1				Neither
720	neon	Ne		A1				Neither
728	nitrogen	N_2		A1				Neither
732	oxygen	O_2						Neither
740	argon	Ar		A1				Neither
744	carbon dioxide	CO_2	5000	A1	30,000	3.4	54	Neither
744A	nitrous oxide	N_2O						Neither
764	sulfur dioxide	SO_2		B1				Neither

Table 9.1 Refrigerant Data and Safety Classifications [Std 34-2019, Tbl 4-1] ***(Continued)***

Refrigerant No.	Chemical Name[a,b]	Chemical Formula[a]	OEL[f], ppm v/v	Safety Group	RCL[c] (ppm v/v)	RCL[c] (lb/Mcf)	RCL[c] (g/m^3)	Highly Toxic or Toxic[d] Under Code Classification
Unsaturated Organic Compounds								
1130(E)	trans-1,2-dichloroethene	CHCl=CHCl	200	B1	100	0.25	4	Neither
1132a	1,1-difluoroethylene	CF_2=CH_2	500	A2	13,000	2.0	33	Neither
1150	ethene (ethylene)	CH_2=CH_2	200	A3				Neither
1224yd(Z)	(Z)-1-chloro-2,3,3,3-tetrafluoropropene	CF3CF=CHCl	1000	A1	60,000	23	360	Neither
1233zd(E)	trans-1-chloro-3,3,3-trifluoro-1-propene	CF_3CH=CHCl	800	A1	16,000	5.3	85	Neither
1234yf	2,3,3,3-tetrafluoro-1-propene	CF_3CF=CH_2	500	A2L	16,000	4.7	75	Neither
1234ze(E)	trans-1,3,3,3-tetrafluoro-1-propene	CF_3CH=CFH	800	A2L	16,000	4.7	75	Neither
1270	propene (propylene)	CH_3CH=CH_2	500	A3	1000	0.11	1.7	Neither
1336mzz(E)	trans-1,1,1,4,4,4-hexafluoro-2-butene	CF_3CH=CHCF_3	400	A1	7200	3.0	48	Neither
1336mzz(Z)	cis-1,1,1,4,4,4-hexaflouro-2-butene	CF_3CHCHCF_3	500	A1	13,000	5.4	87	Neither

a. The chemical name and chemical formula are not part of this standard. Chemical names conform to IUPAC nomenclature[6,7] except where shortened, unambiguous names are used following ANSI/ASHRAE Standard 34 convention.

b. The preferred chemical name is followed by the popular name in parentheses.

c. Data taken from J.M. Calm, "ARTI Refrigerant Database," Air- Conditioning and Refrigeration Technology Institute (ARTI), Arlington, VA, July 2001; J.M. Calm, "Toxicity Data to Determine Refrigerant Concentration Limits," Report DE/CE 23810-110, Air- Conditioning and Refrigeration Technology Institute (ARTI), Arlington, VA, September 2000; J.M. Calm, "The Toxicity of Refrigerants," *Proceedings of the 1996 International Refrigeration Conference*, Purdue University, West Lafayette, IN, pp. 157–62, 1996; D.P. Wilson and R.G. Richard, "Determination of Refrigerant Lower Flammability Limits (LFLs) in Compliance with Proposed Addendum p to ANSI/ASHRAE Standard 34-1992 (1073-RP)," *ASHRAE Transactions* 2002, 108(2); D.W. Coombs, "HFC-32 Assessment of Anesthetic Potency in Mice by Inhalation," Huntingdon Life Sciences Ltd., Huntingdon, Cambridgeshire, England, February 2004 and amendment February 2006; D.W. Coombs, "HFC-22 An Inhalation Study to Investigate the Cardiac Sensitization Potential in the Beagle Dog," Huntingdon Life Sciences Ltd., Huntingdon, Cambridgeshire, England, August 2005; and other toxicity studies.

d. *Highly toxic*, *toxic*, or *neither*, where *highly toxic* and *toxic* are as defined in the *International Fire Code*, *Uniform Fire Code*, and OSHA regulations, and *neither* identifies those refrigerants having lesser toxicity than either of those groups[1,2,3].

e. At locations with altitudes higher than 4920 ft, the ODL and RCL shall be 69,100 ppm.

f. The OELs are eight-hour TWAs, as defined in Section 3, unless otherwise noted; a "C" designation denotes a ceiling limit.

g. At locations with altitudes higher than 3300 ft but below or equal to 4920 ft, the ODL and RCL shall be 112,000 ppm, and at altitudes higher than 4920 ft, the ODL and RCL shall be 69,100 ppm.

Table 9.2 Data and Safety Classifications for Refrigerant Blends [Std 34-2019, Tbl 4-2]

Refrigerant No.	Composition (Mass%)	Composition Tolerances	OEL[h], ppm v/v	Safety Group	RCL[a] (ppm v/v)	RCL[a] (lb/Mcf)	RCL[a] (g/m³)	Highly Toxic or Toxic[f] Under Code Classification
Zeotropes								
400	R-12/114 (must be specified)			A1				Neither
	(50.0/50.0)		1000	A1	28,000	10	160	
	(60.0/40.0)		1000	A1	30,000	11	170	
401A	R-22/152a/124 (53.0/13.0/34.0)	(±2.0/+0.5, −1.5/±1.0)	1000	A1	27,000	6.6	110	Neither
401B	R-22/152a/124 (61.0/11.0/28.0)	(±2.0/+0.5, −1.5/±1.0)	1000	A1	30,000	7.2	120	Neither
401C	R-22/152a/124 (33.0/15.0/52.0)	(±2.0/+0.5, −1.5/±1.0)	1000	A1	20,000	5.2	84	Neither
402A	R-125/290/22 (60.0/2.0/38.0)	(±2.0/+0.1, −1.0/±2.0)	1000	A1	66,000	17	270	Neither
402B	R-125/290/22 (38.0/2.0/60.0)	(±2.0/+0.1, −1.0/±2.0)	1000	A1	63,000	15	240	Neither
403A	R-290/22/218 (5.0/75.0/20.0)	(+0.2, −2.0/±2.0/±2.0)	1000	A2	33,000	7.6	120	Neither
403B[g]	R-290/22/218 (5.0/56.0/39.0)	(+0.2, −2.0/±2.0/±2.0)	1000	A1	70,000	18	290	Neither
404A[i]	R-125/143a/134a (44.0/52.0/4.0)	(±2.0/±1.0/±2.0)	1000	A1	130,000	31	500	Neither
405A	R-22/152a/142b/C318 (45.0/7.0/5.5/42.5)	Individual components = (±2.0/±1.0/±1.0/±2.0); sum of R-152a and R-142b = (+0.0, −2.0)	1000		57,000	16	260	Neither
406A	R-22/600a/142b (55.0/4.0/41.0)	(±2.0/±1.0/±1.0)	1000	A2	21,000	4.7	25	Neither
407A[g]	R-32/125/134a (20.0/40.0/40.0)	(±2.0/±2.0/±2.0)	1000	A1	83,000	19	300	Neither
407B[g]	R-32/125/134a (10.0/70.0/20.0)	(±2.0/±2.0/±2.0)	1000	A1	79,000	21	330	Neither
407C[g]	R-32/125/134a (23.0/25.0/52.0)	(±2.0/±2.0/±2.0)	1000	A1	81,000	18	290	Neither
407D	R-32/125/134a (15.0/15.0/70.0)	(±2.0/±2.0/±2.0)	1000	A1	68,000	16	250	Neither
407E[g]	R-32/125/134a (25.0/15.0/60.0)	(±2.0/±2.0/±2.0)	1000	A1	80,000	17	280	Neither
407F	R-32/125/134a (30.0/30.0/40.0)	(±2.0/±2.0/±2.0)	1000	A1	95,000	20	320	Neither
407G	R-32/125/134a (2.5/2.5/95.0)	(±0.5/±0.5/±1.0)	1000	A1	52,000	13	210	Neither
407H	R-32/125/134a (32.5/15.0/52.5)	(±1.0/±1.0/±2.0)	1000	A1	92,000	19	300	Neither

Table 9.2 Data and Safety Classifications for Refrigerant Blends [Std 34-2019, Tbl 4-2] ***(Continued)***

Refrigerant No.	Composition (Mass%)	Composition Tolerances	OEL[h], ppm v/v	Safety Group	RCL[a] (ppm v/v)	RCL[a] (lb/Mcf)	RCL[a] (g/m^3)	Highly Toxic or Toxic[f] Under Code Classification
407I	R-32/125/134a (19.5/8.5/72.0)	(+1.0, –2.0/+2.0, –1.0/±2.0)	1000	A1	71,100	16	250	Neither
408A[g]	R-125/143a/22 (7.0/46.0/47.0)	(±2.0/±1.0/±2.0)	1000	A1	95,000	21	340	Neither
409A	R-22/124/142b (60.0/25.0/15.0)	(±2.0/±2.0/±1.0)	1000	A1	29,000	7.1	110	Neither
409B	R-22/124/142b (65.0/25.0/10.0)	(±2.0/±2.0/±1.0)	1000	A1	30,000	7.3	120	Neither
410A[i]	R-32/125 (50.0/50.0)	(+0.5, –1.5/+1.5, –0.5)	1000	A1	140,000	26	420	Neither
410B[i]	R-32/125 (45.0/55.0)	(±1.0/±1.0)		A1	140,000	27	430	Neither
411A[e]	R-1270/22/152a (1.5/87.5/11.0)	(+0.0, –1.0/+2.0, –0.0/+0.0, –1.0)	990	A2	14,000	2.9	46	Neither
411B[e]	R-1270/22/152a (3.0/94.0/3.0)	(+0.0, –1.0/+2.0, –0.0/+0.0, –1.0)	980	A2	13,000	2.8	45	Neither
412A	R-22/218/142b (70.0/5.0/25.0)	(±2.0/±2.0/±1.0)	1000	A2	22,000	5.1	82	Neither
413A	R-218/134a/600a (9.0/88.0/3.0)	(±1.0/±2.0/+0.0, –1.0)	1000	A2	22,000	5.8	94	Neither
414A	R-22/124/600a/142b (51.0/28.5/4.0/16.5)	(±2.0/±2.0/±0.5/+0.5, –1.0)	1000	A1	26,000	6.4	100	Neither
414B	R-22/124/600a/142b (50.0/39.0/1.5/9.5)	(±2.0/±2.0/±0.5/+0.5, –1.0)	1000	A1	23,000	6.0	95	Neither
415A	R-22/152a (82.0/18.0)	(±1.0/±1.0)	1000	A2	14,000	2.9	47	Neither
415B	R-22/152a (25.0/75.0)	(±1.0/±1.0)	1000	A2	12,000	2.1	34	Neither
416A[e]	R-134a/124/600 (59.0/39.5/1.5)	(+0.5, –1.0/+1.0, –0.5/+1.0, –0.2)	1000	A1	14,000	3.9	62	Neither
417A[e]	R-125/134a/600 (46.6/50.0/3.4)	(±1.1/±1.0/+0.1, –0.4)	1000	A1	13,000	3.5	56	Neither
417B	R-125/134a/600 (79.0/18.3/2.7)	(±1.0/±1.0/+0.1, –0.5)	1000	A1	15,000	4.3	70	Neither
417C	R-125/134a/600 (19.5/78.8/1.7)	(±1.0/±1.0/+0.1, –0.5)	1000	A1	21,000	5.4	87	Neither
418A	R-290/22/152a (1.5/96.0/2.5)	(±0.5/±1.0/±0.5)	1000	A2	22,000	4.8	77	Neither
419A[g]	R-125/134a/E170 (77.0/19.0/4.0)	(±1.0/±1.0/±1.0)	1000	A2	15,000	4.2	67	Neither
419B	R-125/134a/E170 (48.5/48.0/3.5)	(±1.0/±1.0/±0.5)	1000	A2	17,000	4.6	74	Neither
420A	R-134a/142b (88.0/12.0)	(+1.0, –0.0/+0.0, –1.0)	1000	A1	45,000	12	190	Neither
421A	R-125/134a (58.0/42.0)	(±1.0/±1.0)	1000	A1	61,000	17	280	Neither

Table 9.2 Data and Safety Classifications for Refrigerant Blends [Std 34-2019, Tbl 4-2] ***(Continued)***

Refrigerant No.	Composition (Mass%)	Composition Tolerances	OEL[h], ppm v/v	Safety Group	RCL[a] (ppm v/v)	RCL[a] (lb/Mcf)	RCL[a] (g/m³)	Highly Toxic or Toxic[f] Under Code Classification
421B	R-125/134a (85.0/15.0)	(±1.0/±1.0)	1000	A1	69,000	21	330	Neither
422A	R-125/134a/600a (85.1/11.5/3.4)	(±1.0/±1.0/+0.1, –0.4)	1000	A1	63,000	18	290	Neither
422B	R-125/134a/600a (55.0/42.0/3.0)	(±1.0/±1.0/+0.1, –0.5)	1000	A1	56,000	16	250	Neither
422C	R-125/134a/600a (82.0/15.0/3.0)	(±1.0/±1.0/+0.1, –0.5)	1000	A1	62,000	18	290	Neither
422D	R-125/134a/600a (65.1/31.5/3.4)	+0.9, –1.1/±1.0/+0.1, –0.4)	1000	A1	58,000	16	260	Neither
422E	R-125/134a/600a (58.0/39.3/2.7)	(±1.0/+1.7, –1.3/+0.3, –0.2)	1000	A1	57,000	16	260	Neither
423A	R-134a/227ea (52.5/47.5)	(±1.0/±1.0)	1000	A1	59,000	19	310	Neither
424A[e]	R-125/134a/600a/600/601a (50.5/47.0/0.9/1.0/0.6)	(±1.0/±1.0/+0.1, –0.2/+0.1, +0.2/+0.1, –0.2)	970	A1	23,000	6.2	100	Neither
425A	R-32/134a/227ea (18.5/69.5/12.0)	(±0.5/±0.5/±0.5)	1000	A1	72,000	16	260	Neither
426A[e]	R-125/134a/600/601a (5.1/93.0/1.3/0.6)	(±1.0/±1.0/+0.1, –0.2/+0.1, –0.2)	990	A1	20,000	5.2	83	Neither
427A	R-32/125/143a/134a (15.0/25.0/10.0/50.0)	(±2.0/±2.0/±2.0/±2.0)	1000	A1	79,000	18	290	Neither
428A	R-125/143a/290/600a (77.5/20.0/0.6/1.9)	(±1.0/±1.0/+0.1, –0.2/+0.1, –0.2)	1000	A1	83,000	23	370	Neither
429A	R-E170/152a/600a (60.0/10.0/30.0)	(±1.0/±1.0/±1.0)	1000	A3	6300	0.81	13	Neither
430A	R-152a/600a (76.0/24.0)	(±1.0/±1.0)	1000	A3	8000	1.3	21	Neither
431A	R-290/152a (71.0/29.0)	(±1.0/±1.0)	1000	A3	5500	0.69	11	Neither
432A	R-1270/E170 (80.0/20.0)	(±1.0/±1.0)	700	A3	1200	0.13	2.1	Neither
433A	R-1270/290 (30.0/70.0)	(±1.0/±1.0)	880	A3	3100	0.34	5.5	Neither
433B	R-1270/290 (5.0/95.0)	(±1.0/±1.0)	950	A3	4500	0.51	8.1	Neither
433C	R-1270/290 (25.0/75.0)	(±1.0/±1.0)	790	A3	3600	0.41	6.6	Neither
434A[g]	R-125/143a/134a/600a (63.2/18.0/16.0/2.8)	(±1.0/±1.0/±1.0/+0.1, –0.2)	1000	A1	73,000	20	320	Neither
435A	R-E170/152a (80.0/20.0)	(±1.0/±1.0)	1000	A3	8500	1.1	17	Neither
436A	R-290/600a (56.0/44.0)	(±1.0/±1.0)	1000	A3	4000	0.50	8.1	Neither

Table 9.2 Data and Safety Classifications for Refrigerant Blends [Std 34-2019, Tbl 4-2] ***(Continued)***

Refrig-erant No.	Composition (Mass%)	Composition Tolerances	OEL[h], ppm v/v	Safety Group	RCL[a] (ppm v/v)	RCL[a] (lb/Mcf)	RCL[a] (g/m³)	Highly Toxic or Toxic[f] Under Code Classification
436B	R-290/600a (52.0/48.0)	(±1.0/±1.0)	1000	A3	4000	0.51	8.2	Neither
436C	R-290/600a (95.0/5.0)	(±1.2/±1.2)	990	A3	5000	0.57	9.1	Neither
437A	R-125/134a/600/601 (19.5/78.5/1.4/0.6)	(+0.5, –1.8/+1.5, –0.7/+0.1, –0.2/+0.1, –0.2)	990	A1	19,000	5.0	82	Neither
438A	R-32/125/134a/600/601a (8.5/45.0/44.2/1.7/0.6)	(+0.5, –1.5/±1.5/±1.5/+0.1, –0.2/+0.1, –0.2)	990	A1	20,000	4.9	79	Neither
439A	R-32/125/600a (50.0/47.0/3.0)	(±1.0/±1.0/±0.5)	990	A2	26,000	4.7	76	Neither
440A	R-290/134a/152a (0.6/1.6/97.8)	(±0.1/±0.6/±0.5)	1000	A2	12,000	1.9	31	Neither
441A	R-170/290/600a/600 (3.1/54.8/6.0/36.1)	(±0.3/±2.0/±0.6/±2.0)	1000	A3	3200	0.39	6.3	Neither
442A	R-32/125/134a/152a/227ea (31.0/31.0/30.0/3.0/5.0)	(±1.0/±1.0±/1.0/±0.5/±1.0)	1000	A1	100,000	21	330	Neither
443A	R-1270/290/600a (55.0/40.0/5.0)	(±2.0/±2.0/±1.2)	580	A3	1700	0.19	3.1	Neither
444A	R-32/152a/1234ze(E) (12.0/5.0/83.0)	(±1.0/±1.0/±2.0)	850	A2L	21,000	5.1	81	Neither
444B	R-32/152a/1234ze(E) (41.5/10.0/48.5)	(±1.0/±1.0/±1.0)	890	A2L	23,000	4.3	69	Neither
445A	R-744/134a/1234ze(E) (6.0/9.0/85.0)	(±1.0/±1.0/±2.0)	930	A2L	16,000	4.2	67	Neither
446A	R-32/1234ze(E)/600 (68.0/29.0/3.0)	(+0.5, –1.0/+2.0, –0.6/+0.1, –1.0)	960	A2L	16,000	2.5	39	Neither
447A	R-32/125/1234ze(E) (68.0/3.5/28.5)	(+1.5, –0.5/+1.5, –0.5/+1.0, –1.0)	900	A2L	16,000	2.6	42	Neither
447B	R-32/125/1234ze(E) (68.0/8.0/24.0)	(+1.0, –2.0/+2.0, –1.0/+1.0, –2.0)	970	A2L	30,000	23	360	Neither
448A	R-32/125/1234yf/134a/1234ze(E) (26.0/26.0/20.0/21.0/7.0)	(+0.5, –2.0/+2.0, –0.5/+0.5, –2.0/+2.0, –1.0/+0.5, –2.0)	890	A1	110,000	24	390	Neither
449A	R-32 /125 /1234yf /134a (24.3/24.7/25.3/25.7)	(+0.2, –1.0/+1.0, –0.2/+0.2, –1.0/+1.0, –0.2)	830	A1	100,000	23	370	Neither
449B	R-32/125/1234yf/134a (25.2/24.3/23.2/27.3)	(+0.3, –1.5/+1.5, –0.3/+0.3, –1.5/+1.5, –0.3)	850	A1	100,000	23	370	Neither
449C	R-32/125/1234yf/134a (20.0/20.0/31.0/29.0)	(+0.5, –1.5/+1.5, –0.5/+0.5, –1.5/+1.5, –0.5)	800	A1	98,000	23	360	Neither

Table 9.2 **Data and Safety Classifications for Refrigerant Blends** [Std 34-2019, Tbl 4-2] ***(Continued)***

Refrigerant No.	Composition (Mass%)	Composition Tolerances	OEL[h], ppm v/v	Safety Group	RCL[a] (ppm v/v)	RCL[a] (lb/Mcf)	RCL[a] (g/m^3)	Highly Toxic or Toxic[f] Under Code Classification
450A	R-134a/1234ze(E) (42.0/58.0)	(±2.0/±2.0)	880	A1	72,000	20	320	Neither
451A	R-1234yf/134a (89.8/10.2)	(±0.2/±0.2)	520	A2L	18,000	5.3	81	Neither
451B	R-1234yf/134a (88.8/11.2)	(±0.2/±0.2)	530	A2L	18,000	5.3	81	Neither
452A	R-32/125/1234yf (11.0/59.0/30.0)	(±1.7/±1.8/+0.1, −1.0)	780	A1	10,000	27	440	Neither
452B	R-32/125/1234yf (67.0/7.0/26.0)	(±2.0/±1.5/±2.0)	870	A2L	30,000	23	360	Neither
452C	R-32/125/1234yf (12.5/61.0/26.5)	(+0.5, −1.5/±1.0/+0.5, −1.5)	800	A1	100,000	27	430	Neither
453A	R-32/125/134a/227ea/600/601a (20.0/20.0/53.8/5.0/0.6/0.6)	(±1.0/±1.0/±1.0/±0.5/+0.1, −0.2/+0.1, −0.2)	1000	A1	34,000	7.8	120	Neither
454A	R-32/1234yf (35.0/65.0)	(+2.0/−2.0, +2.0/−2.0)	690	A2L	16,000	28	450	Neither
454B	R-32/1234yf (68.9/31.1)	(+1.0/−1.0, +1.0/−1.0)	850	A2L	19,000	22	360	Neither
454C	R-32/1234yf (21.5/78.5)	(±2.0/±2.0)	620	A2L	19,000	29	460	Neither
455A	R-744/32/1234yf (3.0/21.5/75.5)	(+2.0, −1.0/+1.0, −2.0/±2.0)	650	A2L	30,000	23	380	Neither
456A	R-32/134a/1234ze(E) (6.0/45.0/49.0)	(±1.0/±1.0/±1.0)	900	A1	77,000	20	320	Neither
457A	R-32/1234yf/152a (18.0/70.0/12.0)	(+0.5, −1.5/+0.5, −1.5/+0.1, −1.9)	650	A2L	15,000	25	400	Neither
458A	R-32/125/134a/227ea/236fa (20.5/4.0/61.4/13.5/0.6)	(±0.5/±0.5/±0.5/±0.5/±0.1)	1000	A1	76,000	18	280	Neither
459A	R-32/1234yf/1234ze(E) (68.0/26.0/6.0)	(+0.5, −1.5/±2.0/+1.5, −0.5)	870	A2L	27,000	23	360	Neither
459B	R-32/1234yf/1234ze(E) (21.0/69.0/10.0)	(+0.5, −1.0/±2.0/±1.0)	640	A2L	16,000	30	470	Neither
460A	R-32/125/134a/1234ze(E) (12.0/52.0/14.0/22.0)	(±1.0/±1.0/±1.0/±1.0)	650	A1	92,000	24	380	Neither
460B	R-32/125/134a/1234ze(E) (28.0/25.0/20.0/27.0)	(±1.0/±1.0/±1.0/±1.0)	950	A1	120,000	25	400	Neither
460C	R-32/125/134a/1234ze(E) (2.5/2.5/46.0/49.0)	(±0.5/±0.5/±1.0/±1.0)	900	A1	73,000	20	310	Neither

Table 9.2 Data and Safety Classifications for Refrigerant Blends [Std 34-2019, Tbl 4-2] ***(Continued)***

Refrigerant No.	Composition (Mass%)	Composition Tolerances	OEL[h], ppm v/v	Safety Group	RCL[a] (ppm v/v)	RCL[a] (lb/Mcf)	RCL[a] (g/m³)	Highly Toxic or Toxic[f] Under Code Classification
461A	R-125/143a/134a/227ea/600a (55.0/5.0/32.0/5.0/3.0)	(±1.0/ ±0.5/±1.0/±0.5/+0.1, –0.4)	1000	A1	61,000	17	270	Neither
462A	R-32/125/143a/134a/600 (9.0/42.0/2.0/44.0/3.0)	(+1.5, –1.0/±2.0/±1.0/±2.0/±1.0)	1000	A2	16,000	3.9	62	Neither
463A	R-744/32/125/1234yf/134a (6.0/36.0/30.0/14.0/14.0)	(+2.0, –1.0/±2.0/±2.0/±2.0/±2.0)	990	A1	98,000	19	300	Neither
464A	R-32/125/1234ze(E)/227ea (27.0/27.0/40.0/6.0)	(±1.0/±1.0/±1.0/±0.5)	930	A1	120,000	27	430	Neither
465A	R-32/290/1234yf (21.0/7.9/71.1)	(+0.5, –1.5/+0.1, –0.9/±1.0)	660	A2	12,000	2.5	40	Neither
Azeotropes[b]								
500	R-12/152a (73.8/26.2)		1000	A1	30,000	7.6	120	Neither
501	R-22/12 (75.0/25.0)[c]		1000	A1	54,000	13	210	Neither
502[g]	R-22/115 (48.8/51.2)		1000	A1	73,000	21	330	Neither
503	R-23/13 (40.1/59.9)		1000					Neither
504[i]	R-32/115 (48.2/51.8)		1000		140,000	28	450	Neither
505	R-12/31 (78.0/22.0)[c]							Neither
506	R-31/114 (55.1/44.9)							Neither
507A[d,i]	R-125/143a (50.0/50.0)		1000	A1	130,000	32	520	Neither
508A[d]	R-23/116 (39.0/61.0)		1000	A1	55,000	14	220	Neither
508B	R-23/116 (46.0/54.0)		1000	A1	52,000	13	200	Neither
509A[d,g]	R-22/218 (44.0/56.0)		1000	A1	75,000	24	390	Neither
510A	R-E170/600a (88.0/12.0)	(±0.5/±0.5)	1000	A3	7300	0.87	14	Neither
511A	R-290/E170 (95.0/5.0)	(±1.0/±1.0)	1000	A3	5300	0.59	9.5	Neither

Table 9.2 Data and Safety Classifications for Refrigerant Blends [Std 34-2019, Tbl 4-2] ***(Continued)***

Refrigerant No.	Composition (Mass%)	Composition Tolerances	OEL[h], ppm v/v	Safety Group	RCL[a] (ppm v/v)	RCL[a] (lb/Mcf)	RCL[a] (g/m^3)	Highly Toxic or Toxic[f] Under Code Classification
512A	R-134a/152a (5.0/95.0)	(±1.0/±1.0)	1000	A2	11,000	1.9	31	Neither
513A	R-1234yf/134a (56.0/44.0)	(±1.0/±1.0)	650	A1	72,000	20	320	Neither
513B	R-1234yf/134a (58.5/41.5)	(±0.5/±0.5)	640	A1	74,000	21	330	Neither
514A	R-1336mzz(Z)/1130 (E) (74.7/25.3)	(+1.5, −0.5/+0.5, −1.5)	320	B1	2400	0.86	14	Neither
515A	R-1234ze(E)/227ea (88.0/12.0)	(+1.0, −2.0/+2.0, −1.0)	810	A1	62,000	19	300	Neither
516A	R-1234yf/134a/152a (77.5/8.5/14.0)	(±1.4/+0.5, −1.5/+0.1, −1.9)	590	A2L	27,000	7.0	110	Neither

a. Data taken from J.M. Calm, "ARTI Refrigerant Database," Air- Conditioning and Refrigeration Technology Institute (ARTI), Arlington, VA, July 2001; J.M. Calm, "Toxicity Data to Determine Refrigerant Concentration Limits," Report DE/CE 23810-110, Air- Conditioning and Refrigeration Technology Institute (ARTI), Arlington, VA, September 2000; J.M. Calm, "The Toxicity of Refrigerants," *Proceedings of the 1996 International Refrigeration Conference*, Purdue University, West Lafayette, IN, pp. 157–62, 1996; D.P. Wilson and R.G. Richard, "Determination of Refrigerant Lower Flammability Limits (LFLs) in Compliance with Proposed Addendum p to ANSI/ASHRAE Standard 34-1992 (1073-RP)," *ASHRAE Transactions* 2002, 108(2); D.W. Coombs, "HFC-32 Assessment of Anesthetic Potency in Mice by Inhalation," Huntingdon Life Sciences Ltd., Huntingdon, Cambridgeshire, England, February 2004 and amendment February 2006; D.W. Coombs, "HFC-22 An Inhalation Study to Investigate the Cardiac Sensitization Potential in the Beagle Dog," Huntingdon Life Sciences Ltd., Huntingdon, Cambridgeshire, England, August 2005; and other toxicity studies.

b. Azeotropic refrigerants exhibit some segregation of components at conditions of temperature and pressure other than those at which they were formulated. The extent of segregation depends on the particular azeotrope and hardware system configuration.

c. The exact composition of this azeotrope is in question, and additional experimental studies are needed.

d. R-507, R-508, and R-509 are allowed alternative designations for R-507A, R-508A, and R-509A due to a change in designations after assignment of R-500 through R-509. Corresponding changes were not made for R-500 through R-506.

e. The RCL values for these refrigerant blends are approximated in the absence of adequate data for a component comprising less than 4% m/m of the blend and expected to have only a small influence in an acute, accidental release.

f. *Highly toxic*, *toxic*, or *neither*, where *highly toxic* and *toxic* are as defined in the *International Fire Code*, *Uniform Fire Code*, and OSHA regulations, and *neither* identifies those refrigerants having lesser toxicity than either of those groups [1,2,3].

g. At locations with altitudes higher than 4920 ft, the ODL and RCL shall be 69,100 ppm.

h. The OELs are eight-hour TWAs as defined in Section 3 unless otherwise noted; a "C" designation denotes a ceiling limit.

i. At locations with altitudes higher than 3300 ft but below or equal to 4920 ft, the ODL and RCL shall be 112,000 ppm, and at altitudes higher than 4920 ft, the ODL and RCL shall be 69,100 ppm.

Refrigerating Machinery Rooms

When required, the machinery room must

- Be dimensioned so parts are accessible with space for service and maintenance.
- Have tight-fitting doors opening outward, self-closing if they open into the building, with no openings permitting passage of escaping refrigerant into the building except gasketed access panels of ductwork and air-handling equipment.
- Contain a leak detector located where refrigerant from a leak will concentrate that actuates visual and audible alarms inside the room and outside each entrance, and activates the mechanical ventilation.
- On alarm, exhaust of $Q_{cfm} = 100 \times G^{0.5}$ where G is pounds of refrigerant in the largest system, with openings for inlet air to avoid recirculation; multiple fans or multispeed fans to operate to reduce airflow for normal operation to at least 0.5 cfm per ft^2 or 20 cfm per person, and operable when occupied to limit temperature rise to 18°F above inlet air or a maximum of 122°F.
- Combustion air can be used for equipment in the machinery room only if ducted from outside the room and sealed from refrigerant entry, and a refrigerant detector is employed to shut off combustion on refrigerant leaks. (Exceptions: CO_2 or water refrigerant; or ammonia only driven by internal combustion engine.)
- Be no airflow to or from an occupied space through a machinery room unless ducted and sealed against refrigerant leaks.
- Restrict access to authorized personnel with clear signage at each entrance. If system is in an open enclosure outdoors more than 20 ft from building openings, mechanical or natural ventilation may be used; free-opening area for natural ventilation must be $F_{sqft} = G^{0.5}$.

The total of Group A2, B2, A3, or B3 refrigerants except R-717 (ammonia) must not exceed 1100 lb without approval of the authority having jurisdiction. Special requirements in Section 7.5 of ANSI/Standard 15 apply relative to recovered, reclaimed, or recycled refrigerants, or mixing of refrigerants, refrigerant, or lubricant conversion. Group A2, A3, B1, B2, or B3 refrigerants must not be used in high-probability systems (where a refrigerant leak can enter occupied space) for human comfort.

Refrigerant Piping

Piping must not be installed in elevators or other shafts that have moving objects or open into living quarters. It must not penetrate floors except the top floor to the roof, or the basement to the first floor, unless enclosed in a gastight, fire-resistive shaft. The piping must be enclosed in a pipe duct if inside floors.

Pressure Relief Protection

Refrigerating systems must be protected by pressure relief devices. ANSI/ASHRAE Standard 15 covers required location and sizing. All pressure relief valves must be marked "UV" or "VR," and all rupture members marked with data required by paragraph UG 127 of Section VIII, Division 1, of the *ASME Boiler and Pressure Vessel Code*; and fusible plugs must be marked with the melting temperature. Generally, pressure relief devices and fusible plugs must discharge to the atmosphere not less than 15 ft above ground and 20 ft from a window, ventilation opening, pedestrian walkway, or exit in any building.

10. REFRIGERATION LOADS AND EQUIPMENT

Transmission Load

Sensible heat gain through walls, floor, and ceiling is calculated at steady state as

$$q = UA\,\Delta t \tag{10.1}$$

where

q	=	heat gain, Btu/h
A	=	outer area of section, ft^2
Δt	=	difference between outdoor air temperature and air temperature of refrigerated space, °F

The overall coefficient of heat transfer U of the wall, floor, or ceiling can be calculated by the following equation:

$$U = \frac{1}{1/h_i + x/k + 1/h_o} \tag{10.2}$$

where

U	=	overall heat transfer coefficient, Btu/h·ft^2·°F
x	=	wall thickness, in.
k	=	thermal conductivity of wall material, Btu·in/h·ft^2·°F
h_i	=	inner surface conductance, Btu/h·ft^2·°F
h_o	=	outer surface conductance, Btu/h·ft^2·°F

A value of 1.6 for h_i and h_o is frequently used for still air. If the outer surface is exposed to 15 mph wind, h_o is increased to 6.

Latent heat gain due to moisture transmission through walls, floors, and ceilings of modern refrigerated facilities is negligible.

Table 10.1 Thermal Conductivity of Cold Storage Insulation [2018R, Ch 24, Tbl 1]

Insulation	Thermal Conductivity[a] k, Btu·in/h·ft^2·°F
Polyurethane board (R-11 expanded)	0.16 to 0.18
Polyisocyanurate, cellular (R-141b expanded)	0.19
Polystyrene, extruded (R-142b)	0.24
Polystyrene, expanded (R-142b)	0.26
Corkboard[b]	0.30
Foam glass[c]	0.31

[a]Values are for a mean temperature of 75°F, and insulation is aged 180 days.
[b]Seldom used. Data are only for reference.
[c]Virtually no effects from aging.

Table 10.2 Minimum Insulation Thickness [2018R, Ch 24, Tbl 2]

Storage Temperature, °F	Expanded Polyisocyanurate Thickness	
	Northern U.S., in.	Southern U.S., in.
50 to 60	2	2
40 to 50	2	2
25 to 40	2	3
15 to 25	3	3
0 to 15	3	4
−15 to 0	4	4
−40 to −15	5	5

Table 10.3 Allowance for Sun Effect [2018R, Ch 24, Tbl 3]

Typical Surface Types	East Wall, °F	South Wall, °F	West Wall, °F	Flat Roof, °F
Dark-colored surfaces				
Slate roofing	8	5	8	20
Tar roofing				
Black paint				
Medium-colored surfaces				
Unpainted wood	6	4	6	15
Brick				
Red tile				
Dark cement				
Red, gray, or green paint				
Light-colored surfaces				
White stone	4	2	4	9
Light-colored cement				
White paint				

Note: Add to the normal temperature difference for heat leakage calculations to compensate for sun effect. Do not use for air-conditioning design.

Product Load

1. Heat removed to cool from initial temperature to some lower temperature above freezing:

$$Q_1 = mc_1(t_1 - t_2) \tag{10.3}$$

2. Heat removed in cooling from the initial temperature to a freezing point of the product:

$$Q_2 = mc_1(t_1 - t_f) \tag{10.4}$$

3. Heat removed to freeze the product:

$$Q_3 = m h_{if} \tag{10.5}$$

4. Heat removed in cooling from the freezing point to the final temperature below the freezing point:

$$Q_4 = mc_2 (t_f - t_3) \tag{10.6}$$

where

Q_1, Q_2, Q_3, Q_4 = heat removed, Btu
m = weight of the product, lb
c_1 = specific heat of the product above freezing, Btu/lb·°F
t_1 = initial temperature of the product above freezing, °F
t_2 = lower temperature of the product above freezing, °F
t_f = freezing temperature of the product, °F
h_{if} = latent heat of fusion of the product, Btu/lb
c_2 = specific heat of the product below freezing, Btu/lb·°F
t_3 = final temperature of the product below freezing, °F

Specific heats above and below freezing for many products are given in Table 3 of Chapter 19 of the 2018 *ASHRAE Handbook—Refrigeration.*

Refrigeration system capacity for products brought into refrigerated spaces is determined from the time allotted for heat removal and assumes that the product is properly exposed to remove the heat in that time. The calculation is:

$$q = \frac{Q_2 + Q_3 + Q_4}{n} \tag{10.7}$$

where

q = product cooling load, Btu/h
n = allotted time period, h

A product's latent heat of fusion is related to its water content and can be estimated by multiplying the product's percent of water (expressed as a decimal) by the water's latent heat of fusion, 144 Btu/lb. Most food products freeze in the range of 26°F to 31°F. When the exact freezing temperature is not known, assume that it is 28°F.

Table 10.4 Heat Gain from Typical Electric Motors [2018R, Ch 24, Tbl 6]

Motor Name-plate or Rated Horse-power	Motor Type	Nominal rpm	Full Load Motor Efficiency, %	Location of Motor and Driven Equipment with Respect to Conditioned Space or Airstream		
				A	B	C
				Motor in, Driven Equipment in, Btu/h	Motor out, Driven Equipment in, Btu/h	Motor in, Driven Equipment out, Btu/h
0.05	Shaded pole	1500	35	360	130	240
0.08				580	200	380
0.125				900	320	590
0.16				1160	400	760
0.25	Split phase	1750	54	1180	640	540
0.33			56	1500	840	660
0.50			60	2120	1270	850
0.75	3-Phase	1750	72	2650	1900	740

Table 10.5 Heat Equivalent of Occupancy [2018R, Ch 24, Tbl 7]

Refrigerated Space Temperature, °F	Heat Equivalent/Person, Btu/h
50	720
40	840
30	950
20	1050
10	1200
0	1300
−10	1400

Note: Heat equivalent may be estimated by the following equation:
$q_p = 1295 - 11.5t$
where t = temperature of refrigerated space, °F

Packaging Related Load

Cardboard and wood used as part of product packaging adsorb or desorb moisture, depending on air temperature and relative humidity. This moisture sorption represents a conversion between sensible and latent heat: the latent heat of sorption is countered by sensible heat transfer between the packaging and the air by convection. The heat load q_t from the i packaging components is

$$q_t = \frac{\sum m_i c_i (t_1 - t_3)}{3600n} \tag{10.8}$$

$$q_l = \frac{\left[\frac{m(X_1 - X_3)L}{1 + X_1}\right]_{wood} + \left[\frac{m(X_1 - X_3)L}{1 + X_1}\right]_{cardboard}}{3600n} \tag{10.9}$$

where

q_l	=	total heat load, Btu
m_i	=	mass of ith packaging component, lb
c_i	=	specific heat of ith packaging component, Btu/lb·°F
X_1	=	entering packaging component moisture content, lb/lb dry basis
X_3	=	packaging component moisture content after time n, lb/lb dry basis
L	=	latent heat of sorption, Btu/lb (1075 Btu/lb)

Typical values of c_i are given in Table 10.6. X_1 can be measured or estimated using moisture sorption isotherms based on the air temperature and relative humidity the packaging experienced before entering the refrigerated space. The moisture sorption isotherms for wood and cardboard are given in Figures 10.1 and 10.2. X_3 can be estimated using Figure 10.3 or Figure 10.4 to get Y and

$$X_3 = X^* + (X_1 - X^*)Y \tag{10.10}$$

where

Y	=	fractional unaccomplished moisture change (Figure 10.4)
X^*	=	equilibrium packaging component moisture content, lb/lb dry basis

X^* can be estimated using the moisture sorption isotherms based on the air temperature and relative humidity in the refrigerated space using Figures 10.1 and 10.2 for wood and cardboard, respectively, where equilibrium moisture content (EMC) is plotted against equilibrium relative humidity (ERH).

Table 10.6 Typical Specific Heat Capacities of Common Packaging Materials [2018R, Ch 24, Tbl 8]

Material	Specific Heat Capacity c, Btu/lb·°F
Wood	0.41
Cardboard	0.33
Plastic	0.38
Aluminum	0.20
Steel	0.12

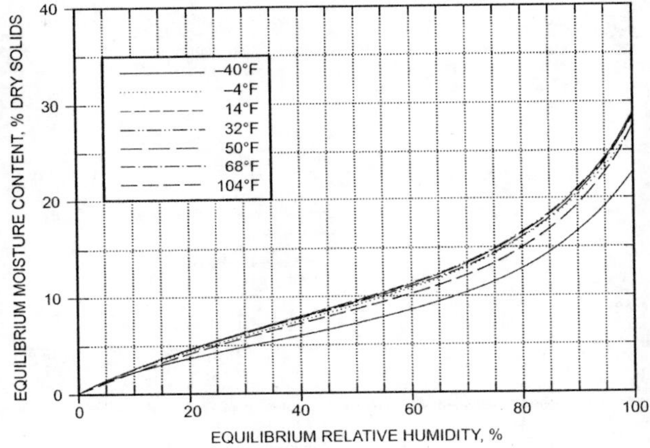

Figure 10.1 Moisture Sorption Isotherms for Wood as Function of Air Temperature and Relative Humidity [2018R, Ch 24, Fig 3]

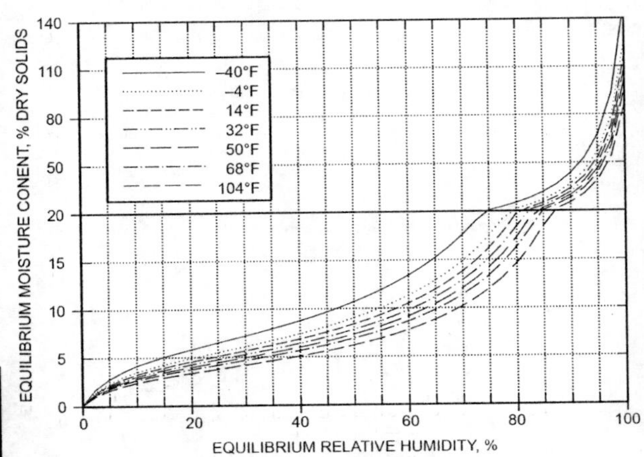

Figure 10.2 Moisture Sorption Isotherms for Cardboard as Function of Air Temperature and Relative Humidity [2018R, Ch 24, Fig 4]

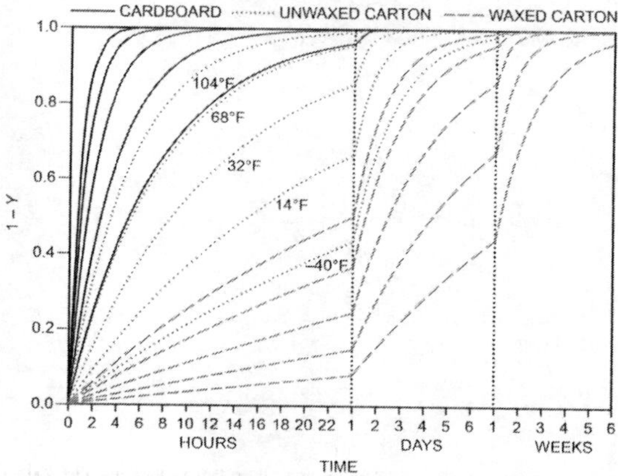

(All plots given in the same temperature order as for unwaxed carton)

Figure 10.3 Fractional Unaccomplished Moisture Change as Function of Time and Temperature for Sheets of Cardboard, Unwaxed Cartons, and Waxed Cartons [2018R, Ch 24, Fig 5]

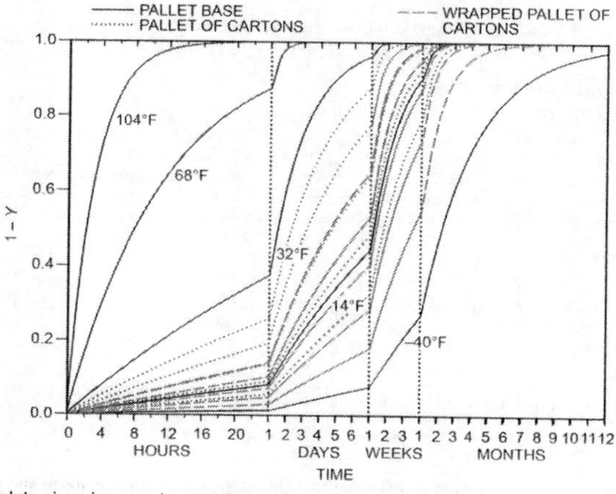

(All plots given in same temperature order as for pallet of cartons)

Figure 10.4 Fractional Unaccomplished Moisture Change as Function of Time and Temperature for Wooden Pallet Bases, Unwrapped Pallets of Cartons, and Wrapped Pallets of Cartons [2018R, Ch 24, Fig 6]

Infiltration Air Load

Heat gain through doorways from air exchange is:

$$q_t = q D_t D_f (1 - E) \tag{10.11}$$

where

q_t	=	average heat gain for the 24 h or other period, Btu/h
q	=	sensible and latent refrigeration load for fully established flow, Btu/h
D_t	=	doorway open-time factor
D_f	=	doorway flow factor
E	=	effectiveness of doorway protective device

$$q = 3790\ WH^{1.5}\ (Q_s/A)(1/R_s) \tag{10.12}$$

where

Q_s/A	=	sensible heat load of infiltration air per square foot of doorway opening as read from Figure 10.5, ton/ft^2
W	=	doorway width, ft
H	=	doorway height, ft
R_s	=	sensible heat ratio of the infiltration air heat gain, from a psychrometric chart

Doorway open-time factor D_t can be calculated as follows:

$$D_t = \frac{(P\theta_p + 60\theta_o)}{3600\theta_d} \tag{10.13}$$

where

D_t	=	decimal portion of time doorway is open
P	=	number of doorway passages
θ_p	=	door open-close time, seconds per passage
θ_o	=	time door simply stands open, min
θ_d	=	the daily (or other) time period, h

Equipment-Related Load

Equipment heat gain is often small at space temperatures above approximately 30°F. Where reheat or other artificial loads are not imposed, total equipment heat gain is about 5% or less of the total load. However, equipment heat gain becomes a major portion of the total load at freezer temperatures. For example, at –20°F the theoretical contribution to total refrigeration load from fan power and coil defrosting alone can exceed, for many cases, 15% of the total load (assuming proper control of defrosting so that the space is not heated excessively).

Safety Factor

The calculated load is typically increased by a safety factor (10% or more is often used) to allow for possible discrepancies between design criteria and actual operation. This factor should be selected in consultation with the facility user and should be applied individually to the first four heat load segments.

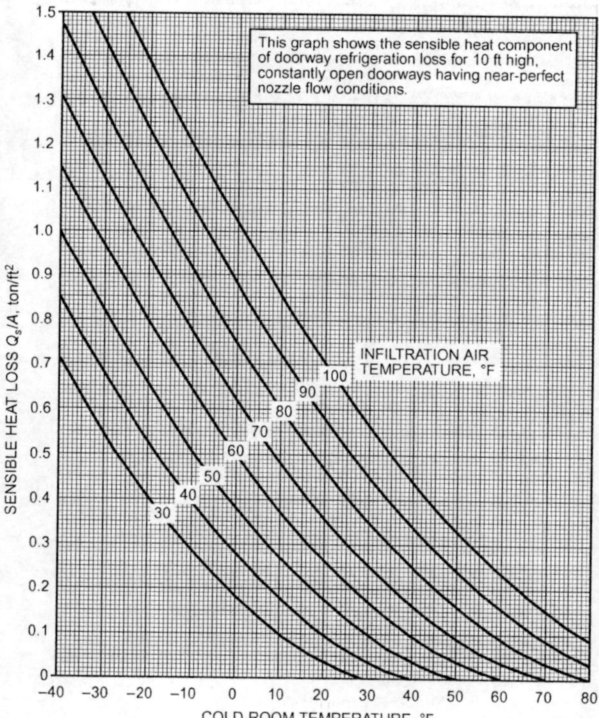

Figure 10.5 Sensible Heat Gain by Air Exchange for Continuously Open Door with Fully Established Flow [2018R, Ch 24, Fig 9]

Refrigeration Equipment

Liquid Coolers

A liquid cooler (hereafter called a cooler) is a heat exchanger in which refrigerant is evaporated, thereby cooling a fluid (usually water or brine) circulating through the cooler.

Various types of liquid coolers and their characteristics are listed in Table 10.7 and Figures 10.6 through 10.12.

Heat transfer for liquid coolers can be expressed by the following steady-state heat transfer equation:

$$q = UA\Delta t_m \tag{10.14}$$

where

q	=	total heat transfer rate, Btu/h
Δt_m	=	mean temperature difference, °F
A	=	heat transfer surface area associated with U, ft^2
U	=	overall heat transfer coefficient, Btu/h·ft^2·°F

The area A can be calculated if the geometry of the cooler is known. The mean temperature difference is

$$\Delta t_m = (\Delta t_1 - \Delta t_2)/\ln(\Delta t_1/\Delta t_2) \tag{10.15}$$

where Δt_1 and Δt_2 are temperature differences between the fluids at each end of the heat exchanger.

U may be calculated by one of the following equations.

Based on inside surface area:

$$U = \frac{1}{1/h_i + [A_i/(A_o h_o)] + (t/k)(A_i/A_m) + r_{fi}} \tag{10.16}$$

Based on outside surface area:

$$U = \frac{1}{[A_o/(A_i h_i)] + 1/h_o + (t/k)(A_o/A_m) + r_{fo}} \tag{10.17}$$

where

h_i	=	inside heat transfer coefficient based on inside surface area, Btu/h·ft^2·°F
h_o	=	outside heat transfer coefficient based on outside surface area, Btu/h·ft^2·°F
A_o	=	outside heat transfer surface area, ft^2
A_i	=	inside heat transfer surface area, ft^2
A_m	=	mean heat transfer area of metal wall, ft^2
k	=	thermal conductivity of heat transfer material, Btu/h·ft·°F
t	=	thickness of heat transfer surface (tube wall thickness), ft
r_{fi}	=	fouling factor of fluid side based on inside surface area, ft^2·h·°F/Btu
r_{fo}	=	fouling factor of fluid side based on outside surface area, ft^2·h·°F/Btu

Note: If fluid is on inside, multiply r_{fi} by A_o/A_i to find r_{fo}.
If fluid is on outside, multiply r_{fo} by A_i/A_o to find r_{fi}.

These equations can be applied to incremental sections of the heat exchanger to include local effects on the value of U, and then the increments summed to obtain a more accurate design.

Over time, most fluids foul the fluid-side heat transfer surface, reducing the cooler's overall heat transfer coefficient. If fouling is expected to be a problem, a mechanically cleanable cooler should be used, such as a flooded, Baudelot, or cleanable direct-expansion tube-in-tube cooler. Direct-expansion shell-and-tube, shell-and-coil, and brazed-plate coolers can be cleaned chemically. Flooded coolers and direct-expansion tube-in-tube coolers with enhanced fluid-side heat transfer surfaces tend to be self-cleaning because of high fluid turbulence, so a smaller fouling factor can probably be used for these coolers. Research shows that negligible fouling occurs in closed-loop evaporator tubes at 3 to 5 fps and 7 fps water velocities. AHRI Standard 480 discusses fouling calculations.

Table 10.7 Types of Coolers [2020S, Ch 42, Tbl 1]

Type of Cooler	Subtype	Usual Refrigerant Feed Device	Usual Capacity Range, tons	Commonly Used Refrigerants
Direct-expansion	Shell-and-tube	Thermal expansion valve	2 to 500	12, 22, 134a, 404A, 407C, 410A, 500, 502, 507A, 717
		Electronic modulation valve	2 to 500	
	Tube-in-tube	Thermal expansion valve	5 to 25	12, 22, 134a, 717
	Brazed-plate	Thermal expansion valve	0.6 to 200	12, 22, 134a, 404A 407C, 410A, 500, 502, 507A, 508B, 717, 744
	Semiwelded plate	Thermal expansion valve	50 to 1990	12, 22, 134a, 500, 502, 507A, 717, 744
Flooded	Shell-and-tube	Low-pressure float	25 to 2000	11, 12, 22, 113, 114
		High-pressure float	25 to 6000	123, 134a, 500, 502, 507A, 717
		Fixed orifice(s)	25 to 6000	
		Weir	25 to 6000	
	Spray shell-and-tube	Low-pressure float	50 to 10,000	11, 12, 13B1, 22
		High-pressure float	50 to 10,000	113, 114, 123, 134a
	Brazed-plate	Low-pressure float	0.6 to 200	12, 22, 134a, 500, 502, 507A, 717, 744
	Semiwelded plate	Low-pressure float	50 to 1990	12, 22, 134a, 500, 502, 507A, 717, 744
Baudelot	Flooded	Low-pressure float	10 to 100	22, 717
	Direct-expansion	Thermal expansion valve	5 to 25	12, 22, 134a, 717
Shell-and-coil	—	Thermal expansion valve	2 to 10	12, 22, 134a, 717

The refrigerant side of the cooler is not subject to fouling, and a fouling factor need not be included for that side.

Typically, the t/k term in Equations 10.16 and 10.17 may be negligible for material with high thermal conductivity. However, with low-thermal-conductivity material or thick-walled tubing, it may become significant. Refer to Chapter 4 of the 2021 *ASHRAE Handbook—Fundamentals* and to Chapter 39 of the 2020 *ASHRAE Handbook—HVAC Systems and Equipment* for further details.

Pressure drop is usually minimal in Baudelot and shell-and-coil coolers but must be considered in direct-expansion and flooded coolers. Both direct-expansion and flooded coolers rely on turbulent fluid flow to improve heat transfer. This turbulence is obtained at the expense of pressure drop.

For air-conditioning, pressure drop is commonly limited to 10 psi to keep pump size and energy cost reasonable. For flooded coolers, see Chapter 39 of the 2020 *ASHRAE Handbook—HVAC Systems and Equipment* for a discussion of pressure drop for flow in tubes. Pressure drop for fluid flow in shell-and-tube direct-expansion coolers depends greatly on tube and baffle geometry. The following equation projects the change in pressure drop caused by a change in flow:

$$\text{New pressure drop} = \text{Original pressure drop}\left[\frac{\text{New rate}}{\text{Original rate}}\right]^{1.8} \tag{10.18}$$

The refrigerant-side pressure drop must be considered for direct-expansion, shell-and-coil, brazed-plate, and (sometimes) Baudelot coolers. When there is a pressure drop on the refrigerant side, the refrigerant inlet and outlet pressures and corresponding saturated temperature are different. This difference changes the mean temperature difference, which affects the total heat transfer rate. If pressure drop is high, expansion valve operation may be affected because of reduced pressure drop across the valve. This pressure drop varies, depending on the refrigerant used, operating temperature, and type of tubing.

When the fluid being cooled is electrically conductive, the system must be grounded to prevent electrochemical corrosion.

The constant superheat thermal expansion valve is the most common control used, located directly upstream of the cooler.

In flooded coolers, an orifice is often used as the throttling device between condenser and cooler.

Freeze prevention must be considered for coolers operating near the fluid's freezing point. In some coolers, freezing causes extensive damage. Two methods can be used for freeze protection: (1) hold saturated suction pressure above the fluid freezing point or (2) shut the system off if fluid temperature approaches the freezing point.

If the cooler is used only when ambient temperature is above freezing, drain the fluid from the cooler for cold weather. Alternatively, if the cooler is used year-round, the following methods can be used to prevent freezing:

- Heat tape or other heating device to keep cooler above freezing
- For water, adding an appropriate amount of ethylene glycol
- Continuous pump operation

Most compressors discharge a small percentage of oil in the discharge gas. This oil mixes with condensed refrigerant in the condenser and flows to the cooler. Because the oil is nonvolatile, it does not evaporate and may collect in the cooler.

In direct-expansion coolers, gas velocity in the tubes and suction gas header is usually sufficient to carry oil from the cooler into the suction line. From there, with proper piping design, it can be carried back to the compressor. At light load and low temperature, oil may gather in the superheat section of the cooler, detracting from performance. For this reason, operating refrigerant circuits at light load for long periods should be avoided, especially under low-temperature conditions.

In flooded coolers, vapor velocity above the tube bundle is usually insufficient to return oil up the suction line, and oil tends to accumulate in the cooler. With time, depending on the compressor oil loss rate, oil concentration in the cooler may become large. When concentration exceeds about 1%, heat transfer performance may be adversely affected if enhanced tubing is used.

It is common in flooded coolers to take some oil-rich liquid and return it to the compressor on a continuing basis, to establish a rate of return equal to the compressor oil loss rate.

Cooler maintenance centers around (1) safety and (2) cleaning the fluid side. Periodically inspect the cooler for any weakening of its pressure boundaries. The manufacturer or a service organization experienced in cooler maintenance should have details for cleaning.

A cooler operating at a saturated suction temperature lower than the ambient-air dew point should be insulated to prevent condensation.

Forced-Circulation Air Coolers

A cooling coil and a motor-driven fan are the basic components, and coil defrosting means are added for low-temperature operations where coil frosting might impede performance. Blow-through direct-drive propeller fans are most common, but for long throws, draw-through configuration is preferred. For loads above 32°F, coil spacing is usually 6 to 8 fins per inch; below 32°F a maximum of 4 fins per inch is preferred. Even distribution of halocarbon refrigerant is usually attained in direct-expansion coils by refrigerant distributors. Units in larger refrigeration systems are often liquid-pumped recirculating types with orifice disks.

Defrost for coils and drain pans of low-temperature units may be hot-gas, electric, or water. Usually defrosting is done with the fan off. Control of defrost is usually by microprocessor, with a thermostat mounted within the coil. Usually a rise to 45°F returns the unit to the operating cycle. Drain lines should be well-pitched, insulated, and trapped outside the refrigerated space.

Capacities of air coolers are usually based on the temperature difference between inlet air and refrigerant in the coil. The higher the TD, the lower the space relative humidity. Between 8°F and 16°F TD is usual, except for packaged products and workrooms where TD of 25°F is common. Low-temperature units generally have TD below 15°F for system economics and limiting defrost frequency.

Most frequent control of refrigerant flow is an expansion valve, most frequently thermostatic type. Electric expansion valves, requiring a valve, controller, and control sensor, are also available.

Large refrigerating systems more frequently have flooded evaporators, most often low-side float valves. Refrigerant valves opening or closing flow are usually solenoid valves. Larger flows may require pilot-operated solenoid valves. When it is desired to limit compressor motor load during pulldown, an evaporator pressure regulating valve may be used to limit compressor suction pressure.

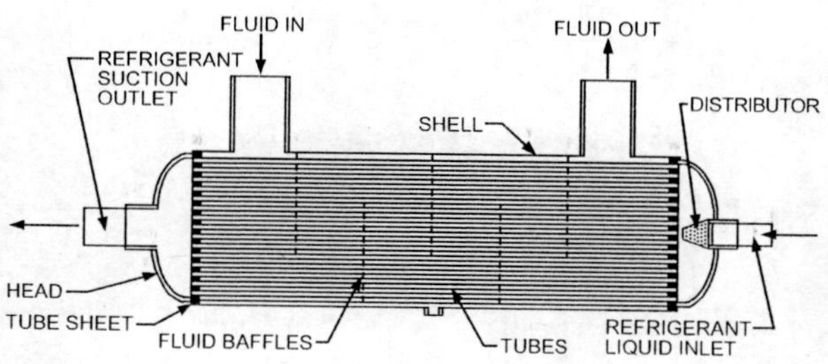

Figure 10.6 Direct-Expansion Shell-and-Tube Cooler [2020S, Ch 42, Fig 1]

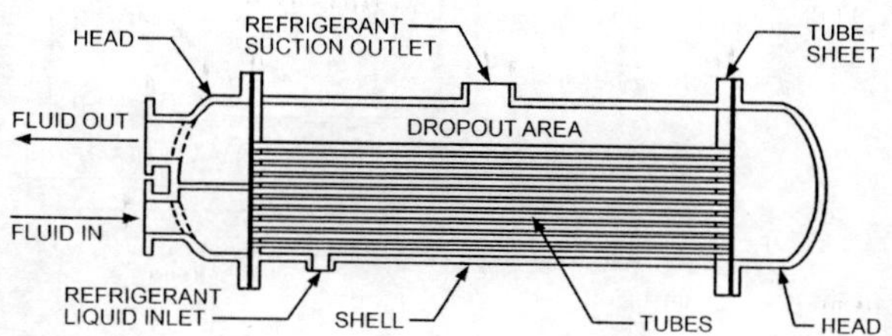

Figure 10.7 Flooded Shell-and-Tube Cooler [2020S, Ch 42, Fig 2]

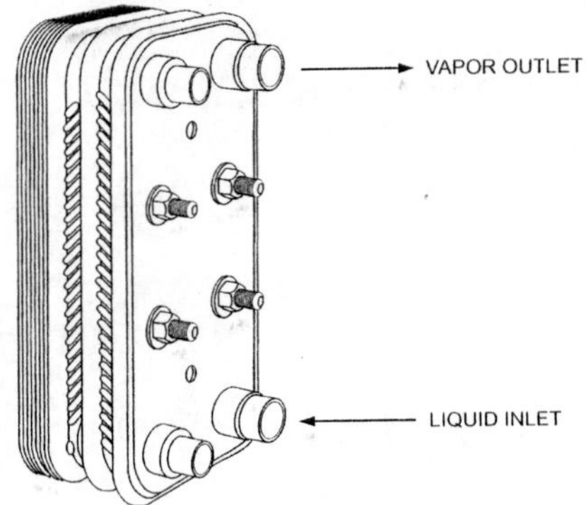

Figure 10.8 Flooded Plate Cooler [2020S, Ch 42, Fig 3]

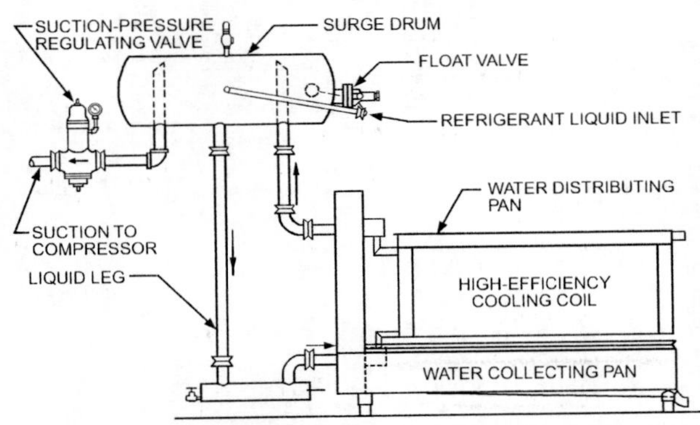

Figure 10.9 Baudelot Cooler [2020S, Ch 42, Fig 4]

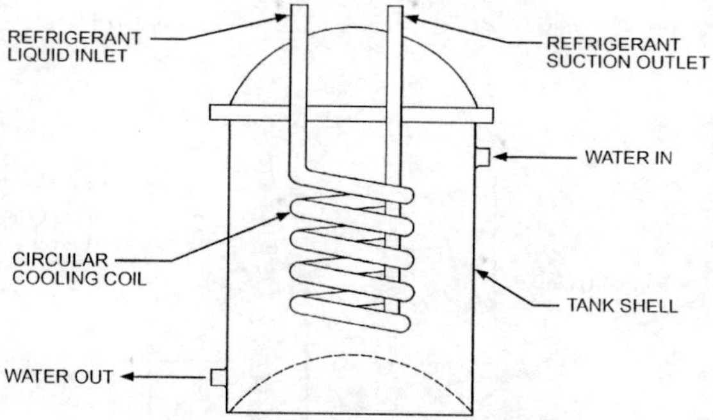

Figure 10.10 Shell-and-Coil Cooler [2020S, Ch 42, Fig 5]

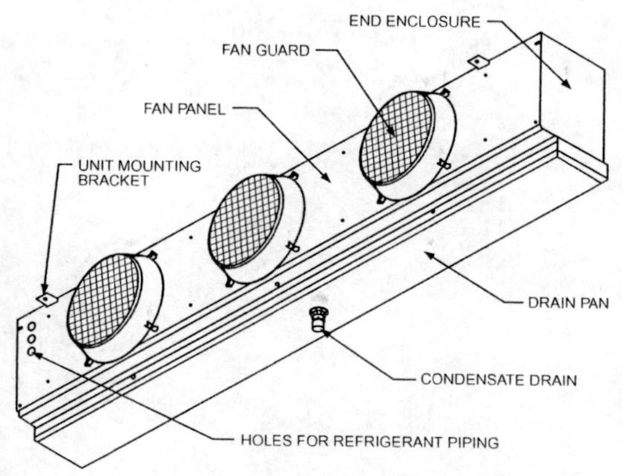

Figure 10.11 Low-Profile Cooler [2018R, Ch 14, Fig 3]

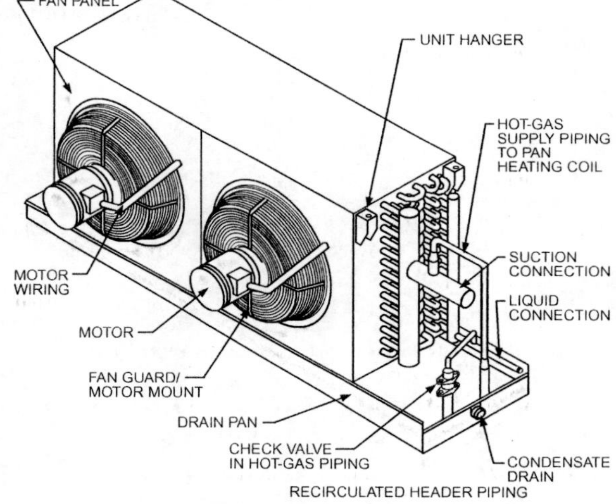

Figure 10.12 Liquid Overfeed Type Unit Cooler [2018R, Ch 14, Fig 4]

11. AIR-CONDITIONING LOAD DATA

Cooling Loads

Cooling loads result from many conduction, convection, and radiation heat transfer processes through the building envelope and from internal sources and system components. Building components or contents that may affect cooling loads include the following:

- **External:** Walls, roofs, windows, skylights, doors, partitions, ceilings, and floors
- **Internal:** Lights, people, appliances, and equipment
- **Infiltration:** Air leakage and moisture migration
- **System:** Outdoor air, duct leakage and heat gain, reheat, fan and pump energy, and energy recovery

ASHRAE provides climatic design information for 9237 locations in the United States, Canada, and around the world. Chapter 14 of the 2021 *ASHRAE Handbook—Fundamentals* provides background discussion on these design data. The complete data tables for all 9237 stations are included with both the PDF version of the Handbook chapter and the Handbook Online version.

ANSI/ASHRAE/ACCA Standard 183 sets the minimum standards for nonresidential load calculations.

Currently there are two ASHRAE cooling load calculation methods. The first is the Heat Balance (HB) method, whose equations are coded in a generic computer program linked to a user interface program. The source code for these programs is in the ASHRAE Load Calculation Toolkit.

The second method is the Radiant Time Series (RTS) method, a simplification of the heat balance method, still requiring a complex computer program for a multiroom building.

Due to the variation in heat transfer coefficients, precision of construction, and manner of actual building operation, a cooling load calculation can never be more than a good estimate of the actual load.

To design and size components of central air-conditioning systems, more than the cooling load is needed. Type of system, fan energy and location, direct heat loss and gain, duct leakage, heat extracted from lights, and type of return system must all be considered.

Heating Loads

Techniques for estimating design heating load for commercial, institutional, and industrial applications are essentially the same as for those estimating design cooling loads for such uses, with the following exceptions:

- Temperatures of outdoor conditioned spaces are generally lower than maintained space temperatures.
- Credit for solar or internal heat gains is not included.
- Thermal storage effect of building structure or content is ignored.

Thermal bridging effects on wall and roof conduction are greater for heating loads than for cooling loads, and greater care must be taken to account for bridging effects on U-factors used in heating load calculations.

Heat losses (negative heat gains) are thus considered to be instantaneous, heat transfer essentially conductive, and latent heat treated only as a function of replacing space humidity lost to the exterior environment.

This simplified approach is justified because it evaluates worst-case conditions that can reasonably occur during a heating season. Therefore, the near-worst-case load is based on the following:

- Design interior and exterior conditions
- Including infiltration and/or ventilation
- No solar effect (at night or on cloudy winter days)
- Before the periodic presence of people, lights, and appliances has an offsetting effect

Typical commercial and retail spaces have nighttime unoccupied periods at a setback temperature where little to no ventilation is required, building lights and equipment are off, and heat loss is primarily through conduction and infiltration. Before being occupied, buildings are warmed to the occupied temperature. During occupied time, building lights, equipment, and people cooling loads can offset conduction heat loss, although some perimeter heat may be required, leaving infiltration and ventilation as the primary heating loads. Ventilation heat load may be offset with heat recovery equipment. These loads (conduction loss, warm-up load, and ventilation load) may not be additive when sizing building heating equipment, and it is prudent to analyze each load and their interactions to arrive at final equipment sizing for heating.

Previous Cooling Load Calculation Methods

Procedures described in Chapters 17 and 18 of the 2021 *ASHRAE Handbook–Fundamentals* are the most current and scientifically derived means for estimating cooling load for a defined building space, but methods in earlier editions of the ASHRAE Handbook are valid for many applications. These earlier procedures are simplifications of the heat balance principles, and their use requires experience to deal with atypical or unusual circumstances. In fact, any cooling or heating load estimate is no better than the assumptions used to define conditions and parameters such as physical makeup of the various envelope surfaces, conditions of occupancy and use, and ambient weather conditions. Experience of the practitioner can never be ignored.

The primary difference between the HB and RTS methods and the older methods is the newer methods' direct approach, compared to the simplifications necessitated by the limited computer capability available previously.

The **transfer function method (TFM)**, for example, required many calculation steps. It was originally designed for energy analysis with emphasis on daily, monthly, and annual energy use, and thus was more oriented to average hourly cooling loads than peak design loads.

The **total equivalent temperature differential method with time averaging (TETD/TA)** has been a highly reliable (if subjective) method of load estimating since its initial presentation in the 1967 *Handbook of Fundamentals*. Originally intended as a manual method of calculation, it proved suitable only as a computer application because of the need to calculate an extended profile of hourly heat gain values, from which radiant components had to be averaged over a time representative of the general mass of the building involved. Because perception of thermal storage characteristics of a given building is almost entirely subjective, with little specific information for the user to judge variations, the TETD/TA method's primary usefulness has always been to the experienced engineer.

The **cooling load temperature differential method with solar cooling load factors (CLTD/CLF)** attempted to simplify the two-step TFM and TETD/TA methods into a single-step technique that proceeded directly from raw data to cooling load without intermediate conversion of radiant heat gain to cooling load. A series of factors were taken from cooling load calculation results (produced by more sophisticated methods) as "cooling load temperature differences" and "cooling load factors" for use in traditional conduction ($q = UA\Delta t$) equations. The results are approximate cooling load values rather than simple heat gain values. The simplifications and assumptions used in the original work to derive those factors limit this method's applicability to those building types and conditions for which the CLTD/CLF factors were derived; the method should not be used beyond the range of applicability.

The TFM, TETD/TA, and CLTD/CLF procedures have not been invalidated or discredited. Experienced engineers have successfully used them in millions of buildings around the world. The accuracy of cooling load calculations in practice depends primarily on the availability of accurate information and the design engineer's judgment in the assumptions made in interpreting the available data. Those factors have much greater influence on a project's success than does the choice of a particular cooling load calculation method.

The primary benefit of HB and RTS calculations is their somewhat reduced dependency on purely subjective input (e.g., determining a proper time-averaging period for TETD/TA; ascertaining appropriate safety factors to add to the rounded-off TFM results; determining whether CLTD/CLF factors are applicable to a specific unique application). However, using the most up-to-date techniques in real-world design still requires judgment on the part of the design engineer and care in choosing appropriate assumptions, just as in applying older calculation methods.

The information that follows includes data on material properties that apply generally to any of the above-mentioned calculation approaches as well as information specific to the CLTD/CLF approach.

Table 11.1 Summary of Load Sources and Equations for Estimating Space Design Cooling Load

[Adapted from *Cooling and Heating Load Calculation Manual,* Second Edition, Tbl 8.1]

Load Source	Equation	Reference, Table, Description
External		
Roof	$q = UA(\mathrm{CLTD})$	Design heat transmission coefficients, Table 11.6 Areas calculated from plans; CLTD from Tables 11.7 through 11.10
Walls	$q = UA(\mathrm{CLTD})$	Design heat transmission coefficients, Table 11.6 Areas calculated from plans; CLTD from Tables 11.11 through 11.13
Glass Conduction	$q = UA(\mathrm{CLTD})$	Glass area calculated from plans U-factors, page 206 CLTD for conduction load through glass, page 206
Glass Solar	$q = A(\mathrm{SC})\mathrm{SCL}$	Solar cooling load (SCL) factors, Table 11.14 Net glass area from plans Shading coefficients for combination of glass and internal shading, Table 11.15 Compute shaded area from building projections Externally shaded glass: use north orientation data
Partitions, Ceilings, Floors	$q = UA(\mathrm{TD})$	Design heat transmission coefficients, Table 11.6 Area calculated from plans
Internal		
Lights	$q = \mathrm{INPUT}$	Input rating from electrical plans or lighting fixture data, Table 11.17
People		
Sensible	$q_s = \mathrm{No.\ (Sens.\ H.G.)}$	Number of people in space Sensible heat gain from occupants, Table 11.16
Latent	$q_l = \mathrm{No.\ (Lat.\ H.G.)}$	Latent heat gain from occupants
Equipment and Appliances	$q_s = \mathrm{HEAT\ GAIN}$	Recommended rate of heat gain, Tables 11.18 through 11.36
Power	$q = \mathrm{HEAT\ GAIN}$	page 236
Infiltration Air		
Sensible	$q_s = 1.10\ (\mathrm{CFM})\ \Delta t$	Inside-outside air temperature difference, °F
Latent	$q_l = 4840\ (\mathrm{CFM})\ \Delta W$	Inside-outside air humidity ratio difference, grains/$\mathrm{lb_{da}}$
Total	$q = 4.5\ (\mathrm{CFM})\ \Delta h$	Inside-outside air enthalpy difference, Btu/$\mathrm{lb_{da}}$

CAUTION: Approximate data—Use for preliminary computations only. See *Load Calculation Applications Manual*, Second Edition, for more details.

Heat Flow Q Through Building Materials

In addition to heat flow through building materials the resistance of surfaces and air spaces must be included in calculating U-factors.

$$Q\text{ (Btu/h)} = U \times \text{Area (ft}^2) \times \text{temperature difference (°F)} \quad (11.1)$$

where U = overall coefficient of heat transmission, Btu/h·ft^2·°F, of materials + interior and exterior resistances:

$$1/U = \Sigma R \text{ (resistance of components)} \quad (11.2)$$

For multiple layers of homogeneous materials, R values are added in series:

$$1/U = R_{cold\ surface} + R_1 + R_2 + R_n ... + R_{warm\ surface} \quad (11.3)$$

For wood stud walls, studs 16 in. on center (series and parallel):

$$1/U = R_{cold\ surface} + \left\{ \frac{+\ 0.25\ R_{stud}}{+\ 0.75\ R_{stud\ space}} \right\} + R_{warm\ surface} \quad (11.4)$$

Plus, in series, $R_{insulation}$, R_{siding}, $R_{wallboard}$, etc.

For metal framed construction, heat flow through the metal causes thermal bridging, increasing the U-factor significantly. For details, see Normative Appendix A of ANSI/ASHRAE/IES Standard 90.1.

Conductive Heat Flow Through Glazing

Solar radiation gain through glazing is usually more significant in cooling load calculations than conductive heat gain. Solar heat gain is neglected in heating load calculations.

Conductive heat flow through glazing including surface resistance (approximate data)
Single glazing $U = 1.1$
Double glazing $U = 0.55$
Triple glazing $U = 0.33$

Table 11.2 Effective Thermal Resistance of Plane Air Spaces,[a,b,c] h·ft²·°F/Btu
[2021F, Ch 26, Tbl 3]

Position of Air Space	Direction of Heat Flow	Air Space Mean Temp.[d], °F	Air Space Temp. Diff.,[d] °F	Effective Emittance ε_{eff}[d,e] 0.5 in. Air Space[c] 0.03	0.05	0.2	0.5	0.82	0.75 in. Air Space[c] 0.03	0.05	0.2	0.5	0.82
Horiz.	Up	90	10	2.13	2.03	1.51	0.99	0.73	2.34	2.22	1.61	1.04	0.75
		50	30	1.62	1.57	1.29	0.96	0.75	1.71	1.66	1.35	0.99	0.77
		50	10	2.13	2.05	1.60	1.11	0.84	2.30	2.21	1.70	1.16	0.87
		0	20	1.73	1.70	1.45	1.12	0.91	1.83	1.79	1.52	1.16	0.93
		0	10	2.10	2.04	1.70	1.27	1.00	2.23	2.16	1.78	1.31	1.02
		−50	20	1.69	1.66	1.49	1.23	1.04	1.77	1.74	1.55	1.27	1.07
		−50	10	2.04	2.00	1.75	1.40	1.16	2.16	2.11	1.84	1.46	1.20
Vertical	Horiz.	90	10	2.47	2.34	1.67	1.06	0.77	3.50	3.24	2.08	1.22	0.84
		50	30	2.57	2.46	1.84	1.23	0.90	2.91	2.77	2.01	1.30	0.94
		50	10	2.66	2.54	1.88	1.24	0.91	3.70	3.46	2.35	1.43	1.01
		0	20	2.82	2.72	2.14	1.50	1.13	3.14	3.02	2.32	1.58	1.18
		0	10	2.93	2.82	2.20	1.53	1.15	3.77	3.59	2.64	1.73	1.26
		−50	20	2.90	2.82	2.35	1.76	1.39	2.90	2.83	2.36	1.77	1.39
		−50	10	3.20	3.10	2.54	1.87	1.46	3.72	3.60	2.87	2.04	1.56
Horiz.	Down	90	10	2.48	2.34	1.67	1.06	0.77	3.55	3.29	2.10	1.22	0.85
		50	30	2.66	2.54	1.88	1.24	0.91	3.77	3.52	2.38	1.44	1.02
		50	10	2.67	2.55	1.89	1.25	0.92	3.84	3.59	2.41	1.45	1.02
		0	20	2.94	2.83	2.20	1.53	1.15	4.18	3.96	2.83	1.81	1.30
		0	10	2.96	2.85	2.22	1.53	1.16	4.25	4.02	2.87	1.82	1.31
		−50	20	3.25	3.15	2.58	1.89	1.47	4.60	4.41	3.36	2.28	1.69
		−50	10	3.28	3.18	2.60	1.90	1.47	4.71	4.51	3.42	2.30	1.71

[a]See Chapter 25 of the 2021 *ASHRAE Handbook—Fundamentals*. Thermal resistance values were determined from $R = 1/C$, where $C = h_c + \varepsilon_{eff} h_r$, h_c is conduction/convection coefficient, $\varepsilon_{eff} h_r$ is radiation coefficient $\approx 0.0068\varepsilon_{eff}[(t_m + 460)/100]^3$, and t_m is mean temperature of air space.

[b]Values apply for ideal conditions (i.e., air spaces of uniform thickness bounded by plane, smooth, parallel surfaces with no air leakage to or from the space). **This table should not be used for hollow siding or profiled cladding.**

[c]A single resistance value cannot account for multiple air spaces; each air space requires a separate resistance calculation that applies only for established boundary conditions. Resistances of horizontal spaces with heat flow downward are substantially independent of temperature difference.

[d]Interpolation is permissible for other values of mean temperature, temperature difference, and effective emittance ε_{eff}. Interpolation and moderate extrapolation for air spaces greater than 3.5 in. are also permissible.

[e]Effective emittance ε_{eff} of air space is given by $1/\varepsilon_{eff} = 1/\varepsilon_1 + 1/\varepsilon_2 - 1$, where ε_1 and ε_2 are emittances of surfaces of air space (see Table 2 of Chapter 26 of the 2021 *ASHRAE Handbook—Fundamentals*). **Also, oxidation, corrosion, and accumulation of dust and dirt can dramatically increase surface emittance. Emittance values of 0.05 should only be used where the highly reflective surface can be maintained over the service life of the assembly.**

Table 11.3 Surface Film Coefficients/Resistances [2021F, Ch 26, Tbl 10]

Position of Surface	Direction of Heat Flow	Surface Emittance, ε					
		Nonreflective $\varepsilon = 0.90$		Reflective			
				$\varepsilon = 0.20$		$\varepsilon = 0.05$	
Indoor		h_i	R_i	h_i	R_i	h_i	R_i
Horizontal	Upward	1.63	0.61	0.91	1.10	0.76	1.32
Sloping at 45°	Upward	1.60	0.62	0.88	1.14	0.73	1.37
Vertical	Horizontal	1.46	0.68	0.74	1.35	0.59	1.70
Sloping at 45°	Downward	1.32	0.76	0.60	1.67	0.45	2.22
Horizontal	Downward	1.08	0.92	0.37	2.70	0.22	4.55
Outdoor (any position)		h_o	R_o				
15 mph wind (for winter)	Any	6.00	0.17	—	—	—	—
7.5 mph wind (for summer)	Any	4.00	0.25	—	—	—	—

Notes:

1. Surface conductance h_i and h_o measured in Btu/h·ft²·°F; resistance R_i and R_o in h·ft²·°F/Btu.
2. No surface has both an air space resistance value and a surface resistance value.
3. Conductances are for surfaces of the stated emittance facing virtual blackbody surroundings at same temperature as ambient air. Values based on surface/air temperature difference of 10°F and surface temperatures of 70°F.
4. See Chapter 4 of the 2021 *ASHRAE Handbook—Fundamentals* for more detailed information.
5. Condensate can have significant effect on surface emittance (see Table 2 of Chapter 26 of the 2021 *ASHRAE Handbook—Fundamentals*). Also, oxidation, corrosion, and accumulation of dust and dirt can dramatically increase surface emittance. Emittance values of 0.05 should only be used where highly reflective surface can be maintained over the service life of the assembly.

Table 11.4 Emissivity of Various Surfaces and Effective Emittances of Facing Air Spaces[a] [2021F, Ch 26, Tbl 2]

Surface	Average Emissivity ε	Effective Emittance ε_{eff} of Air Space: One Surface's Emittance ε; Other, 0.9	Effective Emittance ε_{eff} of Air Space: Both Surfaces' Emittance ε
Aluminum foil, bright	0.05	0.05	0.03
Aluminum foil, with condensate just visible (>0.7 g/ft^2)	0.30[b]	0.29	—
Aluminum foil, with condensate clearly visible (>2.9 g/ft^2)	0.70[b]	0.65	—
Aluminum sheet	0.12	0.12	0.06
Aluminum-coated paper, polished	0.20	0.20	0.11
Brass, nonoxidized	0.04	0.038	0.02
Copper, black oxidized	0.74	0.41	0.59
Copper, polished	0.04	0.038	0.02
Iron and steel, polished	0.2	0.16	0.11
Iron and steel, oxidized	0.58	0.35	0.41
Lead, oxidized	0.27	0.21	0.16
Nickel, nonoxidized	0.06	0.056	0.03
Silver, polished	0.03	0.029	0.015
Steel, galvanized, bright	0.25	0.24	0.15
Tin, nonoxidized	0.05	0.047	0.026
Aluminum paint	0.50	0.47	0.35
Building materials: wood, paper, masonry, nonmetallic paints	0.90	0.82	0.82
Regular glass	0.84	0.77	0.72

[a]Values apply in 4 to 40 μm range of electromagnetic spectrum. Also, oxidation, corrosion, and accumulation of dust and dirt can dramatically increase surface emittance. Emittance values of 0.05 should only be used where the highly reflective surface can be maintained over the service life of the assembly. Except as noted, data from VDI (1999).

[b]Values based on data in Bassett and Trethowen (1984).

Table 11.5 Effective Thermal Resistance of Ventilated Attics[a] (Summer Condition)

Ventilation Air Temp., °F	Sol-Air[e] Temp., °F	Not Ventilation[b]		Natural Ventilation		Power Ventilation[c]					
		Ventilation Rate, cfm/ft^2									
		0		0.1		0.5		1.0		1.5	
		Ceiling Resistance R^d, °F·ft^2·h/Btu									
		10	20	10	20	10	20	10	20	10	20
Part A. Nonreflective Surfaces											
80	120	1.9	1.9	2.8	3.4	6.3	9.3	9.6	16	11	20
	140	1.9	1.9	2.8	3.5	6.5	10	9.8	17	12	21
	160	1.9	1.9	2.8	3.6	6.7	11	10	18	13	22
100	120	1.9	1.9	2.2	2.3	3.3	4.4	4.0	6.0	4.1	6.9
	140	1.9	1.9	2.4	2.7	4.2	6.1	5.8	8.7	6.5	10
	160	1.9	1.9	2.6	3.2	5.0	7.6	7.2	11	8.3	13
Part B. Reflective Surfaces[f]											
80	120	6.5	6.5	8.1	8.8	13	17	17	25	19	30
	140	6.5	6.5	8.2	9.0	14	18	18	26	20	31
	160	6.5	6.5	8.3	9.2	15	18	19	27	21	32
100	120	6.5	6.5	7.0	7.4	8.0	10	8.5	12	8.8	12
	140	6.5	6.5	7.3	7.8	10	12	11	15	12	16
	160	6.5	6.5	7.6	8.2	11	14	13	18	15	20

[a] Although the term effective resistance is commonly used when there is attic ventilation, this table includes values for situations with no ventilation. The effective resistance of the attic added to the resistance (1/U) of the ceiling yields the effective resistance of this combination based on sol-air and room temperatures. These values apply to wood frame construction with a roof deck and roofing that has a conductance of 1.0 Btu/h·ft^2·°F.

[b] This condition cannot be achieved in the field unless extreme measures are taken to tightly seal the attic.

[c] Based on air discharging outward from attic.

[d] When determining ceiling resistance, do not add the effect of a reflective surface facing the attic, as it is accounted for in part B of this table.

[e] Roof surface temperature rather than sol-air temperature can be used if 0.25 is subtracted from the attic resistance shown.

[f] Surfaces with effective emittance $\varepsilon_{eff} = 0.05$ between ceiling joists facing attic space.

Table 11.6 Building and Insulating Materials: Design Values[a] [2021F, Ch 26, Tbl 1]

Description	Density, lb/ft³	Conductivity[b] k, Btu·in/h·ft²·°F	Resistance R, h·ft²·°F/Btu	Specific Heat, Btu/lb·°F
Insulating Materials				
Blanket and batt[c,d]				
Glass-fiber batts				0.2
	0.47 to 0.51	0.32 to 0.33	—	—
	0.61 to 0.75	0.28 to 0.30	—	—
	0.79 to 0.85	0.26 to 0.27	—	—
	1.4	0.23	—	—
Rock and slag wool batts.	—	—	—	0.2
	2 to 2.3	0.25 to 0.26	—	—
	2.8	0.23 to 0.24	—	—
Mineral wool, felted	1 to 3	0.28	—	—
	1 to 8	0.24	—	—
Board and slabs				
Cellular glass	7.5	0.29	—	0.20
Cement fiber slabs, shredded wood with Portland cement binder	25 to 27	0.50 to 0.53	—	—
with magnesia oxysulfide binder	22	0.57	—	0.31
Glass fiber board	—	—	—	0.2
	1.5 to 6.0	0.23 to 0.24	—	—
Expanded rubber (rigid)	4	0.2	—	0.4
Extruded polystyrene, smooth skin	—	—	—	0.35
aged per CAN/ULC Standard S770-2003	1.4 to 3.6	0.18 to 0.20	—	—
aged 180 days	1.4 to 3.6	0.20		
European product	1.9	0.21		
aged 5 years at 75°F	2 to 2.2	0.21	—	—
blown with low global warming potential (GWP) (<5) blowing agent		0.24 to 0.25	—	—

Table 11.6 Building and Insulating Materials: Design Values[a] [2021F, Ch 26, Tbl 1] (*Continued*)

Description	Density, lb/ft^3	Conductivity[b] k, $Btu \cdot in/h \cdot ft^2 \cdot °F$	Resistance R, $h \cdot ft^2 \cdot °F/Btu$	Specific Heat, $Btu/lb \cdot °F$
Expanded polystyrene, molded beads	—	—	—	0.35
	1.0 to 1.5	0.24 to 0.26	—	—
	1.8	0.23	—	—
Mineral fiberboard, wet felted	10	0.26	—	0.2
Rock wool board	—	—	—	0.2
floors and walls	4.0 to 8.0	0.23 to 0.25	—	—
roofing	10. to 11.	0.27 to 0.29	—	0.2
Acoustical tile[g]	21 to 23	0.36 to 0.37	—	0.14 to 0.19
Perlite board	9	0.36	—	—
Polyisocyanurate	—	—	—	0.35
unfaced, aged per CAN/ULC Standard S770-2003	1.6 to 2.3	0.16 to 0.17	—	—
with foil facers, aged 180 days	—	0.15 to 0.16	—	—
Phenolic foam board with facers, aged[f]	—	0.14 to 0.16	—	—
Loose fill				
Cellulose fiber, loose fill	—	—	—	0.33
attic application up to 4 in.	1.0 to 1.2	0.31 to 0.32	—	—
attic application > 4 in.	1.2 to 1.6	0.27 to 0.28	—	—
wall application, densely packed	3.5	0.27 to 0.28	—	—
Perlite, expanded	2 to 4	0.27 to 0.31	—	0.26
	4 to 7.5	0.31 to 0.36	—	—
	7.5 to 11	0.36 to 0.42	—	—
Glass fiber[d]				
attics, ~4 to 12 in.	0.4 to 0.5	0.36 to 0.38	—	—
attics, ~12 to 22 in.	0.5 to 0.6	0.34 to 0.36	—	—
closed attic or wall cavities	1.8 to 2.3	0.24 to 0.25	—	—

Table 11.6 Building and Insulating Materials: Design Values[a] [2021F, Ch 26, Tbl 1] (*Continued*)

Description	Density, lb/ft³	Conductivity[b] k, Btu·in/h·ft²·°F	Resistance R, h·ft²·°F/Btu	Specific Heat, Btu/lb·°F
Rock and slag wool[d]				
attics, ~3.5 to 4.5 in.	1.5 to 1.6	0.34	—	—
attics, ~5 to 17 in.	1.5 to 1.8	0.32 to 0.33	—	—
closed attic or wall cavities	4.0	0.27 to 0.29	—	—
Vermiculite, exfoliated	7.0 to 8.2	0.47	—	0.32
	4.0 to 6.0	0.44	—	—
Spray applied				
Cellulose, sprayed into open wall cavities	1.6 to 2.6	0.27 to 0.28	—	—
Glass fiber, sprayed into open wall or attic cavities	1.0	0.27 to 0.29	—	—
	1.8 to 2.3	0.23 to 0.26	—	—
Polyurethane foam	—	—	—	0.35
low density, open cell	0.45 to 0.65	0.26 to 0.29	—	—
medium density, closed cell, aged 180 days	1.9 to 3.2	0.14 to 0.20	—	—
Building Board and Siding				
Board				
Asbestos/cement board	120	4	—	0.24
Cement board	71	1.7	—	0.2
Fiber/cement board	88	1.7	—	0.2
	61	1.3	—	0.2
	26	0.5	—	0.45
	20	0.4	—	0.45
Gypsum or plaster board	40	1.1	—	0.21
Oriented strand board (OSB) 7/16 in.	41	—	0.62	0.45
1/2 in.	41	—	0.68	0.45

Table 11.6 Building and Insulating Materials: Design Values[a] [2021F, Ch 26, Tbl 1] (*Continued*)

Description		Density, lb/ft³	Conductivity[b] k, Btu·in/h·ft²·°F	Resistance R, h·ft²·°F/Btu	Specific Heat, Btu/lb·°F
Plywood (douglas fir)	1/2 in.	29	—	0.79	0.45
	5/8 in.	34	—	0.85	0.45
Plywood/wood panels	3/4 in.	28	—	1.08	0.45
Vegetable fiber board					
sheathing, regular density	1/2 in.	18	—	1.32	0.31
intermediate density	1/2 in.	22	—	1.09	0.31
nail-based sheathing	1/2 in.	25	—	1.06	0.31
shingle backer	3/8 in.	18	—	0.94	0.3
sound-deadening board	1/2 in.	15	—	1.35	0.3
tile and lay-in panels, plain or acoustic		18	0.4	—	0.14
laminated paperboard		30	0.5	—	0.33
homogeneous board from repulped paper		30	0.5	—	0.28
Hardboard					
medium density		50	0.73	—	0.31
high density, service-tempered and service grades		55	0.82	—	0.32
high density, standard-tempered grade		63	1.0	—	0.32
Particleboard					
low density		37	0.71	—	0.31
medium density		50	0.94	—	0.31
high density		62	1.18	0.85	—
underlayment	5/8 in.	44	0.73	0.82	0.29
Waferboard		37	0.63	0.21	0.45
Shingles					
Asbestos/cement		120	—	0.21	—
Wood, 16 in., 7 1/2 in. exposure		—	—	0.87	0.31

Table 11.6 Building and Insulating Materials: Design Values[a] [2021F, Ch 26, Tbl 1] (*Continued*)

Description		Density, lb/ft^3	Conductivity[b] k, Btu·in/h·ft^2·°F	Resistance R, h·ft^2·°F/Btu	Specific Heat, Btu/lb·°F
Wood, double, 16 in., 12 in. exposure		—	—	1.19	0.28
Wood, plus ins. backer board	5/16 in.	—	—	1.4	0.31
Siding					
Asbestos/cement, lapped	1/4 in.	—	—	0.21	0.24
Asphalt roll siding		—	—	0.15	0.35
Asphalt insulating siding (1/2 in. bed)		—	—	0.21	0.24
Hardboard siding	7/16 in.	—	—	0.15	0.35
Wood, drop, 8 in.	1 in.	—	—	0.79	0.28
Wood, bevel					
8 in., lapped	1/2 in.	—	—	0.81	0.28
10 in., lapped	3/4 in.	—	—	1.05	0.28
Wood, plywood, 3/8 in., lapped		—	—	0.59	0.29
Aluminum, steel, or vinyl,[j,k] over sheathing					—
hollow-backed		—	—	0.62	0.29[i]
insulating-board-backed	3/8 in.	—	—	1.82	0.32
foil-backed	3/8 in.	—	—	2.96	—
insulated vinyl siding	3/4 to 1 1/4 in.[m]			2.0 to 2.7	
Architectural (soda-lime float) glass		158	6.9	—	0.21
Building Membrane					
Vapor-permeable felt		—	—	0.06	—
Vapor: seal, 2 layers of mopped 15 lb felt		—	—	0.12	—
Vapor: seal, plastic film		—	—	Negligible	—
Finish Flooring Materials					
Carpet and rebounded urethane pad	3/4 in.	7	—	2.38	—
Carpet and rubber pad (one-piece)	3/8 in.	20	—	0.68	—

Table 11.6 Building and Insulating Materials: Design Values[a] [2021F, Ch 26, Tbl 1] (*Continued*)

Description		Density, lb/ft^3	Conductivity[b] *k*, $Btu \cdot in/h \cdot ft^2 \cdot °F$	Resistance *R*, $h \cdot ft^2 \cdot °F/Btu$	Specific Heat, $Btu/lb \cdot °F$
Pile carpet with rubber pad	3/8 to 1/2 in.	18	—	1.59	—
Linoleum/cork tile	1/4 in.	29	—	0.51	—
PVC/rubber floor covering		—	2.8	—	—
rubber tile	1.0 in.	119	—	0.34	—
terrazzo	1.0 in.	—	—	0.08	0.19
Metals (See 2021F, Ch 33, Tbl 3)					
Roofing					
Asbestos/cement shingles		120	—	0.21	0.24
Asphalt (bitumen with inert fill)		100	2.98	—	—
		119	4.0	—	—
		144	7.97	—	—
Asphalt roll roofing		70	—	0.15	0.36
Asphalt shingles		70	—	0.44	0.3
Built-up roofing	3/8 in.	70	—	0.33	0.35
Mastic asphalt (heavy, 20% grit)		59	1.32	—	—
Reed thatch		17	0.62	—	—
Roofing felt		141	8.32	—	—
Slate	1/2 in.	—	—	0.05	0.3
Straw thatch		15	0.49	—	—
Wood shingles, plain and plastic-film-faced		—	—	0.94	0.31
Plastering Materials					
Cement plaster, sand aggregate		116	5.0	—	0.2
Sand aggregate	3/8 in.	—	—	0.08	0.2
	3/4 in.	—	—	0.15	0.2

Table 11.6 Building and Insulating Materials: Design Values[a] [2021F, Ch 26, Tbl 1] (*Continued*)

Description		Density, lb/ft³	Conductivity[b] k, Btu·in/h·ft²·°F	Resistance R, h·ft²·°F/Btu	Specific Heat, Btu/lb·°F
Gypsum plaster		70	2.63	—	—
		80	3.19	—	—
Lightweight aggregate	1/2 in.	45	—	0.32	—
	5/8 in.	45	—	0.39	—
on metal lath	3/4 in.	—	—	0.47	—
Perlite aggregate		45	1.5	—	0.32
Sand aggregate		105	5.6	—	0.2
on metal lath	3/4 in.	—	—	0.13	—
Vermiculite aggregate		30	1.0	—	—
		40	1.39	—	—
		45	1.7	—	—
		50	1.8	—	—
		60	2.08	—	—
Perlite plaster		25	0.55	—	—
		38	1.32	—	—
Pulpboard or paper plaster		38	0.48	—	—
Sand/cement plaster, conditioned		98	4.4	—	—
Sand/cement/lime plaster, conditioned		90	3.33	—	—
Sand/gypsum (3:1) plaster, conditioned		97	4.5	—	—
Masonry Materials					
Masonry units					
Brick, fired clay		150	8.4 to 10.2	—	—
		140	7.4 to 9.0	—	—
		130	6.4 to 7.8	—	—
		120	5.6 to 6.8	—	0.19

Table 11.6 Building and Insulating Materials: Design Values[a] [2021F, Ch 26, Tbl 1] (*Continued*)

Description	Density, lb/ft³	Conductivity[b] k, Btu·in/h·ft²·°F	Resistance R, h·ft²·°F/Btu	Specific Heat, Btu/lb·°F
	110	4.9 to 5.9	—	—
	100	4.2 to 5.1	—	—
	90	3.6 to 4.3	—	—
	80	3.0 to 3.7	—	—
	70	2.5 to 3.1	—	—
Clay tile, hollow				
1 cell deep ... 3 in.	—	—	0.80	0.21
... 4 in.	—	—	1.11	—
2 cells deep ... 6 in.	—	—	1.52	—
... 8 in.	—	—	1.85	—
... 10 in.	—	—	2.22	—
3 cells deep ... 12 in.	—	—	2.50	—
Lightweight brick	50	1.39	—	—
	48	1.51	—	—
Concrete blocks[h,i]				
Limestone aggregate				
8 in., 36 lb, 138 lb/ft³ concrete, 2 cores	—	—	—	—
with perlite-filled cores	—	—	2.1	—
12 in., 55 lb, 138 lb/ft³ concrete, 2 cores	—		—	—
with perlite-filled cores	—	—	3.7	—
Normal-weight aggregate (sand and gravel)				
8 in., 33 to 36 lb, 126 to 136 lb/ft³ concrete, 2 or 3 cores	—	—	1.11 to 0.97	0.22
with perlite-filled cores	—	—	2.0	—
with vermiculite-filled cores	—	—	1.92 to 1.37	—
12 in., 50 lb, 125 lb/ft³ concrete, 2 cores	—	—	1.23	0.22

Table 11.6 Building and Insulating Materials: Design Values[a] [2021F, Ch 26, Tbl 1] (*Continued*)

Description	Density, lb/ft^3	Conductivity[b] k, $Btu \cdot in/h \cdot ft^2 \cdot °F$	Resistance R, $h \cdot ft^2 \cdot °F/Btu$	Specific Heat, Btu/lb·°F
Medium-weight aggregate (combinations of normal and lightweight aggregate)				
8 in., 26 to 29 lb, 97 to 112 lb/ft^3 concrete, 2 or 3 cores	—	—	1.71 to 1.28	—
with perlite-filled cores	—	—	3.7 to 2.3	—
with vermiculite-filled cores	—	—	3.3	—
with molded-EPS-filled (beads) cores	—	—	3.2	—
with molded EPS inserts in cores	—	—	2.7	—
Lightweight aggregate (expanded shale, clay, slate or slag, pumice)				
6 in., 16 to 17 lb, 85 to 87 lb/ft^3 concrete, 2 or 3 cores	—	—	1.93 to 1.65	—
with perlite-filled cores	—	—	4.2	—
with vermiculite-filled cores	—	—	3.0	—
8 in., 19 to 22 lb, 72 to 86 lb/ft^3 concrete	—	—	3.2 to 1.90	0.21
with perlite-filled cores	—	—	6.8 to 4.4	—
with vermiculite-filled cores	—	—	5.3 to 3.9	—
with molded-EPS-filled (beads) cores	—	—	4.8	—
with UF foam-filled cores	—	—	4.5	—
with molded EPS inserts in cores	—	—	3.5	—
12 in., 32 to 36 lb, 80 to 90 lb/ft^3, concrete, 2 or 3 cores	—	—	2.6 to 2.3	—
with perlite-filled cores	—	—	9.2 to 6.3	—
with vermiculite-filled cores	—	—	5.8	—
Stone, lime, or sand	180	72	—	—
Quartzitic and sandstone	160	43	—	—
	140	24	—	—
	120	13	—	0.19
Calcitic, dolomitic, limestone, marble, and granite	180	30	—	—
	160	22	—	—

Table 11.6 Building and Insulating Materials: Design Values[a] [2021F, Ch 26, Tbl 1] (*Continued*)

Description	Density, lb/ft^3	Conductivity[b] k, Btu·in/h·ft^2·°F	Resistance R, h·ft^2·°F/Btu	Specific Heat, Btu/lb·°F
	140	16	—	—
	120	11	—	0.19
	100	8	—	—
Gypsum partition tile				
3 by 12 by 30 in., solid	—	—	1.26	0.19
4 cells	—	—	1.35	—
4 by 12 by 30 in., 3 cells	—	—	1.67	—
Limestone	150	3.95	—	0.2
	163	6.45	—	0.2
Concretes[i]				
Sand and gravel or stone aggregate concretes	150	10.0 to 20.0	—	—
(concretes with >50% quartz or quartzite sand have conductivities	140	9.0 to 18.0	—	0.19 to 0.24
in higher end of range)	130	7.0 to 13.0	—	—
Lightweight aggregate or limestone concretes	120	6.4 to 9.1	—	—
expanded shale, clay, or slate; expanded slags; cinders;	100	4.7 to 6.2	—	0.2
pumice (with density up to 100 lb/ft^3); scoria (sanded	80	3.3 to 4.1	—	0.2
concretes have conductivities in higher end of range)	60	2.1 to 2.5	—	—
	40	1.3	—	—
Gypsum/fiber concrete (87.5% gypsum, 12.5% wood chips)	51	1.66	—	0.2
Cement/lime, mortar, and stucco	120	9.7	—	—
	100	6.7	—	—
	80	4.5	—	—
Perlite, vermiculite, and polystyrene beads	50	1.8 to 1.9	—	—
	40	1.4 to 1.5	—	0.15 to 0.23
	30	1.1	—	—

Table 11.6 Building and Insulating Materials: Design Values[a] [2021F, Ch 26, Tbl 1] (*Continued*)

Description	Density, lb/ft³	Conductivity[b] k, Btu·in/h·ft²·°F	Resistance R, h·ft²·°F/Btu	Specific Heat, Btu/lb·°F
	20	0.8	—	—
Foam concretes	120	5.4	—	—
	100	4.1	—	—
	80	3.0	—	—
	70	2.5	—	—
Foam concretes and cellular concretes	60	2.1	—	—
	40	1.4	—	—
	20	0.8	—	—
Aerated concrete (oven-dried)	27 to 50	1.4	—	0.2
Polystyrene concrete (oven-dried)	16 to 50	2.54	—	0.2
Polymer concrete	122	11.4	—	—
	138	7.14	—	—
Polymer cement	117	5.39	—	—
Slag concrete	60	1.5	—	—
	80	2.25	—	—
	100	3	—	—
	125	8.53	—	—
Woods (12% moisture content)[l]				
Hardwoods	—	—	—	*0.39[n]*
Oak	41 to 47	1.12 to 1.25	—	—
Birch	43 to 45	1.16 to 1.22	—	—
Maple	40 to 44	1.09 to 1.19	—	—
Ash	38 to 42	1.06 to 1.14	—	—
Softwoods	—	—	—	*0.39[n]*
Southern pine	36 to 41	1.00 to 1.12	—	—

Table 11.6 Building and Insulating Materials: Design Values[a] [2021F, Ch 26, Tbl 1] (*Continued*)

Description	Density, lb/ft³	Conductivity[b] *k*, Btu·in/h·ft²·°F	Resistance *R*, h·ft²·°F/Btu	Specific Heat, Btu/lb·°F
Southern yellow pine	31	1.06 to 1.16	—	—
Eastern white pine	25	0.85 to 0.94	—	—
Douglas fir/larch	34 to 36	0.95 to 1.01	—	—
Southern cypress	31 to 32	0.90 to 0.92	—	—
Hem/fir, spruce/pine/fir	24 to 31	0.74 to 0.90	—	—
Spruce	25	0.74 to 0.85	—	—
Western red cedar	22	0.83 to 0.86	—	—
West coast woods, cedars	22 to 31	0.68 to 0.90	—	—
Eastern white cedar	23	0.82 to 0.89	—	—
California redwood	24 to 28	0.74 to 0.82	—	—
Pine (oven-dried)	23	0.64	—	0.45
Spruce (oven-dried)	25	0.69	—	0.45

Notes for Table 11.6:

[a]Values are for mean temperature of 75°F. Representative values for dry materials are intended as design (not specification) values for materials in normal use. Thermal values of insulating materials may differ from design values depending on in situ properties (e.g., density and moisture content, orientation, etc.) and manufacturing variability. For properties of specific product, use values supplied by manufacturer or unbiased tests.

[b]Symbol λ also used to represent thermal conductivity.

[c]Does not include paper backing and facing, if any. Where insulation forms boundary (reflective or otherwise) of airspace, see Tables 2 and 3 of Chapter 26 of the 2021 *ASHRAE Handbook—Fundamentals* for insulating value of airspace with appropriate effective emittance and temperature conditions of space.

[d]Conductivity varies with fiber diameter (see Chapter 25 of the 2021 *ASHRAE Handbook—Fundamentals*). Batt, blanket, and loose-fill mineral fiber insulations are manufactured to achieve specified R-values, the most common of which are listed in the table. Because of differences in manufacturing processes and materials, the product thicknesses, densities, and thermal conductivities vary over considerable ranges for a specified R-value.

[e]Values are for aged products with gas-impermeable facers on the two major surfaces. An aluminum foil facer of 0.001 in. thickness or greater is generally considered impermeable to gases. For change in conductivity with age of expanded polyisocyanurate, see SPI Bulletin U108.

[f]Cellular phenolic insulation may no longer be manufactured.

[g]Insulating values of acoustical tile vary, depending on density of board and on type, size, and depth of perforations.

[h]Values for fully grouted block may be approximated using values for concrete with similar unit density.

[i]Values for concrete block and concrete are at moisture contents representative of normal use.

[j]Values for metal or vinyl siding applied over flat surfaces vary widely, depending on ventilation of the airspace beneath the siding; whether airspace is reflective or nonreflective; and on thickness, type, and application of insulating backing-board used. Values are averages for use as design guides, and were obtained from several guarded hot box tests (ASTM Standard C1363) on hollow-backed types and types made using backing of wood fiber, foamed plastic, and glass fiber. Departures of ±50% or more from these values may occur.

[k]Vinyl specific heat = 0.25 Btu/lb·°F

[l]See Adams (1971), MacLean (1941), and Wilkes (1979). Conductivity values listed are for heat transfer across the grain. Thermal conductivity of wood varies linearly with density, and density ranges listed are those normally found for wood species given. If density of wood species is not known, use mean conductivity value. For extrapolation to other moisture contents, the following empirical equation developed by Wilkes (1979) may be used:

$$k = 0.1791 + \frac{(1.874 \times 10^{-2} + 5.753 \times 10^{-4} M)\rho}{1 + 0.01M}$$

where ρ is density of moist wood in lb/ft^3, and M is moisture content in percent.

[m]Dimension referenced is taken at the maximum siding profile thickness. The range of R values and associated thicknesses represent values for products tested to ASTM Standard D7793, which requires applying 15 mph airstream perpendicular to surface of siding during testing.

[n]From Wilkes (1979), an empirical equation for specific heat of moist wood at 75°F is as follows:

$$c_p = \frac{(0.299 + 0.01M)}{(1 + 0.01M)} + \Delta c_p$$

where Δc_p accounts for heat of sorption and is denoted by $\Delta c_p = M(1.921 \times 10^{-3} - 3.168 \times 10^{-5} M)$ where M is moisture content in percent by mass.

[o]Blank space in reference column indicates historical values from previous volumes of ASHRAE Handbook. Source of information could not be determined.

Cooling Load Temperature Differences (CLTDs)

Table 11.7 CLTDs (°F) for Flat Roofs—24°N Latitude, July
[Adapted from *Cooling and Heating Load Calculation Manual*, Second Edition, Tbl 8.2A]

Roof	Solar time, h											
No	2	4	6	8	10	12	14	16	18	20	22	24
1	−2	−5	−6	9	44	76	92	86	58	23	8	2
2	0	−4	−6	1	30	64	86	89	70	36	14	5
3	8	2	−2	3	22	47	68	77	68	47	29	16
4	11	3	−2	−4	5	27	55	75	80	67	43	23
5	16	8	3	1	10	30	52	68	70	59	41	27
8	24	17	11	9	14	27	43	54	58	52	42	32
9	25	16	9	4	5	17	36	54	65	63	51	37
10	31	22	15	9	8	16	30	45	56	59	52	41
13	31	25	20	16	16	23	33	43	49	49	43	37
14	32	27	23	19	19	24	32	40	45	45	42	37

Table 11.8 CLTDs (°F) for Flat Roofs—36°N Latitude, July
[Adapted from *Cooling and Heating Load Calculation Manual*, Second Edition, Tbl 8.2B]

Roof	Solar time, h											
No.	2	4	6	8	10	12	14	16	18	20	22	24
1	−2	−5	−6	12	45	75	90	84	60	26	9	2
2	0	−4	−6	4	32	63	84	87	70	39	15	5
3	8	2	−2	4	24	47	67	75	68	48	30	17
4	11	3	−1	−3	7	29	55	74	79	67	45	24
5	16	8	3	2	12	31	52	67	70	59	42	27
8	25	17	12	9	15	28	42	54	58	53	43	33
9	26	16	9	4	7	19	37	54	64	63	52	38
10	32	23	15	10	9	17	30	45	56	58	52	42
13	31	25	20	16	17	24	33	43	49	49	44	37
14	32	28	23	20	20	25	32	40	45	46	42	37

Table 11.9 CLTDs (°F) for Flat Roofs—48°N Latitude, July
[Adapted from *Cooling and Heating Load Calculation Manual*, Second Edition, Tbl 8.2C]

Roof	Solar time, h											
No.	2	4	6	8	10	12	14	16	18	20	22	24
1	−2	−5	−5	15	44	69	83	79	59	29	9	2
2	0	−4	−5	6	32	60	78	81	68	41	16	5
3	8	2	−1	6	24	45	63	71	65	48	30	17
4	12	3	−1	−2	8	29	52	69	74	65	45	25
5	16	8	3	3	13	31	49	63	66	58	42	27
8	24	17	11	10	16	27	40	51	55	51	42	32
9	26	16	9	5	8	19	35	51	60	61	51	38
10	31	22	15	10	10	17	29	43	53	56	51	41
13	30	25	20	16	18	24	32	41	47	47	43	37
14	32	27	23	20	20	24	31	38	43	44	41	36

CAUTION: Approximate data—Use for preliminary computations only. Also, see notes on next page.

Notes for CLTD Data for Flat Roofs

1. Data apply directly to (1) dark surface, (2) indoor temperature is 78°F, (3) outdoor maximum temperature of 95°F with mean temperature of 85°F and daily range of 21°F, (4) solar radiation typical of clear day on 21st day of month, (5) outside surface film resistance of 0.333 $h \cdot ft^2 \cdot °F/Btu$, and (6) inside surface resistance of 0.685 $h \cdot ft^2 \cdot °F/Btu$.
2. Adjustments to design temperatures

$$\text{Corr. CLTD} = \text{CLTD} + (78 - t_r) + (t_m - 85) \tag{11.5}$$

where t_r = inside temperature and t_m = mean outdoor temperature, or t_m = maximum outdoor temperature − (daily range)/2.

No adjustment recommended for color or for ventilation of air space above a ceiling.

For design purposes, the data suffice for plus or minus 2 weeks from the 21st day of given month.

Table 11.10 Roof Classifications for Use with CLTD Tables for Flat Roofs
[Adapted from *Cooling and Heating Load Calculation Manual*, Second Edition, Tbl 8.4]

Mass Location	Suspended Ceiling	R, $h \cdot ft^2 \cdot °F/Btu$	Wood 1 in.	2 in. (Heavyweight) Concrete	Steel Deck	Attic Ceiling Comb.
Mass inside insul.	Without	0 to 10	*	2	*	*
		10 to 20	*	4	*	*
		20 to 25	*	5	*	*
	With	0 to 5	*	5	*	*
		5 to 10	*	8	*	*
		10 to 20	*	13	*	*
		20 to 25	*	14	*	*
Mass evenly placed	Without	0 to 5	1	2	1	1
		5 to 15	2	*	1	2
		15 to 25	4	*	2	2
	With	0 to 5	*	3	1	*
		5 to 10	4	*	1	*
		10 to 15	5	*	2	
		15 to 20	9	*	2	*
		20 to 25	10	*	4	*
Mass outside insul.	Without	0 to 5	*	2	*	*
		5 to 10	*	3	*	*
		10 to 15	*	4	*	*
		15 to 25	*	5	*	*
	With	0 to 10	*	3	*	*
		10 to 15	*	4	*	*
		15 to 20	*	5	*	*

*Denotes roof that is not possible with the chosen parameters

Table 11.11 Approximate CLTDs (°F) for Sunlit Walls—24°N Latitude, July

[Adapted from *Cooling and Heating Load Calculation Manual*, Second Edition, Tbl 8.3A]

CAUTION: Approximate data—Use for preliminary computations only.

Wall Facing	Solar time, h								Solar time, h								Solar time, h							
	6	8	10	12	14	16	18	20	6	8	10	12	14	16	18	20	6	8	10	12	14	16	18	20
	Low Mass, Low R-Value Wall								**Low Mass, Medium R-Value Wall**								**Low Mass, High R-Value Wall**							
N	−2	13	18	22	28	32	34	17	1	0	6	13	18	23	28	30	−2	2	12	18	23	28	32	29
NE	0	39	53	39	30	30	24	13	0	3	20	36	39	35	32	27	−2	9	36	46	38	32	29	22
E	0	44	63	48	32	30	24	13	1	3	22	43	46	40	34	28	−2	10	42	55	44	35	30	23
SE	−2	25	44	42	32	30	24	13	0	1	13	28	35	35	32	27	−2	4	26	40	38	33	29	22
S	−3	3	12	24	31	30	23	13	0	−1	1	7	16	24	27	25	−2	−1	4	13	24	29	28	22
SW	−3	3	13	22	40	58	52	20	1	−1	1	7	15	29	43	47	−2	−1	5	13	24	42	54	44
W	−3	3	13	22	42	73	75	27	2	0	2	7	15	30	52	61	−1	−1	5	13	23	46	69	61
NW	−3	3	13	22	37	62	67	25	1	0	2	7	15	27	45	54	−1	−1	5	13	22	40	60	55
	High Mass, Low R-Value Wall								**High Mass, Medium R-Value Wall**								**High Mass, High R-Value Wall**							
N	3	3	7	12	16	21	25	27	10	8	8	10	12	15	18	21	12	9	8	8	10	13	16	19
NE	3	6	20	31	33	32	31	27	11	9	14	21	25	26	27	26	13	10	10	15	21	24	27	27
E	4	6	22	36	39	36	33	29	12	10	15	24	29	30	30	29	14	11	11	17	24	28	30	31
SE	3	4	14	25	30	30	30	26	10	8	11	17	21	24	25	25	13	10	9	12	17	21	24	25
S	3	1	3	7	14	20	23	22	8	6	5	6	10	14	17	18	10	8	6	5	7	10	14	17
SW	5	3	4	8	14	26	38	40	13	10	9	9	11	17	24	30	17	13	10	8	9	12	18	25
W	7	4	4	8	15	28	45	51	17	13	11	11	13	18	28	36	21	16	12	10	11	13	20	30
NW	6	3	4	8	14	25	40	46	15	12	10	10	12	17	25	32	19	14	11	9	10	12	18	26

CAUTION: Approximate data—Use for preliminary computations only.

Table 11.12 Approximate CLTDs (°F) for Sunlit Walls—36°N Latitude, July

[Adapted from *Cooling and Heating Load Calculation Manual*, Second Edition, Tbl 8.3B]

CAUTION: Approximate data—Use for preliminary computations only.

Wall Facing	Solar time, h								Solar time, h								Solar time, h							
	6	8	10	12	14	16	18	20	6	8	10	12	14	16	18	20	6	8	10	12	14	16	18	20
	Low Mass, Low R-Value Wall								**Low Mass, Medium R-Value Wall**								**Low Mass, High R-Value Wall**							
N	−1	12	14	21	28	29	30	17	0	0	5	10	16	22	26	27	−2	3	9	15	21	27	28	27
NE	1	41	46	30	29	29	24	14	0	4	21	33	33	31	30	27	−2	12	36	39	32	30	28	23
E	1	49	64	48	31	30	24	14	1	4	26	45	47	40	34	29	−2	14	46	56	45	34	30	23
SE	−1	31	52	52	36	30	24	14	1	2	16	34	44	41	35	29	−2	7	31	48	47	37	31	23
S	−3	4	18	39	47	40	25	14	0	−1	2	11	25	36	38	32	−2	−1	6	21	37	44	37	25
SW	−2	4	13	23	50	67	59	23	1	0	2	8	17	34	51	54	−1	−1	5	13	28	50	62	51
W	−2	4	13	21	42	73	78	31	2	0	2	8	15	30	52	63	−1	−1	5	13	23	46	69	65
NW	−2	4	13	21	29	53	65	28	1	0	2	8	15	24	39	51	−2	−1	5	13	21	33	53	55
	High Mass, Low R-Value Wall								**High Mass, Medium R-Value Wall**								**High Mass, High R-Value Wall**							
N	3	3	6	10	15	20	23	25	9	7	8	9	11	14	17	19	11	9	7	7	9	11	14	17
NE	3	7	20	28	29	29	29	26	10	9	14	20	23	24	25	25	13	10	10	15	19	22	24	25
E	4	8	25	38	40	37	34	29	12	11	17	25	30	31	31	30	15	11	12	18	25	30	31	31
SE	4	5	17	30	37	36	33	29	12	10	13	20	26	29	29	28	14	11	10	14	20	26	29	30
S	3	2	4	11	22	31	33	29	10	8	7	9	14	20	24	25	13	10	7	7	10	15	21	24
SW	6	3	4	8	16	31	44	46	15	12	10	10	13	19	28	34	19	15	11	10	10	14	21	29
W	7	4	5	9	15	28	46	54	17	14	12	11	13	18	28	37	22	17	13	11	11	14	20	30
NW	6	3	4	8	14	22	35	43	14	11	10	10	12	15	22	30	18	14	11	9	10	12	17	24

CAUTION: Approximate data—Use for preliminary computations only.

Table 11.13 Approximate CLTDs (°F) for Sunlit Walls—48°N Latitude, July
[Adapted from *Cooling and Heating Load Calculation Manual*, Second Edition, Tbl 8.3C]
CAUTION: Approximate data—Use for preliminary computations only.

Wall Facing	Solar time, h								Solar time, h								Solar time, h							
	6	8	10	12	14	16	18	20	6	8	10	12	14	16	18	20	6	8	10	12	14	16	18	20
	Low Mass, Low R-Value Wall								**Low Mass, Medium R-Value Wall**								**Low Mass, High R-Value Wall**							
N	3	10	13	21	27	28	27	21	1	2	6	10	16	21	25	26	−1	5	9	14	21	26	27	27
NE	10	42	38	26	28	29	24	15	1	7	23	31	30	29	28	26	0	18	36	34	28	28	28	23
E	10	54	64	47	31	29	25	15	1	8	30	47	48	40	34	29	0	20	49	57	44	34	29	23
SE	4	36	59	61	45	31	25	15	1	4	20	40	51	49	40	32	−1	11	36	55	56	43	33	24
S	−2	5	28	52	62	51	29	15	1	0	3	16	34	48	50	40	−1	0	9	30	50	57	47	30
SW	−1	5	12	29	59	75	65	29	2	0	3	8	20	40	58	61	−1	0	6	14	33	58	69	57
W	−1	5	13	21	41	72	80	41	2	0	3	8	15	29	51	64	−1	0	6	13	22	45	69	69
NW	−2	5	12	21	27	45	62	37	2	0	2	8	14	22	34	47	−1	0	5	13	20	29	46	54
	High Mass, Low R-Value Wall								**High Mass, Medium R-Value Wall**								**High Mass, High R-Value Wall**							
N	3	4	6	10	14	19	22	24	9	8	8	9	11	14	17	19	12	9	8	8	9	11	14	17
NE	4	10	22	26	26	27	27	25	10	10	15	20	22	23	24	24	13	10	12	16	19	22	23	24
E	4	11	28	40	40	37	34	29	12	12	19	27	32	32	32	30	15	12	14	20	27	31	32	32
SE	4	7	20	35	43	42	38	32	13	12	15	23	30	34	34	32	16	12	12	17	24	30	34	34
S	5	3	6	16	31	41	43	37	13	10	9	12	19	27	32	33	16	12	10	10	14	21	28	32
SW	7	4	5	9	19	36	50	52	18	14	12	12	15	23	32	39	22	17	13	11	12	16	24	33
W	8	5	6	9	15	27	45	55	19	15	12	12	14	19	28	38	23	18	14	12	12	14	20	30
NW	6	4	5	8	14	20	31	41	14	11	10	10	12	15	20	28	18	14	11	9	10	12	16	22

Note 1. Apply data directly to (1) dark surface, (2) indoor temperature of 78°F, (3) outdoor maximum temperature of 95°F with mean temperature of 85°F and daily range of 21°F, (4) outside surface film resistance of 0.333 (h·ft^2·°F)/Btu, and (5) inside surface resistance of 0.685 (h·ft^2·°F)/Btu.

Note 2. Adjustments to design temperatures:

$$\text{Corr. CLTD} = \text{CLTD} + (78 - t_r) + (t_m - 85)$$

where t_r = inside temperature and t_m = mean outdoor temperature, or t_m = maximum outdoor temperature − (daily range)/2

Note 3. Adjustments to months other than July: For design purposes, the data suffice for plus or minus 2 weeks from the 21st day of given month.

Table 11.14 Solar Cooling Load for Sunlit Glass (SCL)

[Adapted from *Cooling and Heating Load Calculation Manual*, 2nd Ed., Tbls 8.9A, 8.9B, 8.9C]

Tables do not consider zone type and are conservative.
Use for preliminary computations only.

Glass Facing	Solar time, h																	
	5	6	7	8	9	10	11	12	13	14	15	16	17	18	19	20	21	22
24°N Latitude, July																		
N	0	19	35	36	36	38	40	42	42	40	38	39	43	32	11	6	3	1
NE	0	54	124	150	144	115	78	58	49	44	38	32	25	14	6	3	1	1
E	0	57	139	177	180	154	107	68	54	46	40	33	25	14	6	3	1	1
SE	0	26	74	104	114	106	83	59	50	44	38	32	25	14	6	3	1	1
S	0	5	15	23	30	35	40	43	43	40	37	32	24	14	6	3	1	1
SW	0	5	15	23	30	35	39	42	61	88	110	118	105	62	24	12	6	3
W	0	5	15	23	30	35	39	41	67	116	160	186	184	118	44	21	11	5
NW	0	5	15	23	30	35	39	41	51	83	122	151	158	106	39	19	9	5
Hor	0	10	55	113	170	218	253	271	273	258	225	176	115	54	24	12	6	3
36°N Latitude, July																		
N	0	25	29	28	32	36	39	40	41	39	36	32	33	36	12	6	3	1
NE	0	79	129	139	120	84	58	50	45	41	37	32	26	17	7	3	2	1
E	0	86	153	184	182	155	107	67	54	45	39	33	26	17	7	3	2	1
SE	0	42	90	125	142	140	119	86	58	48	40	34	27	17	7	3	2	1
S	0	8	17	24	36	53	70	80	79	68	52	38	29	18	7	3	2	1
SW	0	8	17	24	30	35	38	57	90	122	141	144	127	85	32	15	8	4
W	0	8	17	24	30	35	38	40	66	115	159	188	191	149	53	25	12	6
NW	0	8	17	24	30	35	38	40	40	56	93	129	148	127	43	21	10	5
Hor	0	20	66	120	171	215	246	263	265	251	221	178	124	66	28	13	7	3
48°N Latitude, July																		
N	14	28	24	27	31	34	37	38	38	37	35	31	27	34	25	9	4	2
NE	32	101	130	126	95	61	49	44	41	38	35	31	26	19	10	4	2	1
E	31	112	165	188	182	153	104	65	51	43	38	32	27	19	10	4	2	1
SE	11	58	106	143	164	168	152	119	77	54	43	35	28	20	10	4	2	1
S	3	11	18	30	58	90	116	130	130	116	88	56	37	24	12	5	3	1
SW	3	11	18	24	30	34	46	82	122	152	168	166	146	106	50	22	11	5
W	3	11	18	24	30	34	36	38	64	112	156	186	193	167	89	36	17	9
NW	3	11	18	24	30	34	36	38	38	40	67	106	134	134	76	30	14	7
Hor	5	32	73	120	163	200	226	241	242	230	205	170	125	76	35	16	8	4

Data apply directly to: (1) standard double strength glass with no inside shade, and (2) clear sky, 21st day of month.

Adjustments to table data:

- Latitudes other than 24, 36 and 48°N
  Linear interpolation is acceptable.
- Months other than July
  For design purposes, data will suffice for plus or minus 2 weeks from the 21st day of given month.
- Other types of glass and internal shade
  Use shading coefficients as multiplier.
- Externally shaded glass
  Use north orientation.

Table 11.15 Shading Coefficients* for Single Glass with Indoor Shading by Venetian Blinds or Roller Shades

[Adapted from *Cooling and Heating Load Calculation Manual*, Second Edition, Tbl 8.10]

Tables do not consider zone type and are conservative.
Use for preliminary computations only.

Type of Glass	Nominal Thickness,[a] in.	Solar Transmittance[b]	Type of Shading				
			Venetian Blinds		Roller Shade		
					Opaque		Translucent
			Medium	Light	Dark	White	Light
Clear	3/32[c]	0.87 to 0.80	0.74[d]	0.67[d]	0.81	0.39	0.44
			(0.63)[e]	(0.58)[e]			
Clear	1/4 to 1/2	0.80 to 0.71					
Clear pattern	1/8 to 1/2	0.87 to 0.79					
Heat-absorbing pattern	1/8	—					
Tinted	3/16, 7/32	0.74, 0.71					
Heat-absorbing[f]	3/16, 1/4	0.46					
Heat-absorbing pattern	3/16, 1/4	—	0.57	0.53	0.45	0.30	0.36
Tinted	1/8, 7/32	0.59, 0.45					
Heat-absorbing or pattern	—	0.44 to 0.30	0.54	0.52	0.40	0.28	0.32
Heat-absorbing[f]	3/8	0.34					
Heat-absorbing or pattern		0.29 to 0.15					
	—	0.24	0.42	0.40	0.36	0.28	0.31
Reflective-coated	S.C. = 0.30[g]		0.25	0.23			
	= 0.40		0.33	0.29			
	= 0.50		0.42	0.38			
	= 0.60		0.50	0.44			

[a]Refer to manufacturers' literature for values.
[b]For vertical blinds with opaque white and beige louvers in the tightly closed position, SC is 0.25 and 0.29 when used with glass of 0.71 to 0.80 transmittance.
[c]Typical residential glass thickness.
[d]From Van Dyck and Konen (1982), for 45° open venetian blinds, 35° solar incidence, and 35° profile angle.
[e]Values for closed venetian blinds. Use these values only when operation is automated for solar gain reduction (as opposed to daylight use).
[f]Refers to gray, bronze, and green tinted heat-absorbing glass.
[g]SC for glass with no shading device.

* Note: Shading coefficient (SC) has been superseded by solar heat gain coefficient (SHGC) including the effect of incident angle of solar radiation on the glass, and the effect of type of framing. This shading coefficient table is sufficiently accurate for the approximate cooling load calculations of this publication. For the glazing portion of single-pane clear and tinted fenestration, SC = SHGC/0.87. This does not include frame effects.

Table 11.16 Representative Rates at Which Heat and Moisture are Given Off by Human Beings in Different States of Activity [2021F, Ch 18, Tbl 1]

Degree of Activity	Location	Total Heat, Btu/h		Sensible Heat, Btu/h	Latent Heat, Btu/h	% Sensible Heat that is Radiant[b]	
		Adult Male	Adjusted, M/F[a]			Low V	High V
Seated at theater	Theater, matinee	390	330	225	105		
Seated at theater, night	Theater, night	390	350	245	105	60	27
Seated, very light work	Offices, hotels, apartments	450	400	245	155		
Moderately active office work	Offices, hotels, apartments	475	450	250	200		
Standing, light work; walking	Department store; retail store	550	450	250	200	58	38
Walking, standing	Drug store, bank	550	500	250	250		
Sedentary work	Restaurant[c]	490	550	275	275		
Light bench work	Factory	800	750	275	475		
Moderate dancing	Dance hall	900	850	305	545	49	35
Walking 3 mph; light machine work	Factory	1000	1000	375	625		
Bowling[d]	Bowling alley	1500	1450	580	870		
Heavy work	Factory	1500	1450	580	870	54	19
Heavy machine work; lifting	Factory	1600	1600	635	965		
Athletics	Gymnasium	2000	1800	710	1090		

Notes:

1. Tabulated values are based on 75°F room dry-bulb temperature. For 80°F room dry bulb, total heat remains the same, but sensible heat values should be decreased by approximately 20%, and latent heat values increased accordingly.
2. Also see Table 4 of Chapter 9 of the 2021 *ASHRAE Handbook—Fundamentals* for additional rates of metabolic heat generation.
3. All values are rounded to nearest 5 Btu/h.

[a] Adjusted heat gain is based on normal percentage of men, women, and children for the application listed, and assumes that gain from an adult female is 85% of that for an adult male, and gain from a child is 75% of that for an adult male.

[b] Values approximated from data in Table 6 of Chapter 9 of the 2021 *ASHRAE Handbook—Fundamentals*, where V is air velocity with limits shown in that table.

[c] Adjusted heat gain includes 60 Btu/h for food per individual (30 Btu/h sensible and 30 Btu/h latent).

[d] Figure one person per alley actually bowling, and all others as sitting (400 Btu/h) or standing or walking slowly (550 Btu/h).

Heat Gain from Lighting

Because lighting is often a major space cooling load component, an accurate estimate of the space heat gain it imposes is needed. Calculation of this load component is not straightforward; the rate of cooling load from lighting at any given moment can be quite different from the heat equivalent of power supplied instantaneously to those lights, because of heat storage.

Instantaneous rate of heat gain from lights, q_{el} Btu/h:

$$q_{el} = 3.41\ WF_{ul}F_{sa} \tag{11.6}$$

where

W	=	total light wattage installed
F_{ul}	=	lighting use factor (proportion in use)
F_{sa}	=	lighting special allowance factor
3.41	=	conversion factor

The **total light wattage** is obtained from the ratings of all lamps installed, both for general illumination and for display use. Ballasts are not included, but are addressed by a separate factor. Wattages of magnetic ballasts are significant; the energy consumption of high-efficiency electronic ballasts might be insignificant compared to that of the lamps.

The **lighting use factor** is the ratio of wattage in use, for the conditions under which the load estimate is being made, to total installed wattage. For commercial applications such as stores, the use factor is generally 1.0.

The **special allowance factor** is the ratio of the lighting fixtures' power consumption, including lamps and ballast, to the nominal power consumption of the lamps. For incandescent lights, this factor is 1. For fluorescent lights, it accounts for power consumed by the ballast as well as the ballast's effect on lamp power consumption. The special allowance factor can be less than 1 for electronic ballasts that lower electricity consumption below the lamp's rated power consumption. Use manufacturers' values for system (lamps + ballast) power, when available.

For high-intensity-discharge lamps (e.g. metal halide, mercury vapor, high- and low-pressure sodium vapor lamps), the actual lighting system power consumption should be available from the manufacturer of the fixture or ballast. Ballasts available for metal halide and high pressure sodium vapor lamps may have special allowance factors from about 1.3 (for low-wattage lamps) down to 1.1 (for high-wattage lamps).

An alternative procedure is to estimate the lighting heat gain on a per square foot basis. Such an approach may be required when final lighting plans are not available. Table 11.17 shows the maximum lighting power density (LPD) (lighting heat gain per square foot) allowed by ANSI/ASHRAE/IES Standard 90.1 for a range of space types.

Table 11.17 Lighting Power Densities Using Space-by-Space Method [2021F, Ch 18, Tbl 2]

Common Space Types[a]	LPD, W/ft^2
Atrium	
<20 ft in height	0.39
≥20 ft and ≤40 ft in height	0.48
>40 ft in height	0.60
Audience Seating Area	
Auditorium	0.61
Gymnasium	0.23
Motion picture theater	0.27
Penitentiary	0.67
Performing arts theater	1.16
Religious building	0.72
Sports arena	0.33
All other audience seating areas	0.23
Banking Activity Area	0.61
Breakroom (*See* Lounge/Breakroom)	
Classroom/Lecture Hall/Training Room	
Penitentiary	0.89
All other classrooms/lecture halls/ training rooms	0.71
Conference/Meeting/Multipurpose Room	0.97
Confinement Cells	0.70
Copy/Print Room	0.31
Corridor[b]	
Facility for visually impaired (and not used primarily by staff)[c]	0.71
Hospital	0.71
All other corridors	0.41
Courtroom	1.20
Computer Room	0.94
Dining Area	
Penitentiary	0.42
Facility for visually impaired (and not used primarily by staff)[c]	1.27
Bar/lounge or leisure dining	0.86
Cafeteria or fast food dining	0.40
Family dining	0.60
All other dining areas	0.43
Electrical/Mechanical Room[f]	0.43
Emergency Vehicle Garage	0.52
Food Preparation Area	1.09

Common Space Types[a]	LPD, W/ft^2
Guest Room	0.41
Laboratory	
In or as classroom	1.11
All other laboratories	1.33
Laundry/Washing Area	0.53
Loading Dock, Interior	0.88
Lobby	
Facility for the visually impaired (and not used primarily by staff)[c]	1.69
Elevator	0.65
Hotel	0.51
Motion picture theater	0.23
Performing arts theater	1.25
All other lobbies	0.84
Locker Room	0.52
Lounge/Breakroom	
Health care facility	0.42
All other lounges/breakrooms	0.59
Office	
Enclosed and ≤250 ft^2	0.74
Enclosed and >250 ft^2	0.66
Open plan	0.61
Parking Area, Interior	0.15
Pharmacy Area	1.66
Restroom	
Facility for the visually impaired (and not used primarily by staff)[c]	1.26
All other restrooms	0.63
Sales Area[d]	1.05
Seating Area, General	0.23
Stairway	
Space containing stairway determines LPD and control requirements for stairway.	
Stairwell	0.49
Storage Room	
<50 ft^2	0.51
>50 ft^2	0.38
Vehicular Maintenance Area	0.60
Workshop	1.26

Table 11.17 Lighting Power Densities Using Space-by-Space Method [2021F, Ch 18, Tbl 2] *(Continued)*

Building-Specific Space Types*	LPD, W/ft^2
Facility for Visually Impaired[c]	
Chapel (used primarily by residents)	0.70
Recreation room/common living room (and not used primarily by staff)	1.77
Automotive (*See* Vehicular Maintenance Area)	
Convention Center, Exhibit Space	0.61
Dormitory/Living Quarters	0.50
Fire Station, Sleeping Quarters	0.23
Gymnasium/Fitness Center	
Exercise area	0.90
Playing area	0.85
Health Care Facility	
Exam/treatment room	1.40
Imaging room	0.94
Medical supply room	0.62
Nursery	0.92
Nurses' station	1.17
Operating room	2.26
Patient room	0.68
Physical therapy room	0.91
Recovery room	1.25
Library	
Reading area	0.96
Stacks	1.18
Manufacturing Facility	
Detailed manufacturing area	0.80
Equipment room	0.76
Extra-high-bay area (>50 ft floor-to-ceiling height)	1.42
High-bay area (25 to 50 ft floor-to-ceiling height)	1.24
Low bay area (<25 ft floor-to-ceiling height)	0.86
Museum	
General exhibition area	0.31
Restoration room	1.10
Performing Arts Theater, Dressing Room	0.41
Post Office, Sorting Area	0.76
Religious Buildings	
Fellowship hall	0.54
Worship/pulpit/choir area	0.85
Retail Facilities	
Dressing/fitting room	0.51
Mall concourse	0.82
Sports Arena, Playing Area[g]	
Class I facility	2.94
Class II facility	2.01
Class III facility	1.30
Class IV facility	0.86
Transportation Facility	
Baggage/carousel area	0.39
Airport concourse	0.25
Ticket counter	0.51
Warehouse—Storage Area	
Medium to bulky, palletized items	0.33
Smaller, hand-carried items[e]	0.69

Source: ANSI/ASHRAE/IES Standard 90.1-2019, Table 9.6.1.

[a] In cases where both a common space type and a building-specific type are listed, the building-specific space type applies.

[b] In corridors, the extra lighting power density allowance is granted when corridor width is <8 ft and is not based on room/corridor ratio (RCR).

[c] A facility for the visually impaired is a facility that can be documented as being designed to comply with light levels in ANSI/IES RP-28 and is (or will be) licensed by local/state authorities for either senior long-term care, adult daycare, senior support, and/or people with special visual needs.

[d] For accent lighting, see Section 9.6.2(b) of ASHRAE/IES Standard 90.1-2019.

[e] Sometimes called a picking area.

[f] An additional 0.52 W/ft^2 shall be allowed, provided that the additional lighting is controlled separately from the base allowance of 0.43 W/ft^2. The additional 0.52 W/ft^2 allowance shall not be used for any other purpose.

[g] Class of play as defined by IES RP-6.

Table 11.18 provides a range of design data under typical operating conditions: airflow 1 cfm/ft^2, supply air between 59°F and 62°F, room temperature between 72°F and 75°F, and lighting heat input in a range from 0.9 to 2.6 W/ft^2. For a fluorescent luminaire without lens, Figure 11.1 gives more precise data. The data should be used with judgment.

Table 11.18 Lighting Heat Gain Parameters for Typical Operating Conditions [2021F, Ch 18, Tbl 3]

Luminaire Category	Space Fraction	Radiative Fraction	Notes
Recessed fluorescent luminaire without lens	0.64 to 0.74	0.48 to 0.68	• Use middle values in most situations • May use higher space fraction, and lower radiative fraction for luminaire with side-slot returns • May use lower values of both fractions for direct/indirect luminaire • May use higher values of both fractions for ducted returns
Recessed fluorescent luminaire with lens	0.40 to 0.50	0.61 to 0.73	• May adjust values in the same way as for recessed fluorescent luminaire without lens
Downlight compact fluorescent luminaire	0.12 to 0.24	0.95 to 1.0	• Use middle or high values if detailed features are unknown • Use low value for space fraction and high value for radiative fraction if there are large holes in luminaire's reflector
Downlight incandescent luminaire	0.70 to 0.80	0.95 to 1.0	• Use middle values if lamp type is unknown • Use low value for space fraction if standard lamp (i.e. A-lamp) is used • Use high value for space fraction if reflector lamp (i.e. BR-lamp) is used
Non-in-ceiling fluorescent luminaire	1.0	0.5 to 0.57	• Use lower value for radiative fraction for surface-mounted luminaire • Use higher value for radiative fraction for pendant luminaire
Recessed LED troffer partial aperture diffuser	0.49 to 0.64	0.37 to 0.47	• Use middle value in most cases • May use higher space fraction for ducted return configuration and lower space fraction for high supply air temperature • May use higher radiant value for ducted return configuration and lower value for large supply airflow rate
Recessed LED troffer uniform diffuser	0.44 to 0.66	0.32 to 0.41	• Use middle value in most cases. • May use higher space fraction for smaller supply airflow rate and lower value for larger supply airflow rate. • May use higher radiant value for ducted return configuration and lower value for larger supply airflow rate.
Recessed high-efficacy LED troffer	0.59	0.51	

Table 11.18 Lighting Heat Gain Parameters for Typical Operating Conditions [2021F, Ch 18, Tbl 3] ***(Continued)***

Luminaire Category	Space Fraction	Radiative Fraction	Notes
Recessed LED downlight	0.40 to 0.56	0.15 to 0.18	• Use middle value in most cases. • May use higher space fraction value for high supply air temperature and lower value for smaller air flowrate. • May use higher radiant value for dimming control and lower value for large supply air flowrate.
Recessed LED retrofit kit 2×4	0.41 to 0.53	0.31 to 0.42	• Use middle value in most cases. • May use higher space fraction value for large supply air flowrate and lower value for ducted return configuration. • May use higher radiant value for ducted return configuration and lower value for larger supply airflow rate.
Recessed LED color tuning fixture	0.53 to 0.56	0.40 to 0.42	Use middle value in most cases.
High-bay LED fixture	1.0	0.42 to 0.51	Use middle value in most cases.
Linear pendant LED fixture	1.0	0.55 to 0.60	Use middle value in most cases.

Sources: Fisher and Chantrasrisalai (2006); Zhou et al. (2016).

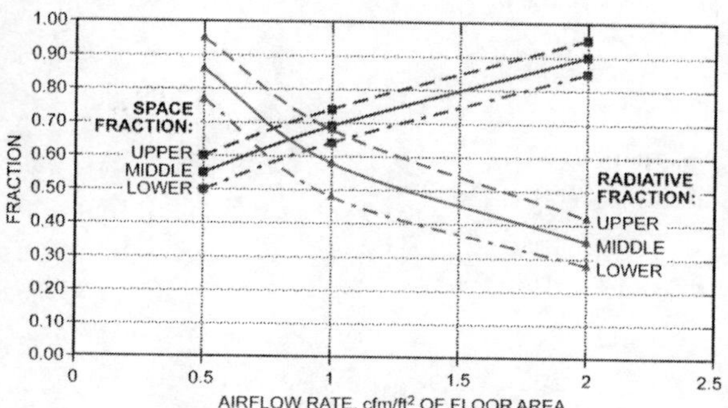

Figure 11.1 Lighting Heat Gain Parameters for Recessed Fluorescent Luminaire Without Lens [2021F, Ch 18, Fig 3]

Heat Gain from Motors and their Loads

Instantaneous rate of heat gain from equipment operated by electric motors within a conditioned space:

$$q_{em} = 2545\ (P/E_M)\ F_{UM}\ F_{LM} \tag{11.7}$$

where

q_{em}	=	heat equivalent of equipment operation, Btu/h
P	=	motor power rating, hp
E_M	=	motor efficiency, decimal fraction < 1.0
F_{UM}	=	motor use factor, 1.0 or decimal fraction <1.0
F_{LM}	=	motor load factor, 1.0 or decimal fraction <1.0
2545	=	conversion factor, Btu/h·hp

When motor is outside the conditioned space or airstream but load is inside:

$$q_{em} = 2545\ P\ F_{UM}\ F_{LM} \tag{11.8}$$

When motor is inside the conditioned space or airstream but load is outside:

$$q_{em} = 2545\ P \left(\frac{1.0 - E_M}{E_M}\right) F_{UM}\ F_{LM} \tag{11.9}$$

Heat output of a motor is generally proportional to motor load, within rated overload limits. Because of typically high no-load motor current, fixed losses, and other reasons, F_{LM} is generally assumed to be unity, and no adjustment should be made for underloading or overloading unless the situation is fixed and can be accurately established, and reduced-load efficiency data can be obtained from the motor manufacturer.

Unless the manufacturer's technical literature indicates otherwise, motor heat gain normally should be equally divided between radiant and convective components for the subsequent cooling load calculations.

Table 11.19 Minimum Nominal Full-Load Efficiency for NEMA Design A, NEMA Design B, and IEC Design N Motors (Excluding Fire Pump Electric Motors) at 60 Hz[a,b] [2021F, Ch 18, Tbl 4A]

Number of Poles ⇒	2	2	4	4	6	6	8	8
Motor Type ⇒	**Enclosed**	**Open**	**Enclosed**	**Open**	**Enclosed**	**Open**	**Enclosed**	**Open**
Motor Horsepower								
1	77.0	77.0	85.5	85.5	82.5	82.5	75.5	75.5
1.5	84.0	84.0	86.5	86.5	87.5	86.5	78.5	77.0
2	85.5	85.5	86.5	86.5	88.5	87.5	84.0	86.5
3	86.5	85.5	89.5	89.5	89.5	88.5	85.5	87.5
5	88.5	86.5	89.5	89.5	89.5	89.5	86.5	88.5
7.5	89.5	88.5	91.7	91.0	91.0	90.2	86.5	89.5
10	90.2	89.5	91.7	91.7	91.0	91.7	89.5	90.2
15	91.0	90.2	92.4	93.0	91.7	91.7	89.5	90.2
20	91.0	91.0	93.0	93.0	91.7	92.4	90.2	91.0
25	91.7	91.7	93.6	93.6	93.0	93.0	90.2	91.0
30	91.7	91.7	93.6	94.1	93.0	93.6	91.7	91.7
40	92.4	92.4	94.1	94.1	94.1	94.1	91.7	91.7
50	93.0	93.0	94.5	94.5	94.1	94.1	92.4	92.4
60	93.6	93.6	95.0	95.0	94.5	94.5	92.4	93.0
75	93.6	93.6	95.4	95.0	94.5	94.5	93.6	94.1
100	94.1	93.6	95.4	95.4	95.0	95.0	93.6	94.1
125	95.0	94.1	95.4	95.4	95.0	95.0	94.1	94.1
150	95.0	94.1	95.8	95.8	95.8	95.4	94.1	94.1
200	95.4	95.0	96.2	95.8	95.8	95.4	94.5	94.1
250	95.8	95.0	96.2	95.8	95.8	95.8	95.0	95.0
300	95.8	95.4	96.2	95.8	95.8	95.8	NA	NA
350	95.8	95.4	96.2	95.8	95.8	95.8	NA	NA
400	95.8	95.8	96.2	95.8	NA	NA	NA	NA
450	95.8	96.2	96.2	96.2	NA	NA	NA	NA
500	95.8	96.2	96.2	96.2	NA	NA	NA	NA

Source: ANSI/ASHRAE/IES Standard 90.1-2019, Table 10.8-1

[a] Nominal efficiencies shall be established in accordance with 10 CFR 431.

[b] For purposes of determining the required minimum nominal full-load efficiency of an electric motor that has a horsepower or kilowatt rating between two horsepower or two kilowatt ratings listed in this table, each such motor shall be deemed to have a listed horsepower or kilowatt rating, determined as follows:

1. A horsepower at or above the midpoint between the two consecutive horsepowers shall be rounded up to the higher of the two horsepowers.
2. A horsepower below the midpoint between the two consecutive horsepowers shall be rounded down to the lower of the two horsepowers.
3. A kilowatt rating shall be directly converted from kilowatts to horsepower using the formula 1 kilowatt = (1/0.746) horsepower. The conversion should be calculated to three significant decimal places, and the resulting horsepower shall be rounded in accordance with paragraph (1) or (2), whichever applies.

Heat Gain From Restaurant Equipment

Heat gain: $q_s = q_{input} F_U F_R$, where F_U is the usage factor and F_R is the radiation factor.

Table 11.20 Recommended Rates of Radiant and Convective Heat Gain from Unhooded Electric Appliances during Idle (Ready-to-Cook) Conditions [2021F, Ch 18, Tbl 5A]

Appliance	Energy Rate, Btu/h		Rate of Heat Gain, Btu/h				Usage Factor F_U	Radiation Factor F_R
	Rated	Standby	Sensible Radiant	Sensible Convective	Latent	Total		
Cabinet: hot serving (large), insulated[a]	6,800	1,200	400	800	0	1,200	0.18	0.33
hot serving (large), uninsulated	6,800	3,500	700	2,800	0	3,500	0.51	0.20
proofing (large)[a]	17,400	1,400	1,200	0	200	1,400	0.08	0.86
proofing (small 15-shelf)	14,300	3,900	0	900	3,000	3,900	0.27	0.00
Cheesemelter[b]	8,200	3,300	1,500	1,800	0	3,300	0.41	0.45
Coffee brewing urn	13,000	1,200	200	300	700	1,200	0.09	0.17
Drawer warmers, 2-drawer (moist holding)[a]	4,100	500	0	0	200	200	0.12	0.00
Egg cooker[b]	8,100	850	200	650	0	850	0.10	0.26
Espresso machine*	8,200	1,200	400	800	0	1,200	0.15	0.33
Food warmer: steam table (2-well-type)	5,100	3,500	300	600	2,600	3,500	0.69	0.09
Freezer (small)	2,700	1,100	500	600	0	1,100	0.41	0.45
Fryer, countertop, open deep fat[b]	15,700	1,500	700	800	0	1,500	0.09	0.47
Griddle, countertop[b]	27,300	6,100	2,900	3,200	0	6,100	0.22	0.48
Hot dog roller[b]	5,500	4,200	900	3,300	0	4,200	0.77	0.22
Hot plate: single element, high speed	3,800	3,400	1,100	2,300	0	3,400	0.89	0.32
Hot-food case (dry holding)[a]	31,100	2,500	900	1,600	0	2,500	0.08	0.36
Hot-food case (moist holding)[a]	31,100	3,300	900	1,800	600	3,300	0.11	0.27
Induction hob, countertop[b]	17,100	0	0	0	0	0	0.00	0.00

Table 11.20 Recommended Rates of Radiant and Convective Heat Gain from Unhooded Electric Appliances during Idle (Ready-to-Cook) Conditions [2021F, Ch 18, Tbl 5A] ***(Continued)***

Appliance	Energy Rate, Btu/h		Rate of Heat Gain, Btu/h				Usage Factor F_U	Radiation Factor F_R
	Rated	Standby	Sensible Radiant	Sensible Convective	Latent	Total		
Microwave oven: commercial	5,800	0	0	0	0	0	0.00	0.00
Oven: countertop conveyorized bake/finishing[b]	17,100	13,500	2,500	11,000	0	13,500	0.79	0.18
Panini[b]	6,100	2,300	700	1,600	0	2,300	0.37	0.29
Popcorn popper[b]	2,900	400	100	300	0	400	0.14	0.24
Rapid-cook oven (quartz-halogen)[a]	41,000	0	0	0	0	0	0.00	0.00
Rapid-cook oven (microwave/convection)[b]	19,400	3,900	300	3,600	0	3,900	0.20	0.08
Reach-in refrigerator[a]	4,800	1,200	300	900	0	1,200	0.25	0.25
Refrigerated prep table[a]	2,000	900	600	300	0	900	0.45	0.67
Rice cooker[b]	5,300	300	50	250	0	300	0.05	0.17
Soup warmer[b]	2,700	1,300	0	200	1,100	1,300	0.49	0.00
Steamer (bun)[b]	5,100	700	100	600	0	700	0.13	0.16
Steamer, countertop[b]	28,300	1,200	0	800	400	1,200	0.04	0.00
Toaster: 4-slice pop up (large): cooking	6,100	3,000	200	1,400	1,000	2,600	0.49	0.07
contact (vertical)[b]	8,900	2,600	600	2,000	0	2,600	0.29	0.24
conveyor (large)	32,800	10,300	3,000	7,300	0	10,300	0.31	0.29
small conveyor[b]	6,000	5,800	1,200	4,600	0	5,800	0.98	0.21
Tortilla grill[b]	7,500	3,600	900	2,700	0	3,600	0.47	0.25
Waffle iron[b]	9,200	900	200	700	0	900	0.10	0.22

Sources: Swierczyna et al. (2008, 2009); with the following exceptions as noted.
[a]Swierczyna et al. (2009) only.
[b]Additions and updates from ASHRAE research project RP-1631 (Kong and Zhang 2016; Kong et al 2016).

Table 11.21 Recommended Rates of Radiant and Convective Heat Gain from Unhooded Electric Appliances during Cooking Conditions [2021F, Ch 18, Tbl 5B]

Appliance	Energy Rate, Btu/h		Rate of Heat Gain, Btu/h				Usage Factor F_U	Radiation Factor F_R
	Rated	Cooking	Sensible Radiant	Sensible Convective	Latent	Total		
Cheesemelter	8,200	9,300	1,500	3,700	2,000	7,200	1.13	0.16
Egg cooker	8,100	4,100	200	1,300	2,200	3,700	0.50	0.05
Fryer, countertop, open deep fryer	15,700	13,000	700	1,700	5,600	8,000	0.83	0.05
Griddle, countertop	27,300	11,200	2,900	2,200	4,400	9,500	0.41	0.26
Hot dog roller	5,500	5,400	900	2,100	2,300	5,300	0.99	0.17
Hot plate, single burner	3,800	3,400	1,100	2,100	200	3,400	0.90	0.32
Induction hob, countertop	17,100	2,200	0	1,100	1,100	2,200	0.13	0.00
Oven, conveyor	17,100	14,600	2,500	8,400	700	11,600	0.86	0.17
Microwave	5,800	8,100	0	3,200	3,400	6,600	1.39	0.00
Rapid cook	19,400	7,900	300	4,200	2,600	7,100	0.41	0.04
Panini grill	6,100	4,700	700	2,400	500	3,600	0.76	0.14
Popcorn popper	2,900	2,000	100	800	700	1,600	0.68	0.05
Rice cooker	5,300	4,000	50	300	200	550	0.75	0.01
Soup warmer	2,700	2,900	0	300	2,400	2,700	1.05	0.00
Steamer (bun)	5,100	2,700	100	800	1,700	2,600	0.53	0.04
Steamer, countertop	28,300	26,400	0	1,700	23,700	25,400	0.93	0.00
Toaster, conveyor	6,000	5,800	1,200	3,300	1,300	5,800	0.98	0.21
Vertical	8,900	6,300	600	2,400	1,100	4,100	0.71	0.10
Tortilla grill	7,500	7,500	900	4,300	2,300	7,500	1.00	0.12
Waffle maker	9,200	4,000	200	1,200	1,900	3,300	0.44	0.05

Source: ASHRAE research project RP-1631 (Zhang et al. 2015).

Table 11.22 Recommended Rates of Radiant Heat Gain from Hooded Electric Appliances during Idle (Ready-to-Cook) Conditions [2021F, Ch 18, Tbl 5C]

Appliance	Energy Rate, Btu/h		Rate of Heat Gain, Btu/h	Usage Factor	Radiation Factor
	Rated	Standby	Sensible Radiant	F_U	F_R
Broiler: underfired 3 ft	36,900	30,900	10,800	0.84	0.35
Cheesemelter*	12,300	11,900	4,600	0.97	0.39
Fryer, kettle	99,000	1,800	500	0.02	0.28
Open deep-fat, 1-vat	47,800	2,800	1,000	0.06	0.36
Pressure	46,100	2,700	500	0.06	0.19
Griddle, double-sided 3 ft (clamshell down)*	72,400	6,900	1,400	0.10	0.20
(Clamshell up)*	72,400	11,500	3,600	0.16	0.31
Flat 3 ft	58,400	11,500	4,500	0.20	0.39
Small 3 ft*	30,700	6,100	2,700	0.20	0.44
Induction cooktop*	71,700	0	0	0.00	0.00
Induction wok*	11,900	0	0	0.00	0.00
Oven, combi: combi-mode*	56,000	5,500	800	0.10	0.15
Convection mode	56,000	5,500	1,400	0.10	0.25
Oven, convection, full-sized	41,300	6,700	1,500	0.16	0.22
Half-sized*	18,800	3,700	500	0.20	0.14
Pasta cooker*	75,100	8,500	0	0.11	0.00
Range top, top off/oven on*	16,600	4,000	1,000	0.24	0.25
3 elements on/oven off	51,200	15,400	6,300	0.30	0.41
6 elements on/oven off	51,200	33,200	13,900	0.65	0.42
6 elements on/oven on	67,800	36,400	14,500	0.54	0.40
Range, hot-top	54,000	51,300	11,800	0.95	0.23
Rotisserie*	37,900	13,800	4,500	0.36	0.33
Salamander*	23,900	23,300	7,000	0.97	0.30
Steam kettle, large (60 gal) simmer lid down*	110,600	2,600	100	0.02	0.04
Small (40 gal) simmer lid down*	73,700	1,800	300	0.02	0.17
Steamer, compartment, atmospheric*	33,400	15,300	200	0.46	0.01
Tilting skillet/braising pan	32,900	5,300	0	0.16	0.00

*Items with an asterisk appear only in Swierczyna et al. (2009); all others appear in both Swierczyna et al. (2008) and (2009).

Table 11.23 Recommended Rates of Radiant Heat Gain from Hooded Gas Appliances during Idle (Ready-to-Cook) Conditions [2021F, Ch 18, Tbl 5D]

Appliance	Energy Rate, Btu/h		Rate of Heat Gain, Btu/h	Usage Factor F_U	Radiation Factor F_R
	Rated	Standby	Sensible Radiant		
Broiler: batch*	95,000	69,200	8,100	0.73	0.12
Chain (conveyor)	132,000	96,700	13,200	0.73	0.14
Overfired (upright)*	100,000	87,900	2,500	0.88	0.03
Underfired 3 ft	96,000	73,900	9,000	0.77	0.12
Fryer: doughnut	44,000	12,400	2,900	0.28	0.23
Open deep-fat, 1 vat	80,000	4,700	1,100	0.06	0.23
Pressure	80,000	9,000	800	0.11	0.09
Griddle: double sided 3 ft, clamshell down*	108,200	8,000	1,800	0.07	0.23
Clamshell up*	108,200	14,700	4,900	0.14	0.33
Flat 3 ft	90,000	20,400	3,700	0.23	0.18
Oven: combi: combi-mode*	75,700	6,000	400	0.08	0.07
Convection mode	75,700	5,800	1,000	0.08	0.17
Convection, full-size	44,000	11,900	1,000	0.27	0.08
Conveyor (pizza)	170,000	68,300	7,800	0.40	0.11
Deck	105,000	20,500	3,500	0.20	0.17
Rack mini-rotating*	56,300	4,500	1,100	0.08	0.24
Pasta cooker*	80,000	23,700	0	0.30	0.00
Range top: top off/oven on*	25,000	7,400	2,000	0.30	0.27
3 burners on/oven off	120,000	60,100	7,100	0.50	0.12
6 burners on/oven off	120,000	120,800	11,500	1.01	0.10
6 burners on/oven on	145,000	122,900	13,600	0.85	0.11

Table 11.23 Recommended Rates of Radiant Heat Gain from Hooded Gas Appliances during Idle (Ready-to-Cook) Conditions [2021F, Ch 18, Tbl 5D] ***(Continued)***

Appliance	Energy Rate, Btu/h		Rate of Heat Gain, Btu/h	Usage Factor F_U	Radiation Factor F_R
	Rated	Standby	Sensible Radiant		
Range: wok*	99,000	87,400	5,200	0.88	0.06
Rethermalizer*	90,000	23,300	11,500	0.26	0.49
Rice cooker*	35,000	500	300	0.01	0.60
Salamander*	35,000	33,300	5,300	0.95	0.16
Steam kettle: large (60 gal) simmer lid down*	145,000	5,400	0	0.04	0.00
Small (10 gal) simmer lid down*	52,000	3,300	300	0.06	0.09
Medium (40 gal) simmer lid down	100,000	4,300	0	0.04	0.00
Steamer: compartment: atmospheric*	26,000	8,300	0	0.32	0.00
Tilting skillet/braising pan	104,000	10,400	400	0.10	0.04

*Items with an asterisk appear only in Swierczyna et al. (2009); all others appear in both Swierczyna et al. (2008) and (2009).

Table 11.24 Recommended Rates of Radiant Heat Gain from Hooded Solid-Fuel Appliances during Idle (Ready-to-Cook) Conditions [2021F, Ch 18, Tbl 5E]

Appliance	Rated	Standby Energy Rate, Btu/h	Rate of Sensible Heat Gain, Btu/h	Usage Factor F_U	Radiation Factor F_R
Broiler: solid fuel: charcoal	40 lb	42,000	6200	N/A	0.15
Broiler: solid fuel: wood (mesquite)	40 lb	49,600	7000	N/A	0.14

Source: Swierczyna et al. (2008).

Table 11.25 Recommended Rates of Sensible and Latent Heat Gain to Space from Warewashing Equipment [2021F, Ch 18, Tbl 5F]

Equipment Type	Supply Water Flow Rate, gpm	Operating Water Temp., °F	Rate of Heat Gain to Space, Btu/h[a]				Usage Factor F_U [c]
			Sensible Radiant[b]	Sensible Convective	Latent	Total	
Pre-Rinse Equipment							
Pre-rinse spray valve	0.65	120	0	200	8200	8400	1
Pre-rinse spray valve	1.2	120	0	300	11,700	12,000	1
Pre-rinse spray valve	4.0	120	0	1100	13,800	14,900	1
3-Compartment sink, rinsing	NA	120	0	900	4900	5800	1
Idle	NA	NA	0	700	2000	2700	NA
Power wash sink, rinsing	NA	120	0	2000	3100	5100	1
Idle	NA	NA	0	1500	1600	3100	NA
Scrapper	18[d]	120	0	1200	11,000	12,200	1
Scrapper with trough	70[d]	120	0	2800	13,900	16,700	1
Unhooded Dishwashers							
Under counter dishwasher, low temperature	0.8	140	0	2200	4900	7100	1
Under counter dishwasher, high temperature	0.8	180	0	4000	4600	8600	1
Under counter dishwasher, high temperature with heat recovery	0.6	180	0	2200	1100	3300	1
Upright door type, low temperature dump and fill	1.0	120	0	3200	3500	6700	1
Upright door type, low temperature with tank	0.7	140	0	3900	13200	17100	1
Upright door type, high temperature	0.9	180	0	8000	21400	29400	1
Upright door type, high temperature with heat recovery	0.9	180	0	4800	13000	17800	1
Pot and pan washer	2.4	180	0	6000	23500	29500	1
Pot and pan washer with heat recovery	2.4	180	0	5500	19000	24500	1

Table 11.25 Recommended Rates of Sensible and Latent Heat Gain to Space from Warewashing Equipment [2021F, Ch 18, Tbl 5F] ***(Continued)***

Equipment Type	Supply Water Flow Rate, gpm	Operating Water Temp., °F	Rate of Heat Gain to Space, Btu/h[a] Sensible Radiant[b]	Sensible Convective	Latent	Total	Usage Factor F_U[c]
44 in. Conveyor dishwasher, unvented	1.8	180	0	10000	59300	69300	1
66 in. Conveyor dishwasher, unvented	1.7	180	0	16100	45000	61100	1
Hooded or Ducted High Temperature Dishwashers							
Upright door type, high temperature under a 3×3 ft hood at 300 cfm	NA	180	0	3500	13000	16500	1
Upright door type, high temperature under a 5×4 ft hood at 500 cfm	NA	180	0	1600	7900	9500	1
44 in. Conveyor, high temperature under a 10 ft hood at 1000 cfm	1.8	190	0	1000	20000	21000	1
Ducted Conveyor Dishwashers							
Ducted 66 in. conveyor dishwasher	1.7	180	0	10600	6300	16900	1
Ducted Flight type conveyor dishwasher	1.0	190	0	13400	8900	22300	1
Ducted Flight type conveyor dishwasher with heat recovery	1.0	190	0	12300	3600	15900	1
Ducted Flight type conveyor dishwasher with blow dryer	1.0	190	0	21200	15700	36900	1

Source: Livchak and Swierczyna (2020)

[a] Heat gain rates for pre-rinse equipment and unhooded dishwashers are for unhooded appliances only. For these equipment items the total appliance heat gain affects the space directly. If an appliance is hooded or vented, the heat gain rates in the hooded and ducted sections of the table must be used. Hooded and ducted line items account for the heat gain captured by the hood or duct and therefore only list the portion of heat gain affecting the space.

[b] Average surface temperature of pre-rinse equipment does not exceed 120°F which is the maximum temperature of water flowing through these devices. Average surface temperatures of the dishwashers are less than the wash tank temperature of 165°F. The surfaces are stainless steel and produce negligible radiant heat gain.

[c] Values given are for continuous rinsing or washing and are peak values. Rinse and wash times usually extend between 1-3 hours after each meal period served by the food service facility. Duration of heat gains will vary based on the operating schedule of the food service.

[d] For scrapper equipment the recirculation flow rate is listed.

Heat Gain From Hospital and Laboratory Equipment

Heat gain varies significantly. In a laboratory, heat gain ranges from 15 to 70 Btu/h·ft^2. Medical equipment is highly varied in type and application. Table 11.26 is relevant for portable and bench-type equipment. For large equipment, such as MRI, obtain heat gain from the manufacturer.

Table 11.26 Recommended Heat Gain from Typical Medical Equipment [2021F, Ch 18, Tbl 6]

Equipment	Nameplate, W	Peak, W	Average, W
Anesthesia system	250	177	166
Blanket warmer	500	504	221
Blood pressure meter	180	33	29
Blood warmer	360	204	114
ECG/RESP	1440	54	50
Electrosurgery	1000	147	109
Endoscope	1688	605	596
Harmonical scalpel	230	60	59
Hysteroscopic pump	180	35	34
Laser sonics	1200	256	229
Optical microscope	330	65	63
Pulse oximeter	72	21	20
Stress treadmill	N/A	198	173
Ultrasound system	1800	1063	1050
Vacuum suction	621	337	302
X-ray system	968		82
	1725	534	480
	2070		18

Source: Hosni et al. (1999)

Table 11.27 Recommended Heat Gain from Typical Laboratory Equipment
[2021F, Ch 18, Tbl 7]

Equipment	Nameplate, W	Peak, W	Average, W
Analytical balance	7	7	7
Centrifuge	138	89	87
	288	136	132
	5500	1176	730
Electrochemical analyzer	50	45	44
	100	85	84
Flame photometer	180	107	105
Fluorescent microscope	150	144	143
	200	205	178
Function generator	58	29	29
Incubator	515	461	451
	600	479	264
	3125	1335	1222
Orbital shaker	100	16	16
Oscilloscope	72	38	38
	345	99	97
Rotary evaporator	75	74	73
	94	29	28
Spectronics	36	31	31
Spectrophotometer	575	106	104
	200	122	121
	N/A	127	125
Spectro fluorometer	340	405	395
Thermocycler	1840	965	641
	N/A	233	198
Tissue culture	475	132	46
	2346	1178	1146

Source: Hosni et al. (1999).

Heat Gain from Office Equipment

Table 11.28 Recommended Heat Gain for Typical Desktop Computers [2021F, Ch 18, Tbl 8A]

Description	Nameplate Power,[a] W	Peak Heat Gain,[b, d] W
Manufacturer 1		
3.0 GHz processor, 4 GB RAM, $n = 1$	NA	83
3.3 GHz processor, 8 GB RAM, $n = 8$	NA	50
3.5 GHz processor, 8 GB RAM, $n = 2$	NA	42
3.6 GHz processor, 16 GB RAM, $n = 2$	NA	66
3.3 GHz processor, 16 GB RAM, $n = 2$	NA	52
4.0 GHz processor, 16 GB RAM, $n = 1$	NA	83
3.3 GHz processor, 8 GB RAM, $n = 1$	NA	84
3.7 GHz processor, 32 GB RAM, $n = 1$	750	116
	NA	102
3.5 GHz processor, 16 GB RAM, $n = 3$[c]	550	144
	NA	93
Manufacturer 2		
3.6 GHz processor, 32 GB RAM, $n = 8$	NA	80
3.6 GHz processor, 16 GB RAM, $n = 1$	NA	78
3.4 GHz processor, 32 GB RAM, $n = 1$	NA	72
3.4 GHz processor, 24 GB RAM, $n = 1$	NA	86
3.50 GHz processor, 4 GB RAM, $n = 1$	NA	26
3.3 GHz processor, 8 GB RAM, $n = 1$	NA	78
3.20 GHz processor, 8 GB RAM, $n = 1$	NA	61
3.20 GHz processor, 4 GB RAM, $n = 1$	NA	44
2.93 GHz processor, 16 GB RAM, $n = 1$	NA	151
2.67 GHz processor, 8 GB RAM, $n = 1$	NA	137
Average 15-min peak power consumption (range)		82 (26-151)

Source: Bach and Sarfraz (2018)

n = number of tested equipment of same configuration.

[a]Nameplate for desktop computer is present on its power supply, which is mounted inside desktop, hence not accessible for most computers, where NA = not available.

[b]For equipment peak heat gain value, highest 15-min interval of recorded data is listed in tables.

[c]For tested equipment with same configuration, increasing power supply size does not increase average power consumption.

[d]Approximately 90% convective heat gain and 10% radiative heat gain.

Table 11.29 Recommended Heat Gain for Typical Laptops and Laptop Docking Station [2021F, Ch 18, Tbl 8B]

Equipment	Description	Nameplate Power,[a] W	Peak Heat Gain,[b, c] W
Laptop computer	Manufacturer 1, 2.6 GHz processor, 8 GB RAM, $n = 1$	NA	46
	Manufacturer 2, 2.4 GHz processor, 4 GB RAM, $n = 1$	NA	59
Average 15-min peak power consumption (range)		53 (46-59)	
Laptop with docking station	Manufacturer 1, 2.7 GHz processor, 8 GB RAM, $n = 1$	NA	38
	1.6 GHz processor, 8 GB RAM, $n = 2$	NA	45
	2.0 GHz processor, 8 GB RAM, $n = 1$	NA	50
	2.6 GHz processor, 4 GB RAM, $n = 1$	NA	51
	2.4 GHz processor, 8 GB RAM, $n = 1$	NA	40
	2.6 GHz processor, 8 GB RAM, $n = 1$	NA	35
	2.7 GHz processor, 8 GB RAM, $n = 1$	NA	59
	3.0 GHz processor, 8 GB RAM, $n = 3$	NA	70
	2.9 GHz processor, 32 GB RAM, $n = 3$	NA	58
	3.0 GHz processor, 32 GB RAM, $n = 1$	NA	128
	3.7 GHz processor, 32 GB RAM, $n = 1$	NA	63
	3.1 GHz processor, 32 GB RAM, $n = 1$	NA	89
Average 15-min peak power consumption (range)		61 (26-151)	

Source: Bach and Sarfraz (2018)

n = number of tested equipment of same configuration.

[a]Voltage and amperage information for laptop computer and laptop docking station is available on power supply nameplates; however, nameplate does not provide information on power consumption, where NA = not available.

[b]For equipment peak heat gain value, the highest 15-min interval of recorded data is listed in tables.

[c]Approximately 75% convective heat gain and 25% radiative heat gain.

Table 11.30 Recommended Heat Gain for Typical Tablet PC [2021F, Ch 18, Tbl 8C]

Description	Nameplate Power,[a] W	Peak Heat Gain,[b] W
1.7 GHz processor, 4 GB RAM, $n = 1$	NA	42
2.2 GHz processor, 16 GB RAM, $n = 1$	NA	40
2.3 GHz processor, 8 GB RAM, $n = 1$	NA	30
2.5 GHz processor, 8 GB RAM, $n = 1$	NA	31
Average 15-min peak power consumption (range)	36 (31-42)	

Source: Bach and Sarfraz (2018)

n = number of tested equipment of same configuration.

[a]Voltage and amperage information for tablet PC is available on power supply nameplate; however, nameplate does not provide information on power consumption, where NA = not available.

[b]For equipment peak heat gain value, highest 15-min interval of recorded data is listed in tables.

Table 11.31 Recommended Heat Gain for Typical Monitors [2021F, Ch 18, Tbl 8D]

Description[a]	Nameplate Power, W	Peak Heat Gain,[b, c] W
Manufacturer 1		
1397 mm LED flat screen, $n = 1$ (excluded from average because atypical size)	240	50
686 mm LED flat screen, $n = 2$	40	26
546 mm LED flat screen, $n = 2$	29	25
Manufacturer 2		
1270 mm 3D LED flat screen, $n = 1$ (excluded from average because atypical size)	94	49
Manufacturer 3		
864 mm LCD curved screen, $n = 1$ (excluded from average because atypical size and curved)	130	48
584 mm LED flat screen, $n = 3$	50	17
584 mm LED flat screen, $n = 1$	38	21
584 mm LED flat screen, $n = 1$	38	14
Manufacturer 4		
610 mm LED flat screen, $n = 1$	42	25
Manufacturer 5		
600 mm LED flat screen, $n = 1$	26	17
546 mm LED flat screen, $n = 1$	29	22
Manufacturer 6		
546 mm LED flat screen, $n = 1$	28	24
Average 15-min peak power consumption (range)	21 (14-26)	

Source: Bach and Sarfraz (2018)

n = number of tested equipment of same configuration.

[a]Screens with atypical size and shape are excluded for calculating average 15-min peak power consumption.

[b]For equipment peak heat gain value, highest 15-min interval of recorded data is listed in tables.

[c]Approximately 60% convective heat gain and 40% radiative heat gain.

Table 11.32 Recommended Heat Gain for Typical Printers [2021F, Ch 18, Tbl 9]

Equipment	Description	Max. Printing Speed, Pages per Minute	Nameplate Power, W	Peak Heat Gain,[a] W
Multifunction printer (copy, print, scan)	Large, multiuser, office type	40	1010	540 (Idle 29 W)
		30	1300	303 (Idle 116 W)
		28	1500	433 (Idle 28 W)
Average 15-min peak power consumption (range)			**425 (303-540)**	
	Multiuser, medium-office type	35	900	732 (Idle 18 W)
	Desktop, small-office type	25	470	56 (Idle 3 W)
Monochrome printer	Desktop, medium-office type	55	1000	222
		45	680	61
Average 15-min peak power consumption (range)			**142 (61-222)**	
Color printer	Desktop, medium-office type	40	620	120
Laser printer	Desktop, small-office type	14	310	89
		24	495	67
		26	1090	65
Average 15-min peak power consumption (range)			**74 (65-89)**	
Plotter	Manufacturer 1		1600	571
	Manufacturer 2		270	173
Average 15-min peak power consumption (range)				**372 (173-571)**
Fax machine	Medium		1090	92
	Small		600	46
Average 15-min peak power consumption (range)			**69 (46-92)**	

Source: Bach and Sarfraz (2018)
[a]Approximately 70% convective heat gain and 30% radiative heat gain.

Table 11.33 Recommended Heat Gain for Miscellaneous Equipment
[2021F, Ch 18, Tbl 10]

Equipment	Nameplate Power,[a] W	Peak Heat Gain,[b] W
Vending machine		
Drinks, 280 to 400 items	NA	940
Snacks	NA	54
Food (e.g., for sandwiches)	NA	465
Thermal binding machine, 2 single documents up to 340 pages	350	28.5
Projector, resolution 1024 × 768	340	308
Paper shredder, up to 28 sheets	1415	265
Electric stapler, up to 45 sheets	NA	1.5
Speakers	220	15
Temperature-controlled electronics soldering station	95	16
Cell phone charger	NA	5
Battery charger		
40 V	NA	19
AA	NA	5.5
Microwave oven, 7 to 9 gal	1000 to 1550	713 to 822
Coffee maker		
Single cup	1400	385
Up to 12 cups	950	780
With grinder	1350	376
Coffee grinder, up to 12 cups	NA	73
Tea kettle, up to 6 cups	1200	1200
Dorm fridge, 3.1 ft^3	NA	57
Freezer, 18 ft^3	130	125
Fridge, 18 to 28 ft^3	NA	387 to 430
Ice maker and dispenser, 20 lb bin capacity	NA	658
Top mounted bottled water cooler	NA	114 to 350
Cash register	25	9
Touch screen computer, 15 in. standard LCD and 2.2 GHz processor	NA	58
Self-checkout machine	NA	15

Source: Bach and Sarfraz (2018)

[a]For some equipment, nameplate power consumption is not available, where NA = not available.

[b]For equipment peak heat gain value, highest 15-min interval of recorded data is listed in tables.

Table 11.34 Recommended Load Factors for Various Types of Offices [2021F, Ch 18, Tbl 11]

Type of Use	Load Factor*, W/ft^2	Description
100% laptop, docking station		
light	0.34	167 ft^2/workstation, all laptop docking station use, 1 printer per 10
medium	0.46	125 ft^2/workstation, all laptop docking station use, 1 printer per 10
50% laptop, docking station		
light	0.44	167 ft^2/workstation, 50% laptop docking station/ 50% desktop, 1 printer per 10
medium	0.59	125 ft^2/workstation, 50% laptop docking station/ 50% desktop, 1 printer per 10
100% desktop		
light	0.54	167 ft^2/workstation, all desktop use, 1 printer per 10
medium	0.72	125 ft^2/workstation, all desktop use, 1 printer per 10
100% laptop, docking station		
2 screens	0.69	125 ft^2/workstation, all laptop docking station use, 2 screens, 1 printer per 10
100% desktop		
2 screens	0.84	125 ft^2/workstation, all laptop use, 2 screens, 1 printer per 10
3 screens	0.96	125 ft^2/workstation, all desktop use, 3 screens, 1 printer per 10
100% desktop		
heavy, 2 screens	1.02	85 ft^2/workstation, all desktop use, 2 screens, 1 printer per 8
heavy, 3 screens	1.16	85 ft^2/workstation, all desktop use, 3 screens, 1 printer per 8
100% laptop, docking station		
full on, 2 screens	1.14	85 ft^2/workstation, all laptop docking use, 2 screens, 1 printer per 8, no diversity
100% desktop		
full on, 2 screens	1.33	85 ft^2/workstation, all desktop use, 2 screens, 1 printer per 8, no diversity
full on, 3 screens	1.53	85 ft^2/workstation, all desktop use, 3 screens, 1 printer per 8, no diversity

Source: Bach and Sarfraz (2018)

*Medium-office type monochrome printer is used for load factor calculator with 15-min peak power consumption of 142 W.

Table 11.35 Diversity Factor for Different Equipment [2021F, Ch 18, Tbl 12]

Equipment	Diversity Factor, %	Diversity Factor,[a] %
Desktop PC	75	75
Laptop docking station	70	NA
Notebook computer	75[b]	75
Screen	70	60
Printer	45	NA

Source: Bach and Sarfraz (2018)
[a]2013 *ASHRAE Handbook—Fundamentals*
[b]Insufficient data from RP-1742; values based on previous data from 2013 *ASHRAE Handbook—Fundamentals* and judgment of Bach and Sarfraz (2018).

Table 11.36 Refrigerating Effect Produced by Open Refrigerated Display Fixtures

	Btu/h·ft of Fixture*		
Type of Display Fixture	**Latent Heat**	**Sensible Heat**	**Total Refrigerating Effect**
Low temperature			
Frozen Food			
Single Deck	38	207	245
Single Deck, Double Island	70	400	470
2 Deck	144	576	720
3 Deck	322	1288	1610
4 or 5 Deck	400	1600	2000
Ice Cream			
Single Deck	64	366	430
Single Deck, Double Island	70	400	470
Standard Temperature			
Meats			
Single Deck	52	298	350
Multideck	219	876	1095
Dairy			
Multideck	196	784	980
Produce			
Single Deck	36	204	240
Multideck	192	768	960

*These figures are general magnitudes for fixtures adjusted for average desired product temperatures and apply to store ambients in front of the display cases of 72°F to 74°F with 50% to 55% rh. Raising the dry bulb only 3°F to 5°F and the humidity 5% to 10% can increase heat removal 25% or more. Equally lower temperatures and humidities as in winter, have an equally marked effect on lowering heat removal from the space.

12. VENTILATION

Residential

Adapted Excerpt from ANSI/ASHRAE Standard 62.2-2019, *Ventilation and Acceptable Indoor Air Quality in Residential Buildings*

(*See complete standard for detailed guidance.*)

A mechanical exhaust system, supply system, or combination thereof, shall be installed to operate for each dwelling unit to provide continuous dwelling-unit ventilation with outdoor air at a rate not less than specified below.

The total required ventilation rate (Q_{tot}) shall be as specified in Table 12.2 or alternatively calculated using Equation 12.1:

$$Q_{tot} = 0.03A_{floor} + 7.5(N_{br} + 1) \tag{12.1}$$

where

Q_{tot} = total required ventilation rate, cfm
A_{floor} = dwelling-unit floor area, ft^2
N_{br} = number of bedrooms (not to be less than 1)

Exception: Dwelling-unit mechanical ventilation systems are not required if the authority having jurisdiction determines that window operation is a locally permissible method of providing ventilation and provided that at least one of the following conditions is met:

1. The building has no mechanical cooling and is in Climate Zone 1 or 2 of the map shown in Figure 8-1 of Standard 62.2.
2. The building is thermally conditioned for human occupancy for less than 876 h per year.

Ventilation air requirements are shown in Table 12.2. Local mechanical exhaust rates are shown in Tables 12.2 and 12.3.

Ventilation openings: not less than 4% of floor nor less than 5 ft^2 for habitable rooms; and not less than 4% of floor space nor less than 1.5 ft^2 for toilets and utility rooms.

Mechanical systems that supply air to an occupiable space through ductwork exceeding 10 ft in length and through a thermal conditioning component, except evaporative coolers, shall be provided with a filter having a designated minimum efficiency of MERV 6 or better when tested in accordance with ANSI/ASHRAE Standard 52.2, or a minimum particle size efficiency of 50% in the 3.0 to 10 μm range in accordance with AHRI Standard 680. The system shall be designed such that all recirculated and mechanically supplied outdoor air is filtered before passing through the thermal conditioning components. The filter shall be located and installed in such a manner as to facilitate access and regular service by the owner.

Airflow quantities refer to the amount of air exhausted by the ventilation system as installed and measured. The prescriptive requirements of Table 12.3 are permitted in place of measurements.

Table 12.1 Ventilation Air Requirements, cfm [Std 62.2-2019, Tbl 4.1a]

Floor Area, ft²	Bedrooms 1	2	3	4	5
<500	30	38	45	53	60
501–1000	45	53	60	68	75
1001–1500	60	68	75	83	90
1501–2000	75	83	90	98	105
2001–2500	90	98	105	113	120
2501–3000	105	113	120	128	135
3001–3500	120	128	135	143	150
3501–4000	135	143	150	158	165
4001–4500	150	158	165	173	180
4501–5000	165	173	180	188	195

Table 12.2 Demand-Controlled Local Ventilation Exhaust Airflow Rates [Std 62.2-2019, Tbl 5-1]

Application	Airflow
Enclosed Kitchen	• Vented range hood (including appliance-range hood combinations): 100 cfm • Other kitchen exhaust fans, including downdraft: 300 cfm or a capacity of 5 ach
Nonenclosed Kitchen	• Vented range hood (including appliance-range hood combinations): 100 cfm • Other kitchen exhaust fans, including downdraft: 300 cfm
Bathroom	50 cfm

Table 12.3 Continuous Local Ventilation Exhaust Airflow Rates [Std 62.2-2019, Tbl 5-2]

Application	Airflow
Enclosed Kitchen	5 ach, based on kitchen volume
Bathroom	20 cfm

Table 12.4 Prescriptive Duct Sizing [Std 62.2-2019, Tbl 5-3]

	Fan Airflow Rating, CFM at minimum static pressure of 0.25 in. of water												
	≤50	≤80	≤100	≤125	≤150	≤175	≤200	≤250	≤350	≤400	≤450	≤700	≤800
Duct Type	Minimum Duct Diameter, in. [a,b]												
Rigid duct	4 [e]	5	5	6	6	7	7	8	9	10	10	12	12 [d]
Flex duct [c]	4	5	6	6	7	7	8	8	9	10	NP	NP	NP

a. For noncircular ducts, calculate the diameter as four times the cross-sectional area divided by the perimeter.
b. NP = application of the prescriptive table is not permitted for this scenario.
c. Use of this table for verification of flex duct systems requires flex duct to be fully extended and any flex duct elbows to have a minimum bend radius to duct diameter ratio of 1.0.
d. For this scenario, use of elbows is not permitted.
e. For this scenario, 4 in. oval duct shall be permitted, provided the minor axis of the oval is greater than or equal to 3 in.

Nonresidential

Adapted Excerpt from ANSI/ASHRAE Standard 62.1-2019, *Ventilation for Acceptable Indoor Air Quality*

(*See complete standard for detailed guidance.*)

General

Use of natural ventilation systems is permitted in lieu of or in conjunction with mechanical ventilation. Naturally ventilated spaces shall be permanently open to operable wall or roof openings to the outdoors; free openable area at least 4% of net occupiable floor area. If interior spaces are ventilated through adjoining rooms, free area between rooms shall be permanently unobstructed and at least 8% of the area of the interior room, nor less than 25 ft^2. Occupants must have ready access to the openings.

All airstream surfaces shall be designed to resist mold growth and resist erosion. Ductwork construction shall meet SMACNA standards. In accordance with manufacturer instructions, fuel-burning appliances shall have sufficient air for combustion and adequate removal of combustion products, which shall be vented directly outdoors. Filters or air cleaners with minimum MERV 8 by ANSI/ASHRAE Standard 52.2 shall be provided upstream of all cooling coils or other devices with wetted surfaces through which air is supplied to occupiable space. Relative humidity should be 65% or less when system performance is analyzed with outdoor at the design dew point and mean coincident dry bulb, sensible and latent space interior loads at cooling design values, and space solar loads at zero. Drain pans slope minimum 1/8 in. per ft to outlet at lowest point, and drain line shall have P-trap or other seal when drain pan is at negative static pressure relative to the outlet. Drain pan shall extend from leading edge of the coil to a distance of half the vertical dimension of the coil.

Discharge from noncombustion equipment that captures contaminants generated by the equipment shall be discharged directly outdoors.

Investigate outdoor air quality. Survey and document local and regional outdoor air quality, with description of noticeable air problems and conditions regarding its acceptability. If unacceptable, treat it. Cleaning for ozone is required only if in a high-ozone area (see Informative Appendix F of the standard) and if the minimum design outdoor airflow is 1.5 air changes or more.

Outdoor air intakes shall be located so the shortest distance from intake to any specific contaminant source shall equal or exceed values in Table 12.5 or that result from the calculation method in Normative Appendix B of ANSI/ASHRAE Standard 62.1.

Design intakes to manage rain and snow entrainment and include bird screens.

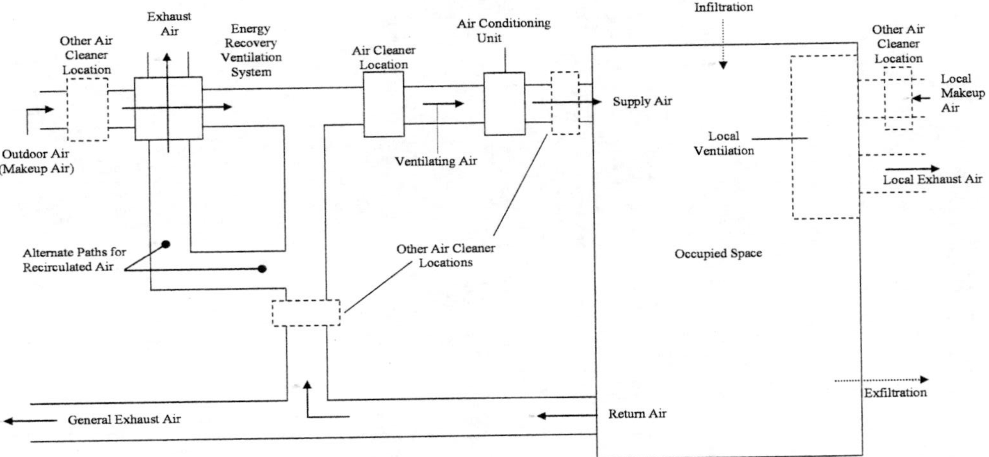

Figure 12.1 Ventilation System [Std 62.1-2019, Fig 3.1]

Table 12.5 Air Intake Minimum Separation Distance [Std 62.1-2019, Tbl 5-1]

Object	Minimum Distance, ft
Class 2 air exhaust/relief outlet[a]	10
Class 3 air exhaust/relief outlet[a]	15
Class 4 air exhaust/relief outlet[b]	30
Plumbing vents terminating less than 3 ft above the level of the outdoor air intake	10
Plumbing vents terminating at least 3 ft above the level of the outdoor air intake	3
Vents, chimneys, and flues from combustion appliances and equipment[c]	15
Garage entry, automobile loading area, or drive-in queue[d]	15
Truck loading area or dock, bus parking/idling area[d]	25
Driveway, street, or parking place[d]	5
Thoroughfare with high traffic volume	25
Roof, landscaped grade, or other surface directly below intake[e,f]	1
Garbage storage/pick-up area, dumpsters	15
Cooling tower intake or basin	15
Cooling tower exhaust	25

a. This requirement applies to the distance from the outdoor air intakes for one ventilation system to the exhaust outlets and relief outlets for any other ventilation system.
b. Minimum distance listed does not apply to laboratory fume hood exhaust air outlets. Separation criteria for fume hood exhaust shall be in compliance with ANSI/AIHA Z9.5. Informative Appendix J contains sources of additional information on separation criteria. These include the *ACGIH Industrial Ventilation Manual*, *ASHRAE Handbook—HVAC Applications*, *ASHRAE Laboratory Design Guide*, and NSF/ANSI 49.
c. The minimum distances relative to fuel-fired appliances shall be as required by ANSI Z223.1/NFPA 54 for fuel gas burning appliances and equipment, NFPA 31 for oil burning appliances and equipment, and NFPA 211 for other combustion appliances and equipment.
d. Distance measured to closest place that vehicle exhaust is likely to be located.
e. The minimum separation distance shall not apply where outdoor surfaces below the air intake are sloped more than 45 degrees from horizontal or where such surfaces are less than 1 in. in width.
f. Where snow accumulation is expected, the surface of the snow at the expected average snow depth shall be considered to be a surface directly below an intake.

Air classifications:

- Class 1: Air with low contaminant concentration, low sensory-irritation intensity, and inoffensive odor.
- Class 2: Air with moderate contaminant concentration, mild sensory-irritation intensity, or mildly offensive odors. (Class 2 air also includes air that is not necessarily harmful or objectionable but that is inappropriate for transfer or recirculation to spaces used for different purposes.)
- Class 3: Air with significant contaminant concentration, significant sensory-irritation intensity, or offensive odor.
- Class 4: Air with highly objectionable fumes or gases or with potentially dangerous particles, bioaerosols, or gases, at concentrations high enough to be considered harmful.

Procedures from ANSI/ASHRAE Standard 62.1-2019

6.1 General. The Ventilation Rate Procedure, the IAQ Procedure, the Natural Ventilation Procedure, or a combination thereof shall be used to meet the requirements of this section. In addition, the requirements for exhaust ventilation in Section 6.5 shall be met regardless of the method used to determine minimum outdoor airflow rates.

Informative Note: Although the intake airflow determined using each of these approaches may differ significantly because of assumptions about the design, any of these approaches is a valid basis for design.

6.1.1 Ventilation Rate Procedure. The prescriptive design procedure presented in Section 6.2, in which outdoor air intake rates are determined based on space type/application, occupancy level, and floor area, shall be permitted to be used for any zone or system.

6.1.2 Indoor Air Quality (IAQ) Procedure. The performance-based design procedure presented in Section 6.3, in which the building outdoor air intake rates and other system design parameters are based on an analysis of contaminant sources, contaminant concentration limits, and level of perceived indoor air acceptability, shall be permitted to be used for any zone or system.

6.1.3 Natural Ventilation Procedure. The prescriptive or engineered system design procedure presented in Section 6.4, in which outdoor air is provided through openings to the outdoors, shall be permitted to be used for any zone or portion of a zone in conjunction with mechanical ventilation systems in accordance with Section 6.4.

6.1.4 Outdoor Air Treatment. Each ventilation system that provides outdoor air shall comply with Sections 6.1.4.1 through 6.1.4.4.

Exception to 6.1.4: Systems supplying air for enclosed parking garages, warehouses, storage rooms, janitor's closets, trash rooms, recycling areas, shipping/receiving/distribution areas.

Informative Note: Occupied spaces ventilated with outdoor air that is judged to be unacceptable are subject to reduced air quality when outdoor air is not cleaned prior to introduction to the occupied spaces.

6.1.4.1 Particulate Matter Smaller than 10 Micrometers (PM10). In buildings located in an area where the national standard or guideline for PM10 is exceeded, particle filters or air-cleaning devices shall be provided to clean the outdoor air at any location prior to its introduction to occupied spaces. Particulate matter filters or air cleaners shall have either

a. MERV of not less than 8 where rated in accordance with ANSI/ASHRAE Standard 52.2 or

b. the minimum efficiency within ISO ePM10 where rated in accordance with ISO 16890.

Informative Note: See Informative Appendix D for resources regarding selected PM10 national standards and guidelines.

Table 12.6 Airstreams or Sources [Std 62.1-2019, Tbl 6-3]

Description	Air Class
Commercial kitchen grease hoods	4
Commercial kitchen hoods other than grease	3
Diazo printing equipment discharge	4
Hydraulic elevator machine room	2
Laboratory hoods	4
Paint spray booths	4
Refrigerating machinery rooms	3
Residential kitchen hoods in transient occupancy	3

6.1.4.2 Particulate Matter Smaller than 2.5 Micrometers (PM2.5). In buildings located in an area where the national standard or guideline for PM2.5 is exceeded, particle filters or air-cleaning devices shall be provided to clean the outdoor air at any location prior to its introduction to occupied spaces. Particulate matter filters or air cleaners shall have either

a. MERV of not less than 11 where rated in accordance with ANSI/ASHRAE Standard 52.2 or
b. the minimum efficiency within ISO ePM2.5 where rated in accordance with ISO 16890.

Informative Note: See Informative Appendix D for resources regarding selected PM2.5 national standards and guidelines.

6.1.4.3 Ozone. Air-cleaning devices for ozone shall be provided when the most recent three-year average annual fourth-highest daily maximum eight-hour average ozone concentration exceeds 0.100 ppm.

Such air-cleaning devices shall have a volumetric ozone removal efficiency of not less than 40% where installed, operated, and maintained in accordance with manufacturer recommendations and shall be approved by the authority having jurisdiction (AHJ). Such devices shall be operated where the outdoor ozone levels are expected to exceed 0.100 ppm.

Exception to 6.1.4.3: Air cleaning for ozone shall not be required where

1. the system design outdoor air intake flow is 1.5 ach or less,
2. controls are provided that sense outdoor ozone level and reduce intake airflow to 1.5 ach or less while complying with the outdoor airflow requirements of Section 6, or
3. outdoor air is brought into the building and heated by direct-fired makeup air units.

Informative Note: In the U.S., a most recent three-year average annual fourth-highest daily maximum eight-hour average ozone concentration exceeding 0.100 ppm equates to a USEPA eight-hour ozone classification of "Serious" or higher (Severe 15, Severe 17, or Extreme).

6.1.4.4 Other Outdoor Contaminants. In buildings located in an area where the national standard for one or more contaminants not addressed in Section 6.1.4 is exceeded, any design assumptions and calculations related to the impact on IAQ shall be included in the design documents.

Table 12.7 Minimum Ventilation Rates in Breathing Zone
[Adapted from Std 62.1-2019, Tbl 6-1]

Occupancy Category	People Outdoor Air Rate R_p	Area Outdoor Air Rate R_a	Default Values Occupant Density	Air Class	OS (6.2.6.1.4)
	cfm/person	cfm/ft²	#/1000 ft²		
Animal Facilities					
Animal exam room (veterinary office)	10	0.12	20	2	
Animal imaging (MRI/CT/PET)	10	0.18	20	3	
Animal operating rooms	10	0.18	20	3	
Animal postoperative recovery room	10	0.18	20	3	
Animal preparation rooms	10	0.18	20	3	
Animal procedure room	10	0.18	20	3	
Animal surgery scrub	10	0.18	20	3	
Large-animal holding room	10	0.18	20	3	
Necropsy	10	0.18	20	3	
Small-animal-cage room (static cages)	10	0.18	20	3	
Small-animal-cage room (ventilated cages)	10	0.18	20	3	
Correctional Facilities					
Booking/waiting	7.5	0.06	50	2	
Cell	5	0.12	25	2	
Dayroom	5	0.06	30	1	
Guard stations	5	0.06	15	1	
Educational Facilities					
Art classroom	10	0.18	20	2	
Classrooms (ages 5 to 8)	10	0.12	25	1	
Classrooms (age 9 plus)	10	0.12	35	1	
Computer lab	10	0.12	25	1	
Daycare sickroom	10	0.18	25	3	
Daycare (through age 4)	10	0.18	25	2	
Lecture classroom	7.5	0.06	65	1	✓
Lecture hall (fixed seats)	7.5	0.06	150	1	✓
Libraries	5	0.12	10		
Media center	10	0.12	25	1	
Multiuse assembly	7.5	0.06	100	1	✓
Music/theater/dance	10	0.06	35	1	✓
Science laboratories	10	0.18	25	2	
University/college laboratories	10	0.18	25	2	
Wood/metal shop	10	0.18	20	2	

Table 12.7 Minimum Ventilation Rates in Breathing Zone
[Adapted from Std 62.1-2019, Tbl 6-1] ***(Continued)***

Occupancy Category	People Outdoor Air Rate R_p	Area Outdoor Air Rate R_a	Default Values: Occupant Density	Air Class	OS (6.2.6.1.4)
	cfm/person	cfm/ft^2	#/1000 ft^2		
Food and Beverage Service					
Bars, cocktail lounges	7.5	0.18	100	2	
Cafeteria/fast-food dining	7.5	0.18	100	2	
Kitchen (cooking)	7.5	0.12	20	2	
Restaurant dining rooms	7.5	0.18	70	2	
General					
Break rooms	5	0.06	25	1	✓
Coffee stations	5	0.06	20	1	✓
Conference/meeting	5	0.06	50	1	✓
Corridors	—	0.06	—	1	✓
Occupiable storage rooms for liquids or gels	5	0.12	2	2	
Hotels, Motels, Resorts, Dormitories					
Barracks sleeping areas	5	0.06	20	1	✓
Bedroom/living room	5	0.06	10	1	✓
Laundry rooms, central	5	0.12	10	2	
Laundry rooms within dwelling units	5	0.12	10	1	
Lobbies/prefunction	7.5	0.06	30	1	✓
Multipurpose assembly	5	0.06	120	1	✓
Miscellaneous Spaces					
Banks or bank lobbies	7.5	0.06	15	1	✓
Bank vaults/safe deposit	5	0.06	5	2	✓
Computer (not printing)	5	0.06	4	1	✓
Freezer and refrigerated spaces (<50°F)	10	0	0	2	
Manufacturing where hazardous materials are not used	10	0.18	7	2	
Manufacturing where hazardous materials are used (excludes heavy industrial and chemical processes)	10	0.18	7	3	
Pharmacy (prep. area)	5	0.18	10	2	
Photo studios	5	0.12	10	1	
Shipping/receiving	10	0.12	2	2	
Sorting, packing, light assembly	7.5	0.12	7	2	
Telephone closets	—	0.00	—	1	
Transportation waiting	7.5	0.06	100	1	✓
Warehouses	10	0.06	—	2	

Table 12.7 Minimum Ventilation Rates in Breathing Zone [Adapted from Std 62.1-2019, Tbl 6-1] *(Continued)*

Occupancy Category	People Outdoor Air Rate R_p	Area Outdoor Air Rate R_a	Default Values Occupant Density	Air Class	OS (6.2.6.1.4)
	cfm/person	cfm/ft²	#/1000 ft²		
Office Buildings					
Breakrooms	5	0.12	50	1	
Main entry lobbies	5	0.06	10	1	✓
Occupiable storage rooms for dry materials	5	0.06	2	1	
Office space	5	0.06	5	1	✓
Reception areas	5	0.06	30	1	✓
Telephone/data entry	5	0.06	60	1	✓
Outpatient Health Care Facilities [a,b]					
Birthing room	10	0.18	15	2	
Class 1 imaging rooms	5	0.12	5	1	
Dental operatory	10	0.18	20	1	
General examination room	7.5	0.12	20	1	
Other dental treatment areas	5	0.06	5	1	
Physical therapy exercise area	20	0.18	7	2	
Physical therapy individual room	10	0.06	20	1	
Physical therapeutic pool area	—	0.48	—	2	
Prosthetics and orthotics room	10	0.18	20	1	
Psychiatric consultation room	5	0.06	20	1	
Psychiatric examination room	5	0.06	20	1	
Psychiatric group room	5	0.06	50	1	
Psychiatric seclusion room	10	0.06	5	1	
Speech therapy room	5	0.06	20	1	
Urgent care examination room	7.5	0.12	20	1	
Urgent care observation room	5	0.06	20	1	
Urgent care treatment room	7.5	0.18	20	1	
Urgent care triage room	10	0.18	20	1	
Public Assembly Spaces					
Auditorium seating area	5	0.06	150	1	✓
Courtrooms	5	0.06	70	1	✓
Legislative chambers	5	0.06	50	1	✓
Libraries	5	0.12	10	1	
Lobbies	5	0.06	150	1	✓
Museums (children's)	7.5	0.12	40	1	
Museums/galleries	7.5	0.06	40	1	✓
Places of religious worship	5	0.06	120	1	✓

Table 12.7 Minimum Ventilation Rates in Breathing Zone
[Adapted from Std 62.1-2019, Tbl 6-1] ***(Continued)***

Occupancy Category	People Outdoor Air Rate R_p	Area Outdoor Air Rate R_a	Default Values: Occupant Density	Air Class	OS (6.2.6.1.4)
	cfm/person	cfm/ft²	#/1000 ft²		
Retail					
Sales (except as below)	7.5	0.12	15	2	
Barbershop	7.5	0.06	25	2	✓
Beauty and nail salons	20	0.12	25	2	
Coin-operated laundries	7.5	0.12	20	2	
Mall common areas	7.5	0.06	40	1	✓
Pet shops (animal areas)	7.5	0.18	10	2	
Supermarket	7.5	0.06	8	1	✓
Sports and Entertainment					
Bowling alley (seating)	10	0.12	40	1	
Disco/dance floors	20	0.06	100	2	✓
Gambling casinos	7.5	0.18	120	1	
Game arcades	7.5	0.18	20	1	
Gym, sports arena (play area)	20	0.18	7	2	
Health club/aerobics room	20	0.06	40	2	
Health club/weight rooms	20	0.06	10	2	
Spectator areas	7.5	0.06	150	1	✓
Stages, studios	10	0.06	70	1	✓
Swimming (pool and deck)	—	0.48	—	2	
Transient Residential					
Common corridors	—	0.06		1	✓
Dwelling unit	5	0.06	F	1	✓

a. Outpatient facilities to which the rates apply are freestanding birth centers, urgent care centers, neighborhood clinics and physicians offices, Class 1 imaging facilities, outpatient psychiatric facilities, outpatient rehabilitation facilities, and outpatient dental facilities.

b. The requirements of this table provide for acceptable IAQ. The requirements of this table do not address the airborne transmission of airborne viruses, bacteria, and other infectious contagions.

Informative Note: These rates are intended only for outpatient dental clinics where the amount of nitrous oxide is limited. They are not intended for dental operatories in institutional buildings where nitrous oxide is piped.

OTHER NOTES

1 The rates in this table are based on all other applicable requirements of ANSI/ASHRAE Standard 62.1 being met.

2 For DCV (demand control ventilation) zones in the occupied standby mode, breathing zone outdoor airflow shall be permitted to be reduced to zero for the occupancy categories indicated "OS," provided that airflow is restored to design value whenever occupancy is detected.

Table 12.8 Minimum Exhaust Rates [Std 62.1-2019, Tbl 6-2]

Occupancy Category	Exhaust Rate, cfm/unit	Exhaust Rate, cfm/ft²	Notes	Air Class
Animal Facilities				
Animal imaging (MRI/CT/PET)	—	0.90		3
Animal operating rooms	—	3.00		3
Animal postoperative recovery room	—	1.50		3
Animal preparation rooms	—	1.50		3
Animal procedure room	—	2.25		3
Animal surgery scrub	—	1.50		3
Large-animal holding room	—	2.25		3
Necropsy	—	2.25		3
Small-animal-cage room (static cages)	—	2.25		3
Small-animal-cage room (ventilated cages)	—	1.50		3
Arenas	—	0.50	B	1
Art classrooms	—	0.70		2
Auto repair rooms	—	1.50	A	2
Barber shops	—	0.50		2
Beauty and nail salons	—	0.60		2
Cells with toilet	—	1.00		2
Copy, printing rooms	—	0.50		2
Darkrooms	—	1.00		2
Educational science laboratories	—	1.00		2
Janitor closets, trash rooms, recycling	—	1.00		3
Kitchenettes	—	0.30		2
Kitchens—commercial	—	0.70		2
Locker rooms for athletic, industrial, and health care facilities	—	0.50		2
All other locker rooms	—	0.25	—	2
Shower rooms	20/50		G,I	2
Paint spray booths	—	—	F	4
Parking garages	—	0.75	C	2
Pet shops (animal areas)	—	0.90	—	2
Refrigerating machinery rooms	—	—	F	3
Residential kitchens	50/100	—	G	2
Soiled laundry storage rooms	—	1.00	F	3
Storage rooms, chemical	—	1.50	F	4
Toilets—private	25/50	—	E, H	2
Toilets—public	50/70	—	D, H	2
Woodwork shop/classrooms	—	0.50	—	2

NOTES:

A Stands where engines are run shall have exhaust systems that directly connect to the engine exhaust and prevent escape of fumes.

B Where combustion equipment is intended to be used on the playing surface, additional dilution ventilation, source control, or both shall be provided.

C Exhaust shall not be required where two or more sides compose walls that are at least 50% open to the outside.

D Rate is per water closet, urinal, or both. Provide the higher rate where periods of heavy use are expected to occur. The lower rate shall be permitted to be used otherwise.

E Rate is for a toilet room intended to be occupied by one person at a time. For continuous system operation during hours of use, the lower rate shall be permitted to be used. Otherwise the higher rate shall be used.

F See other applicable standards for exhaust rate.

G For continuous system operation, the lower rate shall be permitted to be used. Otherwise the higher rate shall be used.

H Exhaust air that has been cleaned to meet Class 1 criteria from Section 5.18.1 shall be permitted to be recirculated.

I Rate is per showerhead.

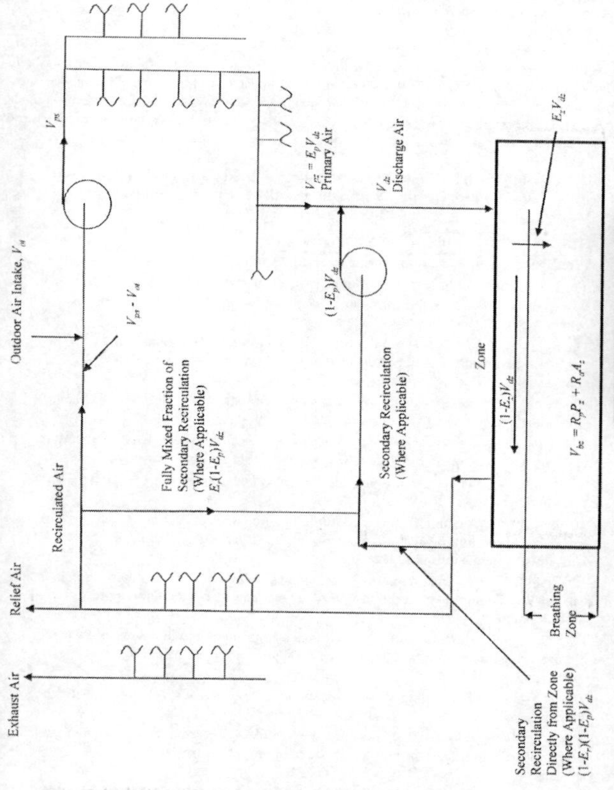

Figure 12.2 Ventilation System Schematic [Std 62.1-2019, Fig A-1]

Operation and Maintenance

An O&M manual, either written or electronic, must be developed and maintained on site or in a centrally accessible location for the working life of the applicable ventilation system equipment or components. This manual must be updated as necessary. The manual must include the O&M procedures, ventilation system operating schedules and any changes made thereto, final design drawings, maintenance schedules based on manufacturer instructions, and the maintenance requirements and frequencies provided in Table 12.9.

Table 12.9 Minimum Maintenance Activity and Frequency for Ventilation System Equipment and Associated Components
[Std 62.1-2019, Tbl 8-1]

Inspection/Maintenance Task	Frequency*
a. Investigate system for water intrusion or accumulation. Rectify as necessary.	As necessary
b. Verify that the space provided for routine maintenance and inspection of open cooling tower water systems, closed cooling tower water systems, and evaporative condensers is unobstructed.	Monthly
c. Open cooling tower water systems, closed cooling tower water systems, and evaporative condensers shall be treated to limit the growth of microbiological contaminants, including *legionella sp.*	Monthly
d. Verify that the space provided for routine maintenance and inspection of equipment and components is unobstructed.	Quarterly
e. Check pressure drop and scheduled replacement date of filters and air-cleaning devices. Clean or replace as necessary to ensure proper operation.	Quarterly
f. Check ultraviolet lamp. Clean or replace as needed to ensure proper operation.	Quarterly
g. Visually inspect dehumidification and humidification devices. Clean and maintain to limit fouling and microbial growth. Measure relative humidity and adjust system controls as necessary.	Quarterly
h. Maintain floor drains and trap primer located in air plenums or rooms that serve as air plenums to prevent transport of contaminants from the floor drain to the plenum.	Semiannually
i. Check ventilation and indoor air quality related control systems and devices for proper operation. Clean, lubricate, repair, adjust, or replace as needed to ensure proper operation.	Semiannually
j. Check P-traps in floor drains located in plenums or rooms that serve as air plenums. Prime as needed to ensure proper operation.	Semiannually
k. Check fan belt tension. Check for belt wear and replace if necessary to ensure proper operation. Check sheaves for evidence of improper alignment or evidence of wear and correct as needed.	Semiannually
l. Check variable-frequency drive for proper operation. Correct as needed.	Semiannually
m. Check for proper operation of cooling or heating coil for damage or evidence of leaks. Clean, restore, or replace as required.	Semiannually
n. Visually inspect outdoor air intake louvers, bird screens, mist eliminators, and adjacent areas for cleanliness and integrity; clean as needed; remove all visible debris or visible biological material observed and repair physical damage to louvers, screens, or mist eliminators if such damage impairs the item from providing the required outdoor air entry.	Semiannually
o. Visually inspect natural ventilation openings and adjacent areas for cleanliness and integrity; clean as needed. Remove all visible debris or visible biological material observed and repair physical damage to louvers, and screens if such damage impairs the item from providing the required outdoor air entry. Manual and/or automatic opening apparatus shall be physically tested for proper operation and repaired or replaced as necessary.	Semiannually

Table 12.9 Minimum Maintenance Activity and Frequency for Ventilation System Equipment and Associated Components [Std 62.1-2019, Tbl 8-1] *(Continued)*

Inspection/Maintenance Task	Frequency*
p. Verify the operation of the outdoor air ventilation system and any dynamic minimum outdoor air controls.	Annually
q. Check air filter fit and housing seal integrity. Correct as needed.	Annually
r. Check control box for dirt, debris, and/or loose terminations. Clean and tighten as needed.	Annually
s. Check motor contactor for pitting or other signs of damage. Repair or replace as needed.	Annually
t. Check fan blades and fan housing. Clean, repair, or replace as needed to ensure proper operation.	Annually
u. Check integrity of all panels on equipment. Replace fasteners as needed to ensure proper integrity and fit/finish of equipment.	Annually
v. Assess field serviceable bearings. Lubricate if necessary.	Annually
w. Check drain pans, drain lines, and coils for biological growth. Check adjacent areas for evidence of unintended wetting. Repair and clean as needed.	Annually
x. Check for evidence of buildup or fouling on heat exchange surfaces. Restore as needed to ensure proper operation.	Annually
y. Inspect unit for evidence of moisture carryover from cooling coils beyond the drain pan. Make corrections or repairs as necessary.	Annually
z. Check for proper damper operation. Clean, lubricate, repair, replace, or adjust as needed to ensure proper operation.	Annually
aa. Visually inspect areas of moisture accumulation for biological growth. If present, clean or disinfect as needed.	Annually
ab. Check condensate pump. Clean or replace as needed.	Annually
ac. Visually inspect exposed ductwork and external piping for insulation and vapor barrier for integrity. Correct as needed.	Annually
ad. Verify the accuracy of permanently mounted sensors whose primary function is outdoor air delivery monitoring, outdoor air delivery verification, or dynamic minimum outdoor air control, such as flow stations at an air handler and those used for demand-control ventilation. A sensor failing to meet the accuracy specified in the O&M manual shall be recalibrated or replaced. Performance verification shall include output comparison to a measurement reference standard consistent with those specified for similar devices in ANSI/ASHRAE Standard 41.2 or ANSI/ASHRAE Standard 111.	5 years
ae. Verify the total quantity of outdoor air delivered by air handlers set to minimum outdoor air mode. If measured minimum airflow rates are less than the design minimum rate documented in the O&M manual, ± a 10% balancing tolerance, (1) confirm the measured rate does not conform with the provisions of this standard and (2) adjust or modify the air-handler components to correct the airflow deficiency. Ventilation systems shall be balanced in accordance with ASHRAE Standard 111 or its equivalent, at least to the extent necessary to verify conformance with the total outdoor airflow and space supply airflow requirements of this standard. **Exception:** Units under 2000 cfm of supply air are exempt from this requirement.	5 years

* Minimum frequencies may be increased or decreased if indicated in the O&M manual.
** National Institute of Standards and Technology, U.S. Department of Commerce, Gaithersburg, MD.

Healthcare Facilities

ANSI/ASHRAE/ASHE Standard 170 provides detailed listings of design parameters for inpatient and outpatient space types based on function. These parameters include the following:

- Pressure relationship to adjacent areas
- Minimum outdoor air changes per hour
- Minimum total air changes per hour
- Requirement that all room air be exhausted directly to outdoors
- Whether air can be recirculated by room units
- Whether unoccupied turndown is permitted
- Minimum filter efficiency
- Design relative humidity
- Design temperature

13. ENVIRONMENTALLY RESPONSIBLE DESIGN

Climate Change

The ASHRAE Position Document on Climate Change states unequivocally that climate change "is the most formidable environmental challenge ever faced by society." Historically, designers and planners assumed a stable climate, and heating and cooling system designs were based on statistics calculated from past weather data, typically for a recent 30-year period. However, we are now experiencing major changes in climate both globally and locally, at rates 10 times greater than those seen since the end of the last ice age 20,000 years ago—over decades instead of centuries or millennia. This presents a challenge for designers of buildings and their systems, as well as for building operators, since buildings are expected to operate robustly for decades.

While there are currently no standardized methods endorsed by ASHRAE to integrate changing climatic information into building and HVAC&R system design, this does not preclude action by practicing engineers and architects. Repeatable and defensible methods can inform and enhance existing ASHRAE standards and guidelines, like those of other professional organizations such as The Chartered Institution of Building Services Engineers (CIBSE), American Society of Civil Engineers (ASCE), American Society of Mechanical Engineers (ASME), and American Association of State Highway and Transportation Officials (AASHTO). Resources for assessing the impact of a changing climate on building and system performance exist, both within and outside ASHRAE. It is important to recognize that, while climate change will have impacts of varying severity and duration around the world, many designers and operators may find that the buildings and systems they are designing or refurbishing currently will end up in a different climate during their operational life.

From the findings of peer-reviewed published research and assessments applying the basic principles of conservation of energy and thermal radiation governed by Planck's law, it is virtually certain that the observed increase in greenhouse gas (GHG) concentrations has had, and is having, a global warming effect, with resulting implications on severe weather, sea level rise, and other aspects of the Earth's climate system.

Temperatures are increasing in the atmosphere (troposphere), on land, and in the oceans. Global decadal averaged temperature (as calculated from instrumental records over both land and oceans) has increased by about 1.9°F since the lowest ten-year average temperature in the decade of 1900 to 1909. This change is by far the largest increase in the globally averaged temperature over at least the last 1700 years and probably much longer. Additionally, this increase is occurring at a much faster rate than the climate tends to change historically. The most recent six years are the six warmest in the instrumental record: 2014 (6th), 2015 (3rd), 2016 (1st), 2017 (4th), 2018 (5th), and 2019 (2nd).

While it has long been recognized that the Earth's climate can change because of natural influences, over the last century it has become increasingly clear that human-related forcings (i.e., drivers for changing the energy balance in the Earth system that lead to climate change) can also have, and are having, a large impact upon the climate system. Though climate drivers of significance over the industrial era include both types of forcings, the most significant factor in the large changes in climate over the last century has been the increasing concentrations in GHGs, especially carbon dioxide (CO_2), methane (CH_4), and nitrous oxide (N_2O). That is, it is very likely that more than half of the observed warming is from anthropogenic forces.

Certain types of extreme weather conditions have changed and have been attributed to global warming. The frequency and intensity of extreme heat has increased, and extreme cold has become less intense in most areas of the globe. Extreme precipitation has become more frequent at most long-term reporting stations, likely the result of larger amounts of water vapor over the warming oceans. Heating degree-days (HDDs) are projected to decrease in most places while cooling degree-days (CDDs) are expected to increase. This change is expected to be neither uniform across the globe nor monotonic for a given weather station. A monotonic change would imply that the given value always either increases or decreases for consecutive time steps but not both. Under a high-emissions (RCP8.5) scenario, climate zones, which are calculated from degree-days, are projected to change all around the world. Recent changes in zone classifications for North America are evident when comparing area classifications based on 2000–2019 data vs data from 1980–1999. These historical changes in climate zones are almost uniformly toward warmer zones (i.e., a lower number in the

ASHRAE system). The changes are clustered at the boundaries between climate zones, and the pattern is particularly clear in central North America. To accommodate warmer climates, a new zone 0 was added in 2016 to extend the climate zone scale.

Both heating and cooling design temperatures are increasing for large numbers of stations around the world and are projected to continue increasing.

Creating projected weather "input files" from global climate models (GCMs) suitable for use in building design and analysis is a complex process. For simulating estimated future building performance, reliable sets of future weather conditions are needed. Similarly, sizing calculations require estimates of future design conditions. Currently, there are no standardized methods to integrate information about a changing climate into building and system design and analysis, but this does not preclude action and the need for professional judgment. The output from GCMs can be useful for stress-testing buildings and systems using multiple plausible futures. This allows a designer to test the impact of multiple plausible acute or chronic climatic events such as heat waves or gradually increasing temperature over decades.

Limiting climate change requires a substantial and sustained global effort to significantly reduce anthropogenic GHG emission rates to avoid further warming and long-lasting changes in all components of the climate system. The consequences of a lack of timely action threaten the health and well-being of both current and future generations. Climate change mitigation (simply called *mitigation*) is an intentional human intervention to reduce the sources or enhance the sinks of GHGs in order to limit the magnitude of future warming. The ultimate goal of mitigation is to stabilize GHG concentrations in the atmosphere at a level that avoids dangerous changes in the climate system. Any changes in climate that are not avoided through mitigation must be considered by engineers as factors to adjust to through climate change adaptation. Mitigation can be understood as "avoiding the unmanageable," whereas adaptation can be understood as "managing the unavoidable."

ASHRAE GreenGuide: Design, Construction, and Operation of Sustainable Buildings, Fifth Edition, provides extensive guidance for designers and building operators to mitigate climate change by modifying their methods, designs, and operations for new buildings; using passive designs; appropriately retrofitting existing buildings by improving energy efficiency; constructing buildings using low-embodied energy materials; and eventually operating buildings using only renewable energy systems (RESs). RESs can be building integrated, on site, or off site. The pursuit of building electrification for both new and existing buildings using electric-powered systems and equipment instead of combustion-based systems will assist in easing the transition from GHG-emitting fossil-fuel sources to RESs. It is also important to reduce the use of fluorinated gases (F-gases) having high global warming potential (GWP) ratings while maintaining system efficiency.

Reduce Carbon Emissions by Design and Construction

Net zero or near zero buildings demonstrate the maximum level of climate change mitigation that can be achieved through building design and operation. These buildings consume minimal energy as limited by energy-efficiency opportunities and are then powered using carbon-free sources of energy. Environmentally friendly building design has progressed beyond simply reducing energy use. Architects, engineers, and other building professionals now aspire to achieving net zero buildings or even negative zero buildings where the building can supply more energy to the grid than it consumes overall. While there are many names, variations, and building certifications for it, net zero building design generally accounts for, and eliminates as much as possible, the carbon emissions from a building over its service life. At a minimum, net zero buildings are designed to use as little energy as possible and source the remaining energy needs from renewable, carbon-free sources. To be considered net zero, direct carbon emissions are usually eliminated completely. This is achieved by forbidding onsite fossil fuel combustion (with the possible exception of emergency generators at least for the near future) and by selecting only electrically powered components and systems for all end uses, since future energy will be provided either as grid or mini-grid electricity or through photovoltaic (PV) solar- or wind-generated on-site electricity. Net zero carbon buildings additionally track the carbon emissions associated with building construction (including embodied energy) and operation and, until energy is produced only by renewable energy, offset the carbon emissions by generating a surplus of renewable energy on site or procuring carbon offsets through a certified carbon offset program.

Table 13.1 Refrigerant Environmental Properties [2021F, Ch 36, Tbl 4]

Refrigerant	Atmospheric Lifetime, years	ODP	GWP100
CFC-11	52	1	5,160
CFC-113	93	0.81	6,080
CFC-114	85	0.5	8,580
CFC-115	540	0.26	7,310
CFC-12	102	0.73	10,300
CFC-13	640	1	13,900
HC-1270	0.001	0	<1
HC-290	0.034	0	<1
HC-600	12 ± 3[a]	0[a]	4[a]
HC-600a	0.016	0	<1
HC-601a	0.009[a]	0[a]	–20[a]
HCFC-123	1.3	0.01	80
HCFC-124	5.9	0.02	530
HCFC-142b	18	0.057	2,070
HCFC-22	12	0.034	1,780
HCFO1224yd(Z)	0.058[a]	0.00012[a]	<1[a]
HCFO1233zd(E)	0.071	0.00034	4
HE-E170	0.015[a]	0[a]	1[a]
HFC/HFC410A		0	1,920[b]
HFC-125	31	0	3,450
HFC-134a	14	0	1,360
HFC-143a	51	0	5,080
HFC-152a	1.6	0	148
HFC-227ea	36	0	3,140
HFC-23	228	0	12,690
HFC-236fa	222	0	7,680
HFC-245fa	7.9	0	880
HFC-32	5.4	0	705
HFO-1234yf	0.029	0	<1
HFO-1234ze(E)	0.045	0	<1
HFO1336mzz(E)	0.045–0.088	0	16
HFO1336mzz(Z)	0.06	0	2
PFC-116	10,000	0	11,100
PFC-218	2,600	0	8,900
PFC-c318	3,200	0	9,540
R-717	(few days)	—	<1
R-744		0	1

Atmospheric lifetime, ODP, and GWP100 from Table A-1 of Fahey et al. (2018) except where indicated.

[a] Chapter 29, 2017 *ASHRAE Handbook—Fundamentals*.

[b] IPCC (2013).

Net zero design fiscal prioritizations include:

- **Step 1:** Assess and prioritize the site and community resources such as optimizing zoning for renewable energy and building proximity to local or community waste heat resources.
- **Step 2:** Maximize architectural passive design strategies to meet property and occupant needs. Passive design strategies can include site planning, building orientation and massing, envelope tightness to reduce infiltration, continuous insulation, window and daylighting optimization, and designing a building to take advantage of natural ventilation and solar thermal opportunities.
- **Step 3:** Anticipate decarbonization of electric grids. Emphasize electric systems or provide dual fuel systems.
- **Step 4:** Maximize mechanical, electrical, and plumbing system efficiencies. Incorporate heat recovery systems, advanced controls, and
- **Step 5:** Offset remaining energy needs with on-site or purchased off-site renewable energy to reduce the facility's carbon footprint.

Climate Change Metrics

Carbon Dioxide Equivalent (MMTCO2Eq): A metric measure used to compare the emissions from various greenhouse gases (GHGs) based on their global warming potential (GWP). Carbon dioxide (CO_2) equivalents are commonly expressed as "million metric tons of carbon dioxide equivalents (MMTCO2Eq)." The CO_2 equivalent for a gas is derived by multiplying the tons of the gas by the associated GWP. MMTCO2Eq = (million metric tons of a gas) × (GWP of the gas).

Carbon Footprint: The total amount of GHGs that are emitted into the atmosphere each year by a person, family, building, organization, or company. A person's carbon footprint includes GHG emissions from fuel that an individual burns directly, such as by heating a home or riding in a car. It also includes GHGs that come from producing the goods or services that the individual uses, including emissions from power plants that make electricity, factories that make products, and landfills where trash gets sent.

CO_2-Equivalent Emission: The amount of CO_2 emission that would cause the same integrated radiative forcing, over a given time horizon, as an emitted amount of a GHG or a mixture of GHGs.

Global Warming Potential (GWP): An index developed to provide a simplified means of describing the relative ability of a chemical compound to affect radiative forcing, if emitted to the atmosphere, over its lifetime in the atmosphere, and thereby to affect the global climate. Radiative forcing reflects the factors that affect the balance between the energy absorbed by the earth and the energy emitted by it in the form of longwave infrared radiation. GWP is defined on a mass basis relative to CO_2. The GWP for a compound must be calculated up to a particular integrated time horizon, for example, 20, 100, or 500 years. The time horizon most widely accepted is 100 years (GWP100).

Ozone Depletion Potential (ODP): A numerical quantity describing the extent of ozone depletion calculated to arise from the release to the atmosphere of 2.2046 lb of a compound relative to the ozone depletion calculated to arise from a similar release of the refrigerant R-11. The calculation is an integration of all known potential effects on ozone over the whole time that any portion of the compound could remain in the atmosphere.

Energy Efficiency

Most energy used in buildings is from nonrenewable resources, the cost of which historically has not considered replenishment or environmental impact. Thus, consideration of energy use in design has been based primarily on economic advantages, which are weighted to encourage more rather than less use.

As resources become less readily available and more exotic, and as replenishable sources are investigated, the need to operate buildings effectively using less energy becomes paramount. Extensive studies since the mid-1970s have shown that building energy use can be significantly reduced by applying the fundamental principles discussed in the following paragraphs.

Energy Ethic-Resource Conservation Design Principles. The basic approach to energy-efficient design is reducing loads (power), improving transport systems, and providing efficient components and "intelligent" controls. Important design concepts include understanding the relationship between energy and power, maintaining simplicity, using self-imposed budgets, and applying energy-smart design practices.

Energy and Power. From an economic standpoint, more energy-efficient systems need not be more expensive than less-efficient systems. Quite the opposite is true because of the simple relationship between energy and power, in which power is simply the time rate of energy use (or, conversely, energy is power times time). The power term *kilowatts* is used in expressing the size of a motor, chiller, boiler, or transformer. Generally, the smaller the equipment, the less it costs. Other things being equal, as smaller equipment operates over time, it consumes less energy. Thus, in designing for energy efficiency, the first objective is always to reduce the power required to the bare minimum necessary to provide the desired performance, starting with the building's heating and cooling loads (a power term, in *kilowatts*) and continuing with the various systems and subsystems.

Simplicity. Complex designs to save energy seldom function in the manner intended unless the systems are continually managed and operated by technically skilled individuals. Experience has shown that long-term, energy-efficient performance with a complex system is seldom achievable. Further, when complex systems are operated by minimally skilled individuals, both energy efficiency and performance suffer. Most techniques discussed in this chapter can be implemented with great simplicity.

Self-Imposed Budgets. Just as an engineer must work to a cost budget with most designs, self-imposed power budgets can be similarly helpful in achieving energy-efficient design. The Advanced Energy Design Guide series, published by ASHRAE, provides guidance on achievable design budgets. For example, the following are possible categories of power (or power-affecting) design budgets for a mid-rise office building:

- Installed lighting (overall), W/ft^2
- Space sensible cooling, Btu/h·ft^2
- Space heating load, Btu/h·ft^2
- Electric power (overall), W/ft^2
- Thermal power (overall), Btu/h·ft^2
- Hydronic system head, ft of water
- Water chiller (water-cooled), kW/ton (COP)
- Chilled-water system auxiliaries, kW/ton
- Unitary air-conditioning systems, kW/ton (COP)
- Annual electric energy, kWh/ft^2·yr
- Annual thermal energy, Btu/ft^2·yr·°F·day

As the building and systems are designed, all decisions become interactive as each subsystem's power or energy performance is continually compared to the budget.

Design Process for Energy-Efficient Projects. Consider energy efficiency at the beginning of the building design process, because energy-efficient features are most easily and effectively incorporated at that time. Seek the active participation of all members of the design team, including the owner, architect, engineer, and often the contractor, early in the design process. Consider building attributes such as function, form, orientation, window-to-wall ratio, and HVAC system types early in the process, because each has major energy implications. Identify meaningful energy performance benchmarks suited to the project and set project-specific goals. Energy benchmarks for a sample project are shown in Table 13.2. Consider energy resources, on-site energy sources, and use of renewable energy, credits, utility rebates, or carbon offsets to mitigate environmental impacts of energy use.

Table 13.2 Example Benchmark and Energy Targets for University Research Laboratory [2021F, Ch 35, Tbl 1]

	Gross	Lit/ Conditioned						
Building area, ft²	**170,000**	**110,500**						
Electric	**Electricity for Lighting**	**Electricity for Ventilation (Fans)**	**Electricity for In-Building Pumps**	**Electricity for Plug Loads**	**Electricity for Unidentified Loads**	**Total Electricity**	**Cogenerated Electricity**	**Grid Electricity**
Design load, W/ft² gross	0.52	0.50	0.60	0.97	—	2.60	—	
Peak demand, W/ft² gross	0.42	0.50	0.42	0.73	0.00016	2.07	—	
Peak demand, kW (Projected submetered peak)	71	85	72	124	20	372	—	
Annual consumption, kWh/yr (Projected submetered reading)	218,154	346,598	191,245	891,503	175,200	1,823,000	966,000	857,000
Annual use index goal, kWh/yr	1.28	2.04	1.12	5.24	1.03	10.72		
Annual use index goal, site Btu/ft² gross·yr	4378	6956	3838	17,893	3516	36,583		
Annual use index, kWh/ft² gross·yr*	2.51 to 3.32	4.48 to 6.88	included elsewhere	4.39 to 5.67	NA	14.74 to 17.91		
Annual use index, site Btu/ft² gross·yr*	8564	15,286	—	14,979	—	50,293 to 61,109		

*From Labs21 program of U.S. Environmental Protection Agency (EPA) and U.S. Department of Energy (DOE). See labs21benchmarking.lbl.gov.

Address a building's energy requirements in the following sequence:

1. Minimize the impact of the building's functional requirements by analyzing how the building relates to its external environment. Advocate changes in building form, aspect ratio, and other attributes that reduce, redistribute, or delay (shift) loads. The load calculation should be interactive so that the effect of those factors can be seen immediately.
2. Minimize loads by analyzing external and internal loads imposed on the building's energy-using subsystems, both for peak- and part-load conditions. Design for efficient and effective operation off-peak, where the majority of operating hours and energy use typically occurs.
3. Maximize subsystem efficiency by analyzing the diversified energy and power requirements of each energy-using subsystem serving the building's functional requirements. Consider static and dynamic efficiencies of energy conversion and energy transport subsystems, and consider opportunities to reclaim, redistribute, and store energy for later use.
4. Study alternative ways to integrate subsystems into the building by considering both the power and time components of energy use. Identify, evaluate, and design each of these components to control overall design energy consumption. Consider the following when integrating major building subsystems:
   - Address more than one problem at a time when developing design solutions, and make maximum use of the building's advantageous features (e.g., windows, structural mass).
   - Examine design solutions that consider time (i.e., when energy use occurs), because sufficient energy may already be present from the environment (e.g., solar heat, night cooling) or from internal equipment (e.g., lights, computers) but available at times different from when needed. Storage techniques that are active (e.g., heat pumps with water tanks) or passive (e.g., building mass) may need to be considered.
   - Examine design solutions that consider the anticipated use of space. For example, in large but relatively unoccupied spaces, consider task or zone lighting. Consider transporting excess energy (light and heat) from locations of production and availability to locations of need instead of purchasing additional energy.
   - Evaluate the economic benefit of energy recovery and heat recovery systems whenever waste energy is available at temperatures usable for space conditioning or other practical purposes.
   - Consider or advocate design solutions that provide more comfortable surface temperatures or increase the availability of controlled daylight in buildings where human occupancy is a primary function.
   - Use easily understood design solutions, because they have a greater probability of use by building operators and occupants.
   - Where the functional requirements of a building are likely to change over time, design the installed environmental system to adapt to meet anticipated changes and to provide flexibility in meeting future changes in use, occupancy, or other functions.
   - Develop energy performance benchmarks, metrics, and targets that allow building owners and operators to better achieve the design intent.
   - Differentiate between peak loads for system design and selection and lower operating loads that determine actual energy use.

Building Energy Use Elements

Envelope

- Control thermal conductivity by using insulation (including movable insulation), thermal mass, and/or phase-change thermal storage at levels that minimize net heating and cooling loads on a time-integrated (annual) basis.
- Minimize unintentional or uncontrolled thermal bridges and include them in energy-related calculations because they can radically alter building envelope conductivity. Examples include wall studs, balconies, ledges, and extensions of building slabs.

- Minimize infiltration so that it approaches zero. (An exception is when infiltration provides the sole means of ventilation, such as in small residential units.) This minimizes fan energy consumption in pressurized buildings during occupied periods and minimizes heat loss (or unwanted heat gain, in warm climates) during unoccupied periods. In warm, humid climates, a tight envelope also improves IAQ. Reduce infiltration through design details that enhance the fit and integrity of building envelope joints in ways that may be readily achieved during construction (e.g., caulking, weatherstripping, vestibule doors, revolving doors), with construction meeting accepted specifications. Building envelope commissioning or testing can help verify these design and construction targets.
- Consider operable windows to allow occupant-controlled ventilation. This requires careful design of the building's mechanical system to minimize unnecessary HVAC energy consumption, and building operators and occupants should be cautioned about improper use of operable windows. CIBSE also provides comprehensive design considerations for natural ventilation. See *ASHRAE Design Guide for Natural Ventilation* for more detailed design information.
- Strive to maintain occupant radiant comfort regardless of whether the building envelope is designed to be a static or a dynamic membrane. Design opaque surfaces so that average inside surface temperatures remain within 5°F of room temperature in the coldest anticipated weather (i.e., winter design conditions) and so that the coldest inside surface remains within 25°F of room temperature (but always above the indoor dew point). In a building with time-varying internal heat generation, consider thermal mass for controlling radiant comfort. In the perimeter zone, thermal mass is more effective when it is positioned inside the envelope's insulation.
- Effective control of solar radiation is critical to energy-efficient design because of the high level of internal heat production in most commercial buildings. In some climates, lighting energy consumption savings from daylighting techniques can be greater than the heating and cooling energy penalties that result from the additional glazed surface area required, if the building envelope is properly designed for daylighting and lighting controls are installed and used. In other climates and in buildings with light emitting diode (LED) lighting, there may not be net savings. Daylighting designs are most effective if direct solar beam radiation is not allowed to cause glare in building spaces.
- Design transparent parts of the building envelope to prevent solar radiant gain above that necessary for effective daylighting and solar heating. On south-facing facades (in the northern hemisphere), using low shading coefficients is generally not as effective as using external physical shading devices in achieving this balance. Consider low-emissivity, high-visible-transmittance glazings for effective control of radiant heat gains and losses. For shading control, judicious use of vegetation may block excess gain year round or seasonally, depending on the plant species chosen.
- Use the envelope and roof for photovoltaic or solar thermal panels. The solar energy panels can be part of the envelope (building integrated photovoltaic [BIPV]) or added to roofs and shading devices.

Lighting

Lighting is both a major energy end use in commercial buildings (especially office buildings) and a major contributor to internal loads by increasing cooling loads and decreasing heating loads. Design should both meet the lighting functional criteria of the space and minimize energy use. The Illuminating Engineering Society (IES) recommends illuminance levels for visual tasks and surrounding lighted areas. Principles of energy-conserving design within that context include the following:

- Energy use is determined by the lighting load (demand power) and its duration of use (time). Minimize actual demand load rather than just apparent connected load. Control the load rather than just area switching, if switching may adversely affect the quality of the luminous environment.
- Consider daylighting with proper controls to reduce costs of electric lighting. Design should be sensitive to window glare, sudden changes in luminance, and general user acceptance of daylighting controls. Carefully select window treatment (blinds,

drapes, and shades) and glazing to control direct solar penetration and luminance extremes while maintaining the view and daylight penetration.

- Design the lighting system so that illumination required for tasks is primarily limited to the location of the task and comes from a direction that minimizes direct glare and veiling reflections on the task. When the design is based on nonuniform illuminance, walls should be a light to medium color or illuminated to provide visual comfort. In densely occupied work spaces, uniform distribution of general lighting may be most appropriate. Where necessary, provide supplementary task illumination. General ambient illumination should not be lower than one-third of the luminance required for the task, to help maintain visually comfortable luminance ratios.
- Use local task lighting to accommodate needs for higher lighting levels because of task visual difficulty, glare, intermittently changing requirements, or individual visual differences (poor or aging eyesight).
- Group similar activities so that high illuminance or special lighting for particular tasks can be localized in certain rooms or areas and so that less-efficient fixtures required for critical glare control do not have to be installed uniformly when they are only required sparsely.
- Use lighting controls throughout so lighting is available when and where it is needed but not wasted when tasks are less critical or spaces are not fully occupied. Also consider user acceptance of control strategies to maximize energy savings.
- Use LED lighting. Only use incandescent and fluorescent lamps in applications where their characteristics cannot be duplicated by other sources, because manufacturing of most incandescent and fluorescent lamps will be discontinued during the life of the building.
- Carry lighting design through the rest of the building's interior design. Reduced light absorption may be achieved by using lighter finishes, particularly on ceilings, walls, and partitions.

Other Loads

- Minimize the thermal impact of equipment and appliances on HVAC systems by using hoods, radiation shields, or other confining techniques, and by using controls to turn off equipment when not needed. Where practical, locate major heat-generating equipment where it can balance other heat losses. Computer centers or kitchen areas usually have separate, dedicated HVAC equipment. In addition, consider heat recovery for this equipment.
- Use storage techniques to level or distribute loads that vary on a time or spatial basis to allow operation of a device at maximum (often full-load) efficiency.

HVAC System Design

- Consider separate HVAC systems to serve areas expected to operate on widely differing operating schedules or design conditions. For instance, systems serving office areas should generally be separate from those serving retail areas.
- Arrange systems so that spaces with relatively constant, weather-independent loads are served by systems separate from those serving perimeter spaces. Areas with special temperature or humidity requirements (e.g., computer rooms) should be served by systems separate from those serving areas that require comfort heating and cooling only. Alternatively, provide these areas with supplementary or auxiliary systems.
- Sequence the supply of zone cooling and heating to prevent simultaneous operation of heating and cooling systems for the same space, to the extent possible. Where this is not possible because of ventilation, humidity control, or air circulation requirements, reduce air quantities as much as possible before incorporating reheating, recooling, or mixing hot and cold airstreams. For example, if reheat is needed to dehumidify and prevent overcooling, only ventilation air needs to be treated, not the entire recirculated air quantity. Finally, reset supply air temperature to the extent possible to reduce reheating, recooling, or mixing losses.
- Provide local and central controls to allow operation in occupied and unoccupied modes. In unoccupied mode, ventilation and exhaust systems should be shut off centrally or locally when possible, and comfort heating and cooling systems should be

shut off except to maintain space conditions ready for the next occupancy cycle. Use standby mode with no ventilation for spaces that are unoccupied during the occupied mode but maintain occupied space temperature set points.

- In geographical areas where diurnal temperature swings and humidity levels permit, consider judicious coupling of air distribution and building structural mass to allow nighttime cooling to reduce the requirement for daytime mechanical cooling.
- Use heat recovery and dedicated outdoor air systems (DOASs) to reduce the cooling, dehumidification, humidification, and heating load to reduce the size of components such as coils, pipes, pumps, chillers, boilers, transformers, and other electrical equipment and to reduce the energy consumption. See Chapter 51 of the 2020 *ASHRAE Handbook—HVAC Systems and Equipment* and/or *ASHRAE Design Guide for Dedicated Outdoor Air Systems* for more details on DOASs.

HVAC Equipment Selection

- To allow HVAC equipment operation at the highest efficiencies, match conversion devices to load increments, and sequence the operation of modules. Oversized or large-scale systems should never serve small seasonal loads (e.g., a large heating boiler serving a summer-service water-heated load). Include specific low-load units and auxiliaries where prolonged use at minimal capacities is expected.
- Select the most efficient (or highest-COP) equipment practical at both design and reduced capacity (part-load) operating conditions.
- When selecting large-power devices such as chillers (including their auxiliary energy burdens), perform an economic analysis of the complete life-cycle costs. See Chapter 37 of the 2019 *ASHRAE Handbook—HVAC Applications* for more information on detailed economic analysis.
- Keep fluid temperatures for heating equipment devices as low as practical and for cooling equipment as high as practical, while still meeting loads and minimizing flow quantities.

Energy Transport Systems

Energy should be transported as efficiently as possible. The following options are listed in order of theoretical efficiency, from the lowest energy transport burden (most efficient) to the highest (least efficient):

1. Electric wire or fuel pipe
2. Two-phase fluid pipe (steam or refrigerant)
3. Single-phase liquid/fluid pipe (water, glycol, etc.)
4. Air duct

Select a distribution system that complements other parameters such as control strategies, storage capabilities, conversion efficiency, and utilization efficiency. The following specific design techniques may be applied to thermal energy transport systems:

Steam Systems

- Include provisions for seasonal or non-use shutdown.
- Require that all steam pipe and components are well insulated.
- Minimize venting of steam and ingestion of air, with design directed toward full-vapor performance.
- Avoid subcooling, if practical.
- Return condensate to boilers or source devices at the highest possible temperature.

Hydronic Systems

- Minimize flow quantity by designing for the maximum practical temperature range.
- Vary flow quantity with load where possible.
- Design for the lowest practical pressure loss in the critical pressure path. Require that the differential pressure set point is reset when at part flow.
- Provide operating and idle control modes.
- When locating equipment, identify the critical pressure path and size runs for the minimum reasonable pressure drop.

Air Systems

- Minimize airflow by careful load analysis and an effective distribution system. If the application allows, supply air quantity should vary with sensible load (i.e., variable-air-volume [VAV] systems). Hold the fan pressure requirement to the lowest practical value and avoid using fan pressure as a source for control power. Require that the static pressure set point is reset when at part flow.
- Provide normal and idle control modes for fan and psychrometric systems.
- Keep duct runs as short as possible, and keep runs on the critical pressure path sized for minimum practical pressure drop.

Power Distribution

- Size transformers and generating units as closely as possible to the actual anticipated load (i.e., avoid oversizing to minimize fixed thermal losses).
- Consider distribution of electric power at the highest practical voltage and load selection at the maximum power factor consistent with safety.
- Consider tenant submetering in commercial and multifamily buildings as a cost-effective energy conservation measure. A large portion of energy use in tenant facilities occurs simply because there is no economic incentive to conserve.

Domestic Hot-Water Systems

- Choose showerheads that provide and maintain user comfort and energy savings. They should not have removable flow-restricting inserts to meet flow limitation requirements.
- Consider point-of-use water heaters where their use will reduce energy consumption and annual energy cost.
- Consider using storage to facilitate heat recovery when the heat to be recovered is out of phase with the demand for hot water or when energy use for water heating can be shifted to take advantage of off-peak rates.

Controls

Well-designed digital control provides information to managers and operators as well as to the data processor that serves as the intelligent controller. Include the energy-saving concepts discussed previously throughout the operating sequences and control logic. Energy conservation should not be sought at the expense of adequate performance, however; in a well-designed system, these two parameters are compatible. See Chapter 7 of the 2021 *ASHRAE Handbook—Fundamentals*, Chapter 48 of the 2019 *ASHRAE Handbook—HVAC Applications*, and ASHRAE Guideline 36 for more information on controls.

Commissioning

Building systems are typically complicated and often do not work as intended. This causes reduced comfort levels, reduced IAQ, and/or increased energy consumption. A commissioning process of documentation, adjusting, testing, verification, and training to ensure that the finished facility operates in accordance with the Owner's Project Requirements and the construction documents will improve the performance of the building. As a result of the commissioning process, the facility will be more comfortable, have better IAQ, and/or use less energy. ANSI/ASHRAE/IES Standard 90.1 recognizes this and requires commissioning of the mechanical systems.

ASHRAE has developed an extensive suite of commissioning standards and guidelines that deal with new and existing projects, including ANSI/ASHRAE/IES Standard 202, *Commissioning Process for Buildings and Systems*; ASHRAE Guideline 0, *The Commissioning Process*; and ASHRAE Guideline 0.2, *Commissioning Process for Existing Systems and Assemblies*.

Energy Design Resources

ASHRAE, in conjunction with partner organizations, has developed The Advanced Energy Design Guide series (www.ashrae.org/aedgs), which includes design recommendations to achieve three levels of energy efficiency for a range of building types.

Green Design and Sustainability

Sustainability is defined in *ASHRAE GreenGuide*, Fifth Edition, in general terms, as "providing for the needs of the present without detracting from the ability to fulfill the needs of the future"—a definition very similar to that developed in 1987 by the United Nations' Brundtland Commission. Others have defined sustainability as "the concept of maximizing the effectiveness of resource use while minimizing the impact of that use on the environment" and an environment in which "an equilibrium… exists between human society and stable ecosystems." Sustaining (i.e., keeping up or prolonging) those elements on which humankind's existence and that of the planet depend, such as energy, the environment, and health, are worthy goals.

Sustainability Addresses the Future. Sustainability is focused on the future. Actions taken under the name of sustainability must address the impact of present actions on conditions likely to prevail in that future time frame. As stressed in Chapter 36 of the 2021 *ASHRAE Handbook—Fundamentals*, climates are changing at a faster rate than previously thought. In designing the built environment, the emphasis has often been on the present or the near future, usually in the form of capital (or first-cost) impact. As is apparent when life-cycle cost analysis is applied, capital cost assumes less importance the longer the future period under consideration.

Sustainability Has Many Contributors. Sustainability is not just about energy, carbon emissions, pollution, waste disposal, or population growth. Although these are central ideas in thinking about sustainability, it is an oversimplification to think that addressing one factor, or even any one set of factors, can result in a sustainable future for the planet.

It is likewise a mistake to think that HVAC&R design practitioners, by themselves and just through activities within their purview, can create a sustainable result. To be sure, their activities can contribute to sustainability by creating a sustainable building, development, or other related project. But they cannot by themselves create global sustainability. Such an endeavor depends on many outside factors that cannot be controlled by HVAC&R engineers; however, these engineers should make their fair-share contribution to sustainability in all their endeavors and encourage other individuals and entities to do the same.

Sustainability is Comprehensive. Sustainability has no borders or limits. A good-faith effort to make a project sustainable does not mean that sustainability will be achieved globally. A superb design job on a building with sustainability as a goal will probably not contribute much to the global situation if a significant number of other buildings are not so designed, or if the transportation sector makes an inadequate contribution, or if only a few regions of the world do their fair share toward making the planet sustainable. A truly sustainable outcome depends on comprehensive efforts in all sectors the world around.

Sustainable versus Green. An emphasis on the distant future can differentiate sustainable design from green design. Whereas green design addresses many of the same characteristics as sustainable design, it may also emphasize near-term impacts such as indoor environmental quality, operation and maintenance features, and meeting current client needs. Thus, green design may focus more on the immediate future (i.e., starting when the building is first constructed and then occupied). Sustainable design is of paramount importance to the global environment in the long term while still incorporating features of green design that focus on the present and near future.

The design process is the first crucial element in producing a green building. For design efficiency, it is necessary to define the owner's objectives and criteria, including sustainable/green goals, before beginning the design so as to minimize potential increased design costs. Once designed, the building must be constructed, its performance verified, and it must be operated in a way that supports the green concept. If it is not designed with the intent to make it green, the desired results will never be achieved.

Figure 13.1 conceptually shows the impact of providing design input at succeeding stages of a project, relative to the cost and effort required. The solid curve shows it is much easier to have a major impact on the performance (potential energy savings, water efficiency, maintenance costs, etc.) of a building if one starts at the very earliest stages of the design process. The available impacts diminish thereafter as one proceeds through the subsequent design and construction phases. A corollary to this is the cost of implementing changes to improve build-

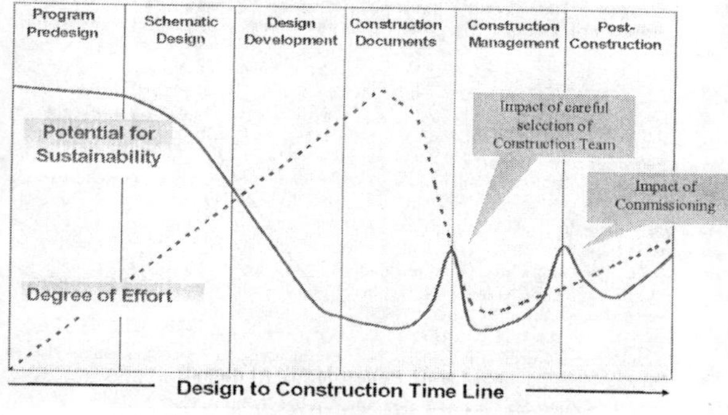

(Image courtesy of Malcolm Lewis, CTG Energetics, Inc.)

Figure 13.1 The Changing Potential for Sustainability over a Project Time Line and the Impact of Commissioning [ASHRAE GreenGuide 5th, Fig 3-2]

ing performance rises at each successive stage of the project (cost is shown as the dotted curve of the graph).

HVAC&R designers know how to design buildings that are much more energy efficient than they have been in the past, but such buildings are still relatively rare, especially in the general commercial market (as opposed to those owned by high-profile entities). ASHRAE's long-standing guidance in designing energy-efficient (now green and/or sustainable) buildings, and the motivation provided by its own and other entities' programs, have pointed the way technologically for the built environment and related industries to make their fair-share contribution to sustainability. Such programs include 1) ASHRAE's net-zero energy buildings (NZEB) thrust, 2) the U.S. Green Building Council (USGBC) Leadership in Energy and Environmental Design (LEED®) Green Building Rating System™, 3) the American Institute of Architects (AIA) 2030 Challenge, 4) the Green Building Institute (GBI) Green Globes program, and 5) the U.S. Environmental Protection Agency (EPA) ENERGY STAR® program.

Embodied Energy and Carbon Emissions

As buildings become more energy efficient and their operational energy is reduced, emphasis will shift toward reducing their embodied energy. Materials used directly in the construction and the components, equipment, and systems for building operation embody the energy and carbon used during their manufacturing, transportation, and installation. Material selection should also consider the environmental impact of demolition and disposal after the service life of the products. Building life-cycle assessment (LCA) focuses on the environmental impact of a product system (from materials acquisition to manufacturing, use, and final disposition) and plays a major role in promoting sustainability. This is a cradle-to-grave approach that evaluates all stages of individual materials and the product's life to determine their cumulative environmental impact. Designers should give preference to resource-efficient materials and reduce waste by recycling and reusing whenever possible.

LCA is an internationally standardized methodology (ISO Standard 14040). Consecutive parts of an LCA include a life-cycle inventory (e.g., collection and analysis of air and water emissions, waste generation, and resource consumption over the product's life) and life-cycle impact assessment (LCIA), which is an estimation of indicators of the environmental pressures in terms of climate change, summer smog, resource depletion, acidification, human health effects, etc., attributable to the product's life cycle. More information on the LCA approach is available online from the EPA (www.epa.gov/saferchoice/design-environment-life-cycle-assessments), the European Commission (ec.europa.eu/environment/ipp/lca.htm), and the Carbon Leadership Forum (http://carbonleadershipforum.org). Various LCA databases and tools available from commercial as well as governmental or public-domain sources can be used to calculate and compare the embodied energy (e.g., total energy per unit mass), related embodied emissions (e.g., total mass of CO_2 per unit mass of material or product), or other embodied environmental impacts of common building materials and products.

A challenge for modeling life-cycle energy use in buildings is using consistent system boundaries and data collection. Available software to address these concerns include Building for Environmental and Economic Sustainability (BEES; www.nist.gov/services-resources/software/bees), the Athena Sustainable Materials Institute's Environmental Impact Estimator (www.athenasmi.org/what-we-do/lca-data-software/), OneClick LCA (www.oneclicklca.com), and the Embodied Carbon in Construction Calculator (EC3) (www.buildingtransparency.org/en/). Regional data are important because conversion factors to primary energy and GHG emissions can differ by country, depending on energy sources used (e.g., coal- or oil-fired power plants versus solar or natural-gas-based generation).

LCA-based information may be in the form of environmental product declarations (EPD) based on CEN Standard 15804 or the product environmental footprints (PEFs) inspired by ISO Standards 14040 and 14044 and voluntary environmental declarations (ISO Standard 14025). They have been gaining in popularity beyond building construction materials, given the growing criteria of green building certifications such as LEED v4 credit, which now rewards selection of HVAC products with EPDs, based on the updated LEED credit interpretation in early 2015.

LCA can also assess specific refurbishments intended to improve energy performance of systems in existing buildings. For example, replacing electric or gas water heaters with solar hot-water systems can provide net emissions savings compared with the conventional systems after 0.6 month to 2.5 years, depending on the auxiliary fuel. For solar domestic hot-water systems and solar central space heating, the energy consumed by producing and installing the solar systems is recovered in about 1.2 years, and the payback time for the systems' embodied energy emissions varies from a few months (for solar domestic water heating) to 9.5 years (for solar central space heating), again depending on the energy carrier for the conventional system and the specific environmental emission indicators considered. The energy payback times of photovoltaic systems have been shown to be between 0.75 and 2 years for a roof-mounted system in a location with 160 kWh per ft^2 irradiation per year and will vary with climate, type of photovoltaic technology, mounting, and other system parameters.

Table 14.1 Characteristics of AC Motors (Nonhermetic) [2020S, Ch 45, Tbl 4]

	Split-Phase	Permanent Split-Capacitor	Capacitor-Start Induction-Run	Capacitor-Start Capacitor-Run	Shaded-Pole	Polyphase, 60-Hz
Connection Diagram	RUN START	RUN CAP. START	RUN CAP. START	RUN START	RUN	
Speed Torque Curves	RUN START F.L. 250 % 125 %	RUN F.L. 250 % 25 %	RUN START F.L. 250 % 350 %	RUN START F.L. 275 %	RUN F.L. 125 % 25 %	START & RUN
Starting Method	Centrifugal switch	None	Centrifugal switch	Centrifugal switch	None	Motor controller
Ratings, hp	0.05 to 0.5	0.05 to 5	0.05 to 5	0.05 to 5	0.01 to 0.25	0.5 and up
Full-Load Speeds at 60-Hz (Two-Pole, Four-Pole)	3450 to 1725	3450 to 1725	3450 to 1725	3500 to 1750	3100 to 1550	3500 to 1750
Torque[a] Locked Rotor	125% to 150%	25%	250% to 350%	250%	25%	150% to 350%
Torque[a] Breakdown	250% to 300%	250% to 300%	250% to 300%	250%	125%	250% to 350%
Speed Classification	Constant	Constant	Constant	Constant	Constant or adjustable	Constant
Full-Load Power Factor	60%	95%	65%	95%	60%	80%
Efficiency	Medium	High	Medium	High	Low	High-Medium

[a] Expressed as percent of rated horsepower torque.

Table 14.2 Motor and Motor Control Equipment Voltages (Alternating Current) [2020S, Ch 45, Tbl 1]

System Nominal Voltage	U.S. Domestic Equipment Nameplate Voltage Ratings (60 Hz)			
	Integral Horsepower		Fractional Horsepower	
	Three-Phase	Single-Phase	Three-Phase	Single-Phase
120	—	115	—	115
208	208/230 or 200/230	208/230 or 200/230	208/230 or 200/230	208/230 or 200/230
240	208/230 or 200/230	208/230 or 200/230	208/230 or 200/230	208/230 or 200/230
277	—	265	—	265
480	460	—	460	—
600*	575	—	575	—
2,400	2,300	—	—	—
4,160	4,000	—	—	—
4,800	4,600	—	—	—
6,900	6,600	—	—	—
13,800	13,200	—	—	—

*Some control and protective equipment has maximum voltage limit of 600 V. Consult manufacturer, power supplier, or both to ensure proper application.

System Nominal Voltage	International Equipment Nameplate Voltage Ratings			
	50 Hz		60 Hz	
	Three-Phase	Single-Phase	Three-Phase	Single-Phase
127	—	127	—	127
200	220/200	200	230/208 or 230/200	—
220	220/240	220/240 or 230/208	230/208 or 230/200	230/208
230	230/208	220/240 or 230/208	230/208 or 230/200	230/208
240	230/208	220/240	230/208	230/208
250	—	250	—	—
380	380/415	—	460/380	—
400	380/415	—	—	—
415	380/415	—	—	—
440	440	—	460	—
480	500	—	—	—

Note: Primary operating voltage for a dual-voltage rating is usually listed first (e.g., 220 is primary for a 220/240 volt rating).

Table 14.3 Motor Full-Load Amperes

Horsepower	Recommended Starter Size Three Phase		Three-Phase AC Squirrel-Cage and Wound-Rotor (Induction Type)			Recommended Starter Size Single Phase	Single-Phase AC			Horsepower
	230 V	460 V	200 V	230 V	460 V	230 V	115 V	200 V	230 V	
1/6						00	4.4	2.5	2.2	1/6
1/4						00	5.8	3.3	2.9	1/4
1/2	00	00	2.3	2	1	00	9.8	5.6	4.9	1/2
3/4	00	00	3.2	2.8	1.4	00	13.8	7.9	6.9	3/4
1	00	00	4.1	3.6	1.8	00	16	9.2	8	1
1.5	00	00	6.0	5.2	2.6	0	20	11.5	10	1.5
2	0	00	7.8	6.8	3.4	0	24	13.8	12	2
3	0	0	11.0	9.6	4.8	1	34	19.6	17	3
5	1	0	17.5	15.2	7.6	1	56	32.2	28	5
7.5	1	1	25.3	22	11	2	80	46	40	7.5
10	2	1	32.2	28	14	2	100	57.5	50	10
15	2	2	48.3	42	21	3				15
20	3	2	62.1	54	27					20
25	3	2	78.2	68	34					25
30	3	3	92	80	40					30
40	4	3	119.6	104	52					40
50	4	3	149.5	130	65					50
60	5	4	177.1	154	77					60
75	5	4	220.8	192	96					75
100	5	4	285.2	248	124					100
125	6	5	358.8	312	156					125
150	6	5	414	360	180					150
200	6	5	552	480	240					200

Values are for motors with normal torque characteristics running at usual belted speeds.

Table 14.4 Useful Electrical Formulas

To Find	Direct Current	Single Phase	Three Phase
Amperes when horsepower known	$\frac{hp \times 746}{E \times \eta}$	$\frac{hp \times 746}{E \times \eta \times F}$	$\frac{hp \times 746}{1.73 \times E \times \eta \times F}$
Amperes when kilowatts known	$\frac{kW \times 1000}{E}$	$\frac{kW \times 1000}{E \times F}$	$\frac{kW \times 1000}{1.73 \times E \times F}$
Amperes when kVA known		$\frac{kVA \times 1000}{E}$	$\frac{kVA \times 1000}{1.73 \times E}$
Kilowatts	$\frac{I \times E}{1000}$	$\frac{I \times E \times F}{1000}$	$\frac{I \times E \times 1.73 \times F}{1000}$
kVA		$\frac{I \times E}{1000}$	$\frac{I \times E \times 1.73}{1000}$
Horsepower—(output)	$\frac{I \times E \times \eta}{746}$	$\frac{I \times E \times \eta \times F}{746}$	$\frac{I \times E \times 1.73 \times \eta \times F}{746}$

I = amperes; E = volts; η = efficiency expressed as decimal; F = power factor; kW = kilowatts; kVA = kilovolt-amperes; hp = horsepower.

Motor Protection and Control

In general, four functions are accomplished by motor protection and control. Separate or integral control components are provided to (1) disconnect the motor and controller from the power supply and protect the operator; (2) start and stop the motor and, in some applications, control the speed or direction of rotation; (3) protect motor branch circuit conductors and control apparatus against short-circuiting; and (4) protect the motor itself from overloading and overheating.

Variable-Frequency Drives (VFDs)

By far the most energy-efficient means of varying flow of fans and pumps driven by electric motors are VFDs. Their application involves careful consideration of their effects (here VFD is considered synonymous with variable-speed drive [VSD], pulse-width modulated drive [PWM drive], adjustable-speed drive [ASD], and adjustable-frequency drive [AFD].) An alternating-current VFD consists of a diode bridge AC-to-DC converter and a pulse-width-modulation (PWM) controller with fast-rise power transistors—usually insulated-gate bipolar transistors (IGBTs)—and an induction motor. The IGBT changes the characteristics of waveforms applied to a motor due to the speed at which the IGBT cycles on and off. At switching speed up to 20 k Hz, the impedance in the connecting cable is far less than the motor impedance, particularly for small motors, causing pulse reflectance at the motor terminals to form damaging high voltage. NEMA motor standard MG1 states PWM drive limits and establishes a peak of 1600 V and a minimum rise time of 0.1 μs for motors rated less than 600 V. Typical manufacturer maximum voltage withstand levels range from 1000 V to 1800 V. When specifying motors for operation on VSDs, the voltage withstand level based on the dV/dt of the drive and the known cable distance should be specified.

Harmonics caused by the portion of a VSD converting line power LDC affect input lines and are termed *line-side harmonics*. Output line harmonics are caused solely by the inverter section of the VSD and are known as load side or motor harmonics. Generally, PWM drives containing internal bus reaction or three-phase AC line reactors do not cause interference with other electrical equipment. There may be problems when a VSD is switched onto a standby generator, or when power factor correction capacitors are used.

Table 15.1 Maximum Capacity of Gas Pipe in Cubic Feet per Hour [2021F, Ch 22, Tbl 40]

Nominal Iron Pipe Size, in.	Internal Diameter, in.	Length of Pipe, ft													
		10	20	30	40	50	60	70	80	90	100	125	150	175	200
1/4	0.364	32	22	18	15	14	12	11	11	10	9	8	8	7	6
3/8	0.493	72	49	40	34	30	27	25	23	22	21	18	17	15	14
1/2	0.622	132	92	73	63	56	50	46	43	40	38	34	31	28	26
3/4	0.824	278	190	152	130	115	105	96	90	84	79	72	64	59	55
1	1.049	520	350	285	245	215	195	180	170	160	150	130	120	110	100
1 1/4	1.380	1,050	730	590	500	440	400	370	350	320	305	275	250	225	210
1 1/2	1.610	1,600	1,100	890	760	670	610	560	530	490	460	410	380	350	320
2	2.067	3,050	2,100	1,650	1,450	1,270	1,150	1,050	990	930	870	780	710	650	610
2 1/2	2.469	4,800	3,300	2,700	2,300	2,000	1,850	1,700	1,600	1,500	1,400	1,250	1,130	1,050	980
3	3.068	8,500	5,900	4,700	4,100	3,600	3,250	3,000	2,800	2,600	2,500	2,200	2,000	1,850	1,700
4	4.026	17,500	12,000	9,700	8,300	7,400	6,800	6,200	5,800	5,400	5,100	4,500	4,100	3,800	3,500

Note: Capacity is in cubic feet per hour at gas pressures of 0.5 psig or less and a pressure drop of 0.3 in. of water; specific gravity = 0.60.

Table 15.2 Typical API Gravity, Density, and Heating Value of Standard Grades of Fuel Oil [2021F, Ch 28, Tbl 10]

Grade No.	API Gravity	Density, lb/gal	Higher Heating Value, Btu/gal
1	38 to 45	6.950 to 6.675	137,000 to 132,900
2	30 to 38	7.296 to 6.960	141,800 to 137,000
4	20 to 28	7.787 to 7.396	148,100 to 143,100
5L	17 to 22	7.940 to 7.686	150,000 to 146,800
5H	14 to 18	8.080 to 7.890	152,000 to 149,400
6	8 to 15	8.448 to 8.053	155,900 to 151,300

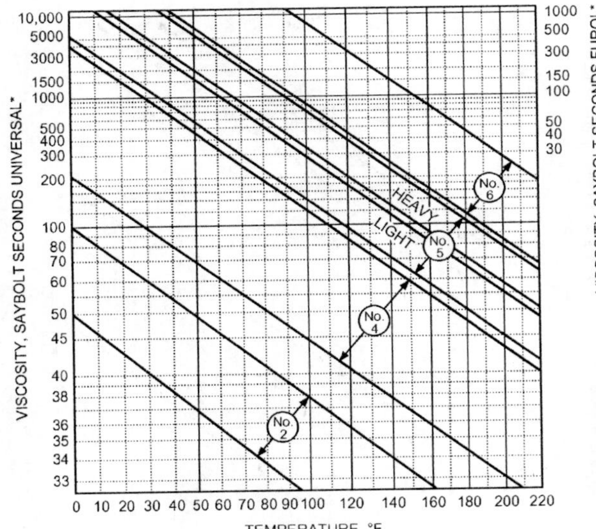

* 1 Saybolt Second (SSU, or SUS) = time required for 60 mL to gravity-flow through Saybolt universal viscometer. (Furol = Fuel and Road Oils)

Figure 15.1 Approximate Viscosity of Fuel Oils [2021F, Ch 28, Fig 2]

Types of Fuel Oils

Fuel oils for heating are broadly classified as distillate fuel oils (lighter oils) or residual fuel oils (heavier oils). ASTM has established specifications for fuel oil properties which subdivide the oils into various grades. Grades No. 1 and 2 are distillate fuel oils. Grades 4, 5 (Light), 5 (Heavy), and 6 are residual fuel oils. Specifications for the grades are based on required characteristics of fuel oils for use in different types of burners.

Grade No. 1 is a light distillate intended for vaporizing-type burners. High volatility is essential to continued evaporation of the fuel oil with minimum residue.

Grade No. 2 is a heavier (API Gravity) distillate than No. 1. It is used primarily with pressure-atomizing (gun) burners that spray the oil into a combustion chamber. The atomized oil vapor mixes with air and burns. This grade is used in most domestic burners and many medium capacity commercial-industrial burners.

Grade No. 4 is an intermediate fuel that is considered either a light residual or a heavy distillate. Intended for burners that atomize oils of higher viscosity than domestic burners can handle, its permissible viscosity range allows it to be pumped and atomized at relatively low storage temperatures.

Grade No. 5 (Light) is a residual fuel of intermediate viscosity for burners that handle fuel more viscous than No. 4 without preheating. Preheating may be necessary in some equipment for burning and, in colder climates, for handling.

Grade No. 5 (Heavy) is a residual fuel more viscous than No. 5 (Light), but intended for similar purposes. Preheating is usually necessary for burning and, in colder climates, for handling.

Grade No. 6, sometimes referred to as Bunker C, is a high-viscosity oil used mostly in commercial and industrial heating. It requires preheating in the storage tank to permit pumping, and additional preheating at the burner to allow atomizing.

Types and Properties of Liquid Fuels for Engines

The primary stationary engine fuels are diesel and gas turbine oils, natural gases, and liquefied petroleum gases. Other fuels include sewage gas, manufactured gas, and other commercial gas mixtures. Gasoline and the JP series of gas turbine fuels are rarely used for stationary engines.

Properties of the three grades of diesel fuel oils (1-D, 2-D, and 4-D) are listed in ASTM Standard D975.

Grade No. 1-D includes the class of volatile fuel oils from kerosene to intermediate distillates. They are used in high-speed engines with frequent and relatively wide variations in loads and speeds and where abnormally low fuel temperatures are encountered.

Grade No. 2-D includes the class of lower volatility distillate gas oils. These fuels are used in high-speed engines with relatively high loads and uniform speeds, or in engines not requiring fuels with the higher volatility or other properties specified for Grade No. 1-D.

Grade No. 4-D covers the class of more viscous distillates and blends of these distillates with residual fuel oils. These fuels are used in low- and medium-speed engines involving sustained loads at essentially constant speed.

Property specifications and test methods for Grade No. 1-D, 2-D, and 4-D diesel fuel oils are essentially identical to specifications of Grade No. 1, 2, and 4 fuel oils, respectively. However, diesel fuel oils have an additional specification for **cetane number**, which measures ignition quality and influences combustion roughness. Cetane number requirements depend on engine design, size, speed and load variations, and starting and atmospheric conditions. An increase in cetane number over values actually required does not improve engine performance. Thus, the cetane number should be as low as possible to assure maximum fuel availability. ASTM Standard D975 provides several methods for estimating cetane number from other fuel oil properties.

ASTM Standard D2880 for gas turbine fuel oils relates gas turbine fuel oil grades to fuel and diesel fuel oil grades.

Table 15.3 Approximate Air Requirements for Stoichiometric Combustion of Various Fuels [2021F, Ch 28, Tbl 13]

Type of Fuel	Theoretical Air Required for Combustion
Solid fuels	lb/lb fuel
Anthracite	9.6
Semibituminous	11.2
Bituminous	10.3
Lignite	6.2
Coke	11.2
Liquid fuels	lb/gal fuel
No. 1 fuel oil	103
No. 2 fuel oil	106
No. 5 fuel oil	112
No. 6 fuel oil	114
Gaseous fuels	ft^3/ft^3 fuel
Natural gas	9.6
Butane	31.1
Propane	24.0

Table 15.4 Approximate Maximum Theoretical (Stoichiometric) CO_2 Values and CO_2 Values of Various Fuels with Different Percentages of Excess Air [2021F, Ch 28, Tbl 15]

Type of Fuel	Theoretical or Maximum CO_2, %	Percent CO_2 at Given Excess Air Values		
		20%	40%	60%
Gaseous Fuels				
Natural gas	12.1	9.9	8.4	7.3
Propane gas (commercial)	13.9	11.4	9.6	8.4
Butane gas (commercial)	14.1	11.6	9.8	8.5
Mixed gas (natural and carbureted water gas)	11.2	12.5	10.5	9.1
Carbureted water gas	17.2	14.2	12.1	10.6
Coke oven gas	11.2	9.2	7.8	6.8
Liquid Fuels				
No. 1 and 2 fuel oil	15.0	12.3	10.5	9.1
No. 6 fuel oil	16.5	13.6	11.6	10.1
Solid Fuels				
Bituminous coal	18.2	15.1	12.9	11.3
Anthracite	20.2	16.8	14.4	12.6
Coke	21.0	17.5	15.0	13.0

Table 15.5 Recommended Nominal Size for Fuel Oil Suction Lines from Tank to Pump (Distillate Grades No. 1 and No. 2) [2021F, Ch 22, Tbl 42]

Pumping Rate, gph	Length of Run in Feet at Maximum Suction Lift of 10 ft									
	25	50	75	100	125	150	175	200	250	300
10	1/2	1/2	1/2	1/2	1/2	1/2	1/2	3/4	3/4	1
40	1/2	1/2	1/2	1/2	1/2	3/4	3/4	3/4	3/4	1
70	1/2	1/2	3/4	3/4	3/4	3/4	3/4	1	1	1
100	1/2	3/4	3/4	3/4	3/4	1	1	1	1	1 1/4
130	1/2	3/4	3/4	1	1	1	1	1	1 1/4	1 1/4
160	3/4	3/4	3/4	1	1	1	1	1 1/4	1 1/4	1 1/4
190	3/4	3/4	1	1	1	1	1 1/4	1 1/4	1 1/4	2
220	3/4	1	1	1	1	1 1/4	1 1/4	1 1/4	1 1/4	2

Table 15.6 Recommended Nominal Size for Fuel Oil Suction Lines from Tank to Pump (Residual Grades No. 5 and No. 6) [2021F, Ch 22, Tbl 41]

Pumping Rate, gph	Length of Run in Feet at Maximum Suction Lift of 15 ft									
	25	50	75	100	125	150	175	200	250	300
10	1 1/2	1 1/2	1 1/2	1 1/2	1 1/2	1 1/2	2	2	2 1/2	2 1/2
40	1 1/2	1 1/2	1 1/2	2	2	2 1/2	2 1/2	2 1/2	2 1/2	3
70	1 1/2	2	2	2	2	2 1/2	2 1/2	2 1/2	3	3
100	2	2	2	2 1/2	2 1/2	3	3	3	3	3
130	2	2	2 1/2	2 1/2	2 1/2	3	3	3	3	4
160	2	2	2 1/2	2 1/2	2 1/2	3	3	3	4	4
190	2	2 1/2	2 1/2	2 1/2	3	3	3	4	4	4
220	2 1/2	2 1/2	2 1/2	3	3	3	4	4	4	4

Notes: 1. Pipe sizes smaller than 1 in. IPS are not recommended for use with residual grade fuel oils.
2. Lines conveying fuel oil from pump discharge port to burners and tank return may be reduced by one or two sizes, depending on piping length and pressure losses.

16. OWNING AND OPERATING

Maintenance Costs

The maintenance cost of mechanical systems varies widely depending on configuration, equipment locations, accessibility, system complexity, service duty, geography, and system reliability requirements.

Dohrmann and Alereza (1986) obtained maintenance costs and HVAC system information from 342 buildings located in 35 states in the United States. In 1983 U.S. dollars, data collected showed a mean HVAC system maintenance cost of $0.32/ft^2 per year, with a median cost of $0.24/ft^2 per year. Building age has a statistically significant but minor effect on HVAC maintenance costs. Analysis also indicated that building size is not statistically significant in explaining cost variation. The type of maintenance program or service agency that building management chooses can also have a significant effect on total HVAC maintenance costs. Although extensive or thorough routine and preventive maintenance programs cost more to administer, they usually extend equipment life; improve reliability; and reduce system downtime, energy costs, and overall life-cycle costs.

Some maintenance cost data are available, both in the public domain and from proprietary sources used by various commercial service providers. These sources may include equipment manufacturers, independent service providers, insurers, government agencies (e.g., the U.S. General Services Administration), and industry-related organizations [e.g., the Building Owners and Managers Association (BOMA)] and service industry publications. More traditional, widely used products and components are likely to have statistically reliable records. However, design changes or modifications necessitated by industry changes, such as alternative refrigerants, may make historical data less relevant.

Newer HVAC products, components, system configurations, control systems and protocols, and upgraded or revised system applications present an additional challenge. Care is required when using data not drawn from broad experience or field reports. In many cases, maintenance information is proprietary or was sponsored by a particular entity or group. Particular care should be taken when using such data. It is the user's responsibility to obtain these data and to determine their appropriateness and suitability for the application being considered.

ASHRAE research project TRP-1237 (Abramson et al. 2005) developed a standardized Internet-based data collection tool and database on HVAC equipment service life and maintenance costs. The database was seeded with data on 163 buildings from around the country. Maintenance cost data were gathered for total HVAC system maintenance costs from 100 facilities. In 2004 dollars, the mean HVAC maintenance cost from these data was $0.47/ft^2, and the median cost was $0.44/ft^2. Table 16.1 compares these figures with estimates reported by Dohrmann and Alereza (1986), both in terms of contemporary dollars, and in 2004 dollars, and shows that the cost per square foot varies widely between studies.

Estimating Maintenance Costs

Total HVAC maintenance cost for new and existing buildings with various types of equipment may be estimated several ways, using several resources. Equipment maintenance requirements can be obtained from the equipment manufacturers for large or custom pieces of equipment. Estimating in-house labor requirements can be difficult; BOMA provides guidance on this topic. Many independent mechanical service companies provide preventative maintenance contracts. These firms typically have proprietary estimating programs developed through their experience, and often provide generalized maintenance costs to engineers and owners upon request, without obligation.

Table 16.1 Comparison of Maintenance Costs Between Studies
[2019A, Ch 38, Tbl 6]

Survey	Cost per ft^2, as Reported		Consumer Price Index	Cost per ft^2, 2004 Dollars	
	Mean	Median		Mean	Median
Dohrmann and Alereza (1986)	$0.32	$0.24	99.6	$0.61	$0.46
Abramson et al. (2005)	$0.47	$0.44	188.9	$0.47	$0.44

When evaluating various HVAC systems during design or retrofit, the absolute magnitude of maintenance costs may not be as important as the relative costs. Whichever estimating method or resource is selected, it should be used consistently throughout any evaluation. Mixing information from different resources in an evaluation may provide erroneous results.

Applying simple costs per unit of building floor area for maintenance is highly discouraged. Maintenance costs can be generalized by system types. When projecting maintenance costs for different HVAC systems, the major system components need to be identified with a required level of maintenance. The potential long-term costs of environmental issues on maintenance costs should also be considered.

Table 16.2 Owning and Operating Cost Data and Summary
[2019A, Ch 38, Tbl 1]

OWNING COSTS	
I. Initial Cost of System	
II. Periodic Costs	
A. Income taxes	
B. Property taxes	
C. Insurance	
D. Rent	
E. Other periodic costs	
Total Periodic Costs	
III. Replacement Cost	
IV. Salvage Value	
Total Owning Costs	
OPERATING COSTS	
V. Annual Utility, Fuel, Water, etc., Costs	
A. Utilities	
1. Electricity	
2. Natural gas	
3. Water/sewer	
4. Purchased steam	
5. Purchased hot/chilled water	
B. Fuels	
1. Propane	
2. Fuel oil	
3. Diesel	
4. Coal	
C. On-site generation of electricity	
D. Other utility, fuel, water, etc., costs	
Total	
VI. Annual Maintenance Allowances/Costs	
A. In-house labor	
B. Contracted maintenance service	
C. In-house materials	
D. Other maintenance allowances/costs (e.g., water treatment)	
Total	
VII. Annual Administration Costs	
Total Annual Operating Costs	
TOTAL ANNUAL OWNING AND OPERATING COSTS	

Economic Analysis Techniques

Simple Payback

In the simple payback technique, a projection of the revenue stream, cost savings, and other factors is estimated and compared to the initial capital outlay. This simple technique ignores the cost of borrowing money (interest) and lost opportunity costs. It also ignores inflation and the time value of money.

Present-Value (Present Worth) Analysis

All sophisticated economic analysis methods use the basic principles of present value analysis to account for the time value of money. The total present value (present worth) for any analysis is determined by summing the present worths of all individual items under consideration, both future single-payment items and series of equal future payments. The scenario with the highest present value is the preferred alternative.

Single-Payment Present-Value Analysis. The cost or value of money is a function of the available interest rate and inflation rate. The future value F of a present sum of money P over n periods with compound interest rate i per period is

$$F = P(1 + i)^n \tag{16.1}$$

Conversely, the present value or present worth P of a future sum of money F is given by

$$P = F/(1 + i)^n \tag{16.2}$$

or

$$P = F \times \text{PWF}(i,n)_{sgl} \tag{16.3}$$

where the single-payment present-worth factor $\text{PWF}(i,n)_{sgl}$ is defined as

$$\text{PWF}(i,n)_{sgl} = 1/(1 + i)^n \tag{16.4}$$

Series of Equal Payments. The present-worth factor for a series of future equal payments (e.g., operating costs) is given by

$$\text{PWF}(i,n)_{ser} = \frac{(1 + I)^n - 1}{i(1 + i)^n} \tag{16.5}$$

The present value P of those future equal payments (PMT) is then the product of the present-worth factor and the payment [i.e., $P = \text{PWF}(i,n)_{ser} \times \text{PMT}$].

The number of future equal payments to repay a present value of money is determined by the capital recovery factor (CRF), which is the reciprocal of the present-worth factor for a series of equal payments:

$$\text{CRF} = \text{PMT}/P \tag{16.6}$$

$$\text{CRF}(i,n)_r = \frac{i(1 + i)^n}{(1 + I)^n - 1} = \frac{i}{1 - (1 + i)^n} \tag{16.7}$$

The CRF is often used to describe periodic uniform mortgage or loan payments.

Note that when payment periods other than annual are to be studied, the interest rate must be expressed per appropriate period. For example, if monthly payments or return on investment are being analyzed, then interest must be expressed per month, not per year, and n must be expressed in months.

Improved Payback Analysis. This somewhat more sophisticated payback approach is similar to the simple payback method except that the cost of money (interest rate, discount rate, etc.) is considered. Solving Equation 16.7 for n yields the following:

$$n = \frac{\ln[\text{CRF}/(\text{CRF} - i)]}{\ln(1 + i)} \tag{16.8}$$

Given known investment amounts and earnings, CRFs can be calculated for the alternative investments. Subsequently, the number of periods until payback has been achieved can be calculated using Equation 16.8.

Accounting for Inflation. Different economic goods may inflate at different rates. Inflation reflects the rise in the real cost of a commodity over time and is separate from the time value of money. Inflation must often be accounted for in an economic evaluation. One way to account for inflation is to substitute effective interest rates that account for inflation into the equations given above.

The effective interest rate i', sometimes called the real rate, accounts for inflation rate j and interest rate i or discount rate i_d; it can be expressed as follows:

$$i' = \frac{1+i}{1+j} - 1 = \frac{i-j}{1+j} \tag{16.9}$$

Different effective interest rates can be applied to individual components of cost. Projections for future fuel and energy prices are available in the *Annual Supplement to NIST Handbook 135*.

The following are three common methods of present-value analysis that include life-cycle cost factors (life of equipment, analysis period, discount rate, energy escalation rates, maintenance cost, etc., as shown in Table 16.2):

- Savings-to-Investment Ratio (SIR)
- Internal Rate of Return (IRR)
- Adjusted Internal Rate of Return (AIRR)

These comparison techniques rely on the same assumptions and economic analysis theories but display the results in different forms. They also use the same definition of each term. All can be displayed as a single calculation or as a cash flow table using a series of calculations for each year of the analysis period.

Table 16.3 Two Alternative Economic Analysis Examples [2019A, Ch 38, Tbl 8]

Alternative 1: Purchase Chilled Water from Utility

	Year										
	0	1	2	3	4	5	6	7	8	9	10
First costs		—	—	—	—	—	—	—	—	—	—
Chilled-water costs		$65,250	$66,881	$68,553	$70,267	$72,024	$73,824	$75,670	$77,562	$79,501	$81,488
Replacement costs		—	—	—	—	—	—	—	—	—	—
Maintenance costs		—	—	—	—	—	—	—	—	—	—
Net annual cash flow		65,250	66,881	68,553	70,267	72,024	73,824	75,670	77,501	79,501	81,488
Present value of cash flow		60,417	57,340	54,420	51,648	49,018	46,522	44,153	41,904	39,770	37,745

		Year									
		11	12	13	14	15	16	17	18	19	20
Financing annual payments		—	—	—	—	—	—	—	—	—	—
Chilled-water costs		$83,526	$85,614	$87,754	$89,948	$92,197	$94,501	$96,864	$99,286	$101,768	$104,312
Replacement costs		—	—	—	—	—	—	—	—	—	—
Maintenance costs		—	—	—	—	—	—	—	—	—	—
Net annual cash flow		83,526	85,614	87,754	89,948	92,197	94,501	96,864	99,286	101,768	104,312
Present value of cash flow		35,823	33,998	32,267	30,624	29,064	27,584	26,179	24,846	23,581	22,380
20-year life-cycle cost	$769,823										

Table 16.3 Two Alternative Economic Analysis Examples [2019A, Ch 38, Tbl 8] ***(Continued)***

Alternative 2: Install Chiller and Tower

	Year										
	0	**1**	**2**	**3**	**4**	**5**	**6**	**7**	**8**	**9**	**10**
First costs	$220,000	—	—	—	—	—	—	—	—	—	—
Energy costs		$18,750	$19,688	$20,672	$21,705	$22,791	$23,930	$25,127	$26,383	$27,702	$29,087
Replacement costs		—	—	—	—	—	—	—	—	—	90,000
Maintenance costs		15,200	15,656	16,126	16,609	17,108	17,621	18,150	18,694	19,255	19,833
Net annual cash flow	220,000	33,950	35,344	36,798	38,315	39,898	41,551	43,276	45,077	46,957	138,920
Present value of cash flow	220,000	31,435	30,301	29,211	28,163	27,154	26,184	25,251	24,354	23,490	64,347

		Year									
		11	**12**	**13**	**14**	**15**	**16**	**17**	**18**	**19**	**20**
Financing annual payments		—	—	—	—	—	—	—	—	—	—
Energy costs		$30,542	$32,069	$33,672	$35,356	$37,124	$38,980	$40,929	$42,975	$45,124	$47,380
Replacement costs		—	—	—	—	—	—	—	—	—	—
Maintenance costs		20,428	21,040	21,672	22,322	22,991	23,681	24,392	25,123	25,877	26,653
Net annual cash flow		50,969	53,109	55,344	57,678	60,115	62,661	65,320	68,099	71,001	74,034
Present value of cash flow		21,860	21,090	20,350	19,637	18,951	18,290	17,654	17,042	16,452	15,884
20-year life-cycle cost	$717,100										

17. SOUND

A primary objective in the design of HVAC systems and equipment is to evaluate noise and vibration to ensure that the acoustical environment in a given space is acceptable for various occupant activities. Sound and vibration are created by a source, are transmitted along one or more paths, and reach a receiver. Treatments and modifications can be applied to any or all of these elements to reduce unwanted noise and vibration, although it is usually most effective and least expensive to reduce noise at the source.

Levels

The magnitude of sound and vibration physical properties are almost always expressed in levels. The level L is based on the common (base 10) logarithm of a ratio of the magnitude of a physical property of power, intensity, or energy to a reference magnitude of the same type of property:

$$L = 10 \log \left(\frac{A}{A_{ref}}\right) \tag{17.1}$$

where A is the magnitude of the physical property of interest and A_{ref} is the reference value. Note that the ratio is dimensionless. In this equation, a factor of 10 is included to convert bels to decibels (dB).

Sound Pressure and Sound Pressure Level

Sound waves in air are variations in pressure above and below atmospheric pressure. **Sound pressure** is measured in pascals (Pa) (SI units are used here rather than I-P because of international agreement). The human ear responds across a broad range of sound pressures; the threshold of hearing to the threshold of pain covers a range of approximately 10^{14}:1. Table 17.1 gives approximate values of sound pressure by various sources at specified distances from the source.

The range of sound pressure in Table 17.1 is so large that it is more convenient to use a scale proportional to the logarithm of this quantity. Therefore, the **decibel** (dB) scale is the preferred method of presenting quantities in acoustics, not only because it collapses a large range of pressures to a more manageable range but also because its levels correlate better with human responses to the magnitude of sound than do sound pressures. Equation 17.2 describes levels of power, intensity, and energy, which are proportional to the square of other physical properties, such as sound pressure and vibration acceleration. Thus, the **sound pressure level** L_p corresponding to a sound pressure is given by

$$L_p = 10 \log \left(\frac{p}{p_{ref}}\right)^2 = 20 \log \left(\frac{p}{p_{ref}}\right) \tag{17.2}$$

where p is the root mean square (RMS) value of acoustic pressure in pascals. The root mean square is the square root of the time average of the square of the acoustic pressure ratio. The ratio p/p_{ref} is squared to give quantities proportional to intensity or energy. A reference quantity is needed so the term in parentheses is nondimensional. For sound pressure levels in air, the reference pressure p_{ref} is 20 μPa, which corresponds to the approximate threshold of hearing for a young person with good hearing exposed to a pure tone with a frequency of 1000 Hz.

The decibel scale is used for many different descriptors relating to sound: source strength, sound level at a specified location, and attenuation along propagation paths; each has a different reference quantity. For this reason, it is important to be aware of the context in which the term *decibel* or *level* is used. For most acoustical quantities, there is an internationally accepted reference value. A reference quantity is always implied even if it does not appear.

Sound pressure level is relatively easy to measure and thus is used by most noise codes and criteria. (The human ear and microphones are pressure sensitive.) Sound pressure levels for the corresponding sound pressures are also given in Table 17.1.

A number of AHRI, AMCA, CTI, and ANSI sound standards are used by equipment manufacturers to provide accurate sound data. Manufacturer-supplied data in accordance with the appropriate standard should be used in preference to empirical information in evaluating the noise resulting from a particular equipment item.

Table 17.1 Typical Sound Pressures and Sound Pressure Levels [2021F, Ch 8, Tbl 1]

Source	Sound Pressure, Pa	Sound Pressure Level, dB re 20 μPa	Subjective Reaction
Military jet takeoff at 100 ft	200	140	Extreme danger
Artillery fire at 10 ft	63.2	130	
Passenger jet takeoff at 50 ft	20	120	Threshold of pain
Loud rock band	6.3	110	Threshold of discomfort
Automobile horn at 10 ft	2	100	
Unmuffled large diesel engine at 130 ft	0.6	90	Very loud
Accelerating diesel truck at 50 ft	0.2	80	
Freight train at 100 ft	0.06	70	
Conversational speech at 3 ft	0.02	60	
Window air conditioner at 3 ft	0.006	50	Moderate
Quiet residential area	0.002	40	
Whispered conversation at 6 ft	0.0006	30	
Buzzing insect at 3 ft	0.0002	20	
Threshold of good hearing	0.00006	10	Faint
Threshold of excellent youthful hearing	0.00002	0	Threshold of hearing

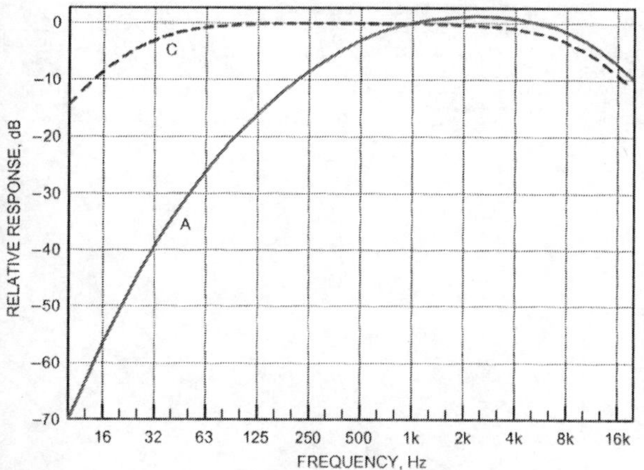

Figure 17.1 Curves Showing A- and C-Weighting Responses for Sound Level Meters [2021F, Ch 8, Fig 1]

Combining Sound Levels

To estimate the levels from multiple sources from the levels from each source, the intensities (not the levels) must be added. Thus, the levels must first be converted to find intensities, the intensities summed, and then converted to a level again, so the combination of multiple levels L_1, L_2, etc., produces a level L_{sum} given by

$$L_{sum} = 10 \log\left(\sum_i 10^{L_i/10}\right) \tag{17.3}$$

where for sound pressure level (L_p), $10^{L_i/10}$ is p_i^2/p_{ref}^2, and L_i is the sound pressure level for the ith source.

A simpler and slightly less accurate method is outlined in Table 17.2. This method, although not exact, results in errors of 1 dB or less. The process with a series of levels may be shortened by combining the largest with the next largest, then combining this sum with the third largest, then the fourth largest, and so on until the combination of the remaining levels is 10 dB lower than the combined level. The process may then be stopped.

Sound Power and Sound Power Level

The **sound power** of a source is its rate of emission of acoustical energy and is expressed in watts. Sound power depends on operating conditions but not distance of observation location from the source or surrounding environment. Approximate sound power outputs for common sources are shown in Table 17.2 with corresponding sound power levels. For **sound power level** L_w, the power reference is 10^{-12} W or 1 picowatt. The definition of sound power level is therefore

$$L_w = 10 \log(w/10^{-12}) \tag{17.4}$$

where w is the sound power emitted by the source in watts.

Table 17.2 Combining Two Sound Levels [2021F, Ch 8, Tbl 3]

Difference between levels to be combined, dB	0 to 1	2 to 4	5 to 9	10 and More
Number of decibels to add to highest level to obtain combined level	3	2	1	0

Table 17.3 Midband and Approximate Upper and Lower Cutoff Frequencies for Octave and 1/3 Octave Band Filters [2021F, Ch 8, Tbl 4]

Octave Bands, Hz			1/3 Octave Bands, Hz		
Lower	Midband	Upper	Lower	Midband	Upper
			11.2	12.5	14
11.2	16	22.4	14	16	18
			18	20	22.4
			22.4	25	28
22.4	31.5	45	28	31.5	35.5
			35.5	40	45
			45	50	56
45	63	90	56	63	71
			71	80	90
			90	100	112
90	125	180	112	125	140
			140	160	180
			180	200	224
180	250	355	224	250	280
			280	315	355
			355	400	450
355	500	710	450	500	560
			560	630	710
			710	800	900
710	1,000	1,400	900	1,000	1,120
			1,120	1,250	1,400
			1,400	1,600	1,800
1,400	2,000	2,800	1,800	2,000	2,240
			2,240	2,500	2,800
			2,800	3,150	3,550
2,800	4,000	5,600	3,550	4,000	4,500
			4,500	5,000	5,600
			5,600	6,300	7,100
5,600	8,000	11,200	7,100	8,000	9,000
			9,000	10,000	11,200
			11,200	12,500	14,000
11,200	16,000	22,400	14,000	16,000	18,000
			18,000	20,000	22,400

Table 17.4 Design Guidelines for HVAC-Related Background Sound in Rooms [2019A, Ch 49, Tbl 1]

Room Types		Octave Band Analysis[a]	Approximate Overall Sound Pressure Level[a]	
		NC/RC[b]	dBA[c]	dBC[c]
Rooms with Intrusion from Outdoor Noise Sources[d]	Traffic noise	N/A	45	70
	Aircraft flyovers	N/A	45	70
Residences, Apartments, Condominiums	Living areas	30	35	60
	Bathrooms, kitchens, utility rooms	35	40	60
Hotels/Motels	Individual rooms or suites	30	35	60
	Meeting/banquet rooms	30	35	60
	Corridors and lobbies	40	45	65
	Service/support areas	40	45	65
Office Buildings	Executive and private offices	30	35	60
	Conference rooms	30	35	60
	Teleconference rooms	25	30	55
	Open-plan offices	40	45	65
	Corridors and lobbies	40	45	65
Courtrooms	Unamplified speech	30	35	60
	Amplified speech	35	40	60
Performing Arts Spaces	Drama theaters, concert and recital halls	20	25	50
	Music teaching studios	25	30	55
	Music practice rooms	30	35	60
Hospitals and Clinics	Patient rooms	30	35	60
	Wards	35	40	60
	Operating and procedure rooms	35	40	60
	Corridors and lobbies	40	45	65

Table 17.4 Design Guidelines for HVAC-Related Background Sound in Rooms [2019A, Ch 49, Tbl 1] ***(Continued)***

Room Types		Octave Band Analysis[a]	Approximate Overall Sound Pressure Level[a]	
		NC/RC[b]	dBA[c]	dBC[c]
Laboratories	Testing/research w/minimal speech communication	50	55	75
	Extensive phone use and speech communication	45	50	70
	Group teaching	35	40	60
Churches, Mosques, Synagogues	General assembly with critical music programs[e]	25	30	55
Schools[f]	Classrooms	30	35	60
	Large lecture rooms with speech amplification	30	35	60
	Large lecture rooms without speech amplification	25	30	55
Libraries		30	35	60
Indoor Stadiums, Gymnasiums	Gymnasiums and natatoriums[g]	45	50	70
	Large-seating-capacity spaces with speech amplification[g]	50	55	75

N/A = Not applicable

[a]Values and ranges are based on judgment and experience, and represent general limits of acceptability for typical building occupancies.

[b]NC: this metric plots octave band sound levels against a family of reference curves, with the number rating equal to the highest tangent line value.
RC: when sound quality in the space is important, the RC metric provides a diagnostic tool to quantify both the speech interference level and spectral imbalance.

[c]dBA and dBC: these are overall sound pressure level measurements with A- and C-weighting, and serve as good references for a fast, single-number measurement. They are also appropriate for specification in cases where no octave band sound data are available for design.

[d]Intrusive noise is addressed here for use in evaluating possible non-HVAC noise that is likely to contribute to background noise levels.

[e]An experienced acoustical consultant should be retained for guidance on acoustically critical spaces (below RC 30) and for all performing arts spaces.

[f]Some educators and others believe that HVAC-related sound criteria for schools, as listed in previous editions of this table, are too high and impede learning for affected groups of all ages. See ANSI/ASA Standard S12.60 for classroom acoustics and a justification for lower sound criteria in schools. The HVAC component of total noise meets the background noise requirement of that standard if HVAC-related background sound is approximately NC/RC 25. Within this category, designs for K-8 schools should be quieter than those for high schools and colleges.

[g]RC or NC criteria for these spaces need only be selected for the desired speech and hearing conditions.

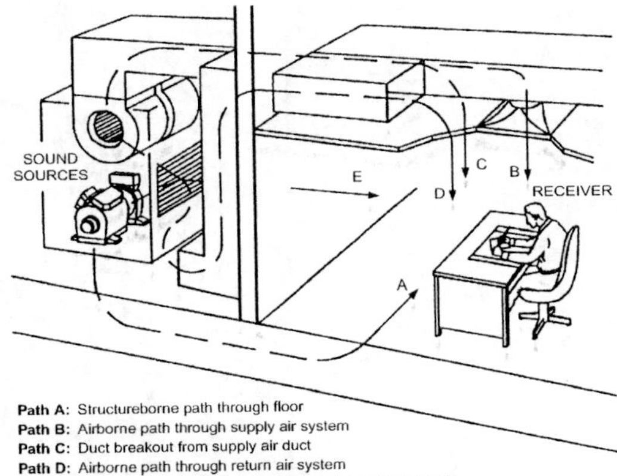

Figure 17.2 Typical Paths of Noise and Vibration Propagation in HVAC Systems [2019A, Ch 49, Fig 1]

Table 17.5 Comparison of Sound Rating Methods [2019A, Ch 49, Tbl 4]

Method	Overview	Considers Speech Interference Effects	Evaluates Sound Quality	Components Presently Rated by Each Method
dBA	No quality assessment Frequently used for outdoor noise ordinances	Yes	No	Cooling towers Water chillers Condensing units
NC	Can rate components Limited quality assessment Does not evaluate low-frequency rumble	Yes	Somewhat	Air terminals Diffusers
RC Mark II	Used to evaluate systems Should not be used to evaluate components Evaluates sound quality Provides improved diagnostics capability	Yes	Yes	Not used for component rating
NCB	Can rate components Some quality assessment	Yes	Somewhat	See NC
RNC	Some quality assessment Attempts to quantify fluctuations	Yes	Somewhat	Not used for component rating

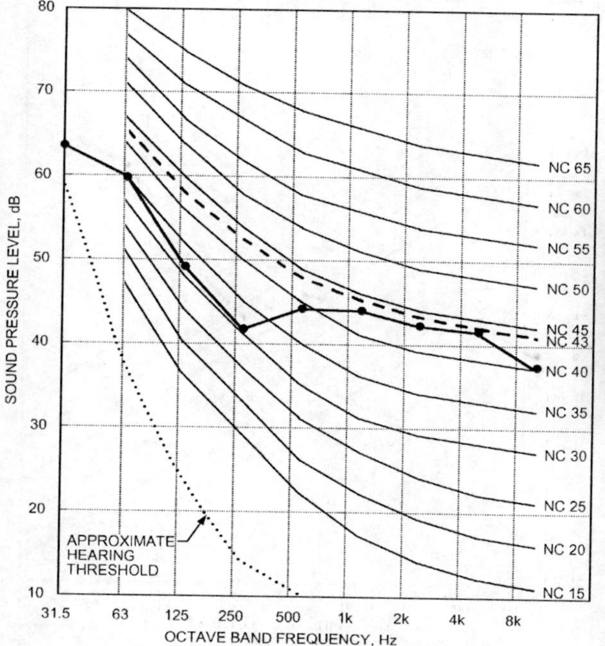

Figure 17.3 NC (Noise Criteria) Curves and Sample Spectrum (Curve with Symbols) [2021F, Ch 8, Fig 7]

Sound

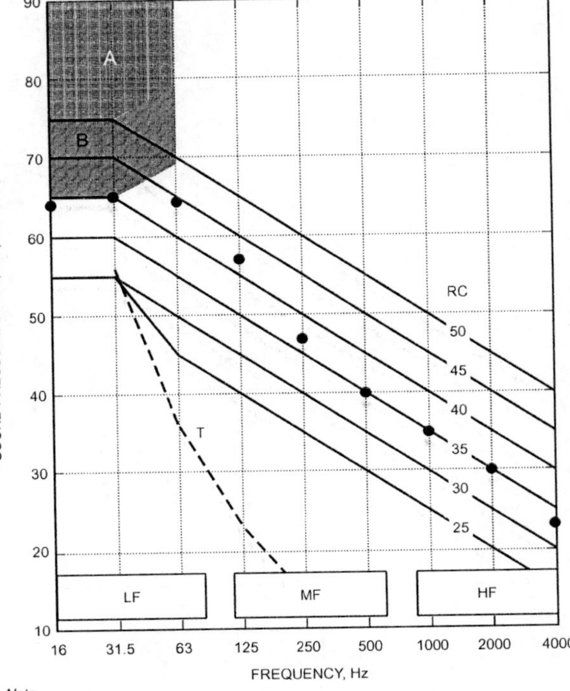

Note:

- Noise levels for lightweight wall and ceiling constructions:
  - In shaded region B are likely to generate vibration that may be perceptible. There is a slight possibility of rattles in light fixtures, doors, windows, etc.
  - In shaded region A have a high probability of generating easily perceptible noise-induced vibration. Audible rattling in light fixtures, doors, windows, etc. may be anticipated.
- LF, MF, and HF refer to low-frequency rumble, mid-frequency roar, and high-frequency hiss, respectively.
- Solid dots are sound pressure levels for the example discussed in Chapter 49 of the 2021 *ASHRAE Handbook—Fundamentals*.

Figure 17.4 Room Criteria Curves, Mark II [2019A, Ch 49, Fig 6]

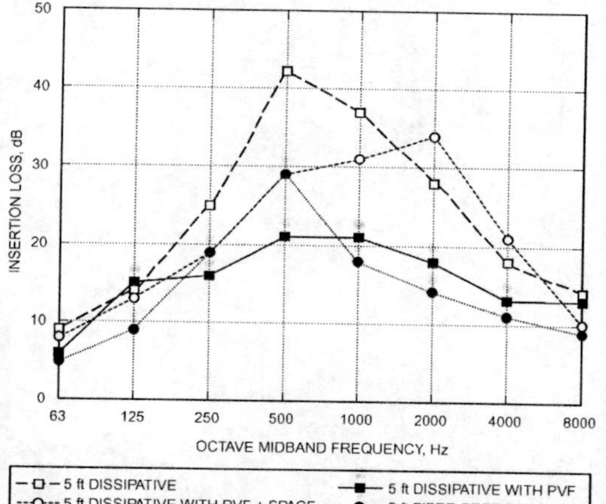

Note: Dissipative silencers use sound-absorptive media such as fiberglass as the primary means of attenuating sound. Reactive silencers are constructed only of metal, both solid and perforated.

Figure 17.5 Comparison of 5 ft Dissipative and Reactive Silencer Performance [2019A, Ch 49, Fig 23]

Sound

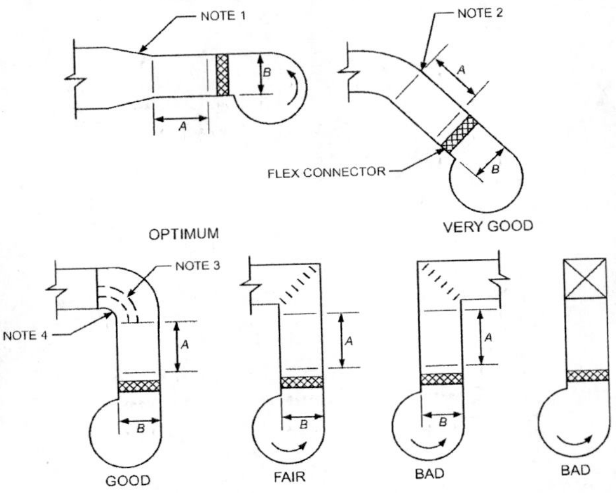

NOTE 1

NOTE 2

FLEX CONNECTOR

OPTIMUM

VERY GOOD

NOTE 3

NOTE 4

GOOD

FAIR

BAD

BAD

Notes:

1. Slopes of 1 in 7 preferred. Slopes of 1 in 4 permitted below 2000 fpm.
2. Dimension *A* should be at least 1.5 times *B*, where *B* is largest discharge duct dimension.
3. Rugged turning vanes should extend full radius of elbow.
4. Minimum 6 in. radius required.

Figure 17.6 Various Outlet Configurations for Centrifugal Fans and Their Possible Rumble Conditions [2019A, Ch 49, Fig 25]

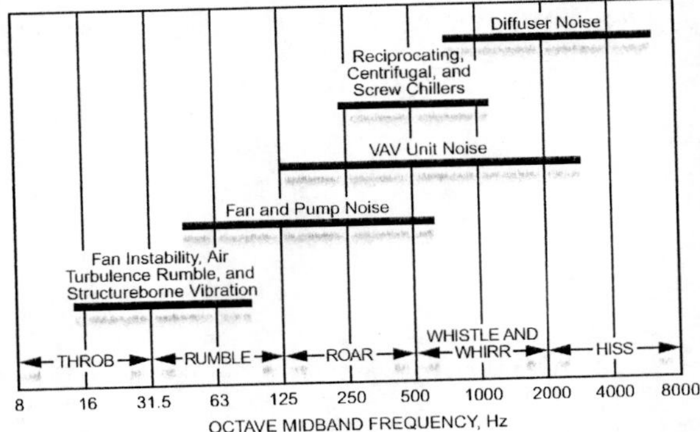

Figure 17.7 Frequencies at Which Different Types of Mechanical Equipment Generally Control Sound Spectra [2019A, Ch 49, Fig 4]

Table 17.6 Sound Transmission Class (STC) and Transmission Loss Values of Typical Mechanical Equipment Room Wall, Floor, and Ceiling Types, dB [2019A, Ch 49, Tbl 40]

Room Construction Type	STC	Octave Midband Frequency, Hz						
		63	125	250	500	1000	2000	4000
8 in. CMU*	50	35	35	41	44	50	57	64
8 in. CMU with 5/8 in. GWB* on furring strips	53	33	32	44	50	56	59	65
5/8 in. GWB on both sides of 3 5/8 in. metal studs	38	18	16	33	47	55	43	47
5/8 in. GWB on both sides of 3 5/8 in. metal studs with fiberglass insulation in cavity	49	16	23	44	58	64	52	53
2 layers of 5/8 in. GWB on both sides of 3 5/8 in. metal studs with fiberglass insulation in cavity	56	19	32	50	62	67	58	63
Double row of 3 5/8 in. metal studs, 1 in. apart, each with 2 layers of 5/8 in. GWB and fiberglass insulation in cavity	64	23	40	54	62	71	69	74
6 in. solid concrete floor/ceiling	53	40	40	40	49	58	67	76
6 in. solid concrete floor with 4 in. isolated concrete slab and fiberglass insulation in cavity	72	44	52	58	73	87	97	100
6 in. solid concrete floor with two layers of 5/8 in. GWB hung on spring isolators with fiberglass insulation in cavity	84	53	63	70	84	93	104	105

Note: Actual material composition (e.g., density, porosity, stiffness) affects transmission loss and STC values.

*CMU = concrete masonry unit; GWB = gypsum wallboard.

Table 17.7 Sound Sources, Transmission Paths, and Recommended Noise Reduction Methods [2019A, Ch 49, Tbl 6]

Sound Source	Path No.
Circulating fans; grilles; registers; diffusers; unitary equipment in room	1
Induction coil and fan-powered VAV mixing units	1, 2
Unitary equipment located outside of room served; remotely located air-handling equipment, such as fans, blowers, dampers, duct fittings, and air washers	2, 3
Compressors, pumps, and other reciprocating and rotating equipment (excluding air-handling equipment)	4, 5, 6
Cooling towers; air-cooled condensers	4, 5, 6, 7
Exhaust fans; window air conditioners	7, 8
Sound transmission between rooms	9, 10

No.	Transmission Paths	Noise Reduction Methods
1	Direct sound radiated from sound source to ear Reflected sound from walls, ceiling, and floor	Direct sound can be controlled only by selecting quiet equipment. Reflected sound is controlled by adding sound absorption to the room and to equipment location.
2	Air- and structureborne sound radiated from casings and through walls of ducts and plenums is transmitted through walls and ceiling into room	Design duct and fittings for low turbulence; locate high-velocity ducts in noncritical areas; isolate ducts and sound plenums from structure with neoprene or spring hangers.
3	Airborne sound radiated through supply and return air ducts to diffusers in room and then to listener by Path 1	Select fans for minimum sound power; use ducts lined with sound-absorbing material; use duct silencers or sound plenums in supply and return air ducts.
4	Noise transmitted through equipment room walls and floors to adjacent rooms	Locate equipment rooms away from critical areas; use masonry blocks or concrete for equipment room walls and floor.
5	Vibration transmitted via building structure to adjacent walls and ceilings, from which it radiates as noise into room by Path 1	Mount all machines on properly designed vibration isolators; design mechanical equipment room for dynamic loads; balance rotating and reciprocating equipment.
6	Vibration transmission along pipes and duct walls	Isolate pipe and ducts from structure with neoprene or spring hangers; install flexible connectors between pipes, ducts, and vibrating machines.
7	Noise radiated to outside enters room windows	Locate equipment away from critical areas; use barriers and covers to interrupt noise paths; select quiet equipment.
8	Inside noise follows Path 1	Select quiet equipment.
9	Noise transmitted to an air diffuser in a room, into a duct, and out through an air diffuser in another room	Design and install duct attenuation to match transmission loss of wall between rooms.
10	Sound transmission through, over, and around room partition	Extend partition to ceiling slab and tightly seal all around; seal all pipe, conduit, duct, and other partition penetrations.

18. VIBRATION

Mechanical vibration and vibration-induced noise are common sources of occupant complaints in modern buildings. Lightweight construction in buildings provides conditions that can result in vibration-related problems. Mandates for energy conservation have resulted in many buildings being designed with variable air volume systems with variable-speed equipment. As rotating equipment spins slower, its forcing frequency approaches the structure's resonant frequency, which can amplify vibration-induced noise and generate vibration at the structure's resonant frequency. Mechanical equipment is often located in penthouses or on the roof, where structures are typically the most susceptible to inducing vibration-related problems. Mechanical equipment rooms are typically located on intermediate level floors, close to the occupied areas they serve.

Occupant complaints associated with building vibration typically take one or more of three forms:

- The level of vibration perceived by building occupants is of sufficient magnitude to cause annoyance, concern, or alarm
- Vibration energy from mechanical equipment, which is transmitted to the building structure, is transmitted to various parts of the building and then is radiated as structureborne noise
- Vibration in a building may interfere with proper operation of sensitive equipment or instrumentation

At the natural frequency (in Hz) of the system, the mass's vibration response in to the applied excitation is a maximum:

$$\text{Natural frequency, } f_n = \frac{1}{2\pi}\sqrt{\frac{k}{M}} \tag{18.1}$$

where k is the stiffness of vibration isolator (lb/in.) and M is the mass of equipment supported by the isolator.

$$f_n = \frac{3.13}{\sqrt{\delta_{st}}} \tag{18.2}$$

where δ_{st} is the static deflection of the isolator in inches.

Transmissibility is the ratio of the amplitudes of the force transmitted to the building structure to the exciting force produced by the vibrating equipment. Transmissibility is inversely proportional to the square of the disturbing frequency f_d to the natural frequency f_n.

$$T = \left|\frac{1}{1-(f_d/f_n)^2}\right| \tag{18.3}$$

At $f_d = f_n$, resonance occurs. Vibration isolation is effective only at a f_d/f_n ratio > 3.5.

When supporting structure stiffness is not large with respect to stiffness of isolator, it becomes a two-degree of freedom system. In this case, choose an isolator that will provide static deflection eight to ten times that of the estimated floor static deflection due to the added weight of the equipment. Seismic snubbers must be included in or with isolators to limit equipment movement.

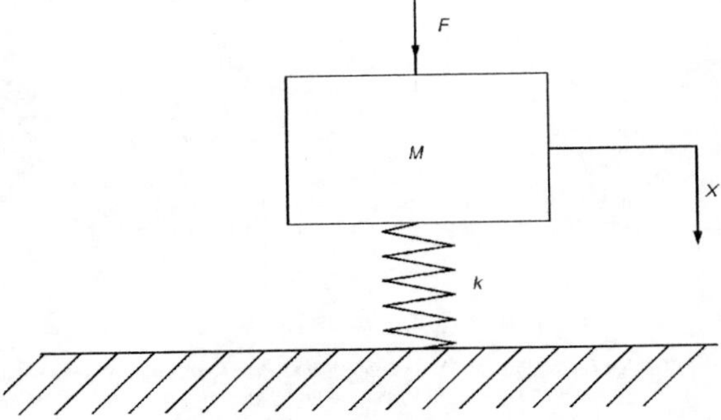

Figure 18.1 Single-Degree-of-Freedom System [2021F, Ch 8, Fig 8]

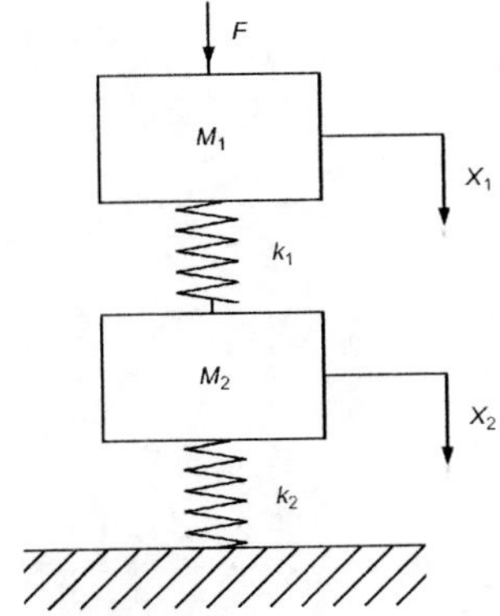

Figure 18.2 Two-Degrees-of-Freedom System [2021F, Ch 8, Fig 11]

Table 18.1 Selection Guide for Vibration Isolation [2019A, Ch 49, Tbl 47]

Equipment Type	Horsepower and Other	RPM	Slab on Grade: Base Type	Slab on Grade: Isolator Type	Slab on Grade: Min. Defl., in.	Floor Span Up to 20 ft: Base Type	Up to 20 ft: Isolator Type	Up to 20 ft: Min. Defl., in.	Floor Span 20 to 30 ft: Base Type	20 to 30 ft: Isolator Type	20 to 30 ft: Min. Defl., in.	Floor Span 30 to 40 ft: Base Type	30 to 40 ft: Isolator Type	30 to 40 ft: Min. Defl., in.	Reference Notes
Refrigeration Machines and Chillers															
Water-cooled reciprocating	All	All	A	2	0.25	A	4	0.75	A	4	1.50	A	4	2.50	2,3,12
Water-cooled centrifugal, scroll	All	All	A	1	0.25	A	4	0.75	A	4	1.50	A	4	1.50	2,3,4,8,12
Water-cooled screw	All	All	A	1	1.00	A	4	1.5	A	4	2.50	A	4	2.50	2,3,4,12
Absorption	All	All	A	4	0.25	A	4	0.75	A	4	1.50	A	4	1.50	
Air-cooled recip., scroll	All	All	A	1	0.25	A	4	1.50	A	4	1.50	A	4	2.50	2,4,5,12
Air-cooled screw	All	All	A	4	1.00	A	4	1.50	B	4	2.50	B	4	2.50	2,4,5,8,12
Air Compressors and Vacuum Pumps															
Tank-mounted horiz.	≤10	All	A	3	0.75	A	3	0.75	A	3	1.50	A	3	1.50	3,15
	≥10	All	C	3	0.75	C	3	0.75	C	3	1.50	C	3	1.50	3,15
Tank-mounted vert.	All	All	C	3	0.75	C	3	0.75	C	3	1.50	C	3	1.50	3,15
Base-mounted	All	All	C	3	0.75	C	3	0.75	C	3	1.50	C	3	1.50	3,14,15
Large reciprocating	All	All	C	3	0.75	C	3	0.75	C	3	1.50	C	3	1.50	3,14,15
Pumps															
Close-coupled	≤7.5	All	B	2	0.25	C	3	0.75	C	3	0.75	C	3	0.75	16
	≥7.5	All	C	3	0.75	C	3	0.75	C	3	1.50	C	3	1.50	16
Inline	5 to 25	All	A	3	0.75	A	3	1.50	A	3	1.50	A	3	1.50	
	≥25	All	A	3	1.50	A	3	1.50	A	3	1.50	A	3	2.50	
End suction and double-suction/split case	≤40	All	C	3	0.75	C	3	0.75	C	3	1.50	C	3	1.50	16
	50 to 125	All	C	3	0.75	C	3	0.75	C	3	1.50	C	3	2.50	10,16
	≥150	All	C	3	0.75	C	3	1.50	C	3	2.50	C	3	3.50	10,16
Packaged pump systems	All	All	A	3	0.75	A	3	0.75	A	3	1.50	C	3	2.50	

Table 18.1 Selection Guide for Vibration Isolation [2019A, Ch 49, Tbl 47] ***(Continued)***

			Equipment Location (see Notes for Table 18.1, Item 1)												
						Floor Span									
			Slab on Grade			Up to 20 ft			20 to 30 ft			30 to 40 ft			
Equipment Type	**Horse-power and Other**	**RPM**	**Base Type**	**Isolator Type**	**Min. Defl., in.**	**Base Type**	**Isolator Type**	**Min. Defl., in.**	**Base Type**	**Isolator Type**	**Min. Defl., in.**	**Base Type**	**Isolator Type**	**Min. Defl., in.**	**Reference Notes**
Cooling Towers	All	Up to 300	A	1	0.25	A	4	3.50	A	4	3.50	A	4	3.50	5,8,18
		301 to 500	A	1	0.25	A	4	2.50	A	4	2.50	A	4	2.50	5,18
		501 and up	A	1	0.25	A	4	0.75	A	4	0.75	A	4	0.75	5,18
Boilers															4
Fire-tube	All	All	A	1	0.25	B B	4	0.75	B	4	1.50	B	4	2.50	
Water-tube, copper fin	All	All	A	1	0.12	A	1	0.12	A	1	0.12	B	4	0.25	
Axial Fans, Plenum Fans, Cabinet Fans, Fan Sections, Centrifugal Inline Fans															
Up to 22 in. diameter	All	All	A	2	0.25	A	3	0.75	A	3	0.75	C	3	0.75	4,9,8
24 in. diameter and up	≤2 in. SP	Up to 300	B	3	2.50	C	3	3.50	C	3	3.50	C	3	3.50	9,8
		301 to 500	B	3	0.75	B	3	1.50	C	3	2.50	C	3	2.50	9,8
		501 and up	B	3	0.75	B	3	1.50	B	3	1.50	B	3	1.50	9,8
		Up to 300	C	3	2.50	C	3	3.50	C	3	3.50	C	3	3.50	3,8,9
	≥2.1 in. SP	301 to 500	C	3	1.50	C	3	1.50	C	3	2.50	C	3	2.50	3,8,9
		501 and up	C	3	0.75	C	3	1.50	C	3	1.50	C	3	2.50	3,8,9
Centrifugal Fans															
Up to 22 in. diameter	All	All	B	2	0.25	B	3	0.75	B	3	0.75	B	3	1.50	9,19
24 in. diameter and up	≤40	Up to 300	B	3	2.50	B	3	3.50	B	3	3.50	B	3	3.50	8,19
		301 to 500	B	3	1.50	B	3	1.50	B	3	2.50	B	3	2.50	8,19
		501 and up	B	3	0.75	B	3	0.75	B	3	0.75	B	3	1.50	8,19
	≥50	Up to 300	C	3	2.50	C	3	3.50	C	3	3.50	C	3	3.50	2,3,8,9,19
		301 to 500	C	3	1.50	C	3	1.50	C	3	2.50	C	3	2.50	2,3,8,9,19
		501 and up	C	3	1.00	C	3	1.50	C	3	1.50	C	3	2.50	2,3,8,9,19
Propeller Fans															
Wall-mounted	All	All	A	1	0.25	A	1	0.25	A	1	0.25	A	1	0.25	
Roof-mounted	All	All	A	1	0.25	A	1	0.25	B	4	1.50	D	4	1.50	

Table 18.1 Selection Guide for Vibration Isolation [2019A, Ch 49, Tbl 47] (*Continued*)

Equipment Type	Horse-power and Other	RPM	Equipment Location (see Notes for Table 18.1, Item 1)												Reference Notes
			Slab on Grade			Floor Span									
						Up to 20 ft			20 to 30 ft			30 to 40 ft			
			Base Type	Isolator Type	Min. Defl., in.	Base Type	Isolator Type	Min. Defl., in.	Base Type	Isolator Type	Min. Defl., in.	Base Type	Isolator Type	Min. Defl., in.	
Heat Pumps, Fan-Coils, Computer Room Units	All	All	A	3	0.75	A	3	0.75	A	3	0.75	A/D	3	1.50	
Condensing Units	All	All	A	1	0.25	A	4	0.75	A	4	1.50	A/D	4	1.50	
Packaged AH, AC, H, and V Units															
All	≤10	All	A	3	0.75	A	3	0.75	A	3	0.75	A	3	0.75	19
	≤15	Up to 300	A	3	0.75	A	3	3.50	A	3	3.50	C	3	3.50	2,4,8,19
		301 to 500	A	3	0.75	A	3	2.50	A	3	2.50	A	3	2.50	4,19
	≤4 in. SP	501 and up	A	3	0.75	A	3	1.50	A	3	1.50	A	3	1.50	4,19
	>15, >4 in. SP	Up to 300	B	3	0.75	C	3	3.50	C	3	3.50	C	3	3.50	2,3,4,8,9
		301 to 500	B	3	0.75	C	3	1.50	C	3	2.50	C	3	2.50	2,3,4,9
		501 and up	B	3	0.75	C	3	1.50	C	3	1.50	C	3	2.50	2,3,4,9
Packaged Rooftop Equipment	All	All	A/D	1	0.25	D	3	0.75	See Reference Note 17						5,6,8,17
Ducted Rotating Equipment															
Small fans, fan-powered boxes	≤600 cfm		A	3	0.50	A	3	0.50	A	3	0.50	A	3	0.50	7
	≥601 cfm		A	3	0.75	A	3	0.75	A	3	0.75	A	3	0.75	7
Engine-Driven Generators	All	All	A	3	0.75	C	3	1.50	C	3	2.50	C	3	3.50	2,3,4
Piping and Ducts (See sections on Isolating Vibration and Noise in Piping Systems and Isolating Duct Vibration for isolator selection.)															

Base Types:
A. No base, isolators attached directly to equipment (Note 28)
B. Structural steel rails or base (Notes 29 and 30)
C. Concrete inertia base (Note 31)
D. Curb-mounted base (Note 32)

Isolator Types:
1. Pad, rubber, or glass fiber (Notes 20 and 21)
2. Rubber floor isolator or hanger (Notes 20 and 25)
3. Spring floor isolator or hanger (Notes 22, 23, and 26)
4. Restrained spring isolator (Notes 22 and 24)
5. Thrust restraint (Note 27)
6. Air spring (Note 25)

Notes for Table 18.1:

These notes are keyed to the column titled Reference Notes in Table 47 of Chapter 49 of the 2019 *ASHRAE Handbook—Applications* and to other reference numbers throughout the table. Although the guide is conservative, cases may arise where vibration transmission to the building is still excessive. If the problem persists after all short circuits have been eliminated, it can almost always be corrected by altering the support path (e.g., from ceiling to floor), increasing isolator deflection, using low-frequency air springs, changing operating speed, improving rotating component balancing, or, as a last resort, changing floor frequency by stiffening or adding more mass. Assistance from a qualified vibration consultant can be very useful in resolving these problems.

Note 1. Isolator deflections shown are based on a reasonably expected floor stiffness according to floor span and class of equipment. Certain spaces may dictate higher levels of isolation. For example, bar joist roofs may require a static deflection of 1.5 in. over factories, but 2.5 in. over commercial office buildings.

Note 2. For large equipment capable of generating substantial vibratory forces and structureborne noise, increase isolator deflection, if necessary, so isolator stiffness is less than one-tenth the stiffness of the supporting structure, as defined by the deflection due to load at the equipment support.

Note 3. For noisy equipment adjoining or near noise-sensitive areas, see the section on Mechanical Equipment Room Sound Isolation.

Note 4. Certain designs cannot be installed directly on individual isolators (type A), and the equipment manufacturer or a vibration specialist should be consulted on the need for supplemental support (base type).

Note 5. Wind load conditions must be considered. Restraint can be achieved with restrained spring isolators (type 4), supplemental bracing, snubbers, or limit stops. Also see Chapter 56 of the 2019 *ASHRAE Handbook—HVAC Applications*.

Note 6. Certain types of equipment require a curb-mounted base (type D). Airborne noise must be considered.

Note 7. See section on Resilient Pipe Hangers and Supports for hanger locations adjoining equipment and in equipment rooms.

Note 8. To avoid isolator resonance problems, select isolator deflection so that resonance frequency is 40% or less of the lowest normal operating speed of equipment (see Chapter 8 in the 2021 *ASHRAE Handbook—Fundamentals*). Some equipment, such as variable-frequency drives, and high-speed equipment, such as screw chillers and vaneaxial fans, contain very-high-frequency vibration. This equipment creates new technical challenges in the isolation of high-frequency noise and vibration from a building's structure. Structural resonances both internal and external to the isolators can significantly degrade their performance at high frequencies. Unfortunately, at present no test standard exists for measuring the high-frequency dynamic properties of isolators, and commercially available products are not tested to determine their effectiveness for high frequencies. To reduce the chance of high-frequency vibration transmission, add a minimum 0.75 in. thick elastomeric pad (type 1, Note 20) to the base plate of spring isolators (type 3, Note 22, 23, 24). For some sensitive locations, air springs (Note 25) may be required. If equipment is located near extremely noise-sensitive areas, follow the recommendations of an acoustical consultant.

Note 9. To limit undesirable movement, thrust restraints (type 5) are required for all ceiling-suspended and floor-mounted units operating at 2 in. of water or more total static pressure.

Note 10. Pumps over 75 hp may need extra mass and restraints.

Note 11. See text for full discussion.

Isolation for Specific Equipment

Note 12. Refrigeration Machines: Large centrifugal, screw, and reciprocating refrigeration machines may generate very high noise levels; special attention is required when such equipment is installed in upper-story locations or near noise-sensitive areas. If equipment is located near extremely noise-sensitive areas, follow the recommendations of an acoustical consultant.

Note 13. Compressors: The two basic reciprocating compressors are (1) single- and double-cylinder vertical, horizontal or L-head, which are usually air compressors; and (2) Y, W, and multihead or multicylinder air and refrigeration compressors. Single- and double-cylinder compressors generate high vibratory forces requiring large inertia bases (type C) and are generally not suitable for upper-story locations. If this equipment must be installed in an upper-story location or at-grade location near noise-sensitive areas, the expected maximum unbalanced force data must be obtained from the equipment manufacturer and a vibration specialist consulted for design of the isolation system.

Note 14. Compressors: When using Y, W, and multihead and multicylinder compressors, obtain the magnitude of unbalanced forces from the equipment manufacturer so the need for an inertia base can be evaluated.

Note 15. Compressors: Base-mounted compressors through 5 hp and horizontal tank-type air compressors through 10 hp can be installed directly on spring isolators (type 3) with structural bases (type B) if required, and compressors 15 to 100 hp on spring isolators (type 3) with inertia bases (type C) weighing 1 to 2 times the compressor weight.

Note 16. Pumps: Concrete inertia bases (type C) are preferred for all flexible-coupled pumps and are desirable for most close-coupled pumps, although steel bases (type B) can be used. Close-coupled pumps should not be installed directly on individual isolators (type A) because the impeller usually overhangs the motor support base, causing the rear mounting to be in tension. The primary requirements for type C bases are strength and shape to accommodate base elbow supports. Mass is not usually a factor, except for pumps over 75 hp, where extra mass helps limit excess movement due to starting torque and forces. Concrete bases (type C) should be designed for a thickness of one-tenth the longest dimension with minimum thickness as follows: (1) for up to 30 hp, 6 in.; (2) for 40 to 75 hp, 8 in.; and (3) for 100 hp and up, 12 in.

Pumps over 75 hp and multistage pumps may exhibit excessive motion at start-up ("heaving"); supplemental restraining devices can be installed if necessary. Pumps over 125 hp may generate high starting forces; consult a vibration specialist.

Note 17. Packaged Rooftop Air-Conditioning Equipment: This equipment is usually installed on lightweight structures that are susceptible to sound and vibration transmission problems. The noise problems are compounded further by curb-mounted equipment, which requires large roof openings for supply and return air.

The table shows type D vibration isolator selections for all spans up to 20 ft, but extreme care must be taken for equipment located on spans of over 20 ft, especially if construction is open web joists or thin, lightweight slabs. The recommended procedure is to determine the additional deflection caused by equipment in the roof. If additional roof deflection is 0.25 in. or less, the isolator should be selected for up to 10 times the additional roof deflection. If additional roof deflection is over 0.25 in., supplemental roof stiffening should be installed to bring the roof deflection down below 0.25 in., or the unit should be relocated to a stiffer roof position.

For mechanical units capable of generating high noise levels, mount the unit on a platform above the roof deck to provide an air gap (buffer zone) and locate the unit away from the associated roof penetration to allow acoustical treatment of ducts before they enter the building.

Some rooftop equipment has compressors, fans, and other equipment isolated internally. This isolation is not always reliable because of internal short-circuiting, inadequate static deflection, or panel resonances. It is recommended that rooftop equipment over 300 lb be isolated externally, as if internal isolation was not used.

Note 18. Cooling Towers: These are normally isolated with restrained spring isolators (type 4) directly under the tower or tower dunnage. High-deflection isolators proposed for use directly under the motor-fan assembly must be used with extreme caution to ensure stability and safety under all weather conditions. See Note 5.

Note 19. Fans and Air-Handling Equipment: Consider the following in selecting isolation systems for fans and air-handling equipment:

1. Fans with wheel diameters of 22 in. and less and all fans operating at speeds up to 300 rpm do not generate large vibratory forces. For fans operating under 300 rpm, select isolator deflection so the isolator natural frequency is 40% or less than the fan speed. For example, for a fan operating at 275 rpm, $0.4 \times 275 = 110$ rpm. Therefore, an isolator natural frequency of 110 rpm or lower is required. This can be accomplished with a 3 in. deflection isolator (type 3).
2. Flexible duct connectors should be installed at the intake and discharge of all fans and air-handling equipment to reduce vibration transmission to air duct structures.
3. Inertia bases (type C) are recommended for all class 2 and 3 fans and air-handling equipment because extra mass allows the use of stiffer springs, which limit heaving movements.
4. Thrust restraints (type 5) that incorporate the same deflection as isolators should be used for all fan heads, all suspended fans, and all base-mounted and suspended air-handling equipment operating at 2 in. or more total static pressure. Restraint movement adjustment must be made under normal operational static pressures.

Vibration Isolators: Materials, Types, and Configurations

Notes 20 through 32 include figures to assist in evaluating commercially available isolators for HVAC equipment. The isolator selected for a particular application depends on the required deflection, life, cost, and compatibility with associated structures.

RUBBER PADS (Type 1)

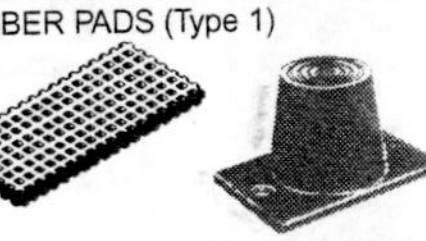

RUBBER MOUNTS (Type 2)

Note 20. Rubber isolators are available in pad (type 1) and molded (type 2) configurations. Pads are used in single or multiple layers. Molded isolators come in a range of 30 to 70 durometer (a measure of stiffness). Material in excess of 70 durometer is usually ineffective because durometers are not a measure of stiffness of an isolator. Isolators are designed for up to 0.5 in. deflection, but are used where 0.3 in. or less deflection is required. Solid rubber and composite fabric and rubber pads are also available. They provide high load capacities with small deflection and are used as noise barriers under columns and for pipe supports. These pad types work well only when they are properly loaded and the weight load is evenly distributed over the entire pad surface. Metal loading plates can be used for this purpose.

GLASS FIBER PADS (Type 1)

Note 21. Glass fiber with elastic coating (type 1). This type of isolation pad is precompressed molded fiberglass pads individually coated with a flexible, moisture-impervious elastomeric membrane. Natural frequency of fiberglass vibration isolators should be essentially constant for the operating load range of the supported equipment. Weight load is evenly distributed over the entire pad surface. Metal loading plates can be used for this purpose.

SPRING ISOLATOR (Type 3) 	**Note 22.** Steel springs are the most popular and versatile isolators for HVAC applications because they are available for almost any deflection and have a virtually unlimited life. Spring isolators may have a rubber acoustical barrier to reduce transmission of high-frequency vibration and noise that can migrate down the steel spring coil. They should be corrosion protected if installed outdoors or in a corrosive environment. The basic types include the following: **Note 23.** *Open spring isolators* (type 3) consist of top and bottom load plates with adjustment bolts for leveling equipment. Springs should be designed with a horizontal stiffness of at least 80% of the vertical stiffness (k_x/k_y) to ensure stability. Similarly, the springs should have a minimum ratio of 0.8 for the diameter divided by the deflected spring height.
RESTRAINED SPRING ISOLATOR (Type 4)	**Note 24.** *Restrained spring isolators* (type 4) have hold-down bolts to limit vertical as well as horizontal movement. They are used with (a) equipment with large variations in mass (e.g., boilers, chillers, cooling towers) to restrict movement and prevent strain on piping when water is removed, (b) outdoor equipment, such as condensing units and cooling towers, to prevent excessive movement due to wind loads, and (c) with any equipment subject to seismic forces. Spring criteria should be the same as open spring isolators, and snubbers should have adequate clearance so that they are activated only when a temporary restraint is needed. See Chapter 56 of the 2019 *ASHRAE Handbook—HVAC Applications* for typical snubber types. *Closed mounts* or *housed spring isolators* consist of two telescoping housings separated by a resilient material. These provide lateral snubbing and some vertical damping of equipment movement, but do not limit the vertical movement. Additional vertical snubbers must be used where vertical travel must be limited (see Chapter 56 of the 2019 *ASHRAE Handbook—HVAC Applications*). Care should be taken in selection and installation to minimize binding and short circuiting.
AIR SPRINGS (Type 6) 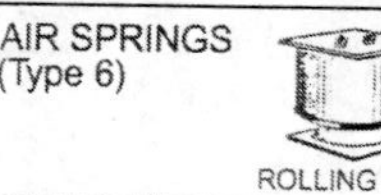    ROLLING LOBE BELLOWS	**Note 25.** Air springs (type 6) can be designed for any frequency, but are economical only in applications with natural frequencies of 1.33 Hz or less (6 in. or greater deflection). They do not transmit high-frequency noise and are often used to replace high-deflection springs on problem jobs (e.g., large transformers on upper-floor installations). A constant air supply (an air compressor with an air dryer) and leveling valves are typically required.

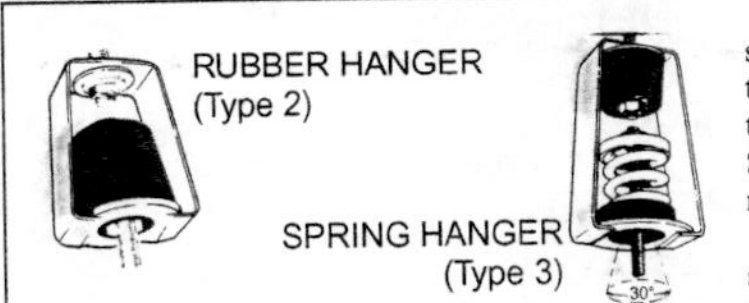 RUBBER HANGER (Type 2) SPRING HANGER (Type 3)	**Note 26.** Isolation hangers (types 2 and 3) are used for suspended pipe and equipment and have rubber, springs, or a combination of spring and rubber elements. Criteria should be similar to open spring isolators, though lateral stability is less important. Where support rod angular misalignment is a concern, use hangers that have sufficient clearance and/or incorporate rubber bushings to prevent the rod from touching the housing. Swivel or traveler arrangements may be necessary for connections to piping systems subject to large thermal movements. *Precompressed spring hangers* incorporate some means of precompression or preloading of the isolator spring to minimize movement of the isolated equipment or system. These are typically used on piping systems that can change weight substantially between installation and operation.
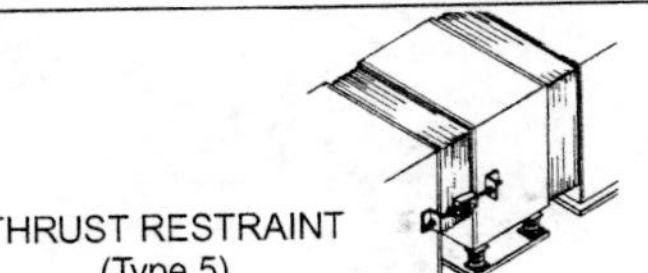 THRUST RESTRAINT (Type 5)	**Note 27.** Thrust restraints (type 5) are similar to spring hangers or isolators and are installed in pairs to resist the thrust caused by air pressure. These are typically sized to limit lateral movement to 0.25 in. or less.
DIRECT ISOLATION (Type A)	**Note 28.** Direct isolation (type A) is used when equipment is unitary and rigid and does not require additional support. Direct isolation can be used with large chillers, some fans, packaged air-handling units, and air-cooled condensers. If there is any doubt that the equipment can be supported directly on isolators, use structural bases (type B) or inertia bases (type C), or consult the equipment manufacturer.
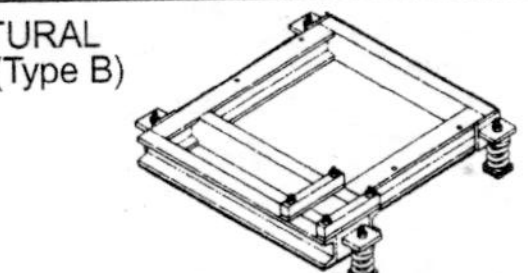 STRUCTURAL BASES (Type B)	**Note 29.** Structural bases (type B) are used where equipment cannot be supported at individual locations and/or where some means is necessary to maintain alignment of component parts in equipment. These bases can be used with spring or rubber isolators (types 2 and 3) and should have enough rigidity to resist all starting and operating forces without supplemental hold-down devices. Bases are made in rectangular configurations using structural members with a depth equal to one-tenth the longest span between isolators. Typical base depth is between 4 and 12 in., except where structural or alignment considerations dictate otherwise.

STRUCTURAL RAILS (Type B) 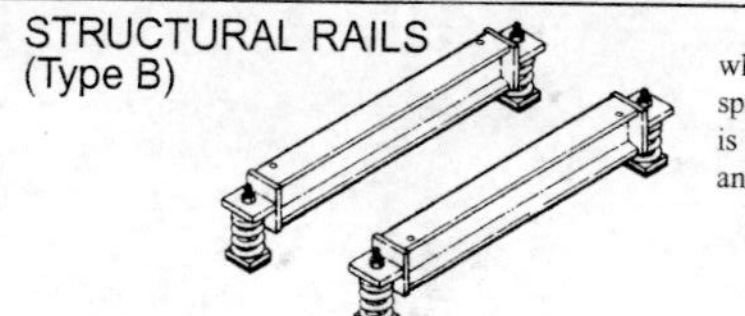	**Note 30.** Structural rails (type B) are used to support equipment that does not require a unitary base or where the isolators are outside the equipment and the rails act as a cradle. Structural rails can be used with spring or rubber isolators and should be rigid enough to support the equipment without flexing. Usual practice is to use structural members with a depth one-tenth of the longest span between isolators, typically between 4 and 12 in., except where structural considerations dictate otherwise.
CONCRETE BASES (Type C) 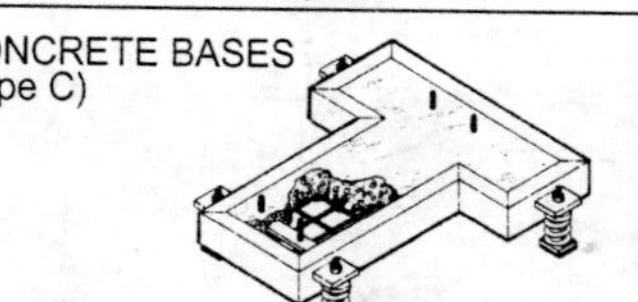	**Note 31.** Concrete bases (type C) are used where the supported equipment requires a rigid support (e.g., flexible-coupled pumps) or excess heaving motion may occur with spring isolators. They consist of a steel pouring form usually with welded-in reinforcing bars, provision for equipment hold-down, and isolator brackets. Like structural bases, concrete bases should be sized to support piping elbow supports, rectangular or T-shaped, and for rigidity, have a depth equal to one-tenth the longest span between isolators. Base depth is typically between 6 and 12 in. unless additional depth is specifically required for mass, rigidity, or component alignment.
CURB ISOLATION (Type D) 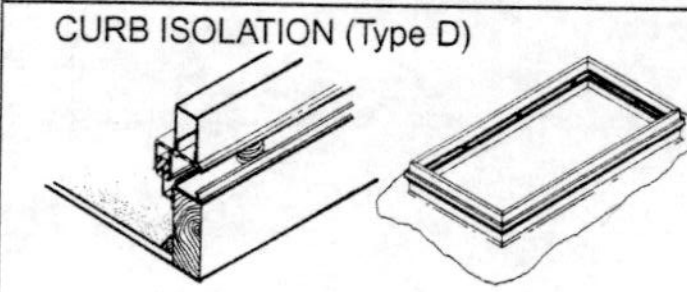	**Note 32.** Curb isolation systems (type D) are specifically designed for curb-supported rooftop equipment and have spring isolation with a watertight, and sometimes airtight, assembly. *Rooftop rails* consist of upper and lower frames separated by nonadjustable springs and rest on top of architectural roof curbs. *Isolation curbs* incorporate the roof curb into their design as well. Both kinds are designed with springs that have static deflections in the 1 to 3 in. range to meet the design criteria described in type 3. Flexible elastomeric seals are typically most effective for weatherproofing between the upper and lower frames. A continuous sponge gasket around the perimeter of the top frame is typically applied to further weatherproof the installation.

19. HVAC SYSTEMS AND EQUIPMENT

For information on boilers, compressors, chillers, and cooling towers, see the 2020 *ASHRAE Handbook—HVAC Systems and Equipment*.

Furnaces

Furnaces are self-enclosed, permanently installed major appliances that provide heated air through ductwork to the space being heated. In addition, a furnace may provide the indoor fan necessary for circulating heated or cooled air from a split or single-package air conditioner or heat pump. Furnaces may be used in either residential or commercial applications, and may be grouped according to the following characteristics:

- Heat source: electricity, natural gas/propane (fan assisted, condensing or noncondensing), or oil (forced draft with power atomizing burner)
- Installation location: within conditioned space (indoors), or outside conditioned space (either outdoors, or inside the structure but not within the conditioned space)
- Combustion air source: direct vent (outdoor air) or indoor air
- Mounting arrangement and airflow: horizontal, vertical upflow, vertical downflow, or multiposition

Furnaces that use electricity as a heat source include one or more resistance-type heating elements that heats the circulating air either directly or through a metal sheath that encloses the resistance element. In gas- or oil-fired furnaces, combustion occurs in the heat exchanger sections or in a combustion chamber, with direct-spark, hot-surface, or electric ignition. Circulating air passes over the outer surfaces of a heat exchanger so that it does not contact the fuel or the products of combustion, which are passed to the outdoor atmosphere through a vent.

In North America, natural gas is the most common fuel supplied for residential heating, and the central-system forced-air furnace (Figure 19.1) is the most common way of heating with natural gas.

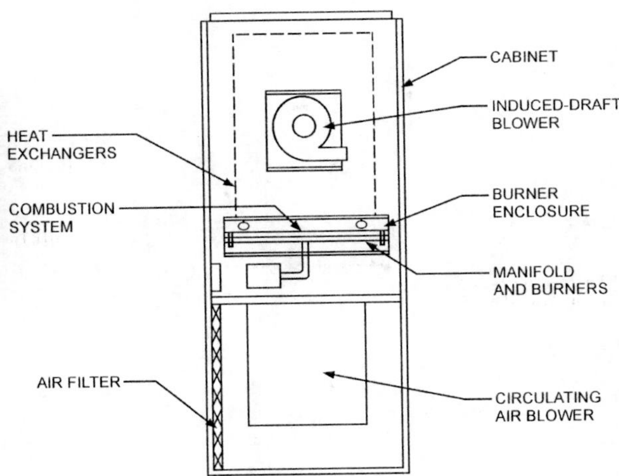

Figure 19.1 Induced-Draft Gas Furnace [2020S, Ch 33, Fig 1]

Furnaces with gas-fired burners have heat exchangers that are typically made either of left/right sets of formed parts that are joined together to form a clamshell, finless tubes bent into a compact form, or finned-tube (condensing) heat exchangers. Standard indoor furnace heat exchangers are generally made of alloy steel. Common corrosion-resistant materials include aluminized steel and stainless steel. Furnaces certified for use downstream of a cooling coil must have corrosion-resistant heat exchangers.

Heat exchangers of oil-fired furnaces are normally heavy-gage steel formed into a welded assembly. Hot flue products flow through the inside of the heat exchanger into the chimney, and conditioned air flows over the outside of the heat exchanger and into the air supply plenum.

Fan-assisted combustion furnaces use a small blower to induce flue products through the furnace. Induced-draft furnaces may or may not have a relief air opening, but they meet the same safety requirements regardless. Residential furnaces built since 1987 are equipped with a blocked-vent shutoff switch to shut down the furnace in case the vent becomes blocked.

Direct-vent furnaces use outdoor air for combustion. Outdoor air is supplied to the furnace combustion chamber by direct connections between the furnace and the outdoor air. If the vent or the combustion air supply becomes blocked, the furnace control system will shut down the furnace.

ANSI Standard Z21.47/CSA 2.3 classifies venting systems. Central furnaces are categorized by temperature and pressure attained in the vent and by the steady-state efficiency attained by the furnace. Although ANSI Standard Z21.47/CSA 2.3 uses 83% as the steady-state efficiency dividing central furnace categories, a general rule of thumb is as follows:

Category I: nonpositive vent pressure and flue loss of 17% or more
Category II: nonpositive vent pressure and flue loss less than 17%
Category III: positive vent pressure and flue loss of 17% or more
Category IV: positive vent pressure and flue loss less than 17%

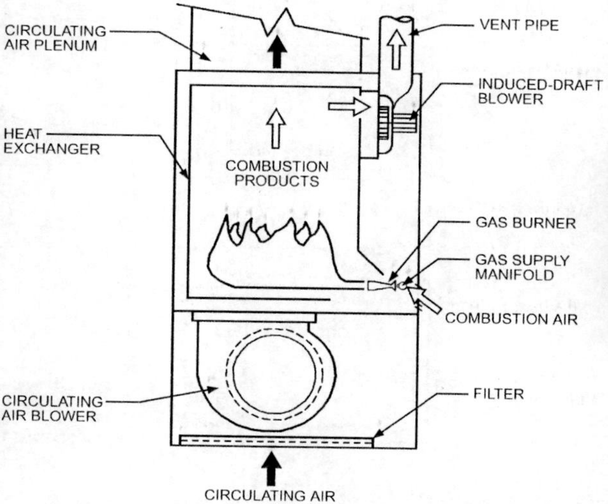

Figure 19.2 Upflow Category I Furnace with Induced-Draft Blower
[2020S, Ch 33, Fig 2]

Furnaces rated in accordance with ANSI Standard Z21.47/CSA 2.3 that are not direct vent are marked to show that they are in one of these four venting categories.

Ducted-system, oil-fired, forced-air furnaces are usually forced draft.

Furnaces with capacities above 150,000 Btu/h are classified as commercial furnaces. The other basic differences between residential and commercial furnaces are available options such as economizers, outdoor air dampers, and the type of electrical service required (three-phase).

Commercial heating equipment comes in almost as many flow arrangements and design variations as residential equipment. Some are identical to residential equipment, whereas others are unique to commercial applications. Some commercial units function as a part of a ducted system, and others operate as unducted space heaters.

Externally, the furnace is controlled by a low-voltage room thermostat.

Several types of gas valves perform various functions within the furnace. The type of valve available relates closely to the type of ignition device used. **Two-stage valves**, available on some furnaces, operate at full gas input or at a reduced rate, and are controlled by either a two-stage thermostat or a software algorithm programmed in the furnace control system.

The **fan control switch** controls the circulating air blower. This switch may be temperature-sensitive and exposed to the circulating airstream in the furnace cabinet, or it may be an electronically operated relay. Blower start-up is typically delayed about 1 min after burner start-up. This delay gives the heat exchangers time to warm up and reduces the flow of cold air when the blower comes on. Blower shutdown is also delayed several minutes after burner shutdown to remove residual heat from the heat exchangers and to improve the annual efficiency of the furnace.

The **limit switch** prevents overheating in the event of severe reduction in circulating airflow. This temperature-sensitive switch is exposed to the circulating airstream and shuts off

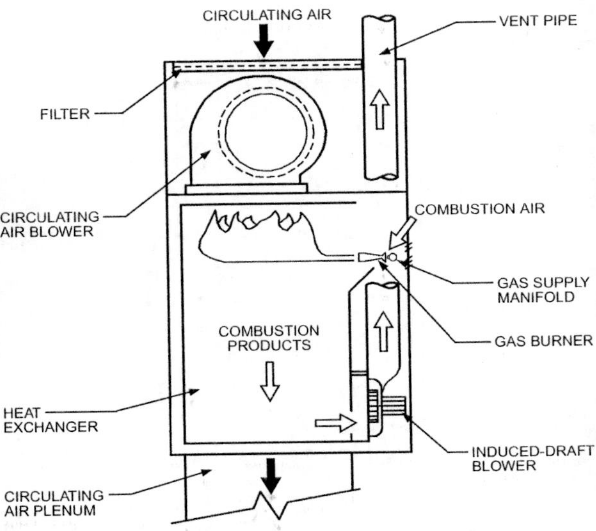

Figure 19.3 Downflow (Counterflow) Category I Furnace with Induced-Draft Blower [2020S, Ch 33, Fig 3]

the heat source (e.g., gas valve or electric element) if the temperature of air leaving the furnace is excessive. The fan control and limit switches are sometimes incorporated in the same housing and may be operated by the same thermostatic element. In the United States, the **blocked-vent shutoff switch** and **flame rollout switch** shut off the gas valve if the vent is blocked or when insufficient combustion air is present.

Furnaces using fan-assisted combustion feature a **pressure switch** to verify the flow of combustion air before opening the gas valve.

Electronic control systems are available in furnaces to provide sequencing of the inducer prepurge, ignition, circulating air blower operation, and inducer postpurge functions according to an algorithm provided by the manufacturer.

Furnaces can be installed inside or outside a building. For ideal air distribution, locate the unit in the center of the structure being heated. Furnaces are typically located in a closet, mechanical room, basement, attic, crawlspace, garage, or outdoors.

The type of fuel selected for heating is based on relative fuel cost, number of heating degree-days, and availability of utilities in the area. The most common fuel is natural gas because of its clean burning characteristics, and because of the continuous supply of this fuel through underground distribution networks to most urban settings. Propane and oil fuels are

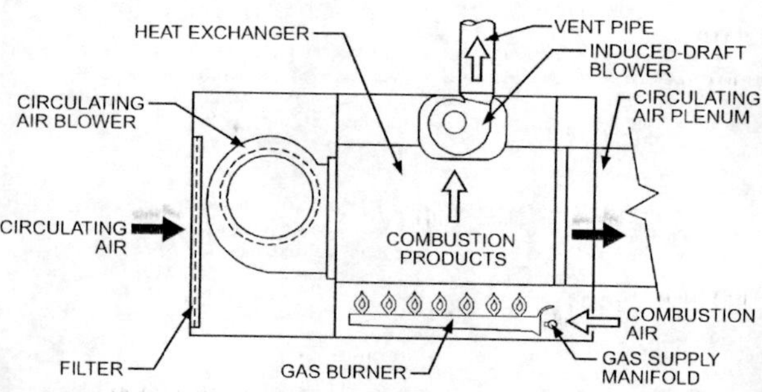

Figure 19.4 Horizontal Category I Furnace with Induced-Draft Blower [2020S, Ch 33, Fig 4]

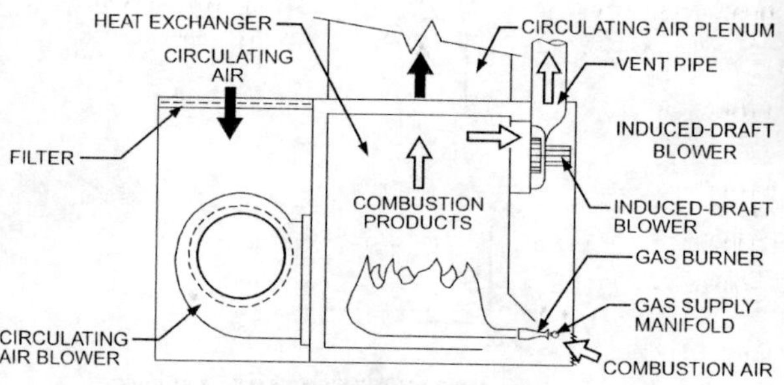

Figure 19.5 Basement (Lowboy) Category I Furnace with Induced-Draft Blower [2020S, Ch 33, Fig 5]

also commonly used. These fuels require on-site storage and periodic fuel deliveries. Electric heat is also continuously available through electrical power grids and is common especially where natural gas is not provided, or where the heating demand is small relative to the cooling demand.

Furnaces are clearly marked for the type of fuel to be used. In some cases, a manufacturer-approved conversion kit may be necessary to convert a furnace from one fuel type to another. If the fuel type is changed after the original installation, the conversion must be done by a qualified service person per the manufacturer's instructions and using the manufacturer's specified conversion kit. After conversion, the unit must be properly inspected by the local code authority.

All fuel-burning furnaces must be properly vented to the outdoors. Metal vents, masonry chimneys, and plastic vents are commonly used for furnaces. Manufacturers provide installation instructions for venting their furnaces, and Chapter 35 of the 2020 *ASHRAE Handbook—HVAC Systems and Equipment* has a detailed discussion on venting.

Air for combustion enters the combustion zone through louvers or pipes. Outdoor air usually has lower levels of pollutants than are typically found in air from indoors, garages, utility rooms, and basements.

The furnace's heating capacity (i.e., the maximum heating rate the furnace can provide) is provided on the appliance rating plate; it is also available through the manufacturers' product literature.

Other factors should be considered when determining furnace capacity. Thermostat setback recovery may require additional heating capacity. Increasing furnace capacity may increase space temperature swing, and thus reduce comfort. Two-stage or step-modulating equipment could help by using the unit's maximum capacity to meet the setback recovery needs, and providing a lower stage of heating capacity at other times.

Fuel-burning furnaces are typically subdivided into two primary categories:

- **Condensing** furnaces typically have high efficiencies, ranging from 89% to 98%, because they have a specially designed secondary heat exchanger that extracts the heat of vaporization of water vapor in the exhaust. The dew-point temperatures of flue gases of condensing furnaces are significantly above the vent temperature, so

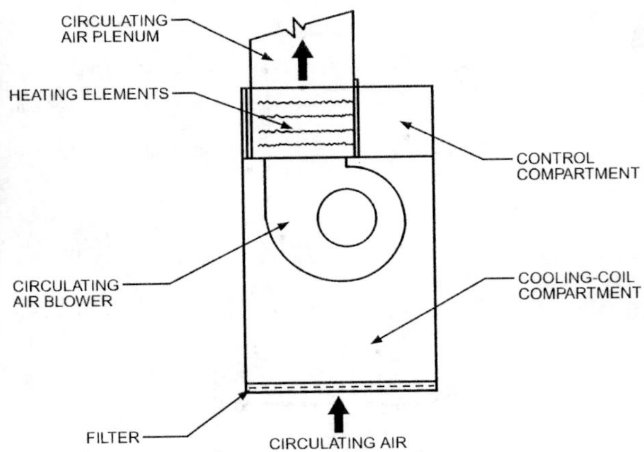

Figure 19.6 Electric Forced-Air Furnace [2020S, Ch 33, Fig 7]

plastic or other corrosion-resistant venting material is required. Condensing furnaces must be plumbed for condensate disposal.

- **Noncondensing** furnaces have generally less than 82% steady-state efficiency. This type of furnace has higher flue gas temperatures and requires either metal, masonry, or a combination of the two for venting materials.

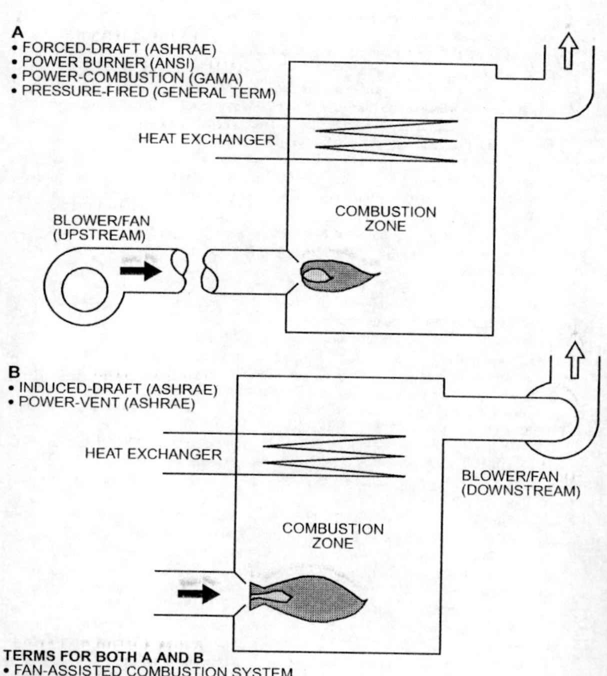

Figure 19.7 Terminology Used to Describe Fan-Assisted Combustion
[2020S, Ch 33, Fig 6]

Hydronic Heating Units and Radiators

Radiators, convectors, and baseboard and finned-tube units are heat-distributing devices used in hot-water and steam heating systems. They supply heat by a **combination of radiation and convection** and maintain the desired air temperature and/or mean radiant temperature in a space without fans. Figure 19.8 shows sections of typical heat-distributing units. In heating systems, radiant panels are also used. Units are inherently self-adjusting in the sense that heat output is based on temperature differentials; cold spaces receive more heat and warmer spaces receive less heat.

The following are the most common types of radiators:

- **Sectional radiators** are fabricated from welded sheet metal sections (generally two, three, or four tubes wide), and resemble freestanding cast-iron radiators.
- **Panel radiators** consist of fabricated flat panels (generally one, two, or three deep), with or without an exposed extended fin surface attached to the rear for increased output. These radiators are most common in Europe.
- **Tubular steel radiators** consist of supply and return headers with interconnecting parallel steel tubes in a wide variety of lengths and heights. They may be specially shaped to coincide with the building structure. Some are used to heat bathroom towel racks.
- **Specialty radiators** are fabricated of welded steel or extruded aluminum and are designed for installation in ceiling grids or floor-mounting. Various unconventional shapes are available.

Pipe coils have largely been replaced by finned tubes. See Table 5 in Chapter 28 of the 1988 *ASHRAE Handbook—Equipment* for the heat emission of such pipe coils.

A **convector** is a heat-distributing unit that operates with gravity-circulated air (natural convection). It has a heating element with a large amount of secondary surface and contains two or more tubes with headers at both ends. The heating element is surrounded by an enclosure with an air inlet below and an air outlet above the heating element.

Baseboard (or baseboard radiation) units are designed for installation along the bottom of walls in place of the conventional baseboard. They may be made of cast iron, with a substantial portion of the front face directly exposed to the room, or with a finned-tube element in a sheet metal enclosure. They use gravity-circulated room air.

Baseboard heat-distributing units are divided into three types: radiant, radiant convector, and finned tube.

- The **radiant** unit, which is made of aluminum, has no openings for air to pass over the wall side of the unit. Most of this unit's heat output is by radiation.
- The **radiant-convector** baseboard is made of cast iron or steel. The units have air openings at the top and bottom to allow circulation of room air over the wall side of the unit, which has extended surface to provide increased heat output. A large portion of the heat emitted is transferred by convection.
- The **finned-tube** baseboard has a finned-tube heating element concealed by a long, low sheet metal enclosure or cover. A major portion of the heat is transferred to the room by convection. The output varies over a wide range, depending on the physical dimensions and the materials used. A unit with a high relative output per unit length compared to overall heat loss (which would result in a concentration of the heating element over a relatively small area) should be avoided. Optimum comfort for room occupants is obtained when units are installed along as much of the exposed wall as possible.

Finned-tube (or fin-tube) units are fabricated from metallic tubing, with metallic fins bonded to the tube. They operate with gravity-circulated room air. Finned-tube elements are available in several tube sizes, in either steel or copper (1 to 2 in. nominal steel or 3/4 to 1 1/4 in. nominal copper) with various fin sizes, spacings, and materials. Resistance to steam or water flow is the same as that through standard distribution piping of equal size and type.

Finned-tube elements installed in occupied spaces generally have covers or enclosures in a variety of designs. When human contact is unlikely, they are sometimes installed bare or provided with an expanded metal grille for minimum protection.

The heat output ratings of heat-distributing units are expressed in Btu/h or in square feet equivalent direct radiation (EDR). By definition, 240 Btu/h = 1 ft^2 EDR with 1 psig steam.

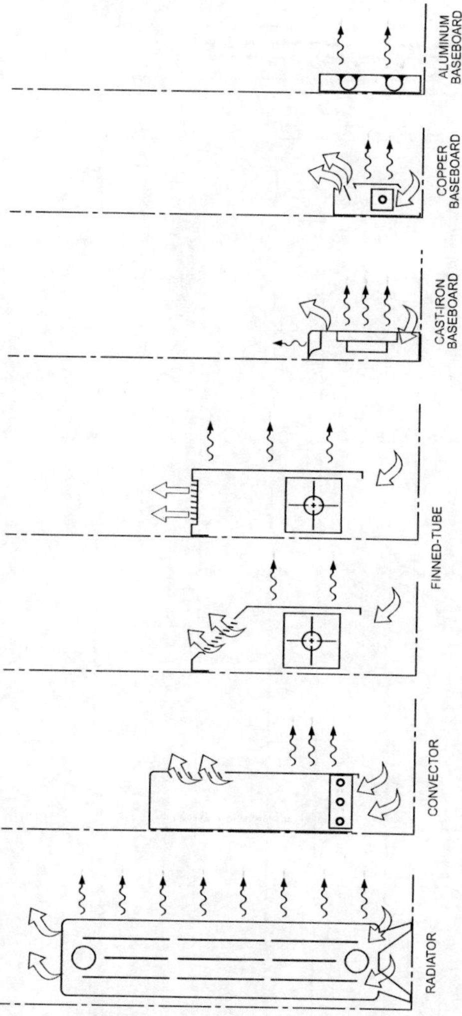

Figure 19.8 Terminal Units [2020S, Ch 36, Fig 1]

Table 19.1 Small-Tube Cast-Iron Radiators [2020S, Ch 36, Tbl 1]

Number of Tubes per Section	Catalog Rating per Section,[a]		Section Dimensions				
			A Height, in.[b]	B Width, in.		C Spacing, in.[c]	D Leg Height, in.[b]
	ft^2	Btu/h		Min.	Max.		
3	1.6	384	25	3.25	3.50	1.75	2.50
4	1.6	384	19	4.44	4.81	1.75	2.50
	1.8	432	22	4.44	4.81	1.75	2.50
	2.0	480	25	4.44	4.81	1.75	2.50
5	2.1	504	22	5.63	6.31	1.75	2.50
	2.4	576	25	5.63	6.31	1.75	2.50
6	2.3	552	19	6.81	8	1.75	2.50
	3.0	720	25	6.81	8	1.75	2.50
	3.7	888	32	6.81	8	1.75	2.50

[a] Ratings based on steam at 215°F and air at 70°F. They apply only to installed radiators exposed in a normal manner, not to radiators installed behind enclosures, behind grilles, or under shelves. For Btu/h ratings at other temperatures, multiply table values by factors found in Table 2 of Chapter 36 of the 2020 *ASHRAE Handbook—HVAC Systems and Equipment*.

[b] Overall height and leg height, as produced by some manufacturers, are 1 in. greater than shown in columns A and D. Radiators may be furnished without legs. Where greater than standard leg heights are required, leg height should be 4.5 in.

[c] Length equals number of sections multiplied by 1.75 in.

Table 19.2 Correction Factors *c* for Various Types of Heating Units [2020S, Ch 36, Tbl 2]

Steam Pressure (Approx.)		Steam or Water Temp., °F	Cast-Iron Radiator Room Temp., °F					Convector Inlet Air Temp., °F					Finned-Tube Inlet Air Temp., °F					Baseboard Inlet Air Temp., °F				
			80	75	70	65	60	75	70	65	60	55	75	70	65	60	55	75	70	65	60	55
		100											0.10	0.12	0.15	0.17	0.20	0.08	0.10	0.13	0.15	0.18
		110											0.15	0.17	0.20	0.23	0.26	0.13	0.15	0.18	0.21	0.25
		120											0.20	0.23	0.26	0.29	0.33	0.18	0.21	0.25	0.28	0.31
		130											0.26	0.29	0.33	0.36	0.40	0.25	0.28	0.31	0.34	0.38
		140											0.33	0.36	0.40	0.42	0.45	0.31	0.34	0.38	0.42	0.45
in. Hg Vac.	**psia**																					
22.4	3.7	150	0.39	0.42	0.46	0.50	0.54	0.35	0.39	0.43	0.46	0.50	0.40	0.42	0.45	0.49	0.53	0.38	0.42	0.45	0.49	0.53
20.3	4.7	160	0.46	0.50	0.54	0.58	0.62	0.43	0.47	0.51	0.54	0.58	0.45	0.49	0.53	0.57	0.61	0.45	0.49	0.53	0.57	0.61
17.7	6.0	170	0.54	0.58	0.62	0.66	0.69	0.51	0.54	0.58	0.63	0.67	0.53	0.57	0.61	0.65	0.69	0.53	0.57	0.61	0.65	0.69
14.6	7.5	180	0.62	0.66	0.69	0.74	0.78	0.58	0.63	0.67	0.71	0.76	0.61	0.65	0.69	0.73	0.78	0.61	0.65	0.69	0.72	0.78
10.9	9.3	190	0.69	0.74	0.78	0.83	0.87	0.67	0.71	0.76	0.81	0.85	0.69	0.73	0.78	0.81	0.86	0.69	0.73	0.78	0.82	0.86
6.5	11.5	200	0.78	0.83	0.87	0.91	0.95	0.76	0.81	0.85	0.90	0.95	0.77	0.81	0.86	0.90	0.95	0.81	0.86	0.92	0.95	1.00
psig	**psia**																					
1	15.6	215	0.91	0.95	1.00	1.04	1.09	0.90	0.95	1.00	1.05	1.10	0.91	0.94	1.00	1.06	1.11	0.91	0.95	1.00	1.05	1.09
6	21	230	1.04	1.09	1.14	1.18	1.23	1.05	1.10	1.15	1.20	1.26	1.03	1.08	1.14	1.19	1.24	1.04	1.09	1.14	1.19	1.25
15	30	250	1.23	1.28	1.32	1.37	1.43	1.27	1.32	1.37	1.43	1.47	1.20	1.26	1.31	1.37	1.43	1.22	1.27	1.32	1.37	1.43
27	42	270	1.43	1.47	1.52	1.56	1.61	1.47	1.54	1.59	1.67	1.72	1.38	1.44	1.50	1.56	1.62	1.43	1.47	1.52	1.59	1.64
52	67	300	1.72	1.75	1.82	1.89	1.92	1.85	1.89	1.96	2.04	2.08	1.67	1.73	1.79	1.86	1.92	1.75	1.82	1.89	1.92	1.96

Note: Use these correction factors to determine output ratings for radiators, convectors, and finned-tube and baseboard units at operating conditions other than standard. Standard conditions in the United States for a radiator are 215°F heating medium temperature and 70°F room temperature (at center of space and at 5 ft level).

Standard conditions for convectors and finned-tube and baseboard units are 215°F heating medium temperature and 65°F inlet air temperature at 29.92 in. Hg atmospheric pressure. Water flow is 3 fps for finned-tube units. Inlet air at 65°F for convectors and finned-tube or baseboard units represents the same room comfort conditions as 70°F room air temperature for a radiator. Standard conditions for radiant panels are 122°F heating medium temperature and 68°F for room air temperature; *c* depends on panel construction.

To determine output of a heating unit under nonstandard conditions, multiply standard heating capacity by appropriate factor for actual operating heating medium and room or inlet air temperatures.

Corrections for Nonstandard Conditions

The heating capacity of a radiator, convector, baseboard, finned-tube heat-distributing unit, or radiant panel is a power function of the temperature difference between the air in the room and the heating medium in the unit, shown as

$$q = c(t_s - t_a)^n \tag{19.1}$$

where

q = heating capacity, Btu/h

c = constant determined by test

t_s = average temperature of heating medium, °F. For hot water, the arithmetic average of the entering and leaving water temperatures is used.

t_a = room air temperature, °F. Air temperature 60 in. above the floor is generally used for radiators, whereas entering air temperature is used for convectors, baseboard units, and finned-tube units.

n = exponent that equals 1.3 for cast-iron radiators, 1.4 for baseboard radiation, 1.5 for convectors, 1.0 for ceiling heating and floor cooling panels, and 1.1 for floor heating and ceiling cooling panels. For finned-tube units, n varies with air and heating medium temperatures. Correction factors to convert heating capacities at standard rating conditions to heating capacities at other conditions are given in Table 19.2.

Equation 19.1 may also be used to calculate heating capacity at nonstandard conditions.

Designing for high temperature drops through the system (as much as 60°F to 80°F in low-temperature water (LTW) systems and as much as 200°F in high-temperature systems) can result in low water velocities in the finned-tube or baseboard element. Applying very short runs designed for conventional temperature drops (i.e., 20°F) can also result in low velocities.

Figure 19.9 shows the effect of water velocity on the heat output of typical sizes of finned-tube elements. The figure is based on work done by Harris (1957) and Pierce (1963) and tests at the Hydronics Institute. The velocity correction factor F_v is

$$F_v = (V/3.0)^{0.04} \tag{19.2}$$

where V = water velocity, fps.

Heat output varies little over the range from 0.5 to 3 fps, where F_v ranges from 0.93 to 1.00. The factor drops rapidly below 0.5 fps because flow changes from turbulent to laminar at around 0.1 fps. Avoid such a low velocity because the output is difficult to predict accurately when designing a system. In addition, the curve is so steep in this region that small changes in actual flow have a significant effect on output. Not only does the heat transfer rate change, but the temperature drop and, therefore, the average water temperature change (assuming a constant inlet temperature).

The designer should check water velocity throughout the system and select finned-tube or baseboard elements on the basis of velocity as well as average temperature. Manufacturers of finned-tube and baseboard elements offer a variety of tube sizes, ranging from 0.5 in. copper tubes for small baseboard elements to 2 in. for large finned-tube units, to aid in maintenance of turbulent flow conditions over a wide range of flow.

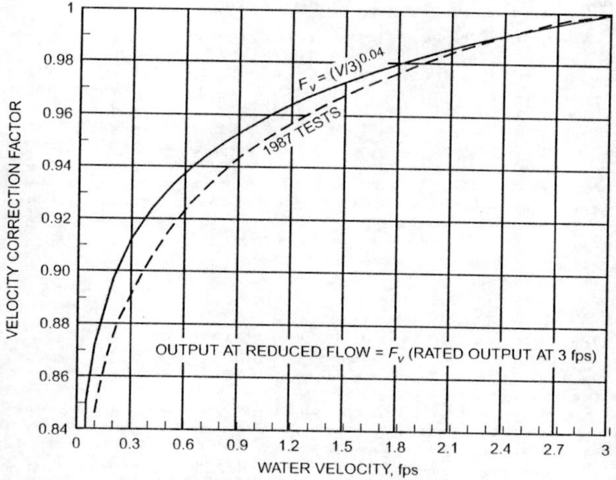

Figure 19.9 Water Velocity Correction Factor for Baseboard and Finned-Tube Radiators [2020S, Ch 36, Fig 3]

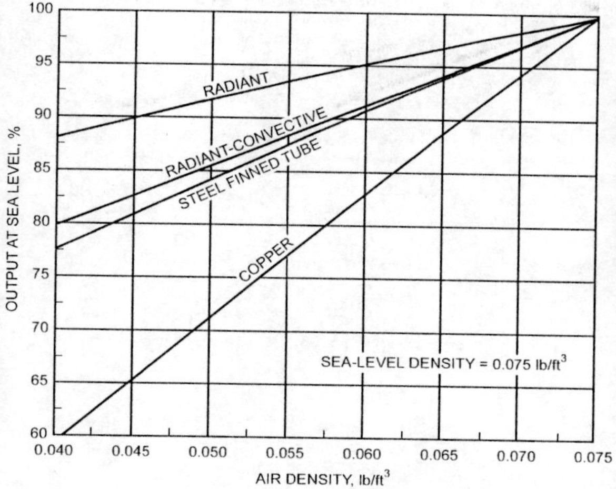

Figure 19.10 Effect of Air Density on Radiator Output [2020S, Ch 36, Fig 4]

Unit Ventilators, Unit Heaters, and Makeup Air Units

A heating unit ventilator is an assembly whose principal functions are to heat, ventilate, and cool a space by introducing outdoor air in quantities up to 100% of its rated capacity. The heating medium may be steam, hot water, gas, or electricity. The essential components of a heating unit ventilator are the fan, motor, heating element, damper, filter, automatic controls, and outlet grille, all of which are encased in a housing.

An **air-conditioning unit ventilator** is similar to a heating unit ventilator; however, in addition to the normal winter function of heating, ventilating, and cooling with outdoor air, it is also equipped to cool and dehumidify during the summer. It is usually arranged and controlled to introduce a fixed quantity of outdoor air for ventilation during cooling in mild weather. The air-conditioning unit ventilator may be provided with a various of combinations of heating and air-conditioning elements. Some of the more common arrangements include

- Combination hot- and chilled-water coil (two-pipe)
- Separate hot- and chilled-water coils (four-pipe)
- Hot-water or steam coil and direct-expansion coil
- Electric heating coil and chilled-water or direct-expansion coil
- Gas-fired furnace with direct-expansion coil

The typical unit ventilator has controls that allow heating, ventilating, and cooling to be varied while the fans operate continuously. In normal operation, the discharge air temperature from a unit is varied in accordance with the room requirements. The heating unit ventilator can provide **ventilation cooling** by bringing in outdoor air whenever the room temperature is above the room set point. Air-conditioning unit ventilators can provide refrigerated cooling when the outdoor air temperature is too high to be used effectively for ventilation cooling.

Unit ventilators are available for floor mounting, ceiling mounting, and recessed applications. They are available with various airflow and capacity ratings, and the fan can be arranged so that air is either blown through or drawn through the unit. With direct-expansion refrigerant cooling, the condensing unit can either be furnished as an integral part of the unit ventilator assembly or be remotely located.

Unit ventilators are used primarily in schools, meeting rooms, offices, and other areas where the density of occupancy requires controlled ventilation to meet local codes.

Floor-model unit ventilators are normally installed on an outer wall near the centerline of the room. Ceiling models are mounted against either the outer wall or one of the inside walls. Ceiling models discharge air horizontally. Best results are obtained if the unit can be placed so that the airflow is not interrupted by ceiling beams or surface-mounted lighting fixtures.

Table 19.3 Typical Unit Ventilator Capacities [2020S, Ch 28, Tbl 1]

Airflow, cfm	Heating Unit Ventilator Total Heating Capacity, Btu/h	A/C Unit Ventilator Total Cooling Capacity, Btu/h
500	38,000	19,000
750	50,000	28,000
1000	72,000	38,000
1250	85,000	47,000
1500	100,000	56,000

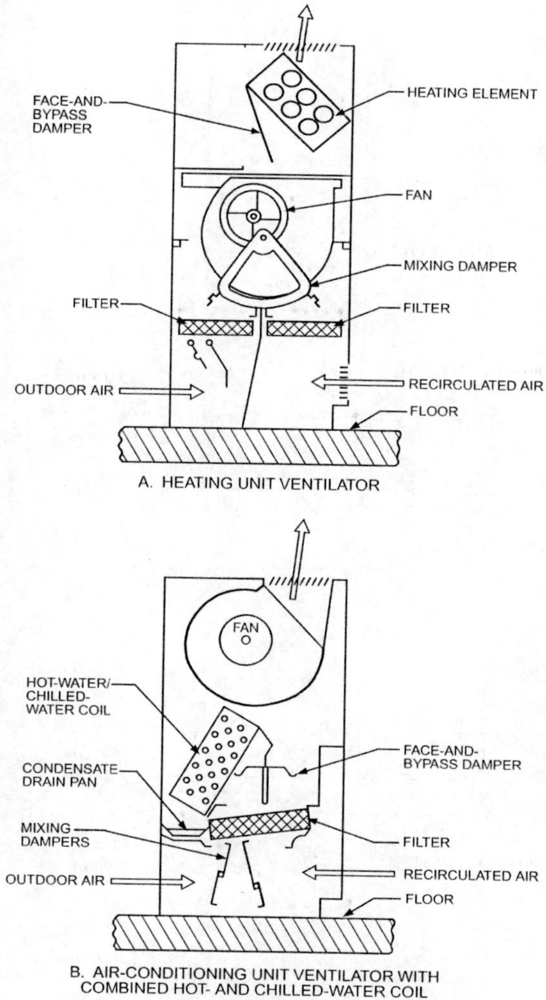

FACE-AND-BYPASS DAMPER
HEATING ELEMENT
FAN
MIXING DAMPER
FILTER
FILTER
OUTDOOR AIR
RECIRCULATED AIR
FLOOR

A. HEATING UNIT VENTILATOR

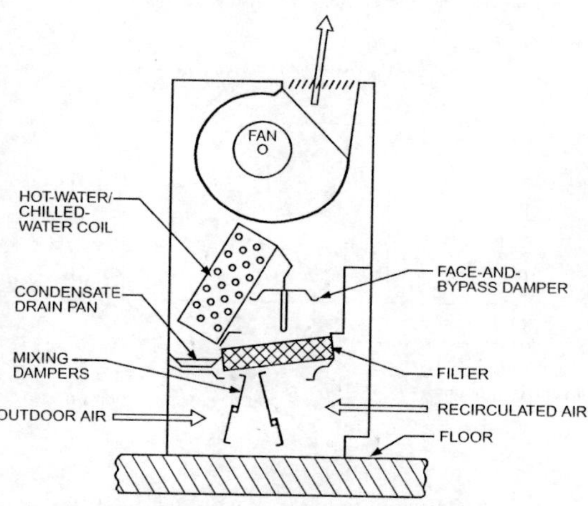

B. AIR-CONDITIONING UNIT VENTILATOR WITH COMBINED HOT- AND CHILLED-WATER COIL

Figure 19.11 Typical Unit Ventilators [2020S, Ch 28, Fig 1]

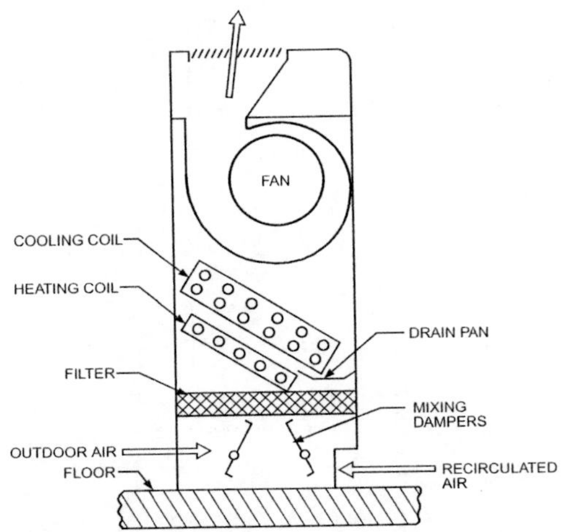

C. AIR-CONDITIONING UNIT VENTILATOR WITH SEPARATE COILS

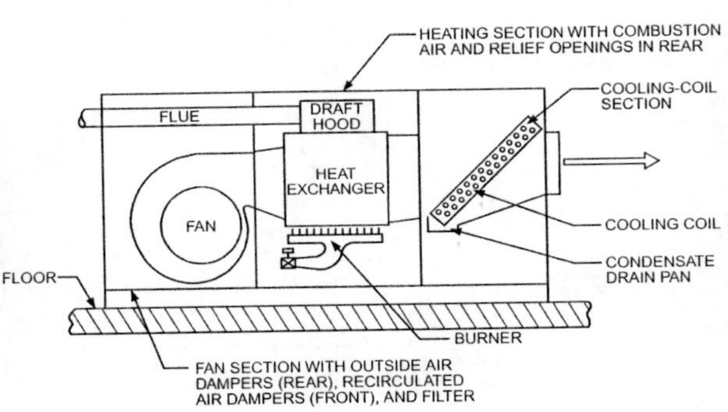

D. GAS-FIRED AIR-CONDITIONING UNIT VENTILATOR

Figure 19.11 Typical Unit Ventilators [2020S, Ch 28, Fig 1]
(Continued)

Unit Heaters

A unit heater is an assembly of elements with the main function of heating a space. The essential elements are a fan and motor, a heating element, and an enclosure. Filters, dampers, directional outlets, duct collars, combustion chambers, and flues may also be included. Some types of unit heaters are shown in Figure 19.12.

Unit heaters have the following principal characteristics:

- Relatively large heating capacities in compact casings
- Ability to project heated air in a controlled manner over a considerable distance
- Relatively low installed cost per unit of heat output
- Application where an elevated sound level is permissible

They are, therefore, usually placed in applications where the heating capacity requirements, physical volume of the heated space, or both, are too large to be handled adequately or economically by other means. By eliminating extensive duct installations, the space is freed for other use.

Unit heaters are mostly used for heating commercial and industrial structures such as garages, factories, warehouses, showrooms, stores, and laboratories, as well as corridors, lobbies, vestibules, and similar auxiliary spaces in all types of buildings. Unit heaters may often be used to advantage in specialized applications requiring spot or intermittent heating, such as at outer doors in industrial plants or in corridors and vestibules. Cabinet unit heaters may be used where heated air must be filtered.

The following factors should be considered when selecting a unit heater:

Heating Medium. The proper heating medium is usually determined by economics and requires examining initial cost, operating cost, and conditions of use.

Steam or **hot-water unit heaters** are relatively inexpensive but require a boiler and piping system. The unit cost of such a system generally decreases as the number of units increases. Therefore, steam or hot-water heating is most frequently used (1) in new installations involving a relatively large number of units, and (2) in existing systems that have sufficient capacity to handle the additional load. High-pressure steam or high-temperature hot-water units are normally used only in very large installations or when a high-temperature medium is required for process work. Low-pressure steam and conventional hot-water units are usually selected for smaller installations and for those concerned primarily with comfort heating.

Gas and **oil indirect-fired unit heaters** are frequently preferred in small installations where the number of units does not justify the expense and space requirements of a new boiler system or where individual metering of the fuel supply is required, as in a shopping center. Gas indirect-fired units usually have either horizontal propeller fans or industrial centrifugal fans. Oil indirect-fired units largely have industrial centrifugal fans. Some codes limit the use of indirect-fired unit heaters in some applications. Indirect-fired oil and gas units are of blow-through design to mitigate the possibility of combustion products entering the occupied space.

Electric unit heaters are used when the cost of available electric power is lower than that of alternative fuel sources and for isolated locations, intermittent use, supplementary heating, or temporary service. Typical applications are ticket booths, security offices, factory offices, locker rooms, and other isolated rooms scattered over large areas. Electric units are particularly useful in isolated and untended pumping stations or pits, where they may be thermostatically controlled to prevent freezing.

Propeller fan units are generally used in non-ducted applications where the heating capacity and distribution requirements can best be met by units of moderate output and where heated air does not need to be filtered. Horizontal-blow units are usually installed in buildings with low to moderate ceiling heights. Downblow units are used in spaces with high ceilings and where floor and wall space limitations dictate that heating equipment be kept out of the way. Downblow units may have an adjustable diffuser to vary the discharge pattern from a high-velocity vertical jet (to achieve the maximum distance of downward throw) to a horizontal discharge of lower velocity (to prevent excessive air motion in the zone of occupancy). Revolving diffusers are also available.

Cabinet unit heaters are used when a more attractive appearance is desired. They are suitable for free-air delivery or low static pressure duct applications. They may be equipped with filters, and they can be arranged to discharge either horizontally or vertically up or down.

Industrial centrifugal fan units are applied where heating capacities and space volumes are large or where filtration of the heated air or operation against static resistance is required. Downblow or horizontal-blow units may be used, depending on the requirements.

Duct unit heaters are used where the air handler is remote from the heater. These heaters sometimes provide an economical means of adding heating to existing cooling or ventilating systems with ductwork. They require flow and temperature limit controls.

Location for Proper Heat Distribution. Units must be selected, located, and arranged to provide complete heat coverage while maintaining acceptable air motion and temperature at an acceptable sound level in the working or occupied zone. Proper application depends on size, number, and type of units; direction of airflow and type of directional outlet used; mounting height; outlet velocity and temperature; and air volumetric flow. Many of these factors are interrelated.

The mounting height may be governed by space limitations or by the presence of equipment such as display cases or machinery. The higher a downblow heater is mounted, the lower the temperature of air leaving the heater must be to force the heated air into the occupied zone. Also, the distance that air leaving the heater travels depends largely on the air temperature and initial velocity. A high discharge temperature reduces the area of effective heat coverage because of its buoyancy.

For area heating, place horizontal-blow unit heaters in exterior zones such that they blow either along the exposure or toward it at a slight angle. When possible, arrange multiple units so that the discharge airstreams support each other and create a general circulatory motion in the space. Interior zones under exposed roofs or skylights should be completely blanketed. Arrange downblow units so that the heated areas from adjacent units overlap slightly to provide complete coverage.

For spot heating of individual spaces in larger unheated areas, single unit heaters may be used, but allowance must be made for the inflow of unheated air from adjacent spaces and the consequent reduction in heat coverage. Such spaces should be isolated by partitions or enclosures, if possible.

Horizontal unit heaters should have discharge outlets located well above head level. Both horizontal and vertical units should be placed so that the heated airstream is delivered to the occupied zone at acceptable temperature and velocity. Outlet air temperature of free-air delivery unit heaters used for comfort heating should be 50°F to 60°F higher than the design room temperature. When possible, locate units so that they discharge into open spaces, such as aisles, and not directly on the occupants.

Manufacturers' catalogs usually include suggestions for the best arrangements of various unit heaters, recommended mounting heights, heat coverage for various outlet velocities, final temperatures, directional outlets, and sound level ratings.

The following factors should be considered when evaluating capacity ratings:

Steam or Hot Water. Heating capacity must be determined at a standard condition. Variations in entering steam or water temperature, entering air temperature, and steam or water flow affect capacity. Typical standard conditions for rating steam unit heaters are dry saturated steam at 2 psig pressure at the heater coil, air at 60°F (29.92 in. Hg barometric pressure) entering the heater, and the heater operating free of external resistance to airflow. Standard conditions for rating hot-water unit heaters are entering water at 200°F, water temperature drop of 20°F, entering air at 60°F and 29.92 in. Hg barometric pressure, and the heater operating free of external resistance to airflow.

Gas-Fired. Gas-fired unit heaters are rated in terms of both input and output, in accordance with the approval requirements of the American Gas Association.

Oil-Fired. Ratings of oil-fired unit heaters are based on heat delivered at the heater outlet.

Electric. Electric unit heaters are rated based on the energy input to the heating element.

Effect of Airflow Resistance on Capacity. Unit heaters are customarily rated at free-air delivery. Airflow and heating capacity decrease if outdoor air intakes, air filters, or ducts on the inlet or discharge are used. The manufacturer should have information on the heat output to be expected at other than free-air delivery.

Effect of Inlet Temperature. Changes in entering air temperature influence the total heating capacity in most unit heaters and the final temperature in all units. Because many unit heaters are located some distance from the occupied zone, possible differences between the temperature of the air actually entering the unit and that of air being maintained in the heated area should be considered, particularly with downblow unit heaters.

Filters. Air from propeller unit heaters cannot be filtered because the heaters are designed to operate with heater friction loss only. If dust in the building must be filtered, centrifugal fan units or cabinet units should be used.

Controls. The controls for a steam or hot water unit heater can provide either (1) on/off operation of the unit fan, or (2) continuous fan operation with modulation of heat output. For on/off operation, a room thermostat is used to start and stop the fan motor or group of fan motors. A limit thermostat, often strapped to the supply or return pipe, prevents fan operation in the event that heat is not being supplied to the unit. An auxiliary switch that energizes the fan only when power is applied to open the motorized supply valve may also be used to prevent undesirable cool air from being discharged by the unit.

Continuous fan operation eliminates both the intermittent blasts of hot air resulting from on/off operation and the stratification of temperature from floor to ceiling that often occurs during off periods. In this arrangement, a proportional room thermostat controls a valve modulating the heat supply to the coil or a bypass around the heating element. A limit thermostat or auxiliary switch stops the fan when heat is no longer available.

One type of control used with downblow unit heaters is designed to automatically return the warm air, which would normally stratify at the higher level, down to the zone of occupancy. Two thermostats and an auxiliary switch are required. The lower thermostat is placed in the zone of occupancy and is used to control a two-position supply valve to the heater. An auxiliary switch is used to stop the fan when the supply valve is closed. The higher thermostat is placed near the unit heater at the ceiling or roof level where the warm air tends to stratify. The lower thermostat automatically closes the steam valve when its setting is satisfied, but the higher thermostat overrides the auxiliary switch so that the fan continues to run until the temperature at the higher level falls below a point sufficiently high to produce a heating effect.

Indirect-fired and electric units are usually controlled by intermittent operation of the heat source under control of the room thermostat, with a separate fan switch to run the fan when heat is being supplied.

Unit heaters can be used to circulate air in summer. In such cases, the heat is shut off and the thermostat has a bypass switch, which allows the fan to run independently of the controls.

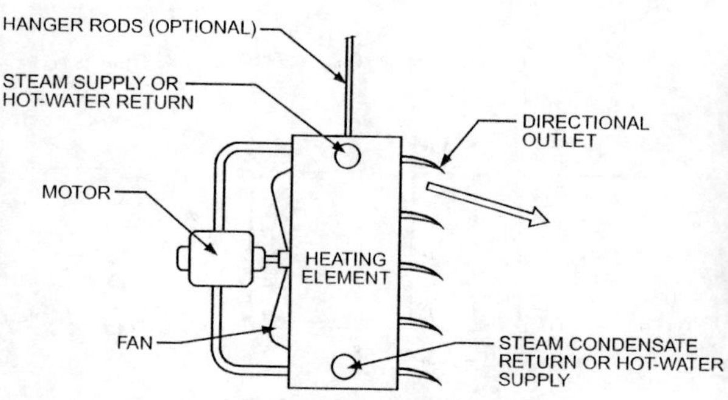

Figure 19.12 Typical Unit Heaters [2020S, Ch 28, Fig 2]

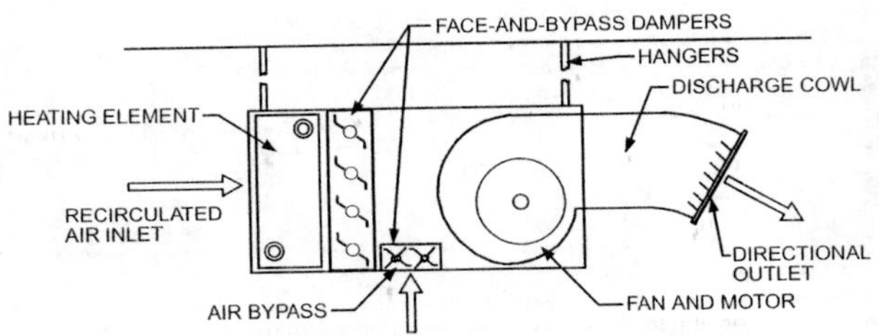

B. SUSPENDED INDUSTRIAL-TYPE WITH CENTRIFUGAL FAN AND BYPASS CONTROL

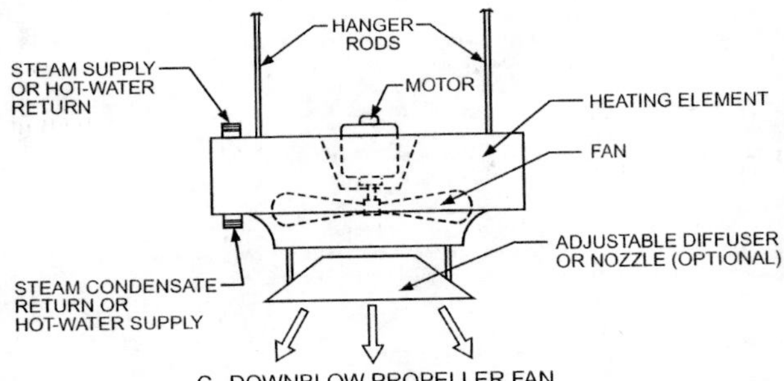

C. DOWNBLOW PROPELLER FAN

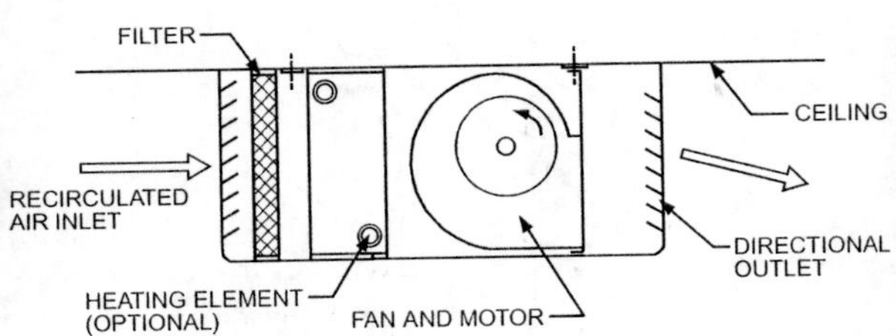

D. SUSPENDED CABINET WITH CENTRIFUGAL FAN

Figure 19.12 Typical Unit Heaters [2020S, Ch 28, Fig 2]
(Continued)

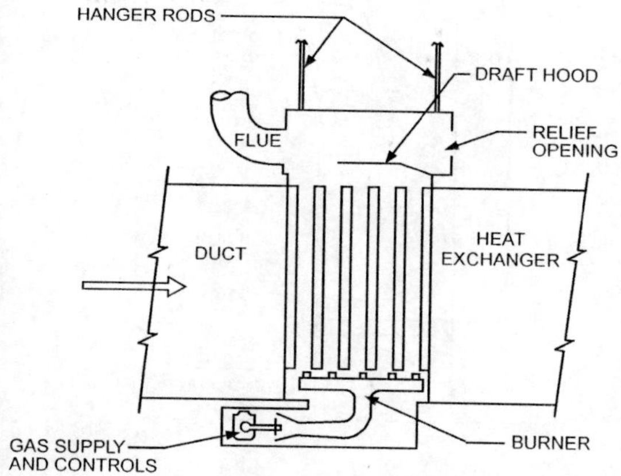

E. GAS INDIRECT-FIRED DUCT MOUNTED

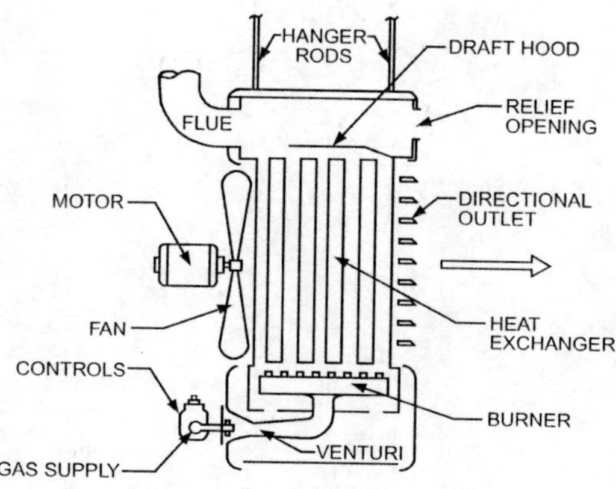

F. GAS INDIRECT-FIRED WITH PROPELLER FAN

Figure 19.12 Typical Unit Heaters [2020S, Ch 28, Fig 2]
(Continued)

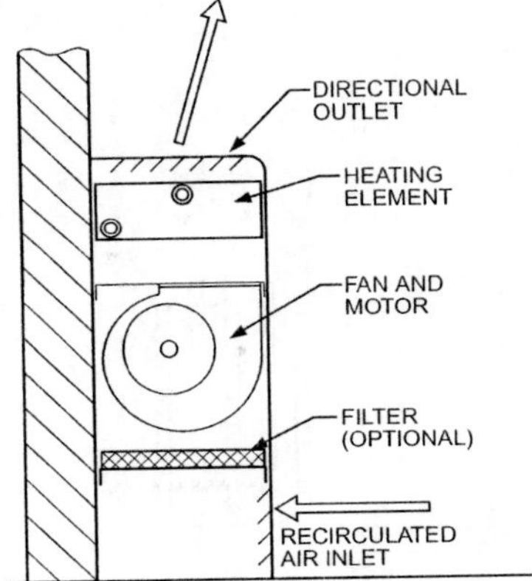

G. FLOOR-MOUNTED CABINET WITH CENTRIFUGAL FAN

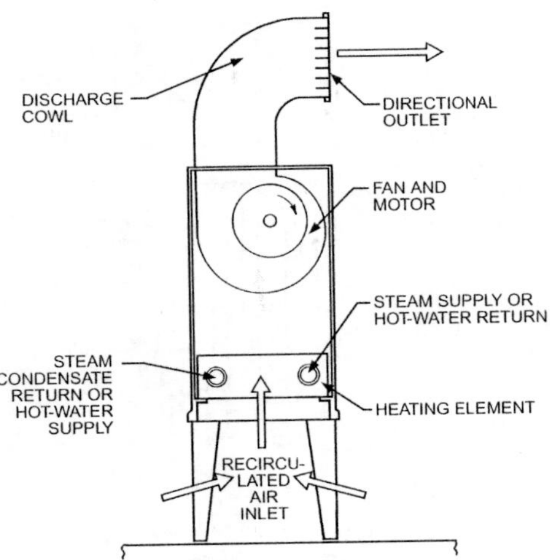

H. FLOOR-MOUNTED INDUSTRIAL-TYPE WITH CENTRIFUGAL FAN

Figure 19.12 Typical Unit Heaters [2020S, Ch 28, Fig 2]
(Continued)

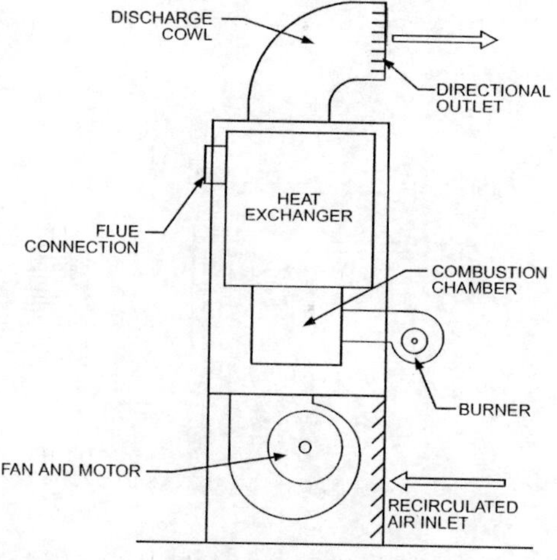

I. FLOOR-MOUNTED, INDUSTRIAL-TYPE, OIL OR GAS INDIRECT-FIRED WITH CENTRIFUGAL FAN

Figure 19.12 Typical Unit Heaters [2020S, Ch 28, Fig 2] ***(Continued)***

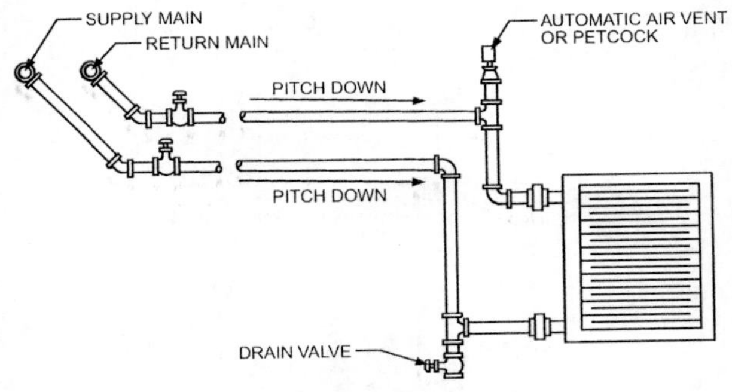

A. OVERHEAD HOT-WATER MAINS

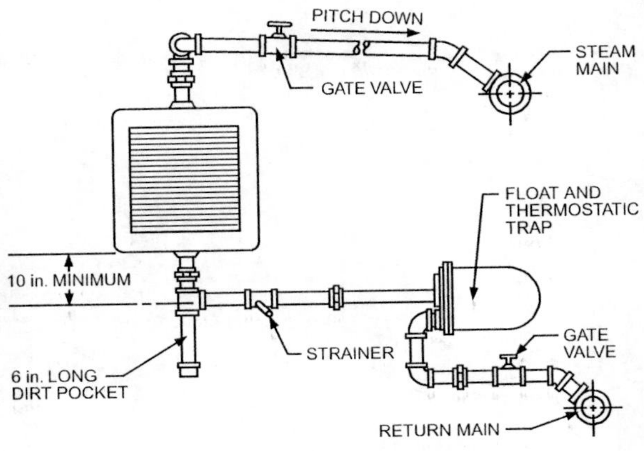

B. LOW-PRESSURE STEAM, OPEN GRAVITY, OR VACUUM RETURN

Figure 19.13 Hot Water and Steam Connections for Unit Heaters
[2020S, Ch 28, Fig 4]

HVAC Systems and Equipment

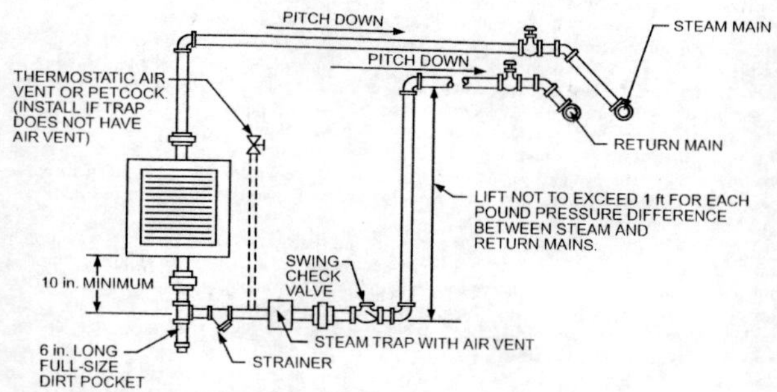

NOTE: This piping arrangement is only for two-position control. Modulating steam control may not provide sufficient pressure to lift condensate to return main in throttled position.

C. OVERHEAD STEAM AND RETURN MAINS

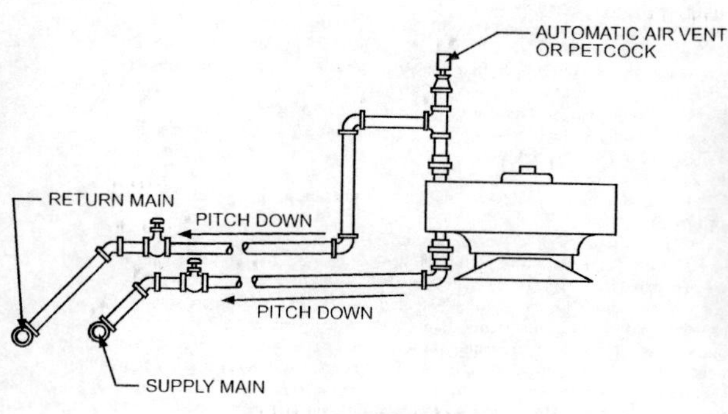

D. LOWER HOT-WATER MAINS

Figure 19.13 Hot Water and Steam Connections for Unit Heaters
[2020S, Ch 28, Fig 4] ***(Continued)***

HVAC Systems and Equipment

Makeup Air Units

Makeup air units are designed to condition ventilation air introduced into a space or to replace air exhausted from a building. The air exhausted may be from a process or general area exhaust, through either powered exhaust fans or gravity ventilators. The units may be used to prevent negative pressure within buildings or to reduce airborne contaminants in a space. The units may heat, cool, humidify, dehumidify, and/or filter incoming air. They may be used to replace air in the conditioned space or to supplement or accomplish all or part of the airflow needed to satisfy the heating, ventilating, or cooling airflow requirements.

Makeup air systems used for ventilation may be (1) sized to balance air exhaust volumes or (2) sized in excess of the exhaust volume to dilute contaminants. In applications where contaminant levels vary, variable-flow units should be considered so that the supply air varies for contaminant control and the exhaust volume varies to track supply volume. In critical spaces, the exhaust volume may be based on requirements to control pressure in the space.

Location. Makeup air units are defined by their location or the use of a key component. Examples are rooftop makeup air units, truss- or floor-mounted units, and sidewall units. Some manufacturers differentiate their units by heating mode, such as steam or direct gas-fired makeup air units.

Rooftop units are commonly used for large single-story industrial buildings to simplify air distribution. Access (via roof walks) is more convenient than access to equipment mounted in the truss; truss units are only accessible by installing a catwalk adjacent to the air units. Disadvantages of rooftop units are (1) they increase foot traffic on the roof, thus reducing its life and increasing the likelihood of leaks; (2) inclement weather reduces equipment accessibility; and (3) units are exposed to weather.

Makeup air units can also be placed around the perimeter of a building with air ducted through the sidewall. This approach limits future building expansion, and the effectiveness of ventilating internal spaces decreases as the building gets larger. However, access to the units is good, and minimum support is required because the units are mounted on the ground.

Heating and Cooling Media. Heaters in makeup air systems may be direct gas-fired burners, electric resistance heating coils, indirect gas-fired heaters, steam coils, or hot-water heating coils. Air distribution systems are often required to direct heat to spaces requiring it.

Mechanical refrigeration with direct-expansion or chilled-water cooling coils, direct or indirect evaporative cooling sections, or well water coils may be used. Air distribution systems are often required to direct cooling to specific spaces that experience or create heat gain.

If direct-expansion coils are used in conjunction with direct-fired gas coils, the cooling coils' headers must be isolated from the airstream and directly vented outdoors.

Filters. High-efficiency filters (approximately MERV 16 for near-HEPA performance) are not normally used in a makeup air unit because of their relatively high cost. HVAC prefilters are generally in the MERV 6 to 13 range, depending on particulate removal needs.

Fans. Follow AMCA Standard 205-12 for fan selection. Fans should have variable-speed drives for possible energy savings or for use in variable-airflow systems.

Fans should have variable-speed drives for possible energy savings or for use in variable-airflow systems.

Controls. Controls for a makeup air unit fall into the following categories: (1) local temperature controls, (2) airflow controls, (3) plant-wide controls for proper equipment operation and efficient performance, (4) safety controls for burner gas, and (5) building smoke control systems.

Safety controls for gas-fired units include components to properly light the burner and to provide a safeguard against flame failure. The heater and all attached inlet ducting must be purged with at least four air changes before initiating an ignition sequence and before reignition after a malfunction. A flame monitor and control system must be used to automatically shut off gas to the burner upon burner ignition or flame failure. Critical malfunctions include flame failure, supply fan failure, combustion air depletion, power failure, control signal failure, excessive or inadequate inlet gas supply pressure, excess air temperature, and gas leaks in motorized valves or inlet gas supply piping.

Makeup air units should be interlocked with exhaust units to avoid overpressurization, and should include shutoff dampers with limit switches for when not in use. Damper leakage rates should be within limits set in ANSI/ASHRAE/IES Standard 90.1. These units should also be interlocked to the building's fire alarm system to shut down in the case of a fire, where required by applicable codes.

Consider using automatic safety shutoff valves on interconnecting piping systems where there are risks of overtemperature, overpressure, or gas leaks.

Small Forced-Air Heating and Cooling Systems

Forced-air systems are heating and/or cooling systems that use motor-driven blowers to distribute heated, cooled, and otherwise treated air to multiple outlets for the comfort of individuals in confined spaces. A typical residential or small commercial system includes (1) a heating and/or cooling unit, (2) supply and return ductwork (including registers and grilles), (3) accessory equipment, and (4) controls (see Figure 19.14).

Three types of forced-air heating and cooling devices are (1) furnaces, (2) air conditioners, and (3) heat pumps.

Furnaces are the basic component of most forced-air heating systems. They are manufactured to use specific fuels such as oil, natural gas, or liquefied petroleum gas, and are augmented with an air-conditioning coil when cooling is included. The fuel used dictates installation requirements and safety considerations.

Common **air-conditioning** systems use a split configuration with an air-handling unit, such as a furnace. The air-conditioning evaporator coil (indoor unit) is installed on the discharge air side of the air handler. The compressor and condensing coil (outdoor unit) are located outside the structure, and refrigerant lines connect the outdoor and indoor units.

Self-contained air conditioners contain all necessary air-conditioning components, including circulating air blowers, and may or may not include fuel-fired heat exchangers or electric heating elements.

Heat pumps cool and heat using the refrigeration cycle. They are available in split and packaged (self-contained) configurations. Generally, air-source heat pumps require supplemental heating; therefore, electric heating elements are usually included with the heat pump as part of the forced-air system. Heat pumps offer high efficiency at mild temperatures, but may be combined with fossil-fuel furnaces to minimize heating cost. Heat pump supplemental heating also may be provided by thermostat-controlled gas heating appliances (e.g., fireplaces, free-standing stoves).

Ground-source heat pumps (GSHPs) are becoming more common in residential housing, especially in colder climates. Because underground temperatures are mild year-round, GSHPs typically do not use supplemental heating except in emergency mode (i.e., when the heat pump does not provide enough heat).

Forced-air systems may be equipped with **accessories** that further condition the air. They may modify humidity, remove contaminants, mix outdoor air with the recirculating air, or transfer energy in other ways. Disposable air filters on the return side of forced-air systems are so common that they are not considered accessories.

A simple thermostat controlling on/off cycling of central equipment may be all that is used or needed for temperature **control**. Such thermostats typically have a switch for automatic or continuous fan operation, and another to choose heating, cooling, or neither.

More complex systems may provide control features for timed variations (from simple night setback to a weekly schedule of temperatures); multiple independent zones, power stages, or fan speeds; influence of outdoor sensors; humidity; automatic switching between heating and cooling modes, etc.

The overall system design should proceed as follows:

1. Estimate heating and cooling loads, including target values for duct losses.
2. Determine preliminary ductwork location and materials of ductwork and outlets.
3. Determine heating and cooling unit location.
4. Select accessory equipment. Accessory equipment is not generally provided with initial construction; however, the system may be designed for later addition of these components.
5. Select control components.
6. Select heating/cooling equipment.
7. Determine maximum airflow (cooling or heating) for each supply and return location.
8. Determine airflow at reduced heating and cooling loads (two-speed and variable-speed fans).
9. Finalize heating/cooling equipment.
10. Finalize control system.
11. Finalize duct design and size.
12. Select supply and return grilles.
13. When the duct system is in place, measure duct leakage and compare results with target values used in step 1.

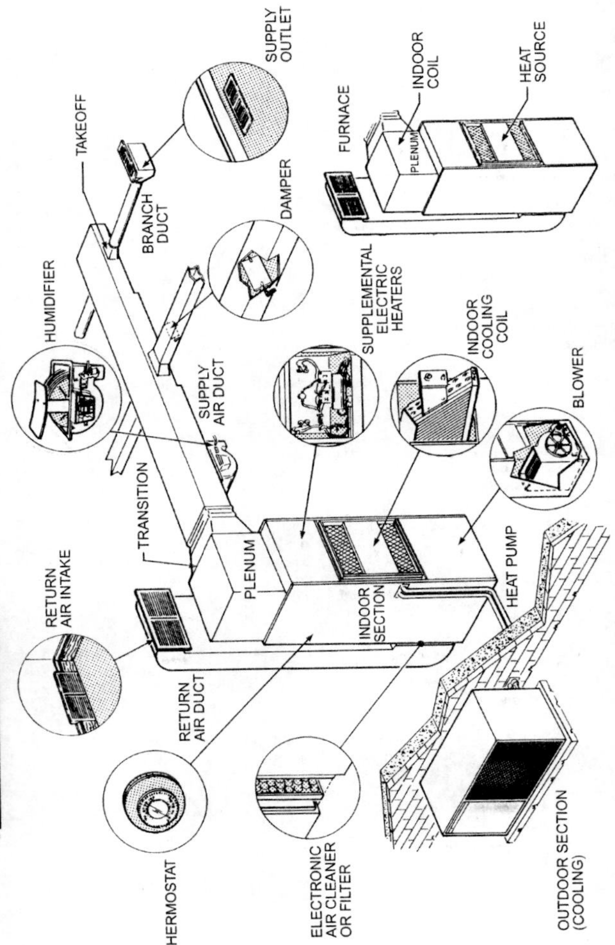

Figure 19.14 Heating and Cooling Components [2020S, Ch 10, Fig 1]

For maximum energy efficiency, ductwork and equipment should be installed in the conditioned space. ANSI/ASHRAE/IES Standard 90.2 gives a credit for installation in this location. The next best location is in a full basement. If a structure has an insulated, unvented, and sealed crawlspace, the ductwork and equipment can be located there (with appropriate provision for combustion air, if applicable), or the equipment can be placed in a closet or utility room. Vented attics and vented crawlspaces are the least preferred locations for ductwork and HVAC equipment.

Furnace heating output should match or slightly exceed the estimated design load. The Air Conditioning Contractors of America (ACCA *Manual* S) recommends a 40% limit on oversizing for fossil fuel furnaces. This limit minimizes venting problems associated with oversized equipment and improves part-load performance. Note that the calculated load must include duct loss, humidification load, and night setback recovery load, as well as building conduction and infiltration heat losses.

To help conserve energy, manufacturers have added features to improve furnace efficiency. Electric ignition has replaced the standing pilot; vent dampers and more efficient motors are also available. Furnaces with fan-assisted combustion systems (FACSs) and condensing furnaces also improve efficiency. Two-stage heating and cooling, variable-speed heat pumps, and two-speed and variable-speed blowers are also available.

Research on the effect of blower performance on residential forced-air heating system performance suggested reductions of 180 to 250 kWh/yr for automatic furnace fan operation and 2600 kWh/yr for continuous fan operation by changing from permanent split capacitor (PSC) blower motors to brushless permanent electronically commutated magnet motors (ECMs) (Phillips 1998).

A system designed to both heat and cool and that cycles cooling equipment on and off by sensing dry-bulb temperature alone should be sized to match the design heat gain as closely as possible. Oversizing under this control strategy could lead to higher-than-desired indoor humidity levels. Chapter 17 of the 2021 *ASHRAE Handbook—Fundamentals* recommends that cooling units not be oversized. Other sources suggest limiting oversizing to 15% of the sensible load. A heat pump should be sized for the cooling load with supplemental heat provided to meet heating requirements. Size air-source heat pumps in accordance with the equipment manufacturer recommendations. ACCA *Manual* S can also be used to assist in the selection and sizing of equipment.

The required airflow and the blower's static pressure limitation are the parameters around which the duct system is designed. The heat loss or gain for each space determines the proportion of the total airflow supplied to each space. Static pressure drop in supply registers should be limited to about 0.03 in. of water. The required pressure drop must be deducted from the static pressure available for duct design.

The flow delivered by a single supply outlet should be determined by considering the (1) space limitations on the number of registers that can be installed, (2) pressure drop for the register at the flow rate selected, (3) adequacy of air delivery patterns for offsetting heat loss or gain, and (4) space use pattern.

Manufacturers' specifications include blower airflow for each blower speed and external static pressure combination. Determining static pressure available for duct design should include the possibility of adding accessories in the future (e.g., electronic air cleaners or humidifiers). Therefore, the highest available fan speed should not be used for design.

For systems that heat only, the blower rate may be determined from the manufacturer's data. The temperature rise of air passing through the heat exchanger of a fossil-fuel furnace must be within the manufacturer's recommended range (usually 40°F to 80°F). The possible later addition of cooling should also be considered by selecting a blower that operates in the midrange of the fan speed and settings.

For cooling only, or for heating and cooling, the design flow can be estimated by Equation 19.3:

$$Q = \frac{q_s U}{\rho c_p \Delta t} \tag{19.3}$$

where

Q = flow rate, cfm
q_s = sensible load, Btu/h
ρ = air density assumed to equal 0.075 lb/ft^3
c_p = specific heat of air = 0.24 Btu/lb·°F
Δt = dry-bulb temperature difference between air entering and leaving equipment, °F
U = unit conversion factor, 1 h/60 min

Replacing all constant values gives the simplified equation in the given units.

$$Q = \frac{1}{1.08} \times \frac{q_s}{\Delta t} = \frac{q_s}{1.08 \Delta t} \tag{19.4}$$

For preliminary design, an approximate Δt is as follows:

Sensible Heat Ratio (SHR)	Δt, °F
0.75 to 0.79	21
0.80 to 0.85	19
0.85 to 0.90	17

SHR = Calculated sensible load/Calculated total load

For example, if calculation indicates the sensible load is 23,000 Btu/h and the latent load is 4900 Btu/h, the SHR is calculated as follows:

$$\text{SHR} = \frac{23{,}000}{23{,}000 + 4900} = 0.82 \tag{19.5}$$

and

$$Q = \frac{23{,}000}{1.08 + 19} = 1121 \text{ cfm} \tag{19.6}$$

This value is the estimated design flow. The exact design flow can only be determined after the cooling unit is selected. The unit that is ultimately selected should supply an airflow in the range of the estimated flow, and must also have adequate sensible and latent cooling capacity when operating at design conditions.

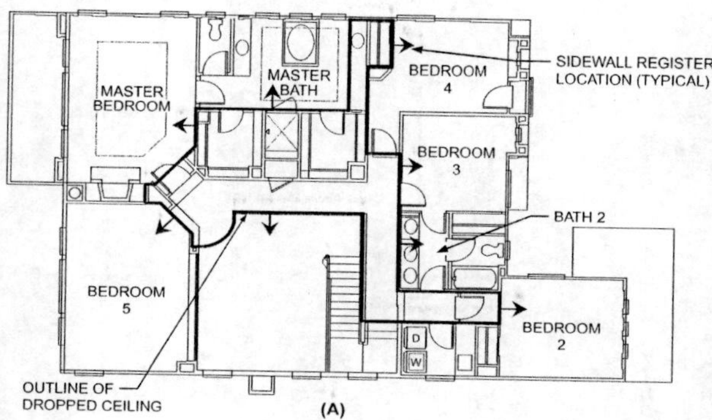

(A)

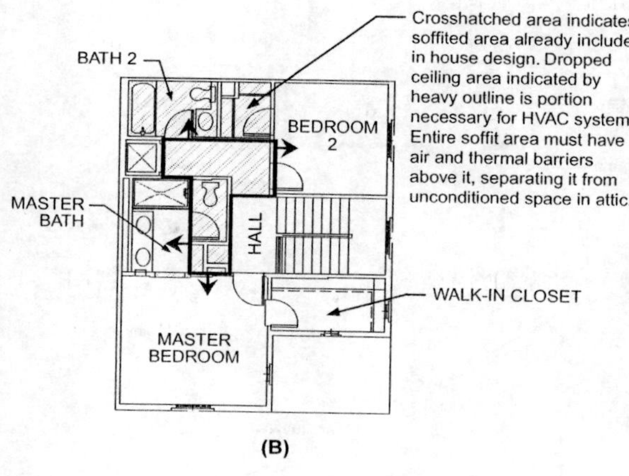

(B)

(Hedrick 2002)

Figure 19.15 Sample Floor Plans for Locating Ductwork in Second Floor of (A) Two-Story House and (B) Townhouse [2020S, Ch 10, Fig 2]

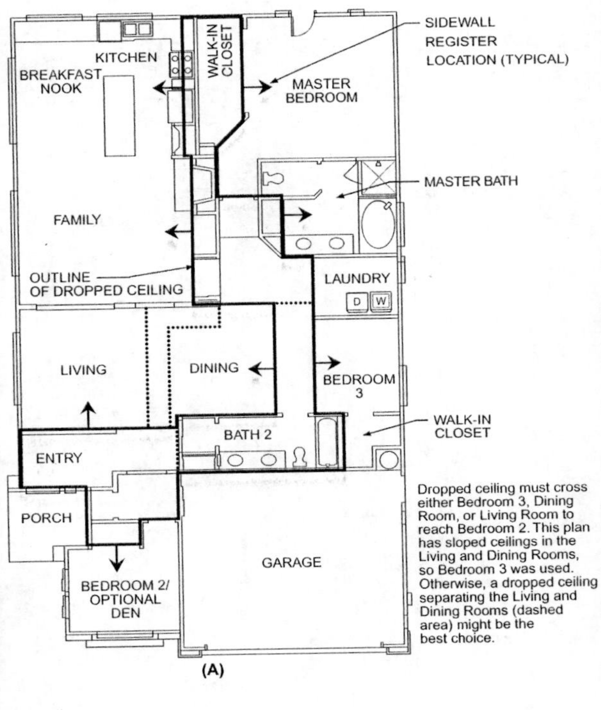

(EPA 2000)

Figure 19.16 Sample Floor Plans for One-Story House with (A) Dropped Ceilings, (B) Ducts in Conditioned Spaces, and (C) Right-Sized Air Distribution in Conditioned Spaces [2020S, Ch 10, Fig 3]

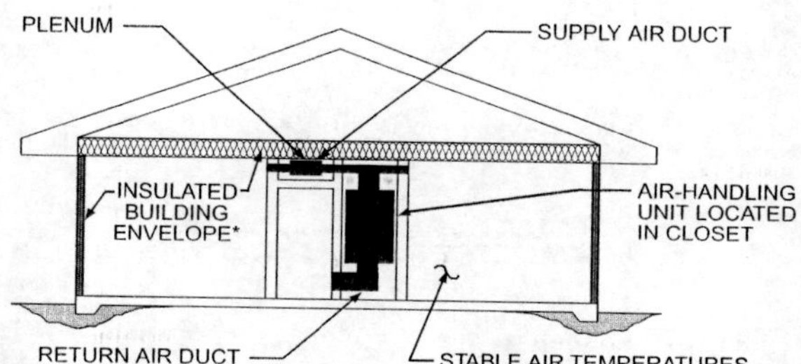

*To minimize duct leakage to attic, continuous drywall or other air barrier is needed at ceiling below insulation in all plenum areas.

(B)

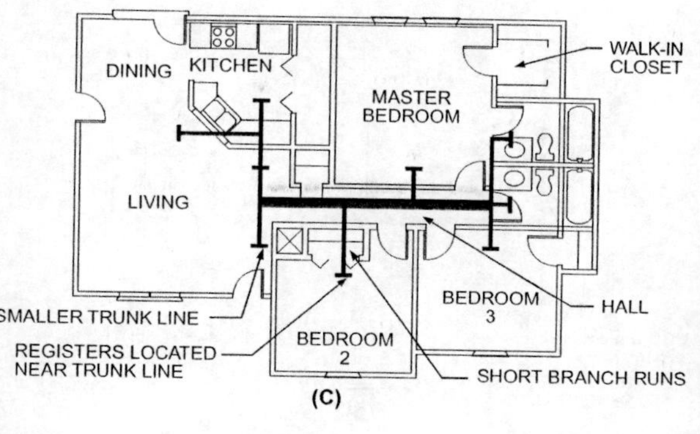

(C)

(EPA 2000)

Figure 19.16 Sample Floor Plans for One-Story House with (A) Dropped Ceilings, (B) Ducts in Conditioned Spaces, and (C) Right-Sized Air Distribution in Conditioned Spaces
[2020S, Ch 10, Fig 3] ***(Continued)***

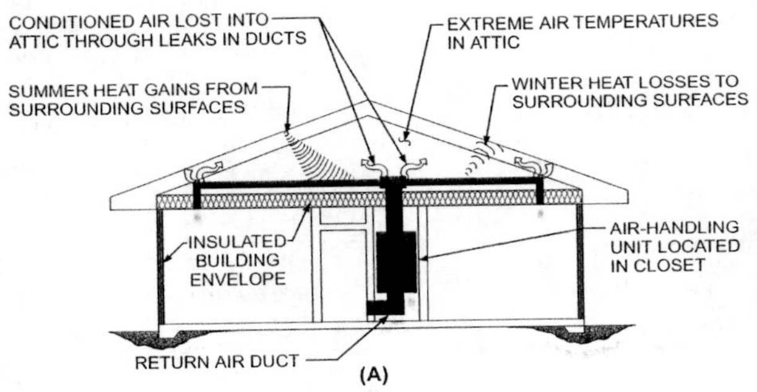

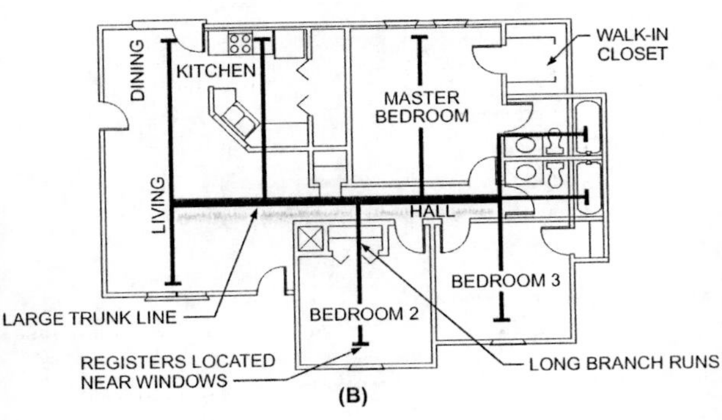

(EPA 2000)

Figure 19.17 (A) Ducts in Unconditioned Spaces and (B) Standard Air Distribution System in Unconditioned Spaces [2020S, Ch 10, Fig 4]

Unitary Air Conditioners and Heat Pumps

Unitary air conditioners are factory-made assemblies that normally include an evaporator or cooling coil and a compressor/ condenser combination, and possibly provide heating as well. An **air-source unitary heat pump** normally includes an indoor conditioning coil, compressor(s), and an outdoor coil. It must provide heating and possibly cooling as well. A **water-source heat pump** rejects or extracts heat to and from a water loop instead of from ambient air. A unitary air conditioner or heat pump with more than one factory-made assembly (e.g., indoor and outdoor units) is commonly called a **split system**.

Unitary equipment is divided into three general categories: residential, light commercial, and commercial. Residential equipment is single-phase unitary equipment with a cooling capacity of 65,000 Btu/h or less and is designed specifically for residential application. Light commercial equipment is generally three-phase, with cooling capacity up to 135,000 Btu/h, and is designed for small businesses and commercial properties. Commercial unitary equipment has cooling capacity higher than 135,000 Btu/h and is designed for large commercial buildings.

Unitary equipment is available in many configurations, such as

- **Single-zone, constant-volume**, which consists of one controlled space with one thermostat that controls to maintain a set point. This equipment may be single stage, multistage, or variable capacity.
- **Multizone, constant-volume**, which has several controlled spaces served by one unit that supplies air of different temperatures to different zones as demanded (Figure 19.18).
- **Single-package, variable-volume,** which consists of several controlled spaces served by one unit. Supply air from the unit is at a constant temperature, with air volume to each space varied to satisfy space demands (Figure 19.19).
- **Multisplit,** which consists of several controlled spaces, each served by a separate indoor unit. All indoor units are connected to an outdoor condensing unit (Figure 19.20). When each indoor unit varies its refrigerant flow in response to heating or cooling load demand, the system is called **variable refrigerant flow (VRF)**.

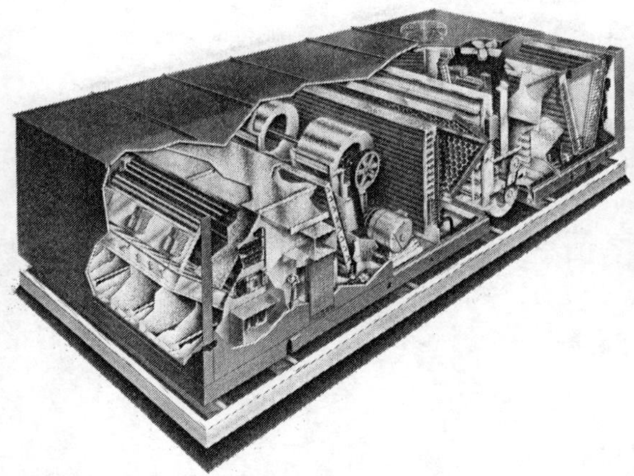

Figure 19.18 Typical Rooftop Air-Cooled Single-Package Air Conditioner
[2020S, Ch 48, Fig 1]

In general, roof-mounted single-package unitary equipment is limited to five or six stories because duct space and available blower power become excessive in taller buildings. Split units are limited by the maximum distance allowed between the indoor and outdoor sections because of losses in refrigerant piping, compressor capability, and refrigerant oil management. Indoor, single-zone equipment is generally less expensive to maintain and service than multizone or multisplit units.

Manufacturers' literature has detailed information about geometry, performance, electrical characteristics, application, and operating limits. The system designer selects suitable equipment with the capacity for the application.

Unitary equipment is designed to keep installation costs low. Adequate planning is important for installing large, roof-mounted equipment because special rigging equipment is frequently required. ACCA Standard 5 describes minimum criteria for the proper installation of HVAC systems in residential and commercial installations.

An advantage of packaged unitary equipment is that proper installation minimizes the risk of field contamination of the circuit. Care must be taken to properly install split-system interconnecting tubing (e.g., proper cleanliness, brazing, and evacuation to remove moisture and other noncondensables). Split systems should be charged according to the manufacturer's instructions. Filter-driers are necessary; if they are not installed at the factory, they should be field installed. When installing split, multisplit, and VRF systems, lines must be properly routed and sized to ensure proper oil return to the compressor.

Unitary equipment must be located to avoid noise and vibration problems. Single-package equipment of over 20 ton capacity should be mounted on concrete pads if vibration control is a concern. Large-capacity equipment should be roof mounted only after the roof's structural adequacy has been evaluated. If they are located over occupied space, roof-mounted units with return fans that use ceiling space for the return plenum should have a lined return plenum according to the manufacturer's recommendations. Use duct silencers where low sound levels are desired. Weight and sound data are available from many manufacturers. Additional installation guidelines include the following:

- In general, install products containing compressors on solid, level surfaces.
- Avoid mounting products containing compressors (such as remote units) on or touching the foundation of a house or building, or outside bedroom windows. A separate pad that does not touch the foundation is recommended to reduce any noise and vibration transmission through the slab.
- Do not box in outdoor air-cooled units with fences, walls, overhangs, or bushes. Doing so reduces the air-moving capability of the unit, reducing efficiency. Manufacturers include minimum clearances in literature.

Figure 19.19 Single-Package Air Equipment with Variable Air Volume
[2020S, Ch 48, Fig 2]

- For a split-system remote unit, choose an installation site that is close to the indoor part of the system to minimize pressure drop in the connecting refrigerant tubing. Comply with manufacturers' refrigerant line length limits and required accessories listed in their literature.
- For VRF units, locate the refrigerant pipes' headers so that the length of refrigerant pipes is minimized.
- Contact the manufacturer or consult installation instructions for further information on installation procedures.

Unitary equipment should be listed or certified by nationally recognized testing laboratories to ensure safe operation and compliance with government and utility regulations. Equipment should also be installed to comply with agency standards' rating and application requirements to ensure that it performs according to industry criteria. Larger and more specialized equipment often does not carry agency labeling. However, power and control wiring practices should comply with the *National Electrical Code*® (NFPA Standard 70). Consult local codes before the installation is designed, and consult local inspectors before installation.

Unitary air conditioners have factory-matched refrigerant circuit components that are applied in the field to fulfill the user's requirements. The manufacturer often incorporates a heating function compatible with the cooling system and a control system that requires minimal field wiring.

Products are available to meet the objectives of nearly any system. Many different heating sections (gas- or oil-fired, electric, or condenser reheat), air filters, and heat pumps, which are a specialized form of unitary product, are available. Such matched equipment, selected with compatible accessory items, requires little field design or field installation work.

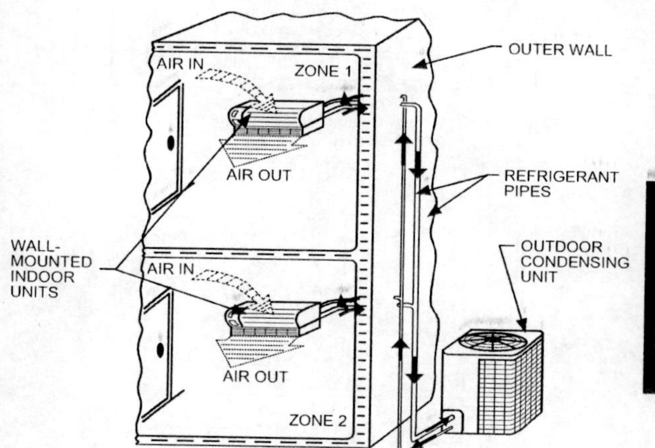

Figure 19.20 Example of Two-Zone Ductless Multisplit System in Typical Residential Installation [2020S, Ch 48, Fig 3]

HVAC Systems and Equipment

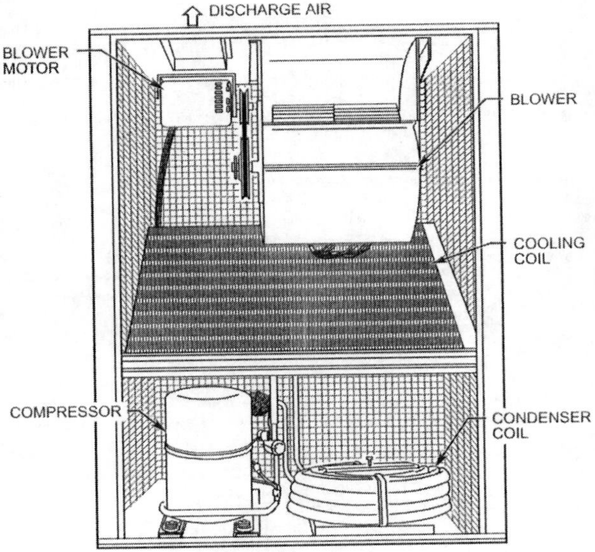

DISCHARGE AIR
BLOWER MOTOR
BLOWER
COOLING COIL
COMPRESSOR
CONDENSER COIL

Figure 19.21 Water-Cooled Single-Package Air Conditioner
[2020S, Ch 48, Fig 4]

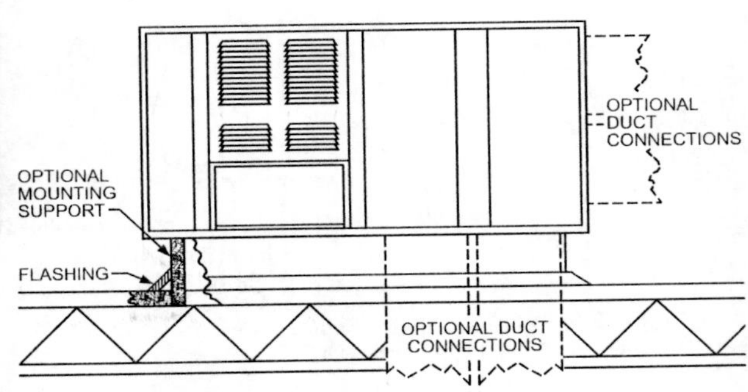

Figure 19.22 Rooftop Installation of Air-Cooled Single-Package Unit
[2020S, Ch 48, Fig 5]

SUPPLY DUCT
PACKAGE ROOFTOP UNIT
RETURN DUCT

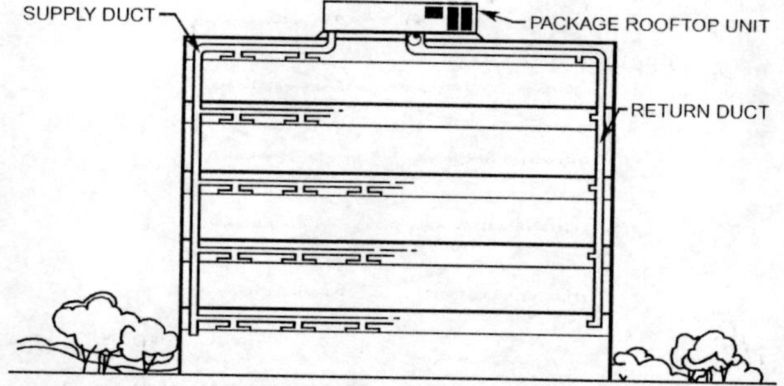

Figure 19.23 Multistory Rooftop Installation of Single-Package Unit [2020S, Ch 48, Fig 6]

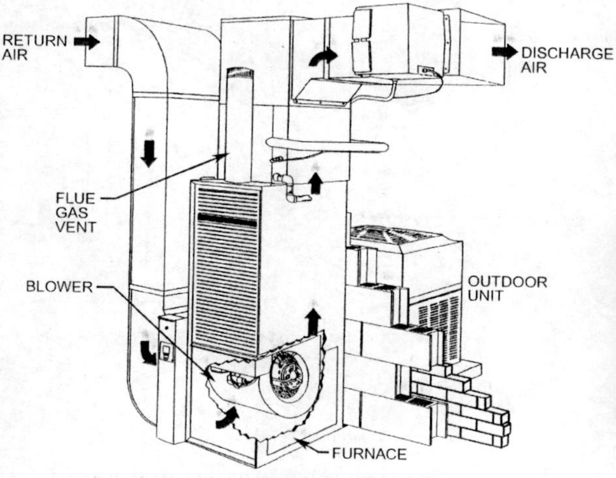

RETURN AIR
DISCHARGE AIR
FLUE GAS VENT
BLOWER
OUTDOOR UNIT
FURNACE

Figure 19.24 Residential Installation of Split-System Air-Cooled Condensing Unit with Coil and Upflow Furnace [2020S, Ch 48, Fig 8]

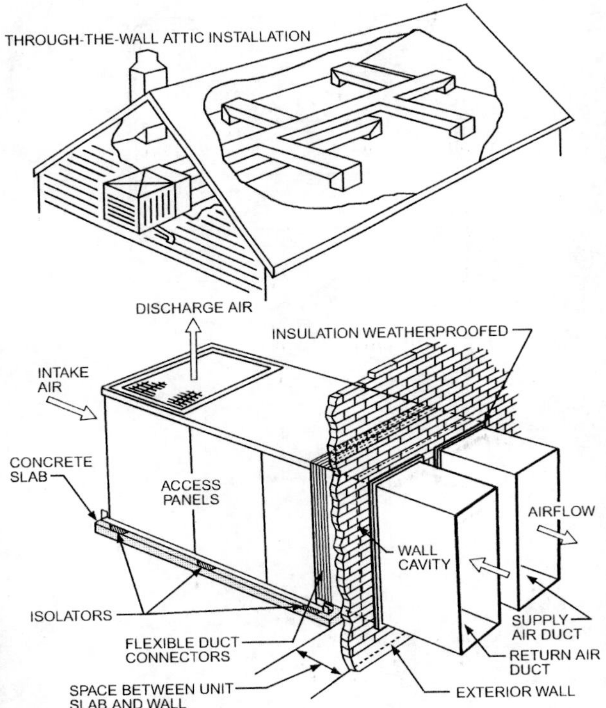

Figure 19.25 Through-the-Wall Installation of Air-Cooled Single-Package Unit
[2020S, Ch 48, Fig 7]

HVAC Systems and Equipment

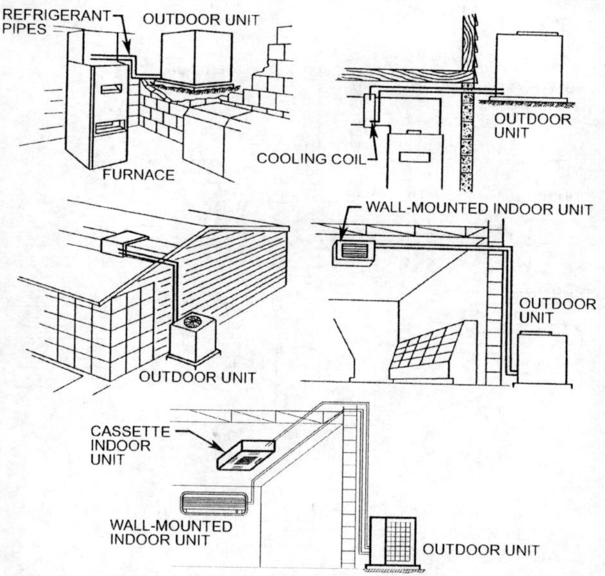

REFRIGERANT PIPES
OUTDOOR UNIT
FURNACE
OUTDOOR UNIT
COOLING COIL
OUTDOOR UNIT
WALL-MOUNTED INDOOR UNIT
OUTDOOR UNIT
CASSETTE INDOOR UNIT
WALL-MOUNTED INDOOR UNIT
OUTDOOR UNIT

Figure 19.26 Outdoor Installations of Split-System Air-Cooled Condensing Units with Coil and Upflow Furnace or with Indoor Blower-Coils [2020S, Ch 48, Fig 9]

SUPPLY DUCT
OUTDOOR UNIT
REFRIGERANT PIPES

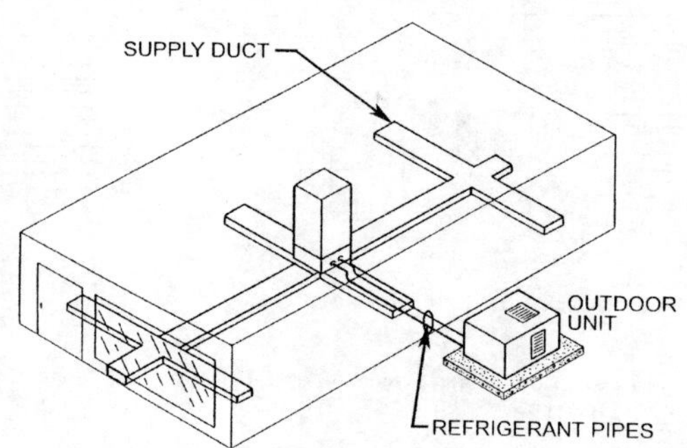

Figure 19.27 Outdoor Installation of Split-System Air-Cooled Condensing Unit with Indoor Coil and Downflow Furnace [2020S, Ch 48, Fig 10]

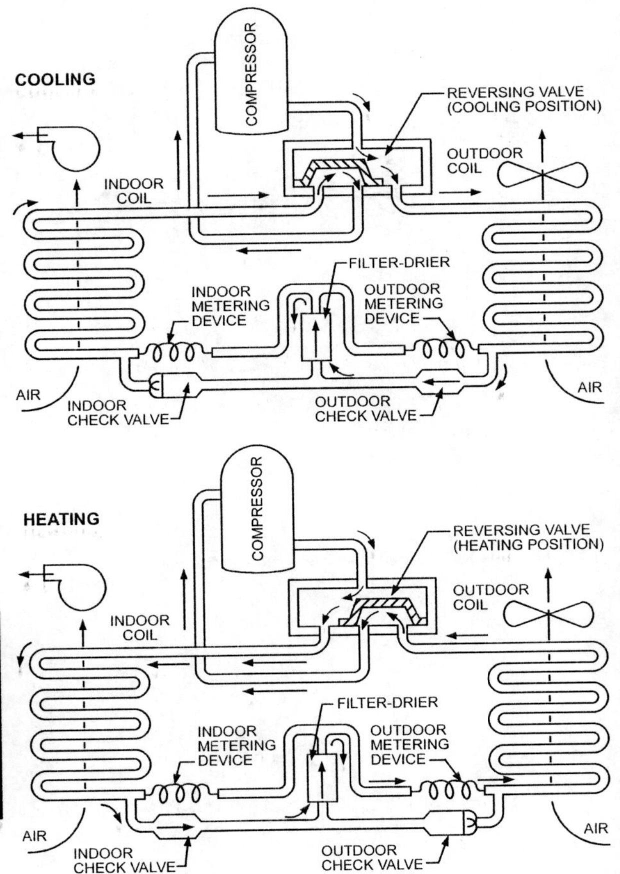

Figure 19.28 Schematic Typical of Air-to-Air Heat Pump System
[2020S, Ch 48, Fig 12]

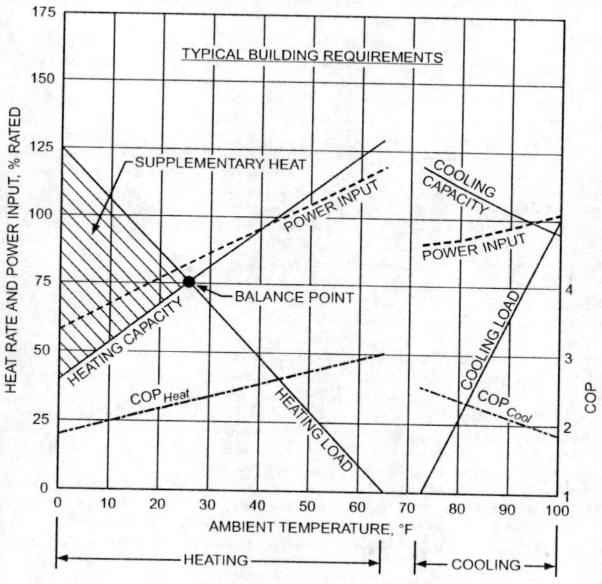

Figure 19.29 Operating Characteristics of Single-Stage Unmodulated Heat Pump [2020S, Ch 48, Fig 13]

HVAC Systems and Equipment

Water-Source Heat Pumps

A water-source heat pump (WSHP) is a single-package reverse-cycle heat pump that uses water as the heat source for heating and as the heat sink for cooling. The water supply may be a recirculating closed loop, a well, a lake, or a stream. Water for closed-loop heat pumps is usually circulated at 2 to 3 gpm per ton of cooling capacity.

WSHPs are used in a variety of systems, such as the following:

A **water-loop heat pump (WLHP)** uses a circulating water loop as the heat source and heat sink. When loop water temperature exceeds a certain level during cooling, a cooling tower dissipates heat from the water loop into the atmosphere. When loop water temperature drops below a prescribed level during heating, heat is added to the circulating loop water, usually with a boiler. In multiple-unit installations, some heat pumps may operate in cooling mode while others operate in heating, and controls are needed to keep loop water temperature within the prescribed limits. Chapter 9 of the 2020 *ASHRAE Handbook—HVAC Systems and Equipment* has more information on water-loop heat pumps.

A **groundwater heat pump (GWHP)** passes groundwater from a nearby well through the heat pump's water-to-refrigerant heat exchanger, where it is warmed or cooled, depending on the operating mode. It is then discharged to a drain, stream, or lake, or is returned to the ground through a reinjection well.

Many state and local jurisdictions have ordinances about use and discharge of groundwater. Because aquifers, the water table, and groundwater availability vary from region to region, these regulations cover a wide spectrum.

A **surface-water heat pump (SWHP)** uses water from a nearby lake, stream, or canal. After passing through the heat pump heat exchanger, it is returned to the source or a drain several degrees warmer or cooler, depending on the operating mode of the heat pump. **Closed-loop** surface water heat pumps use a closed water or brine loop that includes pipes or tubing submerged in the surface water (river, lake, or large pond) that serves as the heat exchanger. The adequacy of the total thermal capacity of the body of water must be considered.

A **ground-coupled heat pump (GCHP), ground-source heat pump (GSHP),** or **geothermal heat pump (GHP)** system uses the earth as a heat source and sink. Usually, plastic

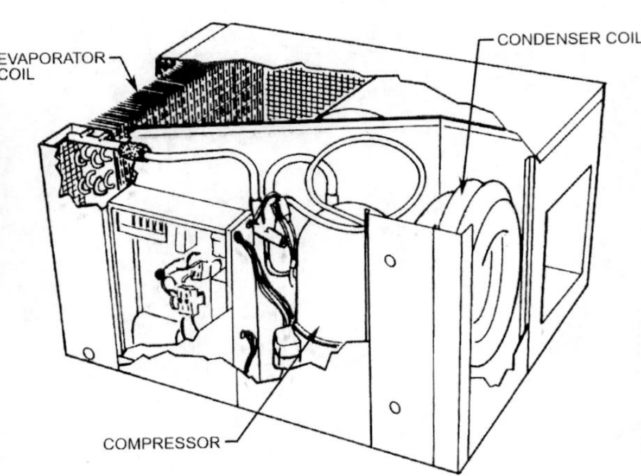

Figure 19.30 Typical Horizontal Water-Source Heat Pump
[2020S, Ch 48, Fig 15]

piping is installed in either a shallow horizontal or deep vertical array to form the heat exchanger. The massive thermal capacity of the earth provides a temperature-stabilizing effect on the circulating loop water or brine. Installing this type of system requires detailed knowledge of the climate; site; soil temperature, moisture content, and thermal characteristics; and performance, design, and installation of water-to-earth heat exchangers. Additional information on GCHP systems is presented in Chapter 35 of the 2019 *ASHRAE Handbook—HVAC Applications*.

Entering Water Temperatures. These various water sources provide a wide range of entering water temperatures to WSHPs. Entering water temperatures vary not only by water source, but also by climate and time of year. Because of the wide range of entering water or brine temperatures encountered, it is not feasible to design a universal packaged product that can handle the full range of possibilities effectively. Therefore, WSHPs are rated for performance at a number of standard rating conditions.

Compressors. WSHPs usually have single-speed compressors, although some high-efficiency models use multispeed compressors. Higher-capacity equipment may use multiple compressors. Compressors may be reciprocating, rotary, or scroll. Single-phase units are available at voltages of 115, 208, 230, and 265. All larger equipment is for three-phase power supplies with voltages of 208, 230, 460, or 575. Compressors usually have electromechanical protective devices.

Indoor Air System. Console WSHP models are designed for free delivery of conditioned air. Other models have ducting capability. Smaller WSHPs have multispeed, direct-drive centrifugal blower wheel fan systems. Large-capacity equipment has belt-drive systems. All units have provisions for fiberglass, metal, or plastic foam air filters.

Indoor Air Heat Exchanger. The indoor air heat exchanger of WSHP units is usually a conventional plate-fin coil of copper tubes and aluminum fins. Microchannel evaporators are also used in some products. The indoor air heat exchanger must be circuited so that it can function effectively as an evaporator with refrigerant flow in one direction and as a condenser when refrigerant flow is reversed.

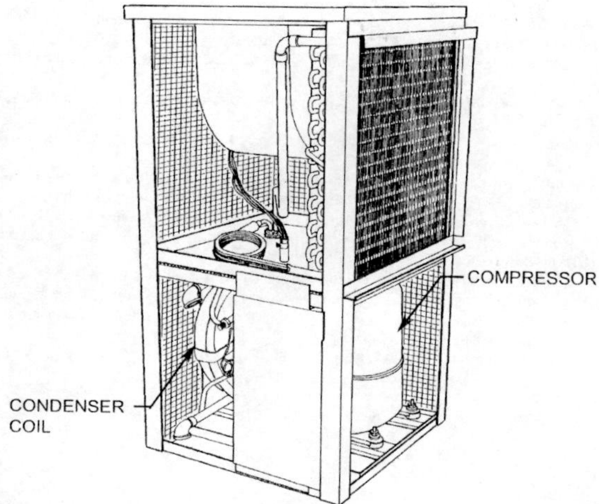

Figure 19.31 Typical Vertical Water-Source Heat Pump [2020S, Ch 48, Fig 16]

Table 19.4 Space Requirements for Typical Packaged Water-Source Heat Pumps [2020S, Ch 48, Tbl 4]

Water-to-Air Heat Pump	Length × Width × Height, ft	Weight, lb
1.5 ton vertical unit	2.0 × 2.0 × 3.0	180
3 ton vertical unit	2.5 × 2.5 × 4.0	250
3 ton horizontal unit	3.5 × 2.0 × 2.0	250
5 ton vertical unit	3.0 × 2.5 × 4.0	330
11 ton vertical unit	3.5 × 3.0 × 6.0	720
26 ton vertical unit	3.5 × 5.0 × 6.0	1550

Note: See manufacturers' specification sheets for actual values.

Refrigerant-to-Water Heat Exchanger. The heat exchanger, which couples the heat pump to source/sink water, is tube-in-tube, tube-in-shell, or brazed-plate. It must function in either condensing or evaporating mode, so special attention is given to refrigerant-side circuitry. Heat exchanger construction is usually of copper and steel, and the source/sink water is exposed only to the copper portions. Cupronickel options to replace the copper are usually available for use with brackish or corrosive water. Brazed-plate heat exchangers are usually constructed of stainless steel, which reduces the need for special materials.

Refrigerant Expansion Devices. These WSHPs operate over a narrow range of entering water temperatures and typically use simple capillaries as expansion devices. However, units may also use thermostatic expansion valves for improved performance over a broader range of inlet fluid temperatures.

Refrigerant-Reversing Valve. The refrigerant-reversing valves in WSHPs are identical to those used in air-source heat pumps.

Condensate Disposal. Condensate, which forms on the indoor coil when cooling, is collected and conveyed to a drain system.

Controls. Console WSHP units have built-in operating mode selector and thermostatic controls. Ducted units use low-voltage remote heat/cool thermostats.

Size. Typical space requirements and weights of WSHPs are presented in Table 19.4.

Special Features. Some WSHPs include the following:

- *Desuperheater.* Uses discharge gas in a special water/refrigerant heat exchanger to heat water for a building.
- *Capacity modulation.* May use multiple compressors, multispeed compressors, or hot-gas bypass.
- *Variable air volume (VAV).* Reduces fan energy usage and requires some form of capacity modulation.
- *Automatic water valve.* Closes off water flow through the unit when the compressor is off and allows variable water volume in the loop, which reduces pumping energy.
- *Outdoor air economizer.* Cools directly with outdoor air to reduce or eliminate the need for mechanical refrigeration during mild or cold weather when outdoor humidity levels and air quality are appropriate.
- *Water-side economizer.* Cools with loop water to reduce or eliminate the need for mechanical refrigeration during cold weather; requires a hydronic coil in the indoor air circuit that is valved into the circulating loop when loop temperatures are relatively low and cooling is required.
- *Electric heaters.* Used in WLHP systems that do not have a boiler as a source for loop heating.

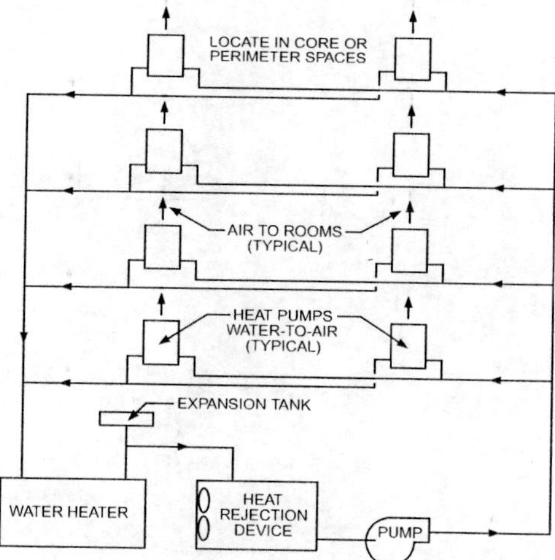

A. WATER-LOOP HEAT PUMP SYSTEM

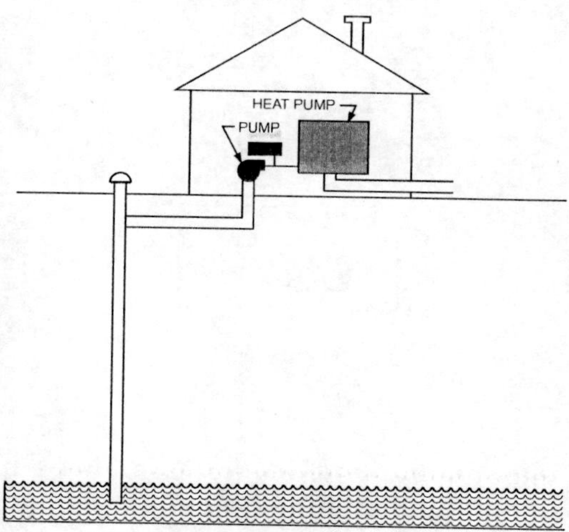

B. GROUNDWATER HEAT PUMP SYSTEM

Figure 19.32 Water-Source Heat Pump Systems [2020S, Ch 48, Fig 17]

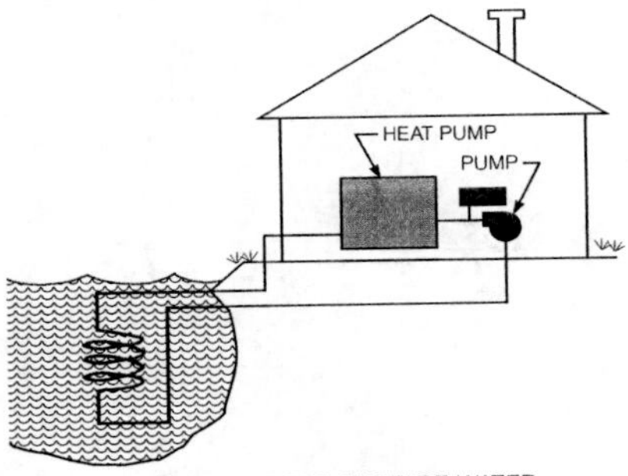

C. CLOSED-LOOP SURFACE-WATER HEAT PUMP SYSTEM

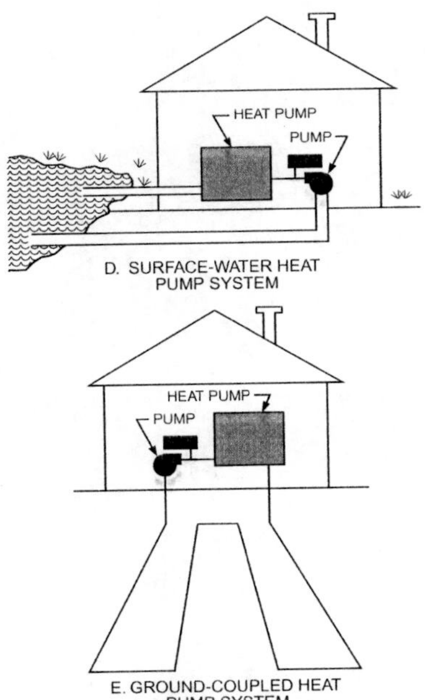

D. SURFACE-WATER HEAT PUMP SYSTEM

E. GROUND-COUPLED HEAT PUMP SYSTEM

Figure 19.32 Water-Source Heat Pump Systems [2020S, Ch 48, Fig 17] ***(Continued)***

Variable-Refrigerant-Flow Heat Pumps

A variable-refrigerant-flow (VRF) system typically consists of a condensing section housing compressor(s) and condenser heat exchanger interconnected by a single set of refrigerant piping to multiple indoor direct-expansion (DX) evaporator fan-coil units. Thirty or more DX fan-coil units can be connected to a single condensing section, depending on system design, and with capacity ranging from 0.5 to 8 tons.

The DX fan-coils are constant air volume, but use variable refrigerant flow through an electronic expansion valve. The electronic expansion valve reacts to several temperature-sensing devices such as return air, inlet and outlet refrigerant temperatures, or suction pressure. The electronic expansion valve modulates to maintain the desired set point.

Application. VRF systems are most commonly air-to-air, but are also available in a water-source (water-to-refrigerant) configuration. They can be configured for simultaneous heating and cooling operation (some indoor fan-coil units operating in heating and some in cooling, depending on requirements of each building zone).

Indoor units are typically direct-expansion evaporators using individual electronic expansion devices and dedicated microprocessor controls for individual control. Each indoor unit can be controlled by an individual thermostat. The outdoor unit may connect several indoor evaporator units with capacities 130% or more than the outdoor condensing unit capacity.

Categories. VRF equipment is divided into three general categories: residential, light commercial, and applied. Residential equipment is single-phase unitary equipment with a cooling capacity of 65,000 Btu/h or less. Light commercial equipment is generally three-phase, with cooling capacity greater than 65,000 Btu/h, and is designed for small businesses and commercial properties. Applied equipment has cooling capacity higher than 135,000 Btu/h and is designed for large commercial buildings.

Refrigerant Circuit and Components. VRF heat pump systems use a two-pipe (liquid and suction gas) system; simultaneous heat and cool systems use the same system, as well as a gas flow device that determines the proper routing of refrigerant gas to a particular indoor unit.

VRF systems use a sophisticated refrigerant circuit that monitors mass flow, oil flow, and balance to ensure optimum performance. This is accomplished in unison with variable-speed compressors and condenser fan motors. Both of these components adjust their frequency in reaction to changing mass flow conditions and refrigerant operating pressures and temperatures. A dedicated microprocessor continuously monitors and controls these key components to ensure proper refrigerant is delivered to each indoor unit in cooling or heating.

Heating and Defrost Operation. In heating mode, VRF systems typically must defrost like any mechanical heat pump, using reverse-cycle valves to temporarily operate the outdoor coil in cooling mode. Oil return and balance with the refrigerant circuit is managed by the microprocessor to ensure that any oil entrained in the low side of the system is brought back to the high side by increasing the refrigerant velocity using a high-frequency operation performed automatically based on hours of operation.

More information on VRF heat pumps can be found in Chapter 18 of the 2020 *ASHRAE Handbook—HVAC Systems and Equipment*, and information on performance-rating these systems can be found in AHRI Standard 1230.

Room Air Conditioners and Packaged Terminal Air Conditioners

Room Air Conditioners

Room air conditioners are encased assemblies designed primarily for mounting in a window or through a wall. They are designed to deliver cool or warm conditioned air to the room, either without ducts or with very short ducts (up to a maximum of about 48 in.). Each unit includes a prime source of refrigeration and dehumidification and a means for circulating and filtering air; it may also include a means for ventilating and/or exhausting and heating.

The basic function of a room air conditioner is to provide comfort by cooling, dehumidifying, filtering or cleaning, and circulating the room air. It may also provide ventilation by introducing outdoor air into the room and/or exhausting room air to the outdoors. Room temperature may be controlled by an integral thermostat. The conditioner may provide heating by heat pump operation, electric resistance elements, or a combination of the two.

Figure 19.33 shows a typical room air conditioner in cooling mode. Warm room air passes over the cooling coil and transfers sensible and latent heat. The conditioned air is then recirculated in the room by a fan or blower.

Heat from the warm room air vaporizes the cold (low-pressure) liquid refrigerant flowing through the evaporator. The vapor then carries the heat to the compressor, which compresses the vapor and increases its temperature above that of the outdoor air. In the condenser, the hot (high-pressure) refrigerant vapor liquefies, transferring the heat from the room air to outdoor air. Next, the high-pressure liquid refrigerant passes through a restrictor, which reduces its pressure and temperature. The cold (low-pressure) liquid refrigerant then enters the evaporator to repeat the refrigeration cycle.

Room air conditioners have line cords, which may be plugged into standard or special electric circuits. Most units in the United States are designed to operate at 115, 208, or 230 V; single-phase; 60 Hz power. Some units are rated at 265 V or 277 V, for which the chassis or chassis assembly must provide permanent electrical connection. The maximum amperage of 115 V units is generally 12 A, which is the maximum current permitted by NFPA Standard 70 [the *National Electrical Code*® (NEC)] for a single-outlet, 15 A circuit. Models designed for

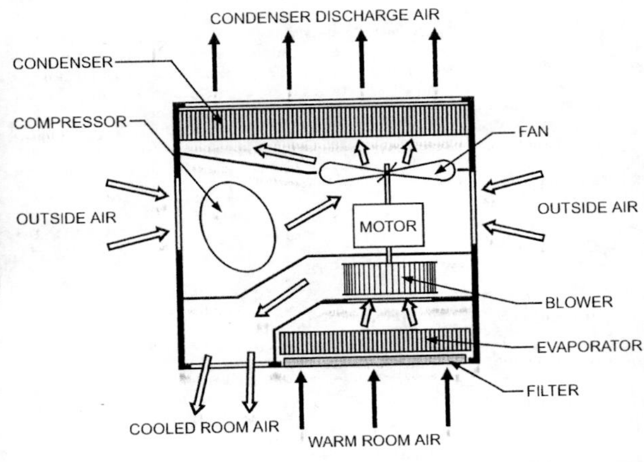

Figure 19.33 Schematic View of Typical Room Air Conditioner
[2020S, Ch 49, Fig 1]

HVAC Systems and Equipment

countries other than the United States are generally for 50 or 60 Hz systems, with typical design voltage ranges of 100 to 120 and 200 to 240 V, single-phase.

Popular 115 V models have capacities in the range of 5000 to 8000 Btu/h, and are typically used in single-room applications. Larger-capacity 115 V units are in the 12,000 to 15,000 Btu/h range. Capacities for 230, 208, or 230/208 V units range from 8000 to 36,000 Btu/h. These higher-voltage units are typically used in multiple-room installations.

Heat pump models are also available, usually for 208 or 230 V applications. These units are generally designed for reversed-refrigerant-cycle operation as the normal means of supplying heat, but may incorporate electrical-resistance heat either to supplement heat pump capacity or to provide the total heating capacity when outdoor temperatures drop below a set value.

Another type of heating model incorporates electrical heating elements in regular cooling units so that heating is provided entirely by electrical resistance heat.

Installation procedures vary because units can be mounted in various ways. It is important to select the mounting for each installation that best satisfies the user and complies with applicable building codes. Common mounting methods include the following:

- **Indoor flush mounting.** Interior face of conditioner is approximately flush with inside wall.
- **Balance mounting.** Unit is approximately half inside and half outside window.
- **Outdoor flush mounting.** Outer face of unit is flush with or slightly beyond outside wall.
- **Special mounting.** Examples include casement windows, horizontal sliding windows, and office windows with swinging units (or swinging windows) to allow window washing, and transoms over doorways.
- **Through-the-wall mounts or sleeves.** This mounting is used for installing window-type chassis, complete units, or consoles in walls of apartment buildings, hotels, motels, and residences. Although very similar to window-mounted units, through-the-wall models do not have side louvers for condenser air; air comes from the outdoor end of the unit.

Room air conditioners have become more compact to minimize both loss of window light and projection inside and outside the structure. Several types of expandable mounts are now available for fast, dependable installation in single- and double-hung windows, as well as in horizontal sliding windows. Window air conditioners should fit in the opening without too much space around the sides; most units come with accordion-style flaps attached to the sides, used to fill the open space around the unit. Installation kits include all parts needed for structural mounting, such as gaskets, panels, and seals for weathertight assembly. Sealing the space around the unit (e.g., with caulk or foam seals) is important to prevent air from escaping and limit seeping of hot outdoor air into the conditioned space, and to achieve energy savings during operation.

Adequate wiring and proper breakers or fuses must be provided for the service outlet. Necessary information is usually given on instruction sheets or stamped on the air conditioner near the service cord or on the serial plate. It is important to follow the manufacturer's recommendation for size and type of breaker or fuse. All units are equipped by the manufacturer with grounding plug caps on the service cord. Receptacles with grounding contacts correctly designed to fit these plug caps should be used when units are installed.

Units rated 265 or 277 V must provide for permanent electrical connection with armored cable or conduit to the chassis or chassis assembly. Manufacturers usually provide an adequate cord and plug cap in the chassis assembly to facilitate installation and service.

One type of room air conditioner is the integral chassis design, with the outer cabinet fastened permanently to the chassis. Most electrical components can be serviced by partially dismantling the control area without removing the unit from the installation. Another type is the **slide-out chassis** design, which allows the outer cabinet to remain in place while the chassis is removed for service.

Effective condensate management should be considered during the installation of the air conditioner. Many window air conditioners have connection points for condensate drains. Follow plumbing and building code requirements for handling discharge of the condensate produced when the air conditioner is operating.

Packaged Terminal Air Conditioners

A packaged terminal air conditioner (PTAC) includes a wall sleeve and a separate unencased combination of heating and cooling assemblies intended for mounting through the wall. A PTAC includes refrigeration components, separable outdoor louvers, forced ventilation, and heating by hot water, steam, or electric resistance. PTAC units with indirect-fired gas heaters are also available from some manufacturers. A packaged terminal heat pump (PTHP) is a heat pump version of a PTAC that provides heat with a reverse-cycle operating mode. A PTHP should provide a supplementary heat source, which can be hot water, steam, electric resistance, or another source.

PTACs are designed primarily for commercial installations to provide the total heating and cooling functions for a room or zone and are specifically for through-the-wall installation. The units are mostly used in relatively small zones on the perimeter of buildings such as hotels and motels, apartments, hospitals, nursing homes, and office buildings. In larger buildings, they may be combined with nearly any system selected for environmental control of the building core.

PTACs and PTHPs are similar in design and construction. The most apparent difference is the addition of a refrigerant-reversing valve in the PTHP. Optional components that control the heating functions of the heat pump include an outdoor thermostat to signal the need for changes in heating operating modes, and, in more complex designs, frost sensors, defrost termination devices, and base pan heaters.

PTACs/PTHPs are available in a wide range of rated cooling capacities, typically 6000 to 18,000 Btu/h, with comparable levels of heating output. Units are available as sectional types or integrated types. A sectional-type unit (Figure 19.34) has a separate cooling chassis; an integrated-type unit (Figure 19.35) has an electric or a gas heating option added to the chassis. Hot-water or steam heating options are usually part of the cabinet or wall box. Both types include the following:

- Heating elements available in hot water, steam, electric, or gas heat
- Integral or remote temperature and operating controls
- Wall sleeve or box
- Removable (or separable) outdoor louvers
- Room cabinet
- Means for controlled forced ventilation
- Means for filtering air delivered to the room

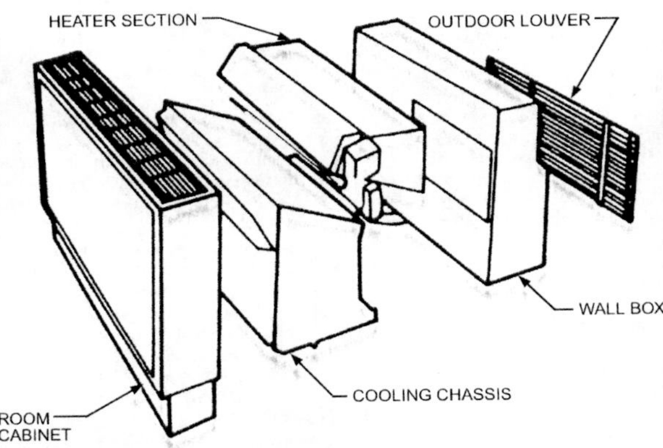

Figure 19.34 Sectional Packaged Terminal Air Conditioner
[2020S, Ch 49, Fig 2]

PTAC assemblies are intended for use in free conditioned-air distribution, but a particular application may require minimal ductwork with a total external static resistance up to 0.1 in. of water.

Packaged terminal air conditioners and packaged terminal heat pumps allow the HVAC designer to integrate the exposed outdoor louver or grille with the building design. Various grilles are available to blend with or accent most construction materials. Because the product becomes part of the building's facade, the architect must consider the product during the conception of the building. Wall sleeve installation is usually done by ironworkers, masons, or carpenters. All-electric units dominate the market.

All the energy of all-electric versions is dispersed through the building via electrical wiring, so the electric designer and electrical contractor play a major role. Final installation is reduced to sliding in the chassis and plugging the unit into an adjacent receptacle. For these all-electric units, the traditional HVAC contractor's work involving ducting, piping, and refrigeration systems is bypassed. This results in a low-cost installation and allows installation of the PTAC/PTHP chassis to be deferred until just before occupancy.

When comparing a gas-fired PTAC to a PTAC with electric resistance heat or a PTHP, evaluate both operating and installation costs. Generally, a gas-fired PTAC is more expensive to install but less expensive to operate in heating mode. A life-cycle cost comparison is recommended (see Chapter 38 of the 2019 *ASHRAE Handbook—HVAC Applications*).

One main advantage of the PTAC/PTHP concept is that it provides excellent zoning capability. Units can be shut down or operated in a holding condition during unoccupied periods. Present equipment efficiency-rating criteria are based on full-load operation, so an efficiency comparison to other approaches may suffer.

The designer must also consider that total capacity is the sum of the peak loads of each zone rather than the peak load of the building. Therefore, total cooling capacity of the zonal system will exceed that of a central system.

Because PTAC units are located in the conditioned space, both appearance and sound level of the equipment are important considerations. Sound attenuation in ducting is not available with the free-discharge PTAC units.

The designer must also consider the added infiltration and thermal leakage load resulting from perimeter wall penetrations. These losses are accounted for during the *on* cycle in equipment cooling ratings and PTHP heating ratings, but during the *off* cycle or with other forms of heating, they could be significant.

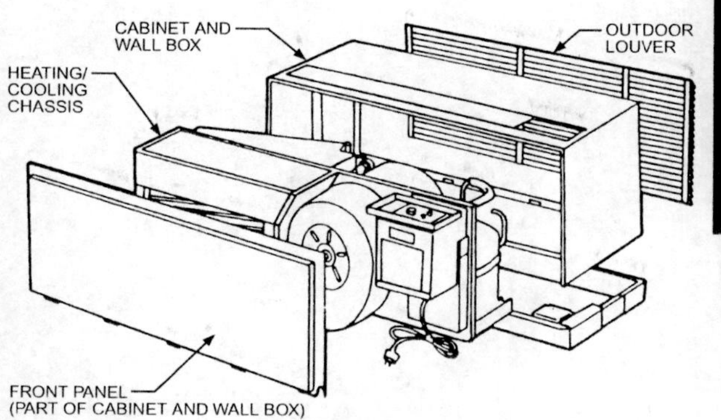

Figure 19.35 Integrated Packaged Terminal Air Conditioner
[2020S, Ch 49, Fig 3]

Most packaged terminal equipment is designed to fit into a wall aperture approximately 42 in. wide and 16 in. high. Although unitary products can increase in size with increasing cooling capacity, PTAC/PTHP units, regardless of cooling capacity, are usually constrained to a few cabinet sizes. The exterior of the equipment must be essentially flush with the exterior wall to meet most building codes. In addition, cabinet structural requirements and the slide-in chassis reduce the available area for outdoor air inlet and relief to less than a total of 3.5 ft^2. Manufacturers' specification sheets should be consulted for more accurate and detailed information.

Basic PTHP units can operate in heat pump mode until outdoor temperature is just above the point at which the outdoor heat exchanger would frost. At that point, heat pump mode is locked out, and other forms of heating are required. Some units include two-stage indoor thermostats and automatically switch from heat pump mode to an alternative heat source if space temperature drops too far below the first-stage set point. Some PTHPs use control schemes that extend heat pump operation to lower temperatures. One approach allows heat pump operation down to outdoor temperatures just above freezing. If the outdoor coil frosts, it is defrosted by shutting down the compressor and allowing the outdoor fan to continue circulating outdoor air over the coil. Another approach allows heat pump operation to even lower outdoor temperatures by using a reverse-cycle defrost sequence. In those cases, the heat pump mode is usually locked out for outdoor temperatures below 10°F.

EVAPORATIVE COOLING

Direct Evaporative Air Coolers

Air is drawn through porous wetted pads or a spray, or rigid media; and its sensible heat energy evaporates some water. The heat and mass transfer between the air and water lowers the air dry-bulb temperature and increases the humidity at a constant wet-bulb temperature. The dry-bulb temperature of the nearly saturated air approaches the ambient air's wet-bulb temperature. The process is adiabatic, so no sensible cooling occurs.

The extent to which the leaving air temperature from a direct evaporative cooler approaches the thermodynamic wet-bulb temperature of the entering air or the extent to which complete saturation is approached is expressed as the **direct saturation efficiency**, defined as

$$\varepsilon_e = 100\frac{t_1 - t_2}{t_1 - t_s'} \tag{19.7}$$

where

ε_e	=	direct evaporative cooling or saturation efficiency, %
t_1	=	dry-bulb temperature of entering air, °F
t_2	=	dry-bulb temperature of leaving air, °F
t_s'	=	thermodynamic wet-bulb temperature of entering air, °F

An efficient wetted pad (with high saturation efficiency) can reduce the air dry-bulb temperature by as much as 95% of the wet-bulb depression (ambient dry-bulb temperature less wet-bulb temperature), while an inefficient and poorly designed pad may only reduce this by 50% or less.

Direct evaporative cooling, though simple and inexpensive, has the disadvantage that if the ambient wet-bulb temperature is higher than about 70°F, the cooling effect is not sufficient for indoor comfort but still may be sufficient for relief cooling applications. Direct evaporative coolers should not recirculate indoor air.

Direct evaporative coolers for residences in low-wet-bulb regions typically require 70% less energy than direct-expansion air conditioners.

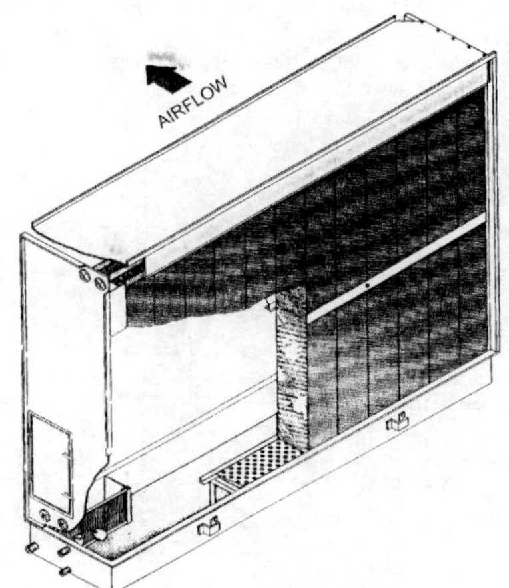

Figure 19.36 Typical Rigid-Media Air Cooler [2020S, Ch 41, Fig 2]

HVAC Systems and Equipment

Indirect Evaporative Air Coolers

Either outdoor or recirculated air may be cooled using indirect evaporative coolers (IECs); commercial IECs commonly cool outdoor air, often as part of a dedicated outdoor air system (DOAS) or variable-air-volume (VAV) air-handler design, whereas in industrial applications and data center cooling designs, process recirculation air is more commonly cooled. Air delivered to the room or process flows through the inside of elliptical-shaped polymer tubes, where it is sensibly cooled. A sump pump recirculates water over the outside of the polymer tubes of this cross-flow air-to-air heat exchanger. Scavenger outdoor air or building return/exhaust air (typical for commercial applications) is drawn upward over the exterior of the wetted polymer tubes.

Polymer tube heat exchangers can provide a 60% to 80% approach of the dry-side entering dry-bulb temperature to the wet-side entering wet-bulb temperature. The heat exchanger efficiency calculation is called *wet-bulb depression efficiency* (WBDE) and is defined as

$$\text{WBDE} = 100\frac{(t_1 - t_2)}{(t_1 - t'_s)} \tag{19.8}$$

where

WBDE = indirect evaporative cooling efficiency,%
t_1 = dry-bulb temperature of entering primary air, °F
t_2 = dry-bulb temperature of leaving primary air, °F
t_s' = wet-bulb temperature of entering secondary air, °F

Supply air-side static pressure losses for these heat exchangers range from 0.25 to 0.75 in. of water. Wet-side airflow pressure drop penalties range from 0.4 to 0.9 in. of water. Secondary airflow ratios are in the range of 1.5 to 1 down to a low of 1 cfm of outdoor air to 0.7 cfm of secondary airflow. The higher the ratios of wet-side air to dry air, the greater the WBDE, with all other factors remaining constant. Cooling energy efficiency ratios (EERs) for this type of heat exchanger range from 40 to 80.

In a two-stage indirect/direct evaporative cooler, a first-stage indirect evaporative cooler lowers both the dry- and wet-bulb temperature of the incoming air. After leaving the indirect stage, the supply air passes through a second-stage direct evaporative cooler.

This method can lower the supply air dry-bulb temperature by 10°F or more below the secondary air wet-bulb temperature.

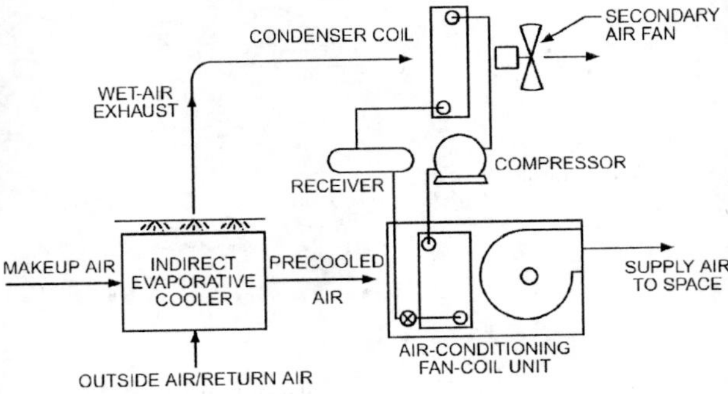

Figure 19.37 Indirect Evaporative Cooler Used as Precooler
[2020S, Ch 41, Fig 4]

In areas with a higher wet-bulb design temperature or where the design requires a supply air temperature lower than that attainable using indirect/direct evaporative cooling, a third cooling stage may be required. This stage may be a direct-expansion refrigeration unit or a chilled-water coil located either upstream or downstream from the direct evaporative cooling stage, but always downstream from the indirect evaporative stage.

Heat Recovery. Indirect evaporative cooling has been used in a number of heat recovery systems, including plate heat exchangers, heat pipe heat exchangers, rotary regenerative heat exchangers, and two-phase thermosiphon loop heat exchangers. Indirect evaporative cooling/heat recovery can be retrofitted on existing systems, lowering operational cost and peak demand. For new installations, equipment can be downsized, lowering overall project and operational costs.

Cooling Tower/Coil Systems. Combining a cooling tower or other evaporative water cooler with a water-to-air heat exchanger coil and water-circulating pump is another type of indirect evaporative cooling. Water flows from the cooling tower reservoir to the coil and returns to the tower's upper distribution header. Both open-water and closed-loop systems are used. Coils in open systems should be cleanable.

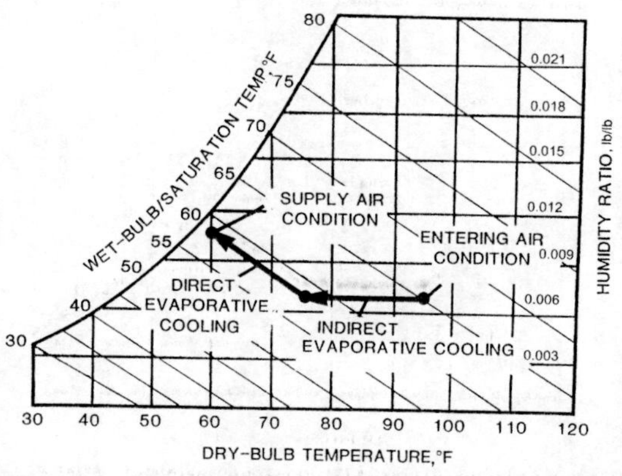

Figure 19.38 Two-Stage Indirect/Direct Evaporative Cooling Process
[2020S, Ch 41, Fig 6]

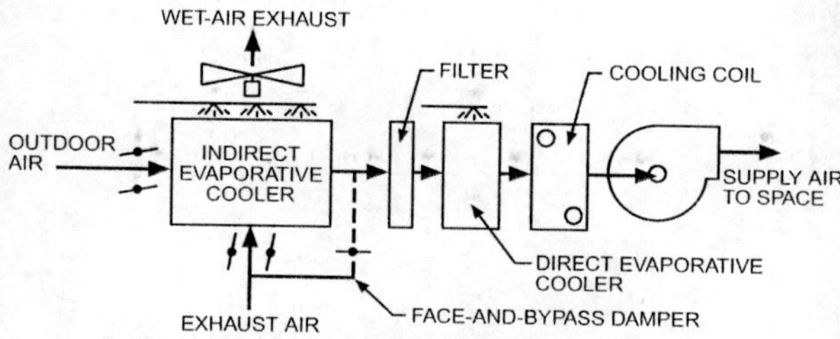

Figure 19.39 Three-Stage Indirect/Direct Evaporative Cooler
[2020S, Ch 41, Fig 8]

Table 19.5 Indirect Evaporative Cooling Systems Comparison [2019A, Ch 53, Tbl 2]

System Type[a]	WBDE,[b] %	Heat Recovery Efficiency, %	Wet-Side Air ΔP, in. of water	Dry-Side Air ΔP, in. of water	Pump hp per 10,000 cfm	Parasitic Loss Range,[e] kW/ton of Cooling	Equipment Cost Range,[f] $/Supply cfm	Notes
Cooling tower to coil	40 to 60	NA	NA	0.4 to 0.7	Varies	Varies	0.50 to 1.00	Best for serving multiple AHUs from a single cooling tower. No winter heat recovery.
Cross-flow plate	60 to 85	40 to 50	0.7 to 1.0	0.4 to 0.7	0.1 to 0.2	0.12 to 0.20	1.20 to 1.70	Most cost-effective for lower airflows. Some cross contamination possible. Low winter heat recovery.
Heat pipe[c]	65 to 75	50 to 60	0.7 to 1.0	0.5 to 0.7	0.2 to 0.4	0.15 to 0.25	1.50 to 2.50	Most cost-effective for large airflows. Some cross contamination possible. Medium winter heat recovery.
Heat wheel[d]	60 to 70	70 to 80	0.6 to 0.9	0.4 to 0.65	0.1 to 0.2	0.2 to 0.3	1.50 to 2.50	Best for high airflows. Some cross contamination. Highest winter heat recovery rates.
Runaround coil[d]	35 to 50	40 to 60	0.6 to 0.8	0.4 to 0.6	Varies	> 0.35	1.00 to 2.00	Best for applications where supply and return air ducts are separated. Lowest summer WBDE.

WBDE = wet-bulb depression efficiency

Notes:

[a]All air-to-air heat exchangers have equal mass flow on supply and exhaust sides.

[b]Plate and heat pipe are direct spray on exhaust side. Heat wheel and runaround coil systems use 90% WBDE direct evaporative cooling media on exhaust air side.

[c]Assumes six-row heat pipe, 11 fpi, with 500 fpm face velocity on both sides.

[d]Assumes 500 fpm face velocity. Parasitic loss includes wheel rotational power.

[e]Includes air-side static pressure and pumping penalty.

[f]Excludes cooling tower cost and assumes less than 200 ft piping between components.

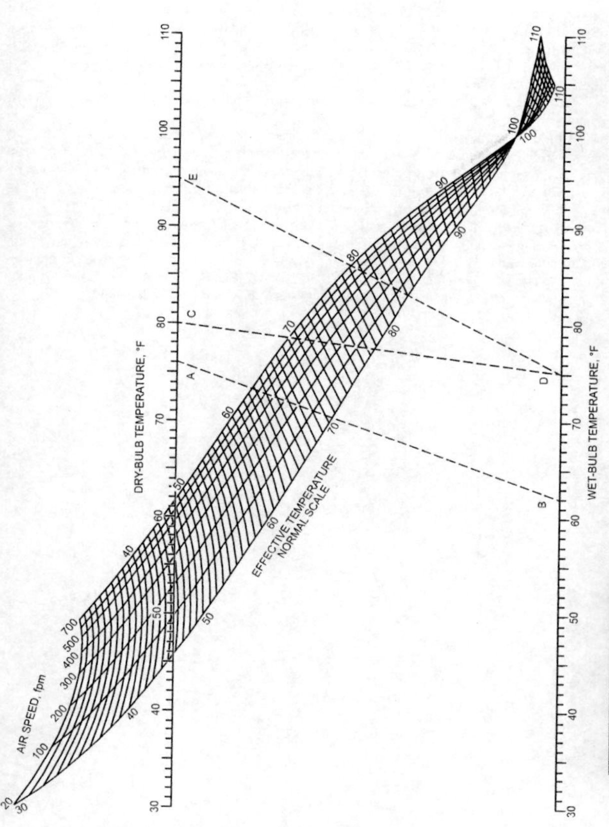

Figure 19.40 Effective Temperature Chart [2019A, Ch 53, Fig 15]

20. AUTOMATIC CONTROLS

Automatic control of HVAC systems and equipment usually includes control of temperature, humidity, pressure, and flow rates of air and water. Automatic controls can sequence equipment operation to meet load requirements and to provide safe equipment operation using direct digital control (DDC), electronic, electrical, mechanical, and/or pneumatic devices. Automatic controls are only fully effective when applied to well-designed mechanical systems; they cannot compensate for misapplied systems, excessive undersizing or oversizing, or highly nonlinear processes.

This chapter illustrates typical control diagrams for common HVAC systems and components.

A building automation system (BAS) with direct digital, electronic, or pneumatic controls has several physical control loops, with each loop including a controlled variable (e.g., temperature), controlled device (e.g., actuator), and the process to be controlled (e.g., heating system). A BAS with DDC controllers can share sensor values with several control loops or have multiple control loops selectively activate an actuator.

A BAS with DDC controllers allows information such as system status or alarms to be shared through a common communication protocol, between HVAC systems or within building systems and services, thereby enabling advanced, energy-saving, system-level applications. ASHRAE Guideline 13 and ANSI/ASHRAE Standard 135 have more detailed discussions of networking and interoperability. See also ASHRAE Guideline 36.

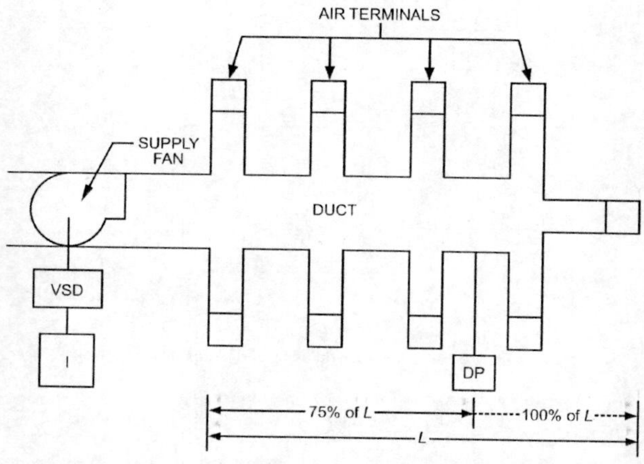

Figure 20.1 Duct Static Pressure Control [2019A, Ch 48, Fig 15]

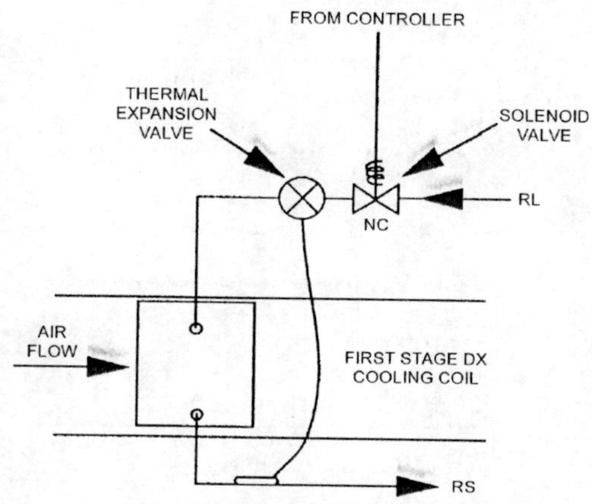

Figure 20.2 Direct Expansion—Two-Position Control

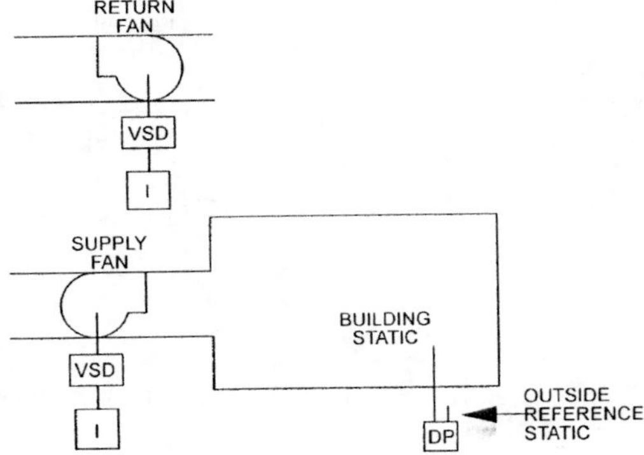

Figure 20.3 Duct Static Control of Return Fan

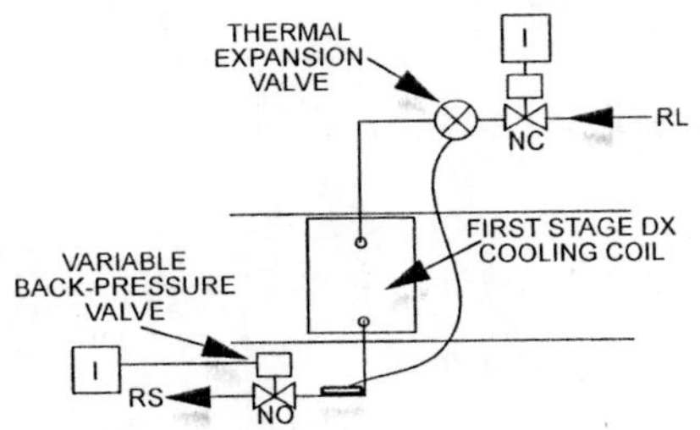

Figure 20.4 Modulating Direct-Expansion Cooling

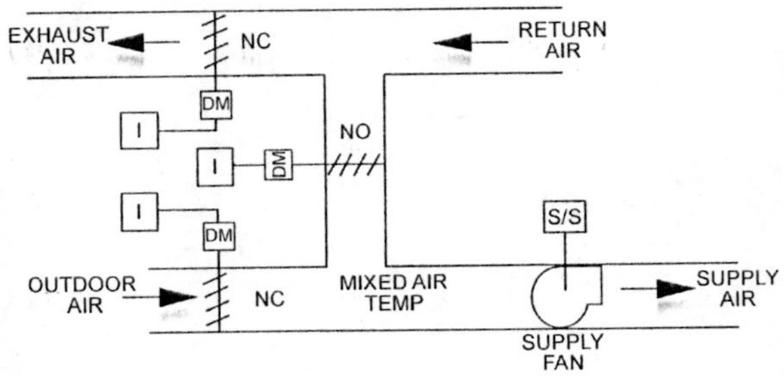

Figure 20.5 Economizer Cycle Control

Automatic Controls

RETURN FAN
FLOW STATION
RETURN AIR
VFD
F
I
F
SUPPLY FAN
FLOW STATION
SUPPLY AIR

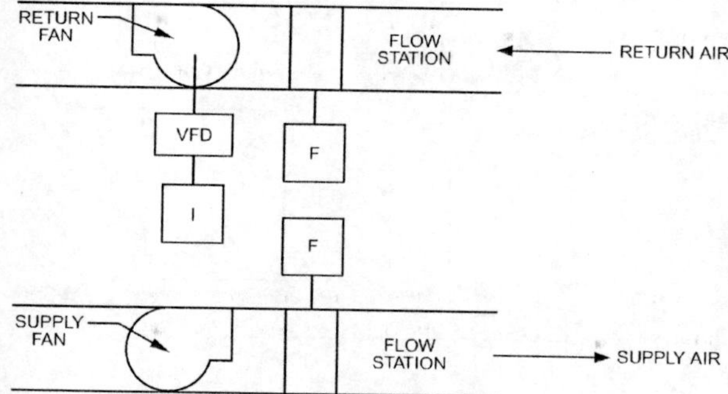

Figure 20.6 Airflow Tracking Control [2019A, Ch 48, Fig 17]

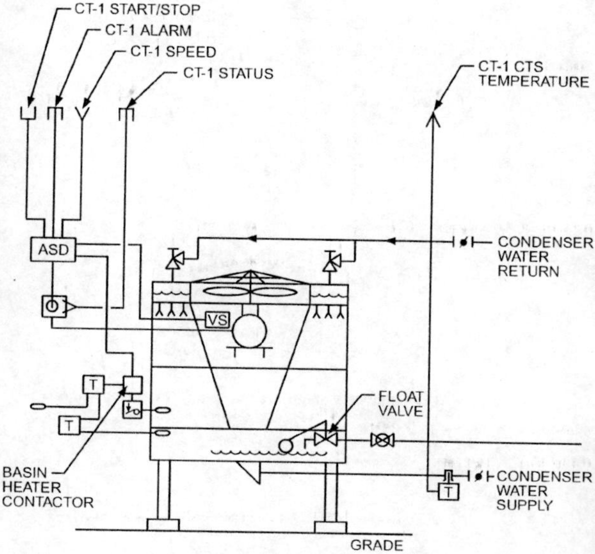

CT-1 START/STOP
CT-1 ALARM
CT-1 SPEED
CT-1 STATUS
CT-1 CTS TEMPERATURE
ASD
CONDENSER WATER RETURN
VS
T
T
FLOAT VALVE
BASIN HEATER CONTACTOR
CONDENSER WATER SUPPLY
T
GRADE

Figure 20.7 Cooling Tower [2019A, Ch 48, Fig 13]

Automatic Controls

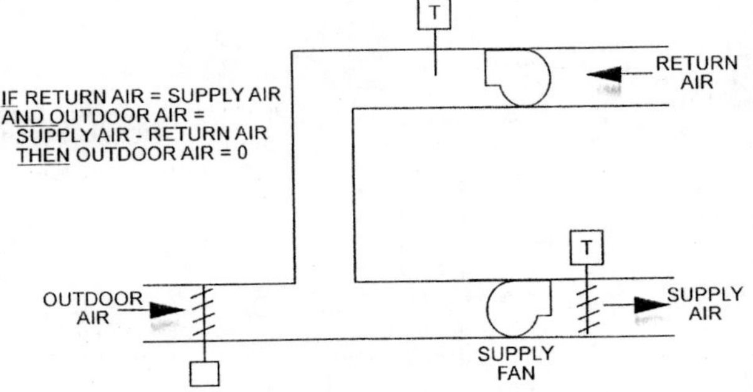

Figure 20.8 Warm-Up Control

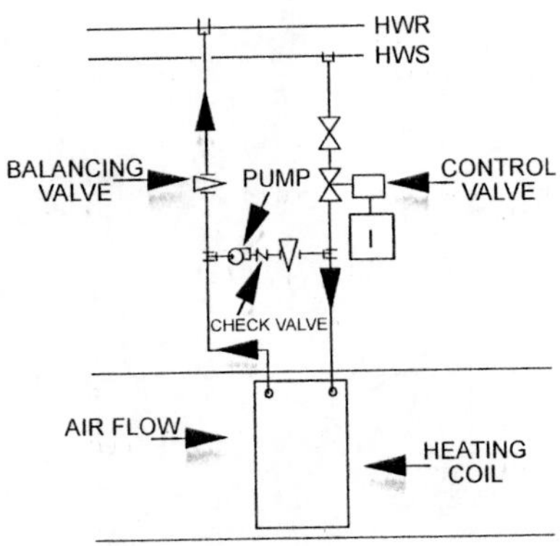

Figure 20.9 Preheat with Secondary Pump and Two-Way Valve

Automatic Controls

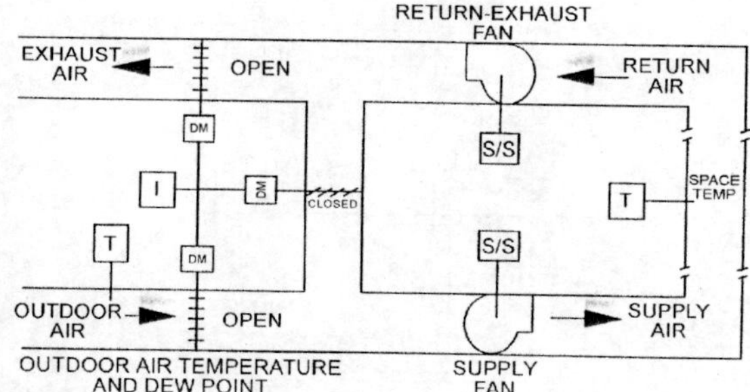

Figure 20.10 Night Cooldown Control

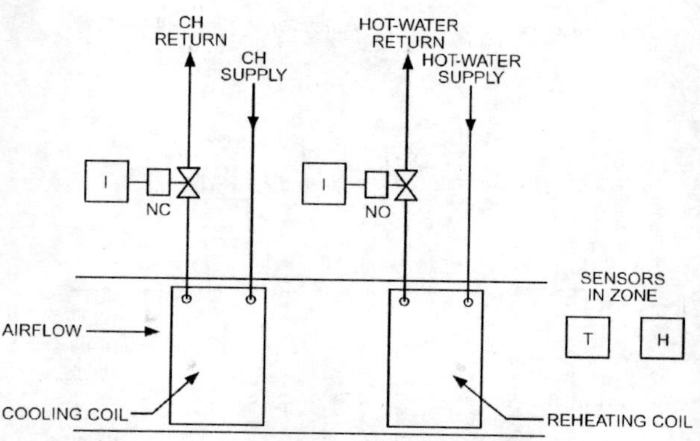

Figure 20.11 Cooling and Dehumidifying with Reheat [2019A, Ch 48, Fig 31]

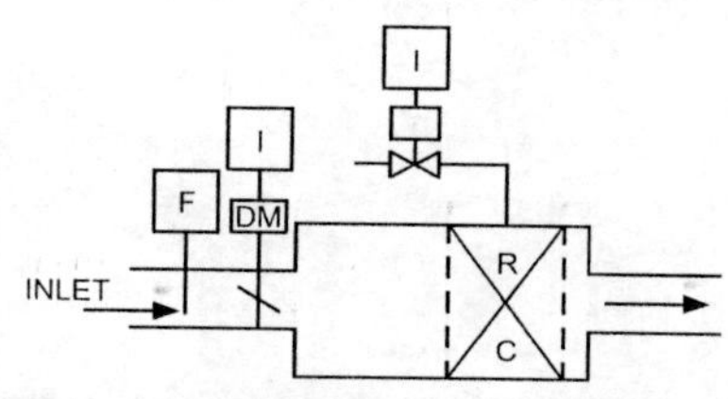

Figure 20.12 Throttling VAV Terminal Unit [2019A, Ch 48, Fig 24]

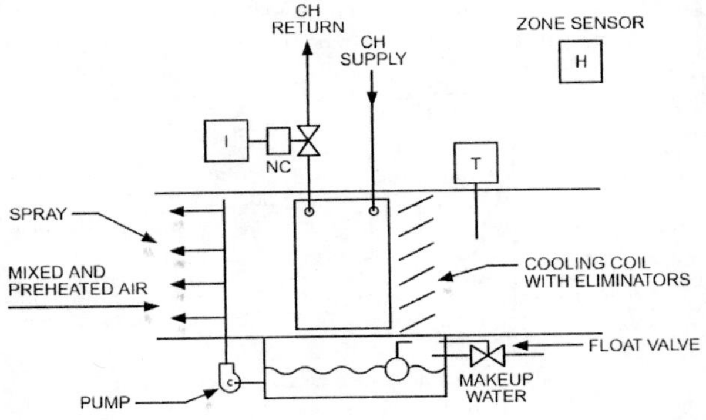

Figure 20.13 Sprayed Coil Dehumidifier [2019A, Ch 48, Fig 32]

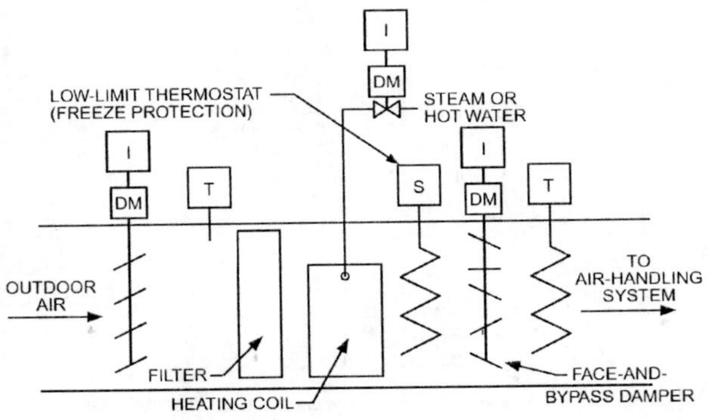

Figure 20.14 Preheat with Face and Bypass Dampers [2019A, Ch 48, Fig 5]

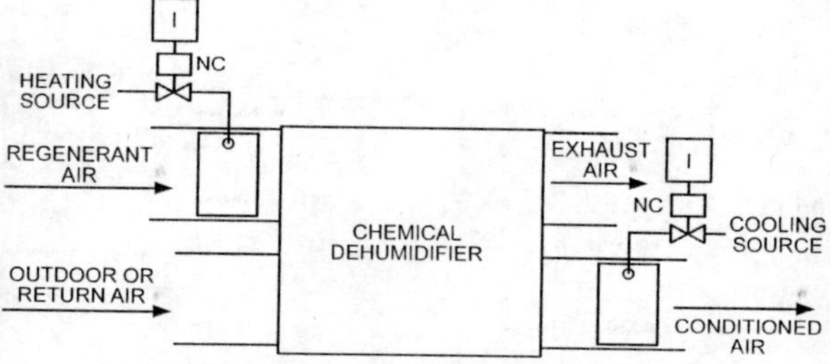

Figure 20.15 Desiccant Dehumidifier [2019A, Ch 48, Fig 34]

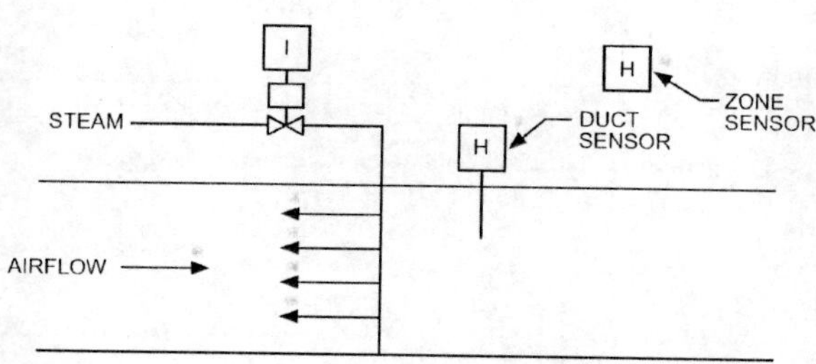

Figure 20.16 Steam Injection Humidifier [2019A, Ch 48, Fig 35]

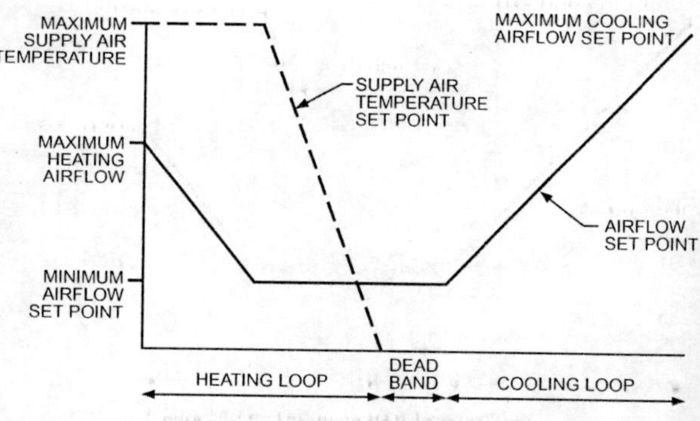

Figure 20.17 Throttling VAV Terminal Unit: Dual Maximum Control Sequence [2019A, Ch 48, Fig 25]

Automatic Controls

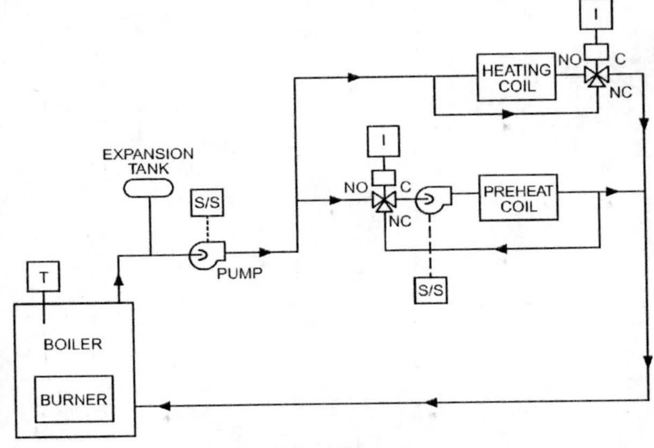

Figure 20.18 Load and Zone Control in Constant-Flow System
[2019A, Ch 48, Fig 3]

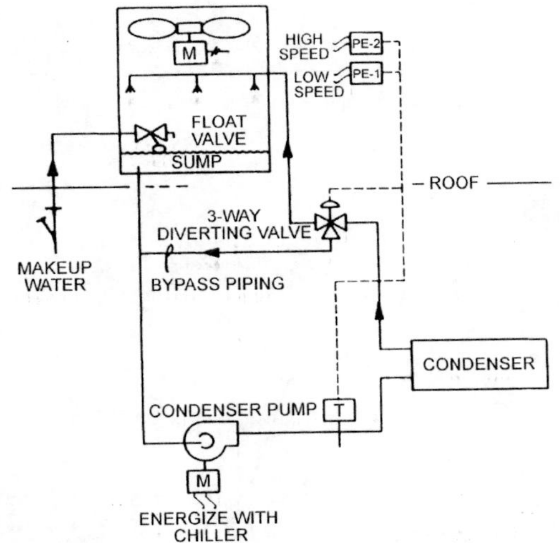

Figure 20.19 Condenser Water Temperature Control

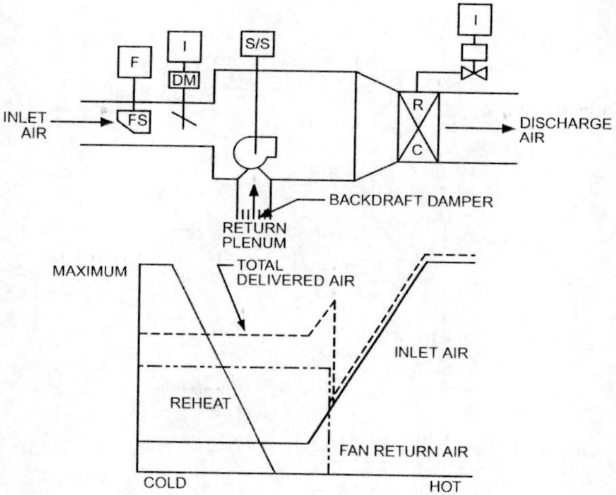

F
I
DM
S/S
I
INLET AIR
FS
R
C
DISCHARGE AIR
BACKDRAFT DAMPER
RETURN PLENUM
MAXIMUM
TOTAL DELIVERED AIR
INLET AIR
REHEAT
FAN RETURN AIR
COLD
HOT

Figure 20.20 Parallel Fan Terminal Unit [2019A, Ch 48, Fig 28]

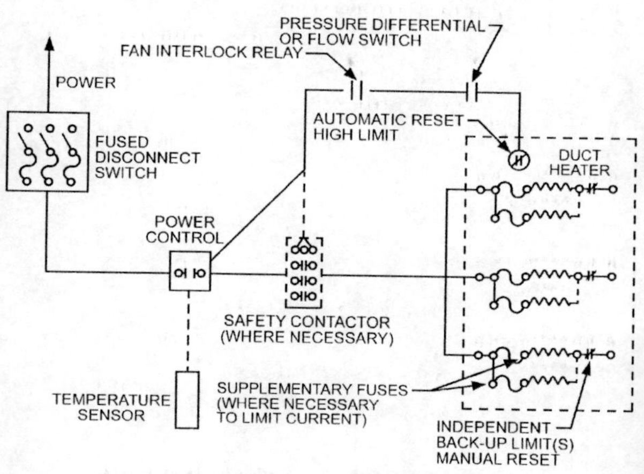

Figure 20.21 Duct Heater Control [2019A, Ch 48, Fig 9]

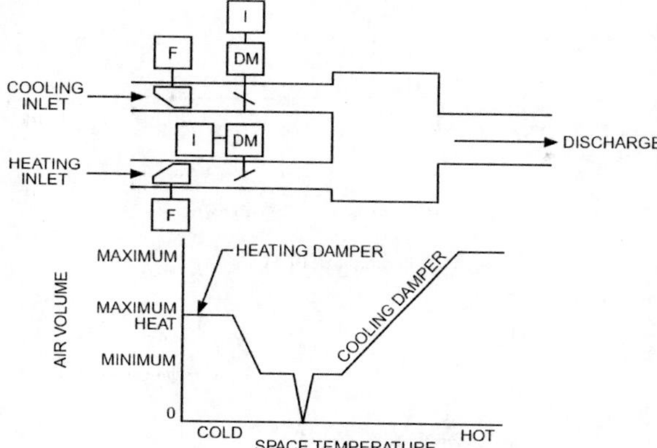

Figure 20.22 Variable-Volume Dual-Duct Terminal Unit [2019A, Ch 48, Fig 29]

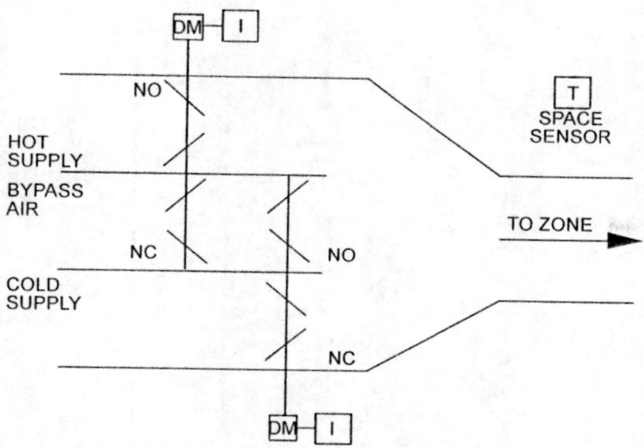

Figure 20.23 Zone Mixing Dampers—Three-Deck Multizone System

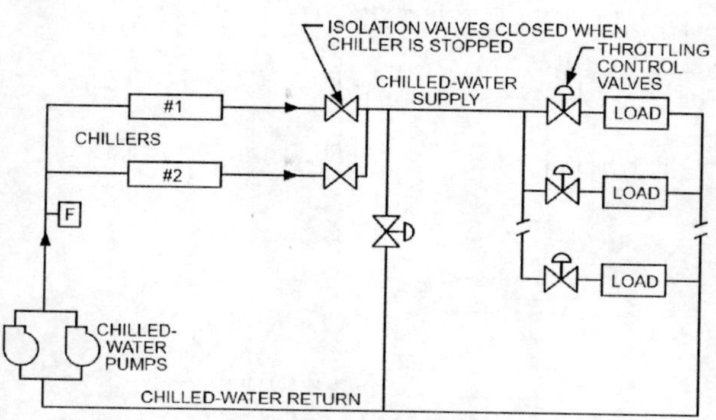

Figure 20.24 Variable-Flow Chilled-Water System (Primary Only)
[2019A, Ch 48, Fig 10]

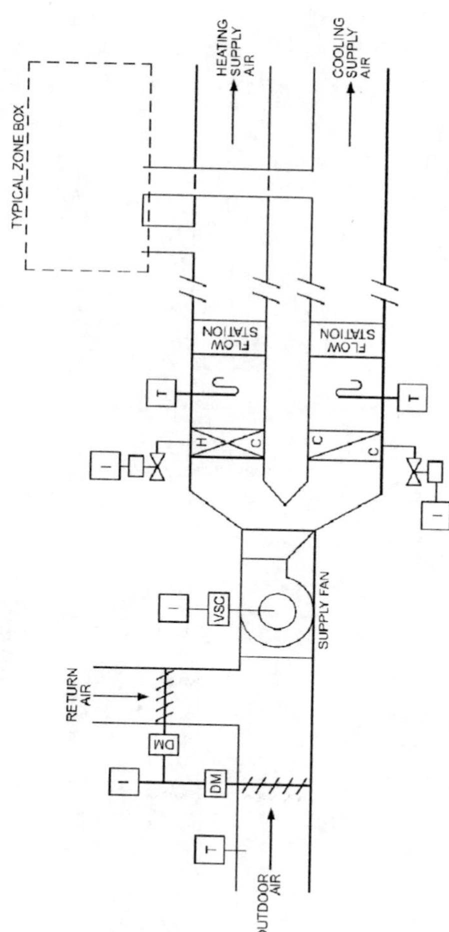

Figure 20.25 Single Fan, Dual-Duct System [2019A, Ch 48, Fig 41]

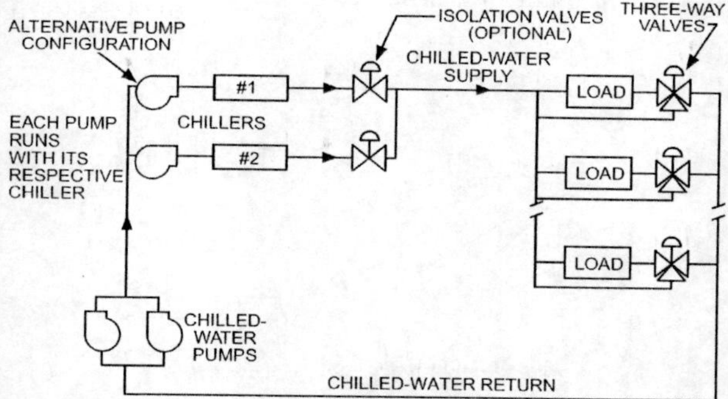

Figure 20.26 Constant-Flow Chilled-Water System (Primary/Only)
[2019A, Ch 48, Fig 12]

Automatic Controls

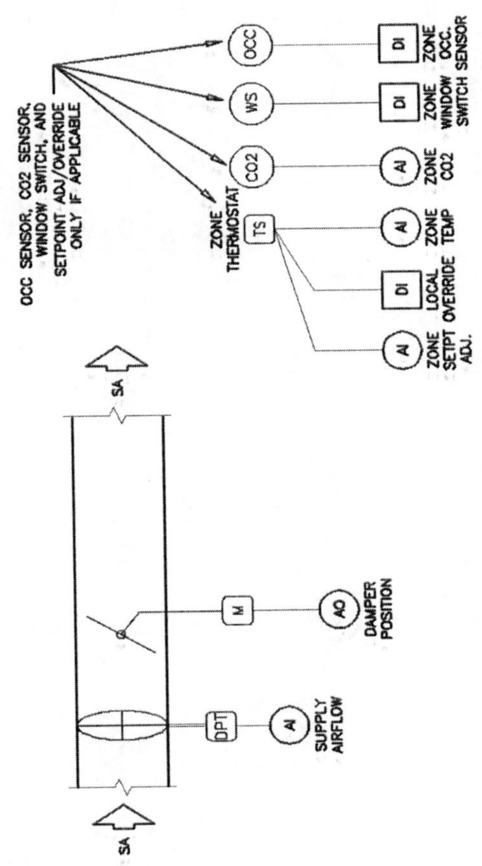

Figure 20.27 VAV Terminal Unit, Cooling Only [Gdln 36-2021, Fig A-1]

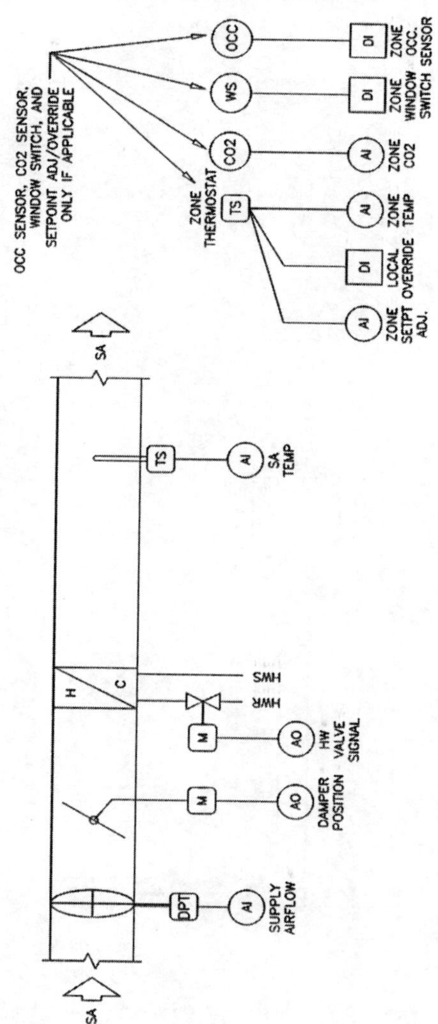

Figure 20.28 VAV Terminal Unit with Reheat [Gdln 36-2021, Fig A-2]

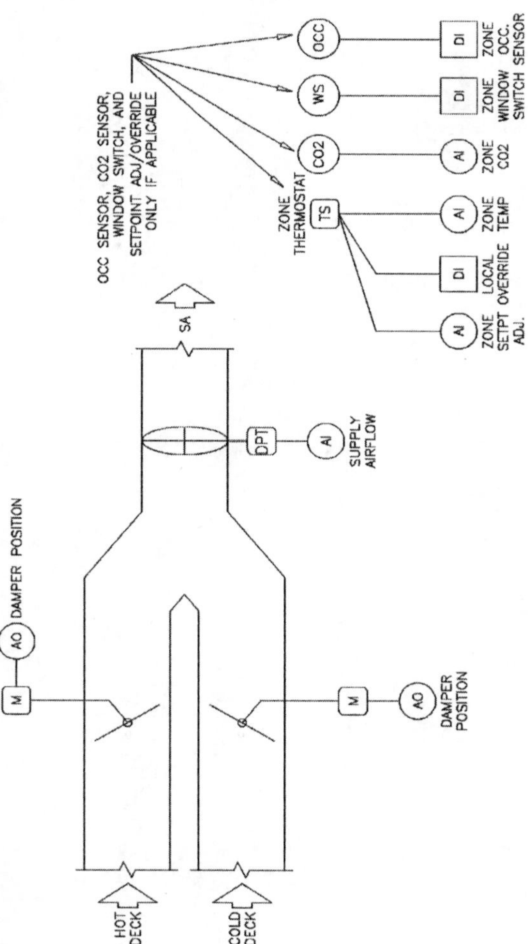

Figure 20.29 Fan-Coil Unit with Variable-Volume Fan, Heating and Cooling Coils [Gdln 36-2021, Fig A-28]

21. OCCUPANT COMFORT

The *operative temperature* (t_o) is the uniform temperature of an imaginary black enclosure, and the air within in, in which an occupant would exchange the same amount of heat by radiation plus convection as in the actual nonuniform environment; calculated in accordance with Normative Appendix A of ANSI/ASHRAE Standard 55-2020, *Thermal Environmental Conditions for Human Occupancy*. (See the complete standard for detailed guidance.)

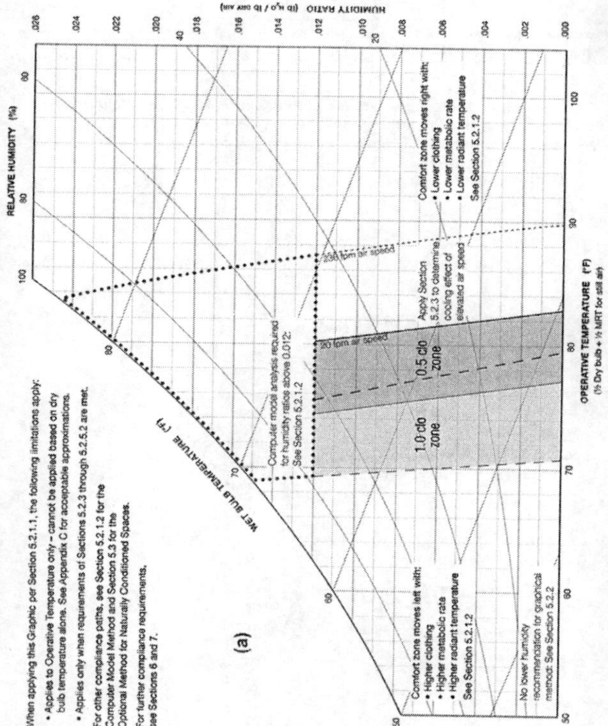

Acceptable ranges of operative temperature and humidity for people in 0.5 to 1.0 clo clothing, activity between 1.0 met and 1.3 met. The operative temperature ranges are based on a 80% satisfaction criterion; 10% general dissatisfaction and 10% partial (local) dissatisfaction.

Figure 21.1 Graphic Comfort Zone Method [Std 55-2013, Fig 5.3.1]

Table 21.1 Acceptable Thermal Environment for General Comfort [Std 55-2020, Tbl H-1]

PPD	PMV Range
< 10	–0.5 < PMV < + 0.5

Table 21.2 Limits on Temperature Drifts and Ramps [Std 55-2020, Tbl 5-12]

Time Period	0.25 h	0.5 h	1 h	2 h	4 h
Maximum Operative Temperature Change Allowed	2.0°F	3.0°F	4.0°F	5.0°F	6.0°F

Table 21.3 Typical Insulation and Permeation Efficiency Values for Western Clothing Ensembles [2021F, Ch 9, Tbl 7]

Ensemble Description[a]	I_{cl}, clo	I_t,[b] clo	f_{cl}	i_{cl}	i_m[b]
Walking shorts, short-sleeved shirt	0.36	1.02	1.10	0.34	0.42
Trousers, short-sleeved shirt	0.57	1.20	1.15	0.36	0.43
Trousers, long-sleeved shirt	0.61	1.21	1.20	0.41	0.45
Same as above, plus suit jacket	0.96	1.54	1.23		
Same as above, plus vest and T-shirt	1.14	1.69	1.32	0.32	0.37
Trousers, long-sleeved shirt, long-sleeved sweater, T-shirt	1.01	1.56	1.28		
Same as above, plus suit jacket and long underwear bottoms	1.30	1.83	1.33		
Sweat pants, sweat shirt	0.74	1.35	1.19	0.41	0.45
Long-sleeved pajama top, long pajama trousers, short 3/4 sleeved robe, slippers (no socks)	0.96	1.50	1.32	0.37	0.41
Knee-length skirt, short-sleeved shirt, panty hose, sandals	0.54	1.10	1.26		
Knee-length skirt, long-sleeved shirt, full slip, panty hose	0.67	1.22	1.29		
Knee-length skirt, long-sleeved shirt, half slip, panty hose, long-sleeved sweater	1.10	1.59	1.46		
Same as above, replace sweater with suit jacket	1.04	1.60	1.30	0.35	0.40
Ankle-length skirt, long-sleeved shirt, suit jacket, panty hose	1.10	1.59	1.46		
Long-sleeved coveralls, T-shirt	0.72	1.30	1.23		
Overalls, long-sleeved shirt, T-shirt	0.89	1.46	1.27	0.35	0.40
Insulated coveralls, long-sleeved thermal underwear, long underwear bottoms	1.37	1.94	1.26	0.35	0.39

Sources: McCullough and Jones (1984) and McCullough et al. (1989).

[a] All ensembles include shoes and briefs or panties. All ensembles except those with panty hose include socks unless otherwise noted.

[b] For $t_r = t_a$ and air velocity less than 40 fpm (I_a = 0.72 clo and i_m = 0.48 when nude).

Table 21.4 Insulation and Permeability Values for a Selection of Non-Western Clothing Ensembles [2021F, Ch 9, Tbl 8]

Ensemble Description[a]	Country	I_{cl} clo	I_t clo	f_{cl}	i_m
Shalwar (pants), kameez (shirt), scarf, sandals (f)	Pakistan	0.69	1.1	1.41	0.32
Shalwar (pants), kameez (shirt), socks, athletic shoes (m)	Pakistan	0.86	1.3	1.36	0.35
Dishdasha (thowb or caftan), short-sleeved t-shirt, long serwal (pants), tagiya (hat), iqal (cord), ghutra (headdress), socks, athletic shoes (m)	Kuwait	1.36	1.7	1.66	0.30
Full slip, double-layer abaya (dress), anta (head cover), hijab (headscarf), sandals (f)	Kuwait	1.27	1.7	1.65	0.33
Underskirt, blouse, sari, sandals (f)	India	0.74	1.2	1.46	0.33
Churidhar pants, churidhar dress, shawl, sandals (f)	India	0.58	1.1	1.28	0.36
Short shirt with long sleeves, long pants, boubou (wide-sleeved robe), kufi (hat), sandals (m)	Nigeria/ Ghana	1.40	1.7	1.96	0.42
Short shirt with long sleeves, long pants, sandals (f)	Nigeria/ Ghana	0.78	1.3	1.35	0.40
Long-sleeved shirt, skirt, headscarf, socks, athletic shoes (f)	Indonesia	0.97	1.4	1.43	0.31
Camisole, short-sleeved qipao (dress), sandals (f)	China	0.42	0.9	1.31	0.40

(f) = clothing traditionally worn by women
(m) = clothing traditionally worn by men
Source: Havenith et al. (2015). Values are the means of manikin-based measurements conducted in three laboratories. All ensembles include bra and panties (female) and briefs (male). For all women's ensembles, I_a = 0.64 clo; for all men's ensembles, I_a = 0.63 clo.

Table 21.5 Expected Percent Dissatisfied Due to Sources of Local Discomfort [Std 55-2020, Tbl I-1]

Draft	Vertical Air Temperature Difference	Warm or Cool Floors	Radiant Asymmetry
<20%	<5%	<10%	<5%

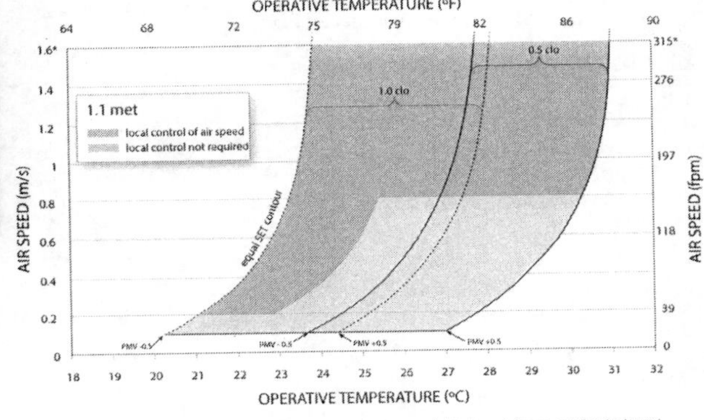

Figure 21.2 Acceptable Ranges of Operative Temperature t_o and Average Air Speed V_a for the 1.0 and 0.5 clo Comfort Zones at Humidity Ratio 0.010 [Std 55-2020, Fig 5-4]

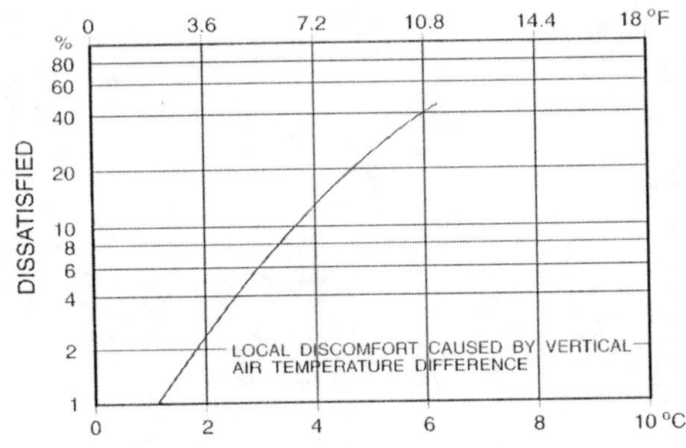

Figure 21.3 Local Thermal Discomfort caused by Vertical Temperature Differences [Std 55-2020, Fig I-3]

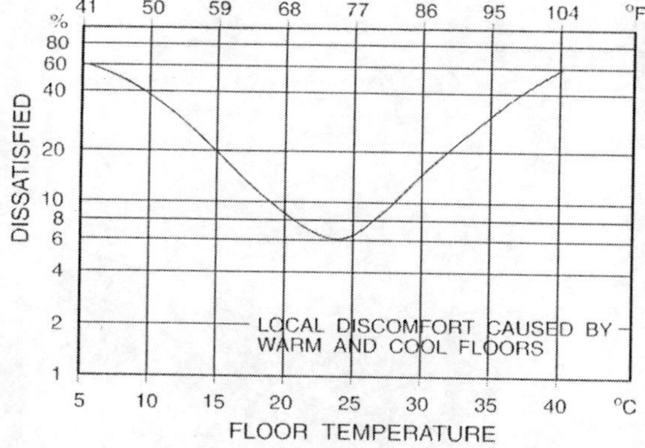

Figure 21.4 Local Discomfort caused by Warm and Cool Floors
[Std 55-2020, Fig I-4]

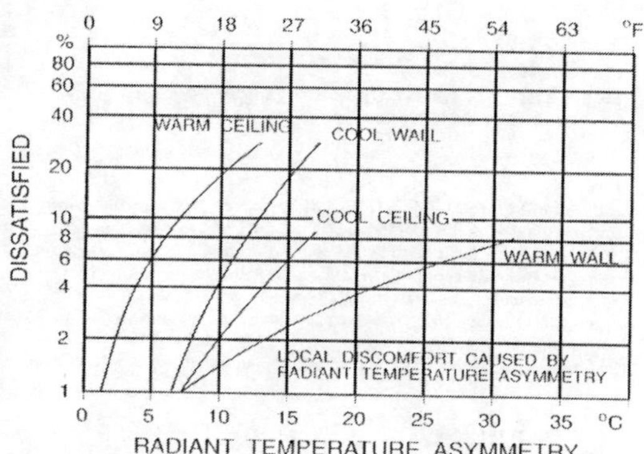

Figure 21.5 Local Thermal Discomfort caused by Radiant Asymmetry
[Std 55-2020, Fig I-1]

Table 21.6 Increases in Acceptable Operative Temperature Limits (Δt_0) in Occupant-Controlled, Naturally Conditioned Spaces (Figure 21.6) Resulting from Increasing Air Speed above 59 fpm [Std 55-2020, Tbl 5-13]

Average Air Speed (V_a) 118 fpm	Average Air Speed (V_a) 177 fpm	Average Air Speed (V_a) 236 fpm
2.2°F	3.2°F	4.0°F

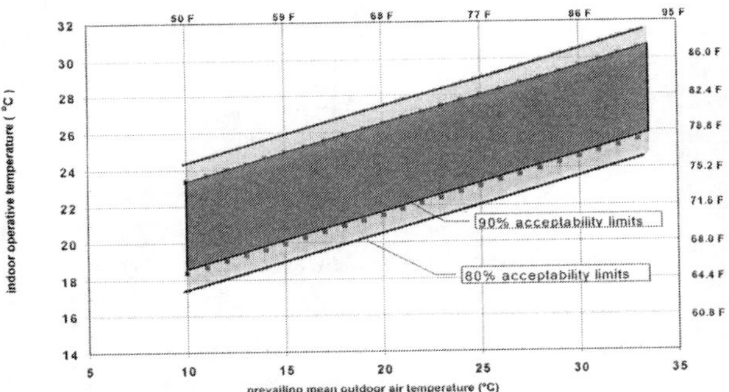

Figure 21.6 Acceptable Operative Temperature t_o Ranges for Naturally Conditioned Spaces [Std 55-2020, Fig 5-8]

Applicability of Figure 21.6. Figure 21.6 defines acceptable thermal environments only for occupant-controlled naturally conditioned spaces that meet all of the following criteria:

- There is no mechanical cooling system (e.g., refrigerated air conditioning, radiant cooling, or desiccant cooling) or heating system in operation.
- Representative occupants have metabolic rates ranging from 1.0 to 1.5 met.
- Representative occupants are free to adapt their clothing to the indoor and/or outdoor thermal conditions within a range at least as wide as 0.5 to 1.0 clo.
- The prevailing mean outdoor temperature is greater than 50°F and less than 92.3°F.

22. COMMISSIONING

Commissioning is a quality-oriented process for achieving, verifying, and documenting that the performance of facilities, systems, and assemblies meets defined objectives and criteria. The defined objectives and criteria are often referred to as the Owner's Project Requirements (OPR).

The commissioning (Cx) process uses the OPR as the reference to determine acceptance of the design and construction. Commissioning includes verifying and documenting that the project operational and maintenance documentation and training of operation and maintenance (O&M) personnel occur. The result should be fully functional systems that can be properly operated and maintained throughout the life of the building.

Recommissioning applies Cx to a project that has been previously delivered using the Cx process. This may be a scheduled recommissioning developed as part of ongoing Cx, or it may be triggered by use change, operational problems, or other needs. Existing building Cx (EBCx, often called *retrocommissioning*) applies Cx to an existing facility that may or may not have been previously commissioned.

Equipment, components, systems, and assemblies have become more complex. More specialization has occurred in the disciplines and trades, with increased interactions between all elements. This increased specialization and interaction requires increased integration between disciplines and specialized systems by the delivery team. Owners often use low-bid policies, and scopes of work for design professionals are often narrowed. The result has been buildings that do not meet owner expectations and often do not work as intended because of programming, design, and construction deficiencies. Commissioning is a value-added service that helps overcome these infrastructure inadequacies and fundamentally improve the performance of building systems and living conditions for occupants.

Key contributors to the commissioning process include the following:

- Owner/end user
- Architect
- Mechanical engineer
- Electrical engineer
- Commissioning provider (CxP)
- Mechanical contractor
- Electrical contractor
- Controls contractor
- Sheet metal contractor
- Testing, adjusting, and balancing (TAB) agency
- Owner's O&M staff
- General contractor/construction manager

New Building Commissioning Process

Commissioning begins during predesign, and formally continues through the first year of occupancy and operations. Although circumstances may require owners to begin Cx at the design or construction stage of a project, such a delayed implementation must capture the same information and verifications developed when Cx begins at project inception. Four phases of the new building and systems Cx process are defined below.

Predesign-Phase Commissioning

The primary activities and objectives of Cx during predesign are to:

- Develop the OPR
- Identify the scope and budget for the Cx process
- Develop the initial Cx plan
- Review and accept predesign-phase Cx-process activities
- Review and use lessons learned from previous projects

Design-Phase Commissioning

Design-phase Cx objectives include the following:

- Update the OPR
- Verify the Basis of Design (BOD) document against the OPR

- Update the design-phase Cx plan developed during predesign
- Develop and incorporate Cx requirements into project specifications
- Develop Cx plan for construction and occupancy/operations phases, including draft construction checklists
- Verify plans and specifications against BOD and OPR
- Begin codeveloping systems manual with relevant discipline design engineer
- Define training requirements for O&M personnel
- Perform Cx-focused design reviews
- Accept design-phase Cx

Construction-Phase Commissioning

Commissioning activities should take place throughout the construction phase and include verification and documentation that:

- All acceptance testing requirements are documented
- All systems and assemblies are provided and installed as specified
- All systems and assemblies are started and function properly
- All record documents are updated
- The systems manual is updated and provided to facility staff
- Facility staff and occupants receive specified training and orientation
- Acceptance testing occurs

Occupancy and Operations-Phase Commissioning

Occupancy and operations phase Cx typically begins with resolving the findings from performance monitoring over the first month or two into occupancy and ends with the completion of the first year of occupancy. The Cx process during this phase should ensure:

- Initial maintenance and operator training is complete
- Systems and assemblies received functional opposite-season verification
- Outstanding performance issues are identified and resolved before warranty expiration
- Commissioning process evaluation is conducted and satisfactorily resolved

Existing Building Commissioning Process (EBCx)

This is a quality-focused process for attaining the current facility requirements (CFR) of an existing facility and/or its systems and assemblies. The process focuses on planning, investigating, implementing, verifying, and documenting that the facility and/or its systems and assemblies are operated and maintained to meet the CFR, with a program to maintain the enhancements for the remaining life of the facility. System performance normally degrades with use and time, at a rate depending on the quality of maintenance and operations and the number of hours of operation. Quality of maintenance also affects equipment life expectancy. An EBCx effort should include updating or developing an owner's CFR, documenting existing systems, surveying the facility to identify operational inefficiencies, quantifying and prioritizing the inefficiencies found, determining how best to optimize equipment or operation, implementing changes, training operating personnel, documenting operations, and then reverifying with ongoing measurements that the EBCx process activities produced and continue to produce the desired effect.

EBCx is used by owners and facility decision makers to optimize the operations of their existing facilities to meet their CFR. The process has five basic steps, with an additional step for multifacility projects:

- Multifacility planning (if multiple buildings are involved)
- Assessment
- Investigation
- Implementation
- Handoff
- Ongoing Cx

ASHRAE Commissioning Documents

ASHRAE has developed numerous Cx process documents to address new and existing buildings and systems, to provide support for HVAC systems Cx efforts, and to assist in the development of Cx documentation. These include:

- ANSI/ASHRAE/IES Standard 202, *Commissioning Process for Buildings and Systems*
- ASHRAE Guideline 0, *The Commissioning Process*
- ASHRAE Guideline 0.2, *Commissioning Process for Existing Systems and Assemblies*
- ASHRAE Guideline 1.1, *HVAC&R Technical Requirements for the Commissioning Process*
- ASHRAE Guideline 1.2, *Technical Requirements for the Commissioning Process for Existing HVAC&R Systems and Assemblies*
- ASHRAE Guideline 1.3, *Building Operations and Maintenance Training for the HVAC&R Commissioning Process*
- ASHRAE Guideline 1.4, *Preparing Systems Manuals for Facilities*
- ASHRAE Guideline 1.5, *The Commissioning Process for Smoke Control Systems*
- *Commissioning Stakeholders' Guide*

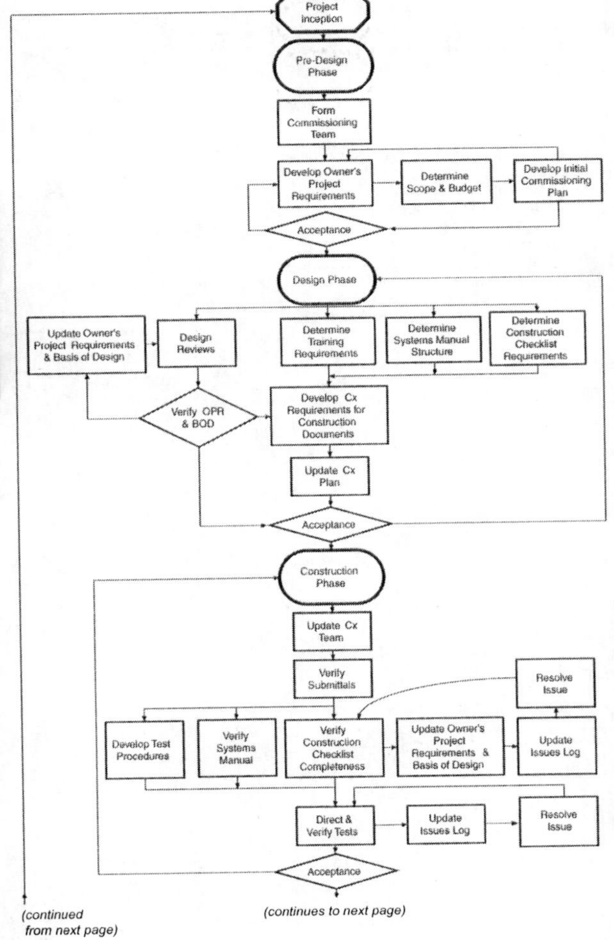

Figure 22.1 Commissioning Process Flowchart for New Buildings and Systems [Gdl 0-2019, Fig B-1]

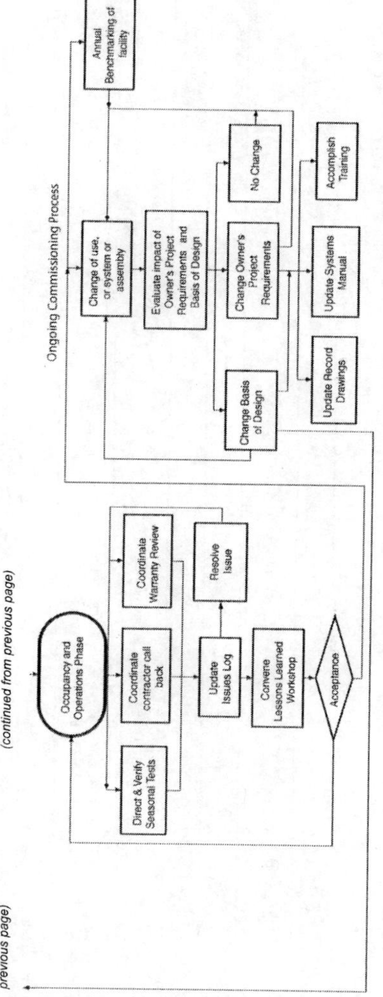

Figure 22.1 Commissioning Process Flow Chart for New Buildings and Systems [Gdl 0-2019, Fig B-1] ***(Continued)***

Table 22.1 Commissioning Process Documentation Matrix for New Building and Systems [Std 202-2018, Tbl A-1]

Phase	Document	Input By	Provided By	Reviewed/ Approved By	Used By	Notes
Project Initiation	OPR	Owner, CxP, O&M, Users, Design Team	Owner, CxP, or Design Team	Owner	CxP, Design Team	Design Team may not be hired yet.
Design	Initial Cx Plan	Owner, Design Team, CxP	Owner or CxP	Owner	CxP, Owner, Design Team, Construction Team	Design Team may not be hired yet.
	Systems Manual Outline	Owner, O&M, CxP	Owner or CxP	Owner	Design Team, Construction Team	Should follow ASHRAE Guideline 1.4.
	Training Requirements Outline	Owner, O&M, Users, CxP, Design Team	Owner or CxP	Owner, CxP	Design Team, Construction Team	Should follow ASHRAE Guideline 1.3 and as defined.
	Issues and Resolution Log Format	Owner, CxP	Owner or CxP	Owner	CxP, Design Team	May be only format at this time.
	Cx Report Format	Owner, CxP	CxP	Owner	Design Team, Owner	Follow requirement in this standard.
	OPR Update	Owner, CxP, O&M, Users, Design Team	CxP or Designer	Owner	CxP, Design Team	
	BoD	Design Team	Design Team	Owner, CxP	Design Team, CxP	
	Construction Specifications for Cx	Design Team, CxP, Owner, O&M	Design Team or CxP	Owner	Contractors, CxP, Design Team	May also be provided by project manager/Owner's representative.
	Systems Manual Outline—Expanded	Design Team, CxP, O&M, Contractor	Design Team or CxP	Owner, CxP	Design Team, Contractor	Contractor may not be hired yet.
	Training Requirements	Owner, CxP O&M, Users,	Owner, CxP, or O&M	Owner	Design Team	Contractor input
	Design Review Comments	CxP	CxP	Design Team, Owner	Design Team	
	Issues and Resolution Log	CxP	CxP	Design Team, Owner	CxP, Design Team	
	Design Cx Report	CxP	CxP	Owner	Owner	

Table 22.1 **Commissioning Process Documentation Matrix for New Building and Systems** [Std 202-2018, Tbl A-1] ***(Continued)***

Phase	Document	Input By	Provided By	Reviewed/ Approved By	Used By	Notes
Construction	OPR Update	Owner, O&M, Users, Design Team	CxP or Designer	Owner	CxP, Design Team, Contractors, Owner	
	BoD Update	Design Team	Design Team	CxP, Owner	Design Team, CxP, Owner	
	Cx Plan Update	Project Team	CxP	Owner	Project Team	
	Submittal Review Comments	CxP	Design Team	Design Team	Contractor	Copy to Owner.
	System Coordination Plans	Contractor, Design Team, CxP	Contractor	CxP, Design Team	Contractor, CxP	
	Evaluation Checklists	CxP, Contractor, Design Team	CxP or Contractor	CxP, Design Team	Contractor	
	Cx Progress Reports	CxP, Contractor	CxP	CxP, Owner	Contractor	
	Test Procedures	Project Team	CxP	CxP, Design Team	Contractor	
	Specified Test Data Submittals	Owner, Design Team, CxP	Contractors, CxP, or Owner	Design Team, CxP	Project Team	
	Cx Meeting Agendas and Minutes	CxP	CxP	All	All	
	Training Plans	Project Team	Contractor or CxP	Owner, CxP	O&M, Users, Contractor	
	Systems Manual	Project Team	Contractor or CxP	Owner, CxP	O&M, Users	See ASHRAE Guideline 1.4.
	Issues and Resolution Log	CxP	CxP	N/A	Project Team	
	Progress Report	CxP	CxP	Owner, Design Team	Project Team	
	Preliminary Construction Cx Report	CxP	CxP	Owner	Owner	Prior to occupancy
	Final Construction Cx Report	CxP	CxP	Owner	Owner	

Table 22.1 Commissioning Process Documentation Matrix for New Building and Systems [Std 202-2018, Tbl A-1] ***(Continued)***

Phase	Document	Input By	Provided By	Reviewed/ Approved By	Used By	Notes
Occupancy and Operations	OPR Update	Owner, O&M, Users, Design Team	CxP or Designer	Owner	CxP, Owner	See ASHRAE Guideline 0.2 for postoccupancy Cx.
	BoD Update	Design Team	Design Team	CxP, Owner	Owner, O&M, CxP	
	Maintenance Program	Owner, O&M, Contractor, CxP	Owner or CxP	Owner, CxP	O&M, Users	
	Test Procedures	CxP	CxP	Design Team, CxP	Contractor, O&M	See Systems Manual.
	Updated Issues and Resolution Log	CxP	CxP	N/A	Project Team	Must be included in final Cx Report.
	Prefinal	Project Team	CxP	N/A	Owner	Typically provided at substantial completion.
	Final Cx Report	Project Team	CxP	N/A	Owner	
	Final Issues and Resolution Log	Project Team	CxP	Owner	Owner	Included in final Cx Report.
	Recommissioning Plan	O&M, Users, CxP	CxP or Owner	Owner	Owner	

Note: See Section 3 of Standard 202-2018 for entities and deliverables contained in this table.

Table 22.2 Example Commissioning Process Design Checklist for Mechanical Engineer's First Submittal [Gdl 1.1-2021, Annex M, Example Checklist 2]

Instructions: Step 1: Circle Yes or No and fill in with requested information.
Step 2: Explain all "No" responses at the bottom of the checklist.

Item	Task Description	Location of Information in the Programming Document	Response
1	**Owner's Project Requirements**		
A	**Key Owner's Project Requirements**		**Complete**
1	Commissioning Plan Updated, provide date and enclose with this submittal		Yes No
2	Basis of Design for controls completed		Yes No
3	Basis of Design for accessibility completed		Yes No
4	Sustainability and LEED issues coordination addressed		Yes No
5	Do the general HVAC&R requirements the current OPR requirements? Has justification been document and approved by owner's Project Manager?		Yes No
6	Control format, BACnet requirements complete and documented		Yes No
B	**Owner's Objectives**		
1	Preliminary mechanical room layout complete		Yes No
2	Energy analysis meeting goal of 30% less than ASHRAE 90?		Yes No
3	Single line diagrams developed for controls and systems		Yes No
4	Report on safety factors and tolerance for facility system operations		Yes No
5	Have chillers been sized and pre-order to meet occupancy goal		Yes No
6	Environmental and sustainability initial design complete		Yes No
C	**General Owner's Needs**		
1	Is current HVAC and control systems budget enclosed and within initial budget		Yes No
2	Mechanical rooms space and location coordinated with shops		Yes No
3	Has Electrical, Plumbing, Lighting and Communications coordination been completed?		Yes No
4	Does the initial design meet all Benchmark Established for HVAC&R? Document?		Yes No
5	Constructability and maintainability analysis completed		Yes No

"No" Responses

Item	Date	Reason for "No" Response

Table 22.3 Example Commissioning Process Construction Checklist for a Hot Water Unit Heater [Gdl 1.1-2021, Annex M, Example Checklist 22]

Instructions: Step 1: Circle Yes or No and fill in with requested information.
Step 2: Explain all "No" responses at the bottom of the checklist.

Item		Task Description	Response	
1		**Delivery Book**		
	A	**Model Verification**	**Submitted**	**Delivered**
	1	Manufacturer		
	2	Model		
	3	Serial number	N/A	
	4	Fan Motor Power (hp)		
	5	Fan Motor Voltage / Phase / Frequency (V / - / Hz)	/ /	/ /
	6	Total Heating Capacity (MBH)		
	7	Heating Fluid Flow / Pressure Drop (gpm/ft wg)	/	/
	B	**Physical Checks**		
	1	Unit is free from physical damage	Yes	No
	2	All components present	Yes	No
	3	The water openings are sealed with plastic plugs	Yes	No
	4	Manufacturer's data readable/accurate	Yes	No
	5	Unit identification attached and visible	Yes	No
2		**Construction Checklist**		
	A	**Installation of Unit Heater**		
	1	Unit supported using adequately sized mounting anchors	Yes	No
	2	Adequate clearance around unit for service	Yes	No
	3	All components accessible for maintenance	Yes	No
	4	Unit can be removed from building	Yes	No
	5	Unit identification attached and visible	Yes	No
	B	**Piping**		
	1	All piping components have been installed (in the correct order) as required by detail drawing	Yes	No
	2	Piping arranged for ease of unit removal	Yes	No
	3	Piping supported as required by specifications	Yes	No
	4	Piping is clean	Yes	No
	5	Piping insulation complete and installed as per specifications	Yes	No
	6	All valves and test ports are easily accessible	Yes	No
	C	**Electrical**		
	1	Local disconnect installed in an accessible location	Yes	No
	2	Motor rotation in the proper direction	Yes	No
	3	All electrical connections are tight	Yes	No
	4	All electrical components are grounded	Yes	No
	D	**Controls**		
	1	Room thermostat installed and calibration verified	Yes	No
	2	Hot water actuator calibration verified	Yes	No
	3	Heating sequence of control verified	Yes	No
	4	Valve tags are attached	Yes	No

Table 22.3 Example Commissioning Process Construction Checklist for a Hot Water Unit Heater [Gdl 1.1-2021, Annex M, Example Checklist 22] ***(Continued)***

Item	Task Description	Response	
E	TAB		
1	Motor rotation in the proper direction	Yes	No
2	Motor overloads verified	Yes	No
3	Motor voltage and amps verified - each phase	Yes	No
4	Entering and leaving air temperatures (°F)	/	/
5	Flow and air/water pressure drops verified	Yes	No

"No" Responses

Item	Date	Reason for "No" Response

Commissioning

Table 22.4 Example Commissioning Process Construction Checklist for a Split System A/C Unit [Gdl 1.1-2021, Annex M, Example Checklist 20]

Instructions: Step 1: Circle Yes or No and fill in with requested information.
Step 2: Explain all "No" responses at the bottom of the checklist.

Item	Task Description	Response	
1	**Delivery Book**		
A	**Model Verification**	**Submitted**	**Delivered**
1	Manufacturer		
2	Model		
3	Serial Number	N/A	
4	Airflow (cfm)		
5	Fan Motor Power (hp)		
6	Fan Motor Voltage / Phase / Frequency (V / - / Hz)	/ /	/ /
7	Total Cooling Capacity (MBH)		
B	**Physical Checks**		
1	Unit is free from physical damage	Yes	No
2	All components present	Yes	No
3	The refrigerant line openings are sealed	Yes	No
4	Installation and startup manual provided	Yes	No
5	Unit tags affixed	Yes	No
2	**Construction Checklist**		
A	**Installation of Split System Coil**		
1	Unit supported using adequately sized mounting anchors	Yes	No
2	Adequate clearance around unit for service	Yes	No
3	All components are accessible for maintenance	Yes	No
4	Unit can be removed from building	Yes	No
5	Condensate drain piping un-trapped and runs to open sight drain	Yes	No
6	Unit labeled and is easy to see	Yes	No
B	**Piping**		
1	All piping components have been installed (in the correct order) as required by detail drawing	Yes	No
2	Piping arranged for ease of unit removal	Yes	No
3	Piping supported as required by specifications	Yes	No
4	Refrigerant lines connected to indoor and outdoor units	Yes	No
5	Piping is clean and free from leaks	Yes	No
6	Piping insulation is complete and installed as per specifications	Yes	No
7	All valves and test ports are easily accessible	Yes	No
8	Valve tags attached	Yes	No
9	Unit filled with correct refrigerant	Yes	No
C	**Electrical**		
1	Local disconnect installed in an accessible location	Yes	No
2	Fan motor rotation in the proper direction	Yes	No
3	All electrical connections are tight	Yes	No
4	All electrical components are grounded	Yes	No

Table 22.4 Example Commissioning Process Construction Checklist for a Split System A/C Unit [Gdl 1.1-2021, Annex M, Example Checklist 20] ***(Continued)***

Item	Task Description	Response	
D	**Controls - Installation**		
1	Room thermostat installed and calibration verified	Yes	No
2	Control wiring provided to outdoor (compressor) unit	Yes	No
3	Communication with outdoor unit verified	Yes	No
E	**Controls - Startup**		
1	Cooling sequence of control verified	Yes	No
2	System starts and runs with no unusual noise or vibration	Yes	No
3	Manufacturer's startup checklist completed and attached	Yes	No
F	**TAB**		
1	Filters installed and are clean	Yes	No
2	Entering and leaving air temperatures (°F)	/	/
3	Airflow (cfm)	/	/

"No" Responses

Item	Date	Reason for "No" Response

Table 22.5 Example Commissioning Process Construction Checklist for an HVAC Pump [Gdl 1.1-2021, Annex M, Example Checklist 19]

Instructions: Step 1: Circle Yes or No and fill in with requested information.
Step 2: Explain all "No" responses at the bottom of the checklist.

Item		Task Description	Response	
1		**Delivery Book**		
	A	**Model Verification**	**Submitted**	**Delivered**
	1	Manufacturer		
	2	Model		
	3	Serial Number	N/A	
	4	Pump Type		
	5	Impeller diameter (in.)		
	6	Inlet / Outlet Sizes (in.)	/	/
	7	Capacity / Head (gpm/ft wg)	/	/
	8	Motor Speed / Power (rpm/hp)	/	/
	9	Motor Voltage / Phase / Frequency (V / - / Hz)	/ /	/ /
	B	**Physical Checks**		
	1	Unit is free from physical damage	Yes	No
	2	All components present	Yes	No
	3	The water openings are sealed with plastic plugs	Yes	No
	4	Unit tags affixed	Yes	No
	5	Installation and startup manual provided	Yes	No
	6	Manufacturer's ratings readable/accurate	Yes	No
2		**Construction Checklist**		
	A	**Installation of Pump**		
	1	Unit secured as required by manufacturer and specifications	Yes	No
	2	Adequate clearance around unit for service	Yes	No
	3	All components accessible for maintenance	Yes	No
	4	Unit can be removed from building	Yes	No
	5	Unit labeled and is easy to see	Yes	No
	B	**Piping**		
	1	All piping components have been installed (in the correct order) as required by detail drawing	Yes	No
	2	Piping arranged for ease of unit removal	Yes	No
	3	Shut-off valves and unions installed on inlet and outlet of pump	Yes	No
	4	Pressure gauges installed on inlet and outlet of pump	Yes	No
	5	Piping supported as required by specifications	Yes	No
	6	Piping is clean	Yes	No
	7	Piping insulation complete and installed as per specifications	Yes	No
	8	All valves and test ports are easily accessible	Yes	No
	9	Valve tags attached	Yes	No
	C	**Electrical**		
	1	Safety disconnect installed in an accessible location	Yes	No
	2	Motor rotation in the proper direction	Yes	No
	3	All electrical connections are tight	Yes	No
	4	All electrical components are grounded	Yes	No

Table 22.5 Example Commissioning Process Construction Checklist for an HVAC Pump [Gdl 1.1-2021, Annex M, Example Checklist 19] ***(Continued)***

Item	Task Description	Response	
D	**Mechanical - Startup**		
1	Unit checked, aligned, and certified prior to startup and report submitted	Yes	No
2	Unit and motor lubricated before startup	Yes	No
3	Pump shaft rotates easily with power turned off	Yes	No
4	System starts and runs without any unusual noise or vibration	Yes	No
5	Manufacturer's startup checklist completed and attached	Yes	No
E	**TAB**		
1	Flow Rate, gpm		
2	Inlet pressure (ft) / Outlet pressure (ft)	/	/
3	Motor rotation in the proper direction	Yes	No
4	Motor overload verified	Yes	No
5	Motor voltage and amps verified - each phase	Yes	No
6	Start-up strainer removed (after 24 hours)	Yes	No

"No" Responses

Item	Date	Reason for "No" Response

Table 22.6 Example Commissioning Process Construction Checklist for a Fire Damper [Gdl 1.1-2021, Annex M, Example Checklist 14]

Instructions:	Step 1: Circle Yes or No and fill in with requested information. Step 2: Explain all "No" responses at the bottom of the checklist.

Item	Task Description	Response	
1	**Delivery Book**		
A	**Model Verification**	**Submitted**	**Delivered**
1	Manufacturer		
2	Model		
3	Style		
4	Width (in.)		
5	Height (in.)		
6	Orientation		
B	**Physical Checks**		
1	Unit is free from physical damage	Yes	No
2	All components/accessories present	Yes	No
3	Installation manual provided	Yes	No
2	**Construction Checklist**		
A	**Installation of Fire Damper**		
1	Unit secured as required by manufacturer and specifications	Yes	No
2	Adequate clearance around unit for maintenance	Yes	No
3	Unit mounted in correct orientation	Yes	No

"No" Responses

Item	Date	Reason for "No" Response

Table 22.7 Example Commissioning Process Test Protocol for Verification of Thermal Comfort OPR [Adapted from Gdl 1.1-2021, Tbl U-1]

Test	Step	Expected	Actual	Pass/Fail
Morning Warm-up – Cloudy Day				
	Set Perimeter Spaces to 64°F (10°F cooler than set point)			
	Set Interior Spaces to 69°F (5°F cooler than set point)			
	Record Results			
	Record Time to Stability	20 min.		
	Record Issues Identified			
Morning Warm-up – Clear Day				
	Set South, West, and North Perimeter Spaces to 64°F (10°F cooler than set point)			
	Set East Perimeter to 79°F (5°F warmer than set point)			
	Set Interior Spaces to 69°F (5°F cooler than set point)			
	Record Results			
	Record Time to Stability	20 min.		
	Record Issues Identified			
Morning Cool-down – Cloudy Day				
	Set Perimeter Spaces to 84°F (10°F warmer than set point)			
	Set Interior Spaces to 79°F (5°F warmer than set point)			
	Record Results			
	Record Time to Stability	20 min.		
	Record Issues Identified			
Morning Cool-down – Clear Day				
	Set South and North Perimeter and Interior Spaces to 79°F (5°F warmer than set point)			
	Set East Perimeter to 84°F (10°F warmer than set point)			
	Set West Perimeter to 76°F (2°F warmer than set point)			
	Record Results			
	Record Time to Stability	20 min.		
	Record Issues Identified			
Peak Cooling				
	Set All Spaces to 84°F (10°F warmer than set point)			
	Record Results			
	Record Time to Stability	20 min.		
	Record Issues Identified			
Peak Heating				
	Set All Spaces to 64°F (10°F cooler than set point)			
	Record Results			
	Record Time to Stability	20 min.		
	Record Issues Identified			
Afternoon Cooling				
	Set West Perimeter to 79°F (5°F warmer than set point)			
	Sell All Other Spaces to 74°F (at set point)			
	Record Results			
	Record Time to Stability	20 min.		
	Record Issues Identified			
Conference Room Load				
	Set Conference Room to 84°F (10°F warmer than set point)			
	Sell All Other Spaces to 78°F (3°F warmer than set point)			
	Record Results			
	Record Time to Stability	20 min.		
	Record Issues Identified			

Table 22.7 Example Commissioning Process Test Protocol for Verification of Thermal Comfort OPR [Adapted from Gdl 1.1-2021, Tbl U-1] ***(Continued)***

Other Observations: The following observations were noted during the implementation of this comfort OPR commissioning process test procedure:

#	Observation
1	
2	
3	
4	
5	
6	

Issues: The following issues were identified during the implementation of this comfort OPR commissioning process test procedure and require follow-up (the detailed issue should be entered into the issues database).

#	Issue Description	Person Responsible
1		
2		
3		
4		
5		

Signatures: The following shall be completed after implementation of the test procedure.

Signature	Signature
Commissioning Authority	BAMS Contractor
Date/Time	Date/Time
Signature	Signature
Mechanical Contractor	Electrical Contractor
Date/Time	Date/Time

23. GENERAL

Table 23.1 General Design Criteria[a, b] [Adapted from 2007A, Ch 3, Tbl 1]

General Category	Specific Category	Inside Design Conditions: Winter	Inside Design Conditions: Summer	Air Movement	Circulation, ach	Noise[c]	Filtering Efficiencies	Load Profile	Comments
Dining and Entertainment Centers	Cafeterias and Luncheonettes	70 to 74°F 20 to 30% rh	78°F[d] 50% rh	50 fpm at 6 ft above floor	12 to 15	NC 40 to 50[e]	MERV 6–8	Peak at 1 to 2 PM 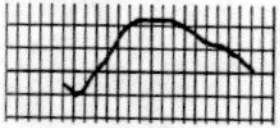	Prevent draft discomfort for patrons waiting in serving lines
	Restaurants	70 to 74°F 20 to 30% rh	74 to 78°F 55 to 60% rh	25 to 30 fpm	8 to 12	NC 35 to 40	MERV 6–8	Peak at 1 to 2 PM 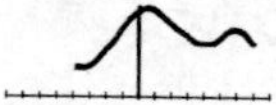	
	Bars	70 to 74°F 20 to 30% rh	74 to 78°F 50 to 60% rh	30 fpm at 6 ft above floor	15 to 20	NC 35 to 50	Use charcoal for odor control with manual purge control for 100% outside air to exhaust MERV 6–8 prefilters	Peak at 5 to 7 PM 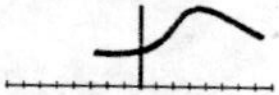	
	Nightclubs and Casinos	70 to 74°F 20 to 30% rh	74 to 78°F 50 to 60% rh	below 25 fpm at 5 ft above floor	20 to 30	NC 35 to 45[f]	Use charcoal for odor control with manual purge control for 100% outside air to exhaust MERV 6–8 prefilters	Nightclubs peak at 8 PM to 2 AM; Casinos peak at 4 PM to 2 AM; Equipment, 24 h/day	Provide good air movement but prevent cold draft discomfort for patrons
	Kitchens	70 to 74°F	85 to 88°F	30 to 50 fpm	12 to 15[g]	NC 40 to 50	N/A	 h	Negative air pressure required for odor control (also see 2019A, Ch 34)

Table 23.1 General Design Criteria[a, b] [Adapted from 2007A, Ch 3, Tbl 1] (*Continued*)

General Category	Specific Category	Inside Design Conditions: Winter	Inside Design Conditions: Summer	Air Movement	Circulation, ach	Noise[c]	Filtering Efficiencies	Load Profile	Comments
Office Buildings		70 to 74°F 20 to 30% rh	74 to 78°F 50 to 60% rh	25 to 45 fpm 0.75 to 2 cfm/ft^2	4 to 10	NC 30 to 40	MERV 6–8	Peak at 4 PM 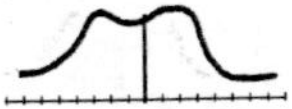	
Museums, Galleries, Libraries, and Archives (also see 2019A, Ch 24)	Average	68 to 72°F 40 to 55% rh		below 25 fpm	8 to 12	NC 35 to 40	MERV 6–8	Peak at 3 PM 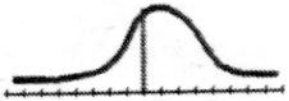	
	Archival	See 2019A, Ch 24		below 25 fpm	8 to 12	NC 35	MERV 8 prefilters plus charcoal filters MERV 11–13 final[i]	Peak at 3 PM 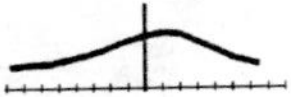	
Bowling Centers		70 to 74°F 20 to 30% rh	75 to 78°F 50 to 55% rh	50 fpm at 6 ft above floor	10 to 15	NC 40 to 50	MERV 3–5	Peak at 6 to 8 PM 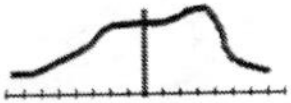	
Communication Centers	Telephone Terminal Rooms	72 to 78°F 40 to 50% rh	72 to 78°F 40 to 50% rh	25 to 30 fpm	8 to 20	to NC 60	MERV 11–13	Varies with location and use	Constant temperature and humidity required
	Radio and Television Studios	74 to 78°F 30 to 40% rh	74 to 78°F 40 to 55% rh	below 25 fpm at 12 ft above floor	15 to 40	NC 15 to 25	MERV 6–8	Varies widely because of changes in lighting and people	Constant temperature and humidity required

Table 23.1 General Design Criteria[a, b] [Adapted from 2007A, Ch 3, Tbl 1] (*Continued*)

General Category	Specific Category	Inside Design Conditions		Air Movement	Circulation, ach	Noise[c]	Filtering Efficiencies	Load Profile	Comments
		Winter	Summer						
Transportation Centers (also see 2019A, Ch 16)	Airport Terminals	70 to 74°F 20 to 30% rh	74 to 78°F 50 to 60% rh	25 to 30 fpm at 6 ft above floor	8 to 12	NC 35 to 50	MERV 6–8 and charcoal filters	Peak at 10 AM to 9 PM	Positive air pressure required in terminal
	Ship Docks	70 to 74°F 20 to 30% rh	74 to 78°F 50 to 60% rh	25 to 30 fpm at 6 ft above floor	8 to 12	NC 35 to 50	MERV 3–5	Peak at 10 AM to 5 PM	Positive air pressure required in waiting area
	Bus Terminals	70 to 74°F 20 to 30% rh	74 to 78°F 50 to 60% rh	25 to 30 fpm at 6 ft above floor	8 to 12	NC 35 to 50	MERV 6–8 with exfiltration	Peak at 10 AM to 5 PM	Positive air pressure required in terminal
	Garages[j]	40 to 55°F	80 to 100°F	30 to 75 fpm	4 to 6	NC 35 to 50	MERV 3–5	Peak at 10 AM to 5 PM	Negative air pressure required to remove fumes; positive air in pressure adjacent occupied spaces
Warehouses		Inside design temperatures for warehouses often depend on the materials stored			1 to 4	to NC 75	MERV 3–5	Peak at 10 AM to 3 PM	

Notes for Table 23.1:

[a]This table shows design criteria differences between various commercial and public buildings. It should not be used as sole source for design criteria. Each type of data contained here can be determined from ASHRAE Handbook and standards. MERV values are approximate equivalents for ASHRAE Standard 52.1 efficiencies listed in the original table.

[b]Consult governing codes to determine minimum allowable requirements. Outside air requirements may be reduced if high-efficiency adsorption equipment or other odor- or gas-removal equipment is used. See ANSI/ASHRAE Standard 62.1 for calculation procedures.

[c]Refer to Chapter 49 of the 2019 *ASHRAE Handbook—HVAC Applications*.

[d]Food in these areas is often eaten more quickly than in a restaurant; therefore, turnover of diners is much faster. Because diners seldom remain for long periods, they do not require the degree of comfort necessary in restaurants. Thus, it may be possible to lower design criteria standards and still provide reasonably comfortable conditions. Although space conditions of 80°F and 50% rh may be satisfactory for patrons when it is 95°F and 50% rh outside, inside conditions of 78°F and 40% rh are better.

[e]Cafeterias and luncheonettes usually have some or all food preparation equipment and trays in the same room with diners. These establishments are generally noisier than restaurants, so noise transmission from air-conditioning equipment is not as critical.

[f]In some nightclubs, air-conditioning system noise must be kept low so patrons can hear the entertainment.

[g]Usually determined by kitchen hood requirements.

[h]Peak kitchen heat load does not generally occur at peak dining load, although in luncheonettes and some cafeterias where cooking is done in dining areas, peaks may be simultaneous.

[i]Methods for removing chemical pollutants must also be considered.

[j]Also includes service stations.

Air-Conditioning Formulas

1 Btu = amount of heat required to raise (or lower) temperature of one pound of water 1°F

1 ton refrigeration = 12,000 Btu/h = 200 Btu/min

1 watt = 3.412 Btu/h

1 horsepower = 2545 Btu/h

1 lb = 7000 grains

1 ft (head) = 0.433 psi

1 square foot EDR (equivalent direct radiation) = 240 Btu/h

1 boiler horsepower = 33,479 Btu/h

No. of air changes (N) = 60 (cfm)/ft^3

Sensible heat (Btu/h) = 1.08 $Q\Delta t$

where Δt = difference between entering and leaving dry-bulb temperature and Q = airflow rate in cubic feet per minute

Latent heat (Btu/h) = 0.68 $Q\Delta g$

where Δg = difference in moisture content of entering and leaving air, grains per pound of dry air

Water quantity (gpm) required for heating and cooling = $q/500\ \Delta t_{water}$

where q = load in Btu/h

Chiller capacity (tons) = gpm (chilled water) × Δt (water)/24

For air:

1 lb/h = 4.5 Q

1 ton = $Q\Delta h/2670$

$$\text{Fan hp} = \frac{\text{cfm} \times \text{static pressure (in. w.g.)}}{6356 \times \text{Efficiency}} \times \frac{\text{Density of air}}{\text{Density of standard air}}$$

For water:

1 lb/h = 500 gpm

1 ton = (gpm) $\Delta t/24$

$$\text{Pump hp} = \frac{\text{gpm} \times \text{ft head}}{3960 \times \text{Efficiency}} \times \text{Specific Gravity}$$

small pumps 0.40 – 0.60 efficiency

large pumps 0.70 – 0.85 efficiency

Control Valves (C_v): Liquid: $= \dfrac{gpm\sqrt{sp\ gr}}{\sqrt{\Delta p_{psi}}}$

Steam: $= \dfrac{(lb\ steam/hr)\sqrt{spec\ vol}}{63.5\sqrt{\Delta p_{psi}}}$

(at 5 psi, specific volume = 20.4; at 30 psi, specific volume = 9.46)

General

Water Out

Btu Added or Removed

Water In

For heating or cooling water:

$$\text{gpm} = \frac{\text{Btuh}}{500 \times (\text{water temp. rise or drop, °F})}$$

Steam or Water in

Water Out

Water In

Outlet

For heating water with steam:

$$\text{lb steam/h} = 0.5\ \text{gpm (water temp. rise, °F)}$$

For heating or cooling water with water:

$$\text{gpm}_1 = \text{gpm}_2 \left(\frac{\text{water}_2\ \text{temp. rise or drop, °F}}{\text{water}_1\ \text{temp. rise or drop, °F}} \right)$$

Steam or Water in

Air

Outlet

For heating air with steam coils:

$$\text{lb steam/h} = \left(\frac{\text{CFM}}{1000} \right) (\text{air temp. rise, °F})$$

For heating air with water coils:

$$\text{gpm} = 2.16 \left(\frac{\text{CFM}}{1000} \right) \left(\frac{\text{air temp. rise, °F}}{\text{water temp. drop, °F}} \right)$$

For radiation:

lb steam/h = 0.25 (sq ft EDR)
(1 sq ft EDR = 240 Btu/h)

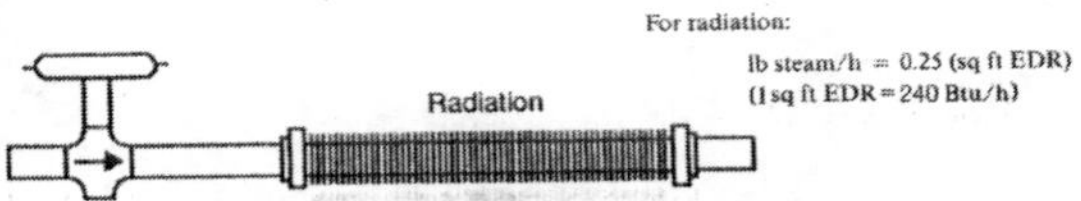

Figure 23.1 Sizing Formulas for Heating/Cooling

Table 23.2 Conversions to I-P and SI Units [2021F, Ch 40, Tbl 1]
(Multiply I-P values by conversion factors to obtain SI;
divide SI values by conversion factors to obtain I-P)

Multiply I-P	By	To Obtain SI
acre (43,560 ft^2)	0.4047	ha
	4046.873	m^2
atmosphere (standard)	*101.325	kPa
bar	*100	kPa
barrel (42 U.S. gal, petroleum)	159.0	L
	0.1580987	m^3
Btu (International Table)	1055.056	J
Btu (thermochemical)	1054.350	J
Btu/ft^2 (International Table)	11,356.53	J/m^2
Btu/ft^3 (International Table)	37,258.951	J/m^3
Btu/gal	278,717.1765	J/m^3
Btu·ft/h·ft^2·°F	1.730735	W/(m·K)
Btu·in/h·ft^2·°F (thermal conductivity k).	0.1442279	W/(m·K)
Btu/h	0.2930711	W
Btu/h·ft^2	3.154591	W/m^2
Btu/h·ft^2·°F (overall heat transfer coefficient U)	5.678263	W/(m^2·K)
Btu/lb	*2.326	kJ/kg
Btu/lb·°F (specific heat c_p)	*4.1868	kJ/(kg·K)
bushel (dry, U.S.)	0.0352394	m^3
calorie (thermochemical)	*4.184	J
centipoise (dynamic viscosity μ)	*1.00	mPa·s
centistokes (kinematic viscosity ν)	*1.00	mm^2/s
clo	0.155	(m^2·K)/W
dyne	1.0×10^{-5}	N
dyne/cm^2	*0.100	Pa
EDR hot water (150 Btu/h)	43.9606	W
EDR steam (240 Btu/h)	70.33706	W
EER	0.293	COP
ft	*0.3048	m
	*304.8	mm
ft/min, fpm	*0.00508	m/s
ft/s, fps	*0.3048	m/s
ft of water	2989	Pa
ft of water per 100 ft pipe	98.1	Pa/m
ft^2	0.092903	m^2
ft^2·h·°F/Btu (thermal resistance R)	0.176110	(m^2·K)/W
ft^2/s (kinematic viscosity ν)	92,900	mm^2/s
ft^3	28.316846	L
	0.02832	m^3
ft^3/min, cfm	0.471947	L/s
To Obtain I-P	**By**	**Divide SI**

General

Table 23.2 Conversions to I-P and SI Units [2021F, Ch 40, Tbl 1] ***(Continued)***

(Multiply I-P values by conversion factors to obtain SI; divide SI values by conversion factors to obtain I-P)

Multiply I-P	By	To Obtain SI
ft^3/s, cfs	28.316845	L/s
ft·lb_f (torque or moment)	1.355818	N·m
ft·lb_f (work)	1.356	J
ft·lb_f/lb (specific energy)	2.99	J/kg
ft·lb_f/min (power)	0.0226	W
footcandle	10.76391	lx
gallon (U.S., *231 in^3)	3.785412	L
gph	1.05	mL/s
gpm	0.0631	L/s
gpm/ft^2	0.6791	L/(s·m^2)
gpm/ton refrigeration	0.0179	mL/J
grain (1/7000 lb)	0.0648	g
gr/gal	17.1	g/m^3
gr/lb	0.143	g/kg
horsepower (boiler) (33,470 Btu/h)	9.81	kW
horsepower (550 ft·lb_f/s)	0.7457	kW
inch	*25.4	mm
in. of mercury (60°F)	3.3864	kPa
in. of water (60°F)	248.84	Pa
in/100 ft, thermal expansion coefficient	0.833	mm/m
in·lb_f (torque or moment)	113	mN·m
in^2	645.16	mm^2
in^3 (volume)	16.3874	mL
in^3/min (SCIM)	0.273117	mL/s
in^3 (section modulus)	16,387	mm^3
in^4 (section moment)	416,231	mm^4
kWh	*3.60	MJ
kW/1000 cfm	2.118880	kJ/m^3
kilopond (kg force)	9.81	N
kip (1000 lb_f)	4.45	kN
kip/in^2 (ksi)	6.895	MPa
litre	*0.001	m^3
met	58.15	W/m^2
micron (μm) of mercury (60°F)	133	mPa
mile	1.609	km
mile, nautical	*1.852	km
mile per hour (mph)	1.609344	km/h
	0.447	m/s
millibar	*0.100	kPa
mm of mercury (60°F)	0.133	kPa
mm of water (60°F)	9.80	Pa
ounce (mass, avoirdupois)	28.35	g
To Obtain I-P	**By**	**Divide SI**

General

Table 23.2 Conversions to I-P and SI Units [2021F, Ch 40, Tbl 1] ***(Continued)***

(Multiply I-P values by conversion factors to obtain SI;
divide SI values by conversion factors to obtain I-P)

Multiply I-P	By	To Obtain SI
ounce (force or thrust)	0.278	N
ounce (liquid, U.S.)	29.6	mL
ounce inch (torque, moment)	7.06	mN·m
ounce (avoirdupois) per gallon	7.489152	kg/m^3
perm (permeance at 32°F)	5.72135×10^{-11}	$kg/(Pa \cdot s \cdot m^2)$
perm inch (permeability at 32°F)	1.45362×10^{-12}	kg/(Pa·s·m)
pint (liquid, U.S.)	4.73176×10^{-4}	m^3
pound		
lb (avoirdupois, mass)	0.453592	kg
	453.592	g
lb_f (force or thrust)	4.448222	N
lb_f/ft (uniform load)	14.59390	N/m
lb/ft·h (dynamic viscosity μ)	0.4134	mPa·s
lb/ft·s (dynamic viscosity μ)	1490	mPa·s
$lb_f \cdot s/ft^2$ (dynamic viscosity μ)	47.88026	Pa·s
lb/h	0.000126	kg/s
lb/min	0.007559	kg/s
lb/h [steam at 212°F (100°C)]	0.2843	kW
lb_f/ft^2	47.9	Pa
lb/ft^2	4.88	kg/m^2
lb/ft^3 (density ρ)	16.0	kg/m^3
lb/gallon	120	kg/m^3
ppm (by mass)	*1.00	mg/kg
psi	6.895	kPa
quad (10^{15} Btu)	1.055	EJ
quart (liquid, U.S.)	0.9463	L
square (100 ft^2)	9.2903	m^2
tablespoon (approximately)	15	mL
teaspoon (approximately)	5	mL
therm (U.S.)	105.5	MJ
ton, long (2240 lb)	1.016046	Mg
ton, short (2000 lb)	0.907184	Mg; t (tonne)
ton, refrigeration (12,000 Btu/h)	3.517	kW
torr (1 mm Hg at 0°C)	133	Pa
watt per square foot	10.76	W/m^2
yd	*0.9144	m
yd^2	0.8361	m^2
yd^3	0.7646	m^3
To Obtain I-P	**By**	**Divide SI**

*Conversion factor is exact.

Notes: 1. Units are U.S. values unless noted otherwise.

2. Litre is a special name for the cubic decimetre. 1 L = 1 dm^3 and 1 mL = 1 cm^3.

24. APPENDIX

DB: Dry-bulb temperature, °F
MCWB: Mean coincident wet-bulb temperature, °F
WB: Wet-bulb temperature, °F
HDD and CDD 65: Annual heating and cooling degree-days, base 65°F, °F-day
DP: Dew-point temperature, °F

Climatic Design Conditions for Selected Locations

Station	Heating DB		Cooling DB/MCWB						Heat./Cool. Degree-Days	
			0.4%		1%		2%			
	99.6%	99%	DB	MCWB	DB	MCWB	DB	MCWB	HDD	CDD 65
United States of America										
Alabama										
AUBURN UNIVERSITY	23.2	27.5	93.4	73.7	91.3	74.1	90.1	73.9	2322	1978
BIRMINGHAM SHUTTLESWORTH	20.7	24.9	95.5	74.5	93.2	74.5	91.1	74.3	2540	2143
CAIRNS AAF	26.6	29.7	95.7	75.9	93.4	76.1	91.5	75.7	1758	2442
DOTHAN	27.2	30.5	96.5	75.5	94.0	75.3	92.1	75.0	1699	2578
HUNTSVILLE INTL	18.5	22.7	95.4	74.9	93.2	74.6	91.1	74.1	2969	1949
MAXWELL AFB	25.2	28.8	97.2	75.8	95.2	76.2	93.2	76.1	1951	2552
MOBILE	27.5	30.9	94.2	77.1	92.3	76.8	90.7	76.4	1600	2591
MONTGOMERY	24.2	27.9	96.7	76.1	94.7	76.0	92.9	75.7	2039	2457
NORTHEAST ALABAMA	18.8	22.7	94.2	75.0	91.6	74.9	90.3	74.7	3086	1682
NORTHWEST ALABAMA	19.5	23.4	96.1	75.3	93.8	75.1	91.7	74.8	2932	1983
TUSCALOOSA	22.1	26.5	97.3	75.4	94.7	75.7	92.6	75.4	2396	2279
Alaska										
ANCHORAGE BRYANT AAF	-18.1	-12.1	75.7	60.8	72.6	59.4	69.3	57.7	10500	10
ANCHORAGE ELMENDORF AFB	-14.7	-9.1	74.5	59.0	71.7	58.1	68.4	56.7	10115	16
ANCHORAGE INTL	-7.4	-2.8	72.5	59.7	69.2	57.9	66.7	56.8	9859	10
ANCHORAGE LAKE HOOD	-7.6	-2.6	74.7	60.1	71.4	58.5	68.3	57.2	9616	22
ANCHORAGE MERRILL FIELD	-9.9	-6.0	74.0	59.8	71.5	58.7	68.5	57.2	9809	19
FAIRBANKS	-42.2	-37.6	80.8	60.9	77.7	59.9	74.5	58.4	13366	67
JUNEAU	5.6	9.8	74.4	59.7	70.5	58.4	67.0	56.7	8295	5
Arizona										
CASA GRANDE	31.7	35.4	108.5	69.7	106.5	69.2	104.9	68.8	1466	3623
DAVIS-MONTHAN AFB	32.1	35.1	105.3	65.3	103.1	65.1	100.8	64.8	1385	3262

Climatic Design Conditions for Selected Locations (*Continued*)

Station	Heating DB		Cooling DB/MCWB						Heat./Cool. Degree-Days	
			0.4%		1%		2%			
	99.6%	99%	DB	MCWB	DB	MCWB	DB	MCWB	HDD	CDD 65
FLAGSTAFF PULLIAM	4.4	9.9	85.9	55.1	83.6	54.8	81.4	54.6	6744	135
LUKE AFB	35.0	37.6	111.0	69.7	108.7	69.6	106.6	69.4	1157	4108
PHOENIX SKY HARBOR	39.3	41.9	110.5	69.2	108.5	69.0	106.7	68.9	874	4698
PRESCOTT	18.2	21.2	94.7	60.3	92.4	60.0	90.3	59.6	4032	1073
TUCSON	32.0	34.7	105.7	65.9	103.6	65.7	101.5	65.4	1328	3373
WINDOW ROCK	0.6	6.1	90.5	56.4	88.2	55.9	86.0	55.3	6242	343
YUMA	42.3	44.8	111.0	72.3	108.9	72.2	107.6	71.6	637	4759
Arkansas										
BENTONVILLE	10.1	15.9	95.3	75.1	91.7	75.2	90.2	74.5	3953	1522
DRAKE FIELD	10.4	16.1	95.2	74.4	92.1	74.9	90.1	74.6	3975	1415
FORT SMITH	17.9	22.3	100.0	75.9	96.9	76.3	94.3	76.0	3063	2193
GRIDER FIELD	21.5	25.2	97.2	77.6	94.9	77.3	92.7	76.8	2746	2226
JONESBORO	16.9	20.7	96.8	76.9	94.2	76.5	92.2	76.2	3461	1978
LITTLE ROCK AFB	17.6	21.7	99.6	77.2	96.7	77.7	94.1	77.4	3117	2125
LITTLE ROCK CLINTON	20.1	24.0	98.5	77.0	95.6	77.1	93.3	76.7	2881	2249
NORTH LITTLE ROCK	18.5	23.3	95.4	76.6	93.0	76.3	90.9	75.6	3158	1937
ROGERS	10.0	15.7	94.7	74.0	91.8	74.4	89.9	73.9	3929	1506
SMITH FIELD	10.3	16.2	97.0	74.6	93.0	74.7	90.5	74.4	3869	1542
TEXARKANA	23.7	26.9	99.2	75.7	96.6	75.8	94.1	75.6	2432	2394
California										
ALAMEDA	40.6	42.6	81.4	64.1	77.3	63.0	73.9	62.0	2484	169
BEALE AFB	31.1	33.8	101.2	70.1	98.4	69.3	95.4	68.1	2413	1523
BROWN FIELD	39.1	41.8	89.9	64.3	85.8	64.6	82.4	64.8	1557	730
CAMARILLO	37.7	40.0	87.8	63.0	83.7	62.9	80.9	63.4	1717	508
CAMP PENDLETON MCAS	31.9	34.6	91.3	65.0	87.5	65.0	84.0	65.2	1904	607
DESERT RESORTS	31.7	34.9	112.6	72.0	109.7	71.5	107.8	71.0	1038	4049
EL TORO MCAS	43.2	45.3	91.9	67.8	88.9	67.5	86.0	66.8	1111	1172

Climatic Design Conditions for Selected Locations (*Continued*)

Station	Heating DB		Cooling DB/MCWB						Heat./Cool. Degree-Days	
			0.4%		1%		2%			
	99.6%	99%	DB / MCWB		DB / MCWB		DB / MCWB		HDD / CDD 65	
FRESNO YOSEMITE	32.5	34.8	103.8	69.6	101.3	68.6	98.8	67.7	2138	2223
FULLERTON	40.0	42.8	95.3	66.8	91.7	66.8	88.7	66.2	1042	1443
HAYWARD	37.0	39.1	87.4	65.0	82.7	64.0	78.8	63.1	2414	319
HOLLYWOOD BURBANK	38.9	41.3	97.9	67.8	94.3	66.8	91.2	66.1	1345	1502
IMPERIAL COUNTY AP	35.9	38.5	111.9	72.7	109.5	72.3	107.8	72.0	893	4263
LANCASTER FOX	21.3	24.9	103.5	65.7	100.9	64.5	98.6	63.6	2883	1968
LEMORE NAS	28.3	31.1	103.7	70.0	101.3	69.1	98.9	68.4	2293	1861
LIVERMORE	30.9	33.4	99.0	67.4	95.0	65.9	91.1	64.9	2587	884
LOMPOC	32.3	35.5	82.1	62.0	78.7	61.4	74.8	60.8	2761	74
LONG BEACH	41.7	43.9	91.8	66.0	88.2	66.0	85.1	65.4	1139	1159
LOS ANGELES HAWTHORNE	44.5	45.9	88.4	63.5	84.6	63.6	81.6	63.9	1039	913
LOS ANGELES INTL	45.0	47.0	84.7	63.3	81.3	64.2	78.6	64.3	1256	672
MARCH AFB	31.5	34.4	101.4	67.6	98.8	66.7	95.8	66.1	1944	1543
MCCLELLAN-PALOMAR	43.0	44.9	84.3	62.9	81.1	64.0	78.5	64.3	1523	594
MEADOWS FIELD	33.3	36.0	103.2	69.8	100.9	69.0	98.6	68.0	1957	2406
MERCED CASTLE	30.0	31.9	102.5	69.6	100.0	68.3	98.3	67.5	2384	1774
MIRAMAR MCAS	39.3	41.7	92.1	65.8	88.5	65.6	85.2	65.5	1393	949
MODESTO CITY	31.2	33.7	101.7	69.4	98.6	68.3	95.8	67.2	2260	1691
MONTEREY	36.8	38.9	79.2	60.0	74.5	59.4	71.6	59.2	3113	64
MONTGOMERY-GIBBS	40.8	43.1	90.8	65.6	87.2	64.8	83.9	65.0	1359	950
MOUNTAIN VIEW MOFFETT	36.4	38.8	88.1	65.6	83.8	64.8	80.5	64.1	2185	451
NAPA COUNTY AP	29.6	32.1	91.1	65.9	86.4	64.9	82.4	64.0	3076	254
NORTH ISLAND NAS	44.9	46.3	85.1	63.8	81.5	65.1	79.1	65.8	1093	801
OAKLAND INTL	36.9	39.2	83.9	64.4	79.5	63.1	75.4	62.1	2602	184
ONTARIO	38.7	41.0	100.4	69.2	97.6	68.3	94.8	67.4	1323	1878
PALM SPRINGS	41.2	43.9	112.4	70.2	109.7	70.2	107.8	69.8	723	4510

Climatic Design Conditions for Selected Locations *(Continued)*

Station	Heating DB		Cooling DB/MCWB						Heat./Cool. Degree-Days	
			0.4%		1%		2%			
	99.6%	99%	DB	MCWB	DB	MCWB	DB	MCWB	HDD	CDD 65
POINT ARGUELLO	45.8	47.6	72.6	N/A	68.5	N/A	65.9	N/A	3411	28
POINT MUGU NAS	38.9	41.1	82.7	61.8	79.4	63.2	76.7	63.3	2033	265
PORTERVILLE	30.2	33.1	101.7	70.8	99.5	69.5	97.4	68.4	2423	1786
REDDING	29.4	31.8	105.4	68.0	102.4	67.1	99.4	66.0	2619	1961
RIVERSIDE	36.6	38.9	100.7	69.1	98.3	68.6	95.1	67.4	1357	1823
SACRAMENTO EXECUTIVE	31.5	34.0	100.2	69.6	97.0	68.3	93.7	67.3	2436	1238
SACRAMENTO INTL	30.8	33.6	100.3	70.1	97.5	69.1	94.6	67.8	2475	1348
SACRAMENTO MATHER	28.2	30.9	101.2	68.7	98.3	67.4	94.8	66.5	2774	1197
SACRAMENTO MCCLELLAN	31.7	34.1	101.8	69.2	99.2	67.8	95.3	66.4	2331	1526
SALINAS	34.3	36.7	83.6	61.9	79.0	61.0	75.3	60.6	2641	122
SAN BERNARDINO	34.5	37.0	103.5	68.7	100.4	67.8	98.3	67.4	1422	2049
SAN DIEGO INTL	45.3	47.2	84.8	64.4	81.6	65.6	79.0	65.8	1101	784
SAN FRANCISCO INTL	40.3	42.2	82.9	62.8	78.1	62.0	74.5	61.5	2606	173
SAN JOSE INTL	36.0	38.3	91.4	66.1	87.7	65.2	83.9	64.2	2102	619
SAN LUIS OBISPO	34.2	36.5	89.9	64.0	85.3	63.3	81.8	62.9	2155	341
SANTA BARBARA	35.4	37.3	83.5	63.5	80.1	63.4	77.2	63.0	2205	231
SANTA MARIA	33.6	35.9	85.1	62.3	80.9	61.8	77.4	61.3	2554	148
SONOMA COUNTY AP	29.3	31.5	94.9	66.5	91.0	65.7	87.3	64.5	2901	386
SOUTHERN CALIFORNIA	25.5	28.3	102.0	64.2	99.8	63.1	97.6	62.4	2596	2025
STOCKTON	30.7	33.1	101.5	69.7	98.3	68.8	95.3	68.0	2377	1419
TRAVIS AFB	30.3	33.2	99.2	67.5	95.4	66.6	91.4	65.6	2483	994
VISALIA	29.9	32.6	100.3	71.8	98.9	71.0	96.7	70.1	2413	1714
Colorado										
BUCKLEY AFB	1.5	8.1	93.4	58.5	90.9	58.6	88.4	58.5	5668	749
CENTENNIAL	0.9	7.1	92.2	59.3	90.0	59.0	87.5	58.7	5915	674

Climatic Design Conditions for Selected Locations (*Continued*)

Station	Heating DB		Cooling DB/MCWB						Heat./Cool. Degree-Days	
			0.4%		1%		2%			
	99.6%	99%	DB / MCWB		DB / MCWB		DB / MCWB		HDD / CDD 65	
COLORADO SPRINGS	2.3	7.4	91.1	58.7	88.7	58.4	86.1	58.3	6013	551
DENVER INTL	-0.2	5.8	94.8	59.8	92.3	59.7	89.6	59.5	5874	827
DENVER STAPLETON	-1.4	5.1	93.9	60.7	91.2	60.0	88.5	59.6	5667	721
FORT COLLINS	-2.6	4.8	90.1	60.9	87.2	60.4	84.4	60.1	6096	462
GRAND JUNCTION	4.9	10.9	97.8	61.2	95.5	60.3	93.1	59.8	5416	1266
GREELEY-WELD COUNTY AP	-7.7	0.3	96.6	62.8	92.8	62.4	90.2	62.3	6471	686
NORTHERN COLORADO	0.0	5.5	94.8	61.1	91.3	61.2	89.5	61.0	6096	683
PUEBLO	1.0	7.2	98.7	62.3	96.2	62.1	93.5	61.7	5378	1025
Connecticut										
BRIDGEPORT SIKORSKY	10.8	15.3	88.3	73.2	85.4	72.0	83.0	70.8	5193	906
HARTFORD BRADLEY	3.9	9.1	91.6	73.4	88.7	71.9	85.8	70.4	5828	827
HARTFORD-BRAINARD	7.3	11.8	91.2	73.4	88.5	72.2	85.8	70.9	5491	912
WATERBURY-OXFORD	3.1	8.5	87.7	73.5	84.0	71.6	81.6	69.9	6341	511
WINDHAM	3.1	8.9	89.8	73.4	87.1	72.1	84.2	70.4	5903	682
Delaware										
DOVER AFB	13.9	18.0	92.4	76.1	90.0	75.3	87.5	74.4	4433	1243
NEW CASTLE	12.8	16.9	92.1	75.2	89.5	74.1	87.0	73.2	4677	1202
Florida										
CECIL FIELD	30.3	34.0	96.6	76.9	94.2	76.5	92.3	76.1	1148	2757
DAYTONA BEACH	35.7	39.6	92.6	77.2	90.9	77.2	89.5	77.1	709	3095
FORT MEYERS SW FLORIDA INTL	41.6	45.6	93.4	76.6	92.2	76.6	91.0	76.5	295	3836
FORT MYERS PAGE FIELD	42.8	46.6	93.3	76.7	92.2	76.7	91.1	76.7	266	3996
FT LAUDERDALE HOLLYWOOD	47.8	51.9	91.5	78.4	90.5	78.3	89.8	78.3	127	4640
GAINESVILLE	29.6	33.3	94.0	76.0	92.4	75.8	90.9	75.6	1108	2771
HOMESTEAD AFB	46.1	50.3	91.3	79.3	90.4	79.1	89.7	78.9	144	4269

Climatic Design Conditions for Selected Locations (*Continued*)

Station	Heating DB		Cooling DB/MCWB						Heat./Cool. Degree-Days	
			0.4%		1%		2%			
	99.6%	99%	DB / MCWB		DB / MCWB		DB / MCWB		HDD / CDD 65	
JACKSONVILLE CRAIG	32.9	36.3	94.4	76.8	92.3	76.6	90.5	76.4	1097	2848
JACKSONVILLE INTL	29.6	32.8	94.5	77.0	92.6	76.8	90.9	76.4	1268	2676
JACKSONVILLE NAS	34.3	37.9	96.0	76.6	93.9	76.3	92.1	76.0	906	3389
KENNEDY SPACE CENTER	39.3	43.1	91.9	78.0	90.5	78.0	89.6	77.9	516	3234
MACDILL AFB	38.9	43.1	93.4	79.0	92.3	78.8	91.0	78.4	490	3671
MAYPORT NAF	34.6	38.7	93.4	77.0	91.3	77.2	89.6	77.1	1011	2986
MIAMI EXECUTIVE	45.6	49.6	92.8	78.0	91.4	77.9	90.5	77.7	162	4207
MIAMI NHC	49.0	52.7	92.0	77.7	90.9	77.7	90.0	77.6	112	4660
NAPLES	44.5	47.9	92.0	78.0	90.9	78.1	90.0	78.0	249	3969
OCALA	29.6	34.0	93.1	75.6	91.4	75.7	90.6	75.5	1011	2832
ORLANDO EXECUTIVE	39.1	43.3	93.7	76.2	92.5	76.1	91.1	75.9	488	3636
ORLANDO INTL	38.4	42.4	93.7	76.6	92.4	76.3	91.1	76.0	512	3480
ORLANDO MELBOURNE INTL	38.7	43.1	91.8	77.6	90.5	77.8	89.6	77.9	452	3555
ORLANDO SANFORD	37.2	41.3	94.4	75.9	92.9	75.8	91.3	75.7	578	3458
PALM BEACH INTL	44.6	48.5	91.8	77.8	90.5	77.8	89.4	77.7	207	4213
PANAMA CITY	31.8	35.7	92.8	76.8	91.1	76.9	90.1	76.7	1242	2847
PENSACOLA INTL	29.9	33.8	93.9	77.6	92.0	77.4	90.3	77.1	1367	2802
PENSACOLA NAS	29.1	32.9	92.8	78.6	91.0	78.3	89.8	78.1	1452	2635
SARASOTA BRADENTON INTL	40.1	44.5	92.4	78.1	91.1	78.0	90.2	78.0	434	3585
ST PETE-CLEARWATER	42.1	45.4	92.4	77.4	91.2	77.4	90.3	77.3	433	3749
TALLAHASSEE NWS	26.5	30.0	96.2	76.2	94.3	75.8	92.5	75.5	1441	2768
TAMPA INTL	39.8	43.7	92.5	76.8	91.3	77.0	90.3	76.9	481	3733
TYNDALL AFB	31.5	35.4	91.2	78.5	90.2	78.5	89.1	78.4	1264	2708
VENICE PIER	41.7	45.7	88.4	76.5	87.1	77.3	86.3	77.4	468	3125
VERO BEACH	38.8	43.2	92.1	77.2	90.8	77.5	89.9	77.5	416	3544

Climatic Design Conditions for Selected Locations *(Continued)*

Station	Heating DB		Cooling DB/MCWB						Heat./Cool. Degree-Days	
			0.4%		1%		2%			
	99.6%	99%	DB / MCWB		DB / MCWB		DB / MCWB		HDD / CDD 65	
Georgia										
ATHENS	22.4	26.3	95.4	74.6	93.2	74.2	90.9	73.9	2698	1869
ATLANTA HARTSFIELD-JACKSON	21.7	26.4	93.7	73.8	91.6	73.6	89.7	73.3	2578	1969
AUGUSTA	22.6	26.1	97.1	75.9	94.9	75.6	92.8	75.3	2325	2142
COLUMBUS	25.7	29.4	96.1	74.5	94.1	74.3	92.3	74.1	1991	2421
DANIEL FIELD	27.5	30.3	97.0	74.7	94.7	74.2	92.6	73.8	2002	2463
DEKALB-PEACHTREE	21.2	25.7	94.1	73.5	92.0	73.4	90.2	72.9	2807	1869
DOBBINS AFB	19.1	24.1	93.1	74.1	91.2	73.9	89.5	73.6	2842	1859
FULTON COUNTY AP	21.0	25.5	93.8	73.8	91.8	73.6	90.2	73.3	2767	1821
HUNTER AAF	27.8	31.6	95.4	77.6	93.3	77.3	91.1	77.1	1588	2606
LAWSON AAF	22.2	25.6	96.8	75.9	94.8	75.9	92.7	75.8	2253	2161
LEE GILMER	21.4	26.2	92.3	73.3	90.5	73.1	88.5	72.7	2927	1701
MIDDLE GEORGIA	23.7	27.2	96.7	75.1	94.5	75.0	92.5	74.8	2223	2196
MOODY AFB	28.5	32.2	95.8	76.4	94.0	76.2	92.4	75.9	1443	2659
PEACHTREE CITY	20.0	24.1	93.7	74.1	91.8	73.9	90.1	73.7	2872	1679
ROBINS AFB	24.7	28.0	96.8	75.8	94.8	75.7	92.7	75.4	2084	2273
ROME RUSSELL	19.4	23.4	95.8	74.4	93.3	74.0	91.2	73.9	2967	1847
SAVANNAH HILTON HEAD INTL	27.5	30.7	95.5	77.1	93.3	76.8	91.4	76.4	1688	2528
SOUTHWEST GEORGIA	26.5	29.5	96.7	76.0	94.8	75.8	92.9	75.6	1701	2630
VALDOSTA	27.6	30.6	96.5	76.6	94.4	76.3	92.6	75.9	1456	2663
Hawaii										
HILO INTL	61.7	62.9	86.3	74.6	85.2	74.0	84.2	73.6	0	3342
HONOLULU INTL	63.5	65.1	89.6	74.1	88.7	73.7	87.8	73.3	0	4721
KALAELOA	60.7	62.6	89.7	74.1	88.4	73.6	87.7	73.4	0	4219
KANEOHE MCAS	63.8	65.8	85.8	75.3	84.5	74.7	83.8	74.5	0	4223

Climatic Design Conditions for Selected Locations (*Continued*)

Station	Heating DB		Cooling DB/MCWB						Heat./Cool. Degree-Days	
			0.4%		1%		2%			
	99.6%	99%	DB / MCWB		DB / MCWB		DB / MCWB		HDD / CDD 65	
Idaho										
BOISE	11.4	16.4	98.7	63.7	95.9	62.9	93.1	61.9	5311	1062
CALDWELL	9.5	15.6	97.3	66.2	93.4	64.9	91.0	64.0	5621	759
COEUR D'ALENE	6.7	11.5	92.0	63.3	89.7	62.9	85.5	61.6	6734	358
IDAHO FALLS	-5.5	0.4	92.2	60.9	89.7	60.5	86.9	59.7	7621	295
LEWISTON	13.8	19.4	98.7	65.3	95.4	64.4	91.8	63.3	5024	913
MAGIC VALLEY	7.0	11.6	95.0	62.6	92.1	62.0	89.7	61.4	6036	773
POCATELLO	-0.5	4.8	94.9	61.5	92.0	60.8	89.1	59.9	6866	458
Illinois										
AURORA	-6.0	0.2	90.6	74.5	88.2	73.4	85.6	72.3	6470	757
CHAMPAIGN WILLARD	-1.7	3.7	91.3	75.0	89.6	74.7	87.1	73.4	5655	1019
CHICAGO DUPAGE	-3.8	1.2	90.3	74.7	87.9	73.5	85.1	71.8	6404	793
CHICAGO EXECUTIVE	-1.0	3.5	91.4	74.0	88.9	72.7	86.2	71.5	6203	896
CHICAGO MIDWAY	0.0	5.0	91.8	74.6	89.5	73.2	86.8	72.0	5814	1100
CHICAGO O'HARE	-1.7	3.3	91.2	74.1	88.5	72.8	86.0	71.5	6157	919
CHICAGO ROCKFORD	-6.2	-0.5	90.7	74.3	88.0	73.0	85.5	71.8	6531	813
DECATUR	1.2	6.7	92.6	76.3	90.4	75.3	88.1	74.2	5374	1124
PEORIA	-1.5	3.7	92.1	76.5	89.7	75.2	87.3	73.7	5669	1118
QUAD CITY	-4.3	1.2	92.3	76.2	89.8	74.9	87.2	73.2	6040	1028
QUINCY	-0.3	4.9	93.1	76.4	90.4	75.4	88.0	74.2	5448	1174
SCOTT AFB	6.6	11.7	95.0	77.7	92.6	76.9	90.2	76.1	4609	1445
SPRINGFIELD LINCOLN	0.5	6.2	92.8	76.8	90.6	75.9	88.4	74.4	5284	1208
ST LOUIS DOWNTOWN	8.2	12.6	95.1	76.6	92.6	76.2	90.5	75.3	4512	1493
Indiana										
EVANSVILLE	8.3	13.8	93.7	75.8	91.4	75.4	89.4	74.6	4353	1489

Climatic Design Conditions for Selected Locations (*Continued*)

Station	Heating DB		Cooling DB/MCWB						Heat./Cool. Degree-Days	
			0.4%		1%		2%			
	99.6%	99%	DB / MCWB		DB / MCWB		DB / MCWB		HDD / CDD 65	
FORT WAYNE INTL	-1.0	4.5	90.7	74.4	88.1	73.0	85.5	71.7	5948	853
GRISSOM AFB	-3.6	3.0	90.4	75.2	87.9	74.2	85.7	72.9	5876	934
INDIANAPOLIS INTL	1.8	7.5	91.1	74.8	88.9	73.9	86.6	72.7	5224	1160
MONROE COUNTY AP	3.1	9.2	91.0	75.1	89.1	74.9	86.8	73.5	5023	1066
PURDUE UNIVERSITY	-0.4	4.9	91.3	75.4	89.2	74.3	86.6	72.8	5561	1004
SOUTH BEND	-0.4	5.0	90.1	73.9	87.5	72.4	84.9	71.2	6187	804
TERRE HAUTE	1.4	7.7	92.1	75.8	90.0	75.4	87.7	74.0	5165	1114
Iowa										
AMES	-6.7	-1.6	90.8	76.1	88.3	74.8	85.8	73.2	6586	826
ANKENY	-4.4	0.4	92.9	75.6	90.2	75.2	87.7	74.0	6212	958
BOONE	-5.9	-0.1	91.0	76.3	88.9	75.3	86.1	73.5	6475	889
DAVENPORT	-7.1	-0.8	90.8	74.9	88.4	74.1	86.1	72.8	6315	926
DES MOINES	-4.4	0.4	93.0	76.1	90.1	75.0	87.4	73.6	6065	1127
DUBUQUE	-8.6	-3.2	88.3	75.1	85.6	73.4	83.2	71.6	7005	653
EASTERN IOWA	-8.8	-3.3	90.1	76.4	87.5	74.7	84.8	73.0	6718	783
SIOUX GATEWAY	-7.0	-2.4	92.9	75.4	90.1	74.4	87.5	73.2	6689	936
WATERLOO	-9.9	-4.7	90.9	75.5	88.1	73.8	85.5	72.3	6977	781
Kansas										
JOHNSON COUNTY EXECUTIVE	4.2	9.2	95.3	75.8	91.9	75.5	89.7	75.1	4822	1405
LAWRENCE	3.1	8.6	98.8	76.7	95.1	76.2	91.8	75.5	4962	1486
MANHATTAN	2.5	8.0	99.9	75.5	96.8	75.5	93.1	74.8	5053	1523
MARSHALL AAF	4.5	8.7	100.0	75.1	96.3	75.3	93.4	74.8	4866	1645
MCCONNELL AFB	8.6	12.8	99.6	73.0	96.7	73.8	93.2	73.7	4247	1766
SALINA	4.6	9.3	101.7	73.9	98.6	74.0	95.3	73.5	4746	1752
TOPEKA BILLARD	4.0	8.9	98.2	76.2	94.9	76.1	92.0	75.2	4823	1557

Climatic Design Conditions for Selected Locations *(Continued)*

Station	Heating DB		Cooling DB/MCWB						Heat./Cool. Degree-Days	
			0.4%		1%		2%			
	99.6%	99%	DB / MCWB		DB / MCWB		DB / MCWB		HDD / CDD 65	
TOPEKA FORBES	3.6	8.8	98.9	76.4	95.0	76.1	92.0	75.2	4881	1519
WICHITA EISENHOWER	7.9	12.4	100.5	73.8	97.3	74.2	94.1	73.9	4370	1788
WICHITA JABARA	6.8	11.4	99.5	73.9	96.6	74.2	92.8	74.0	4453	1642
Kentucky										
BOWLING GREEN	11.6	16.8	94.1	75.2	91.7	75.1	89.9	74.6	3892	1580
CAMPBELL AAF	11.1	16.5	94.0	76.0	91.5	75.7	90.0	75.2	3769	1648
CINCINNATI NORTHERN KENTUCKY	5.3	11.0	91.4	74.1	89.0	73.4	86.8	72.5	4879	1167
HENDERSON	8.5	13.8	93.3	76.4	91.2	75.9	90.0	75.4	4419	1432
LAKE CUMBERLAND	11.8	17.7	93.2	74.2	90.8	73.6	89.1	72.9	3992	1328
LEXINGTON BLUE GRASS	7.7	13.3	91.5	73.8	89.4	73.4	87.3	72.6	4483	1261
LOUISVILLE BOWMAN	9.8	15.6	93.3	75.2	91.2	74.7	89.5	73.8	4116	1555
LOUISVILLE INTL	10.2	15.7	94.0	75.1	91.7	74.8	89.6	74.0	4010	1678
Louisiana										
ALEXANDRIA ESLER	25.9	28.5	97.9	76.7	95.7	77.1	93.6	77.0	1931	2583
ALEXANDRIA INTL	26.9	29.8	97.2	76.8	95.0	76.8	93.0	76.6	1837	2673
BARKSDALE AFB	24.2	27.5	99.1	75.5	96.6	75.7	94.4	75.9	2198	2504
BATON ROUGE	28.2	31.5	95.0	77.4	93.3	77.3	91.9	76.9	1537	2790
LAFAYETTE	29.9	33.5	94.9	77.7	93.2	77.6	91.6	77.3	1388	2945
LAKE CHARLES NWS	30.4	33.7	95.0	77.6	93.2	77.8	91.7	77.6	1387	2941
MONROE	24.9	28.1	98.3	77.7	95.8	77.4	93.7	77.1	2146	2561
NEW ORLEANS INTL	33.1	36.6	94.4	77.8	92.8	77.7	91.2	77.5	1193	3143
NEW ORLEANS LAKEFRONT	35.6	38.9	93.6	78.6	92.6	78.4	91.1	78.0	1045	3477
NEW ORLEANS NAS	30.6	34.2	93.2	77.7	91.8	77.6	90.4	77.4	1322	2820
SHREVEPORT DOWNTOWN	26.8	29.6	99.2	76.3	96.8	76.3	94.5	76.2	2097	2723
SHREVEPORT REGIONAL	25.9	29.0	99.4	75.6	96.9	75.9	94.6	75.9	2043	2694

Climatic Design Conditions for Selected Locations (*Continued*)

Station	Heating DB		Cooling DB/MCWB						Heat./Cool. Degree-Days	
			0.4%		1%		2%			
	99.6%	99%	DB / MCWB		DB / MCWB		DB / MCWB		HDD / CDD 65	
Maine										
AUBURN-LEWISTON	-5.9	0.1	87.8	71.5	83.8	70.0	81.2	67.7	7539	336
BANGOR	-6.8	-1.6	87.5	71.0	84.0	69.2	81.1	67.2	7601	373
BRUNSWICK	-2.3	1.8	85.8	70.6	82.3	68.6	79.9	66.9	7241	355
PORTLAND INTL JETPORT	0.1	5.0	86.6	71.6	83.3	69.9	80.4	68.2	6891	402
SANFORD	-6.0	0.4	89.7	72.3	85.8	70.8	82.3	68.5	7385	379
Maryland										
ANDREWS AFB	14.0	18.1	93.7	74.8	91.0	74.1	88.5	73.0	4348	1300
BALTIMORE-WASHINGTON	13.5	17.5	94.0	75.0	91.3	74.2	88.7	72.9	4475	1314
THOMAS POINT	16.9	21.1	87.0	76.4	85.0	75.9	83.3	75.2	4153	1271
Massachusetts										
BARNSTABLE	9.8	14.5	84.6	73.2	81.9	71.8	79.6	70.6	5739	556
BOSTON LOGAN	7.7	12.8	90.8	73.0	87.7	71.6	84.5	70.0	5498	812
BUZZARDS BAY	12.3	16.6	76.5	N/A	74.9	N/A	73.6	N/A	5392	354
CHATHAM	11.7	16.4	83.4	73.4	80.9	72.0	78.7	70.8	5581	512
LAWRENCE	4.6	9.6	90.8	73.1	88.1	71.8	84.9	70.2	5975	732
MARTHA'S VINEYARD	9.6	14.3	84.2	72.8	81.6	71.7	79.4	70.6	5745	469
NEW BEDFORD	7.5	12.1	88.3	73.8	85.1	71.9	82.3	70.4	5747	610
NORWOOD	2.9	9.0	91.0	73.6	88.3	72.4	85.3	70.6	6046	647
PLYMOUTH	5.5	10.2	89.0	73.1	85.7	71.8	82.6	70.0	5988	603
SOUTH WEYMOUTH NAS	5.9	10.4	91.2	73.8	87.7	72.3	84.7	70.7	5832	646
WORCESTER	1.7	6.8	86.0	71.4	83.4	69.7	81.0	68.2	6561	523
Michigan										
DETROIT CITY	4.1	8.8	90.5	73.2	87.9	71.9	85.3	70.5	5988	901
DETROIT WAYNE COUNTY AP	2.1	7.3	90.3	74.0	87.5	72.4	85.0	70.9	6036	868

Climatic Design Conditions for Selected Locations *(Continued)*

Station	Heating DB		Cooling DB/MCWB						Heat./Cool. Degree-Days	
			0.4%		1%		2%			
	99.6%	99%	DB	MCWB	DB	MCWB	DB	MCWB	HDD	CDD 65
FLINT BISHOP	-1.1	3.9	89.9	73.1	87.1	71.9	84.4	70.2	6636	647
GRAND RAPIDS FORD	2.0	6.8	89.4	72.9	86.7	71.7	84.2	70.2	6486	698
GROSSE ILE	3.4	9.4	88.9	74.3	85.7	73.4	82.4	71.8	5929	849
JACKSON COUNTY AP	-0.4	4.7	88.8	73.2	86.1	71.8	83.5	70.3	6537	618
KALAMAZOO BATTLE CREEK	1.5	7.0	90.1	73.1	87.6	71.8	84.4	70.2	6237	758
LANSING	-1.0	4.3	89.3	72.9	86.4	71.5	83.8	69.9	6702	623
MBS INTL	-0.1	4.1	89.4	73.1	86.4	71.3	83.7	70.1	6774	625
MUSKEGON COUNTY AP	4.7	9.0	86.4	72.1	84.0	70.9	81.8	69.7	6495	574
OAKLAND COUNTY INTL	0.3	4.8	89.7	72.8	86.5	71.0	83.8	69.6	6600	685
SELFRIDGE AFB	0.4	5.4	89.9	74.2	86.5	72.4	84.0	71.1	6409	689
ST CLAIR COUNTY INTL	-1.5	4.6	89.6	73.4	85.7	71.4	82.3	69.6	6799	462
WESTERN MICHIGAN	5.6	9.8	89.1	73.4	86.3	72.0	83.5	70.8	6201	671
WILLOW RUN	0.6	5.8	92.0	73.9	89.2	72.6	86.3	71.0	6194	819
Minnesota										
DULUTH INTL	-17.3	-12.1	84.4	69.7	81.4	67.5	78.6	65.7	9173	242
DULUTH SKY HARBOR	-10.8	-6.4	86.1	71.5	82.3	69.2	80.6	67.9	8552	309
MANKATO	-12.0	-8.1	89.9	73.7	86.4	72.1	83.6	70.8	7586	663
MINNEAPOLIS ANOKA COUNTY AP	-8.8	-4.5	90.1	74.7	87.6	73.6	83.8	71.5	7524	624
MINNEAPOLIS CRYSTAL	-9.7	-6.1	90.4	73.3	87.9	71.9	84.4	69.8	7555	730
MINNEAPOLIS FLYING CLOUD	-10.6	-6.4	90.6	74.0	88.0	72.7	84.6	70.7	7368	809
MINNEAPOLIS-ST PAUL	-10.6	-6.0	90.9	73.3	87.9	72.0	85.2	70.4	7396	834
ROCHESTER INTL	-12.7	-8.1	87.7	73.5	84.7	71.9	82.3	70.5	7779	545
SOUTH ST PAUL	-8.8	-4.6	90.5	72.9	87.9	71.4	84.4	69.6	7339	768
ST CLOUD	-16.8	-11.4	89.3	72.6	86.3	70.7	83.5	68.9	8350	503
ST PAUL DOWNTOWN	-9.7	-5.8	90.4	73.7	87.7	72.5	84.2	70.6	7381	768

Climatic Design Conditions for Selected Locations (*Continued*)

Station	Heating DB		Cooling DB/MCWB						Heat./Cool. Degree-Days	
			0.4%		1%		2%			
	99.6%	99%	DB / MCWB		DB / MCWB		DB / MCWB		HDD / CDD 65	
Mississippi										
HATTIESBURG-LAUREL	25.0	27.8	96.5	75.9	93.2	75.4	91.2	75.3	2018	2323
JACKSON INTL	23.3	26.8	96.4	75.9	94.3	75.9	92.3	75.7	2210	2381
KEESLER AFB	30.2	34.2	94.3	80.0	92.4	79.5	90.8	79.0	1402	2890
MERIDIAN	22.4	25.9	96.3	76.0	94.1	76.1	92.2	75.9	2307	2230
MERIDIAN NAS	21.9	26.1	96.1	75.7	94.2	75.8	92.4	75.7	2343	2266
TUPELO	19.1	23.4	96.0	75.8	93.7	75.7	91.8	75.3	2865	2072
Missouri										
CAPE GIRARDEAU	9.7	15.4	93.9	77.1	91.9	76.7	90.0	75.9	4195	1531
COLUMBIA	3.2	8.9	94.7	75.7	91.9	75.9	89.2	75.0	4843	1341
JEFFERSON CITY	6.2	11.6	95.4	76.1	92.6	75.5	90.4	74.8	4522	1486
KANSAS CITY INTL	2.4	7.2	95.6	76.7	92.4	76.3	89.6	75.5	4977	1409
KANSAS CITY WHEELER	5.8	10.1	97.2	76.4	94.0	76.0	91.4	75.4	4510	1726
SPIRIT OF ST LOUIS	5.6	11.3	95.4	77.3	92.9	76.5	90.5	75.4	4651	1445
SPRINGFIELD-BRANSON	7.0	12.6	95.3	74.1	92.3	74.4	89.8	74.1	4369	1466
ST LOUIS LAMBERT	6.8	12.2	96.1	76.8	93.5	76.2	91.2	75.1	4379	1736
WEBB CITY JOPLIN	8.7	13.7	97.3	75.1	94.3	75.6	91.6	75.2	4010	1717
Montana										
BILLINGS LOGAN	-8.6	-2.7	94.9	62.6	91.7	61.9	88.4	61.3	6746	687
BOZEMAN YELLOWSTONE	-13.4	-6.5	92.0	61.2	88.6	60.3	85.3	59.4	8160	247
BUTTE MOONEY	-16.1	-8.7	88.1	57.4	85.0	56.5	82.0	55.9	9071	84
GREAT FALLS	-15.1	-8.9	92.9	60.9	89.5	60.1	86.1	59.3	7593	350
MALMSTROM AFB	-14.2	-8.8	94.2	62.4	90.6	61.1	87.2	60.0	7162	460
MISSOULA	-1.7	4.3	93.3	61.6	90.0	61.1	86.5	60.2	7331	352

Climatic Design Conditions for Selected Locations *(Continued)*

Station	Heating DB		Cooling DB/MCWB						Heat./Cool. Degree-Days	
			0.4%		1%		2%			
	99.6%	99%	DB	MCWB	DB	MCWB	DB	MCWB	HDD	CDD 65
Nebraska										
CENTRAL NEBRASKA	-3.0	2.0	95.5	74.2	92.4	73.4	89.4	72.3	6051	1087
EPPLEY FIELD	-2.8	1.6	95.0	76.1	92.1	75.3	89.2	73.9	5947	1233
LINCOLN	-2.4	2.2	96.3	75.2	93.2	74.8	90.4	73.7	5913	1230
NORTH OMAHA	-6.1	-0.1	94.0	75.0	90.9	74.6	88.0	73.0	5981	1093
OFFUTT AFB	-2.4	1.5	95.0	76.5	91.6	75.9	89.3	74.6	5934	1188
Nevada										
LAS VEGAS MCCARRAN	32.8	35.4	109.0	67.0	106.7	66.4	104.6	65.7	1841	3681
NELLIS AFB	30.0	32.5	109.2	66.7	107.1	66.2	104.9	65.6	1962	3509
RENO-TAHOE	15.9	19.5	96.9	61.3	94.4	60.4	91.9	59.3	4817	973
New Hampshire										
CONCORD	-3.1	1.9	90.2	71.6	87.2	69.9	84.3	68.6	7010	503
JAFFREY	-2.5	1.9	87.3	70.3	84.1	68.7	81.5	67.2	7234	402
MANCHESTER-BOSTON	1.8	7.0	91.0	71.6	88.4	70.4	85.6	69.0	6191	761
PORTSMOUTH PEASE	2.0	7.3	89.6	72.7	86.2	71.3	83.2	69.8	6390	580
New Jersey										
ATLANTIC CITY INTL	11.6	16.0	92.4	75.3	89.5	74.0	86.8	73.0	4734	1107
MCGUIRE AFB	10.5	15.1	92.9	75.7	90.3	74.6	87.8	73.4	4860	1100
MILLVILLE	10.7	15.4	91.9	75.2	89.3	74.2	86.9	73.1	4835	1087
MONMOUTH JET CENTER	10.8	15.8	91.1	74.3	88.5	73.1	85.7	72.2	4982	975
NEWARK INTL	12.1	16.2	94.0	74.3	91.1	72.8	88.3	71.9	4646	1285
TETERBORO	11.4	15.7	92.6	74.1	90.0	72.9	87.6	71.8	4868	1159
TRENTON-MERCER	11.6	15.7	92.3	74.4	89.8	73.2	87.3	72.3	4873	1103
New Mexico										
ALAMOGORDO WHITE SANDS	20.9	24.9	99.8	63.1	98.6	63.4	95.2	62.9	2885	1923

Climatic Design Conditions for Selected Locations *(Continued)*

Station	Heating DB		Cooling DB/MCWB						Heat./Cool. Degree-Days	
			0.4%		1%		2%			
	99.6%	99%	DB / MCWB		DB / MCWB		DB / MCWB		HDD / CDD 65	
ALBUQUERQUE INTL	19.0	22.4	95.6	59.8	93.4	59.6	91.2	59.4	3873	1488
CANNON AFB	13.9	18.3	98.7	63.1	95.8	63.3	93.3	63.8	3658	1492
CLOVIS	12.1	17.6	97.4	64.4	94.8	64.2	91.8	64.2	3984	1281
FOUR CORNERS	9.1	13.3	96.1	59.4	93.5	58.9	91.3	58.7	5189	1025
HOLLOMAN AFB	18.9	22.4	100.3	62.4	98.4	62.7	96.2	62.6	3076	1985
ROSWELL	17.7	21.6	101.9	64.2	99.2	64.7	96.8	64.7	3051	2042
WHITE SANDS	18.5	22.5	99.0	63.7	96.5	63.9	94.2	63.8	2948	1811
New York										
ALBANY INTL	-0.7	4.3	89.1	72.9	86.3	71.1	83.7	69.8	6418	686
AMBROSE LIGHT	12.9	16.9	84.1	N/A	81.0	N/A	78.5	N/A	4878	729
BUFFALO NIAGARA	2.5	6.8	86.3	71.3	83.9	70.0	81.7	69.1	6449	606
CHAUTAUQUA COUNTY AP	0.1	4.5	82.3	69.7	81.1	68.6	78.9	67.0	7100	322
ELMIRA CORNING	-0.8	4.1	89.6	71.7	86.5	70.4	83.8	69.1	6672	497
FARMINGDALE REPUBLIC	12.2	16.5	89.8	73.8	86.4	72.1	83.7	71.2	5008	946
GREATER BINGHAMTON	-0.6	3.9	85.1	70.0	82.3	68.6	79.8	67.4	7034	415
GREATER ROCHESTER INTL	2.2	6.6	88.9	73.0	86.0	71.4	83.2	69.8	6404	615
GRIFFISS INTL	-7.2	-0.7	87.8	72.3	85.2	70.8	82.6	69.3	7026	521
HUDSON VALLEY	2.4	8.0	91.2	73.6	88.4	72.3	85.7	70.9	5936	758
LONG ISLAND MACARTHUR	11.3	15.7	88.7	73.7	85.9	72.2	83.2	71.3	5169	876
NEW YORK KENNEDY	13.5	17.5	89.8	73.0	86.7	72.1	84.2	71.2	4761	1057
NEW YORK LA GUARDIA	13.6	17.9	92.6	73.9	89.8	72.5	87.2	71.6	4476	1332
NEW YORK STEWART	2.7	7.8	90.3	72.1	87.6	71.5	84.1	69.6	6038	704
NIAGARA FALLS INTL	1.9	6.5	88.0	72.2	85.4	71.0	82.6	69.6	6572	608
ONEIDA COUNTY AP	-5.7	0.8	87.5	72.8	84.4	70.9	82.0	69.4	6983	499
PLATTSBURGH	-8.8	-3.2	87.6	71.6	83.9	70.4	81.3	68.6	7549	407

Climatic Design Conditions for Selected Locations *(Continued)*

Station	Heating DB		Cooling DB/MCWB						Heat./Cool. Degree-Days	
			0.4%		1%		2%			
	99.6%	99%	DB / MCWB		DB / MCWB		DB / MCWB		HDD / CDD 65	
SYRACUSE HANCOCK	-1.5	4.1	89.1	73.1	86.4	71.4	83.8	69.9	6504	644
WESTCHESTER COUNTY AP	8.7	12.9	89.5	73.4	86.4	71.9	83.9	70.6	5437	816
North Carolina										
ASHEVILLE	14.9	19.4	87.9	70.7	85.9	70.2	83.9	69.6	4000	912
CHARLOTTE DOUGLAS	21.0	24.8	94.2	74.6	91.9	74.0	89.8	73.5	3030	1742
FAYETTEVILLE	22.2	26.4	96.4	76.1	93.7	75.2	91.5	74.7	2659	2083
HICKORY	19.3	23.3	92.0	72.6	89.9	72.4	87.9	71.9	3419	1432
NEW RIVER MCAS	22.8	26.5	92.7	77.8	90.6	77.3	88.7	76.5	2518	1977
PIEDMONT TRIAD	18.6	22.2	92.4	74.0	90.3	73.5	88.2	72.9	3495	1513
PITT-GREENVILLE	20.7	24.9	95.0	76.7	92.9	75.4	90.7	74.9	2960	1904
POPE AFB	20.5	24.5	96.8	76.1	94.3	75.6	91.7	75.0	2823	2064
RALEIGH-DURHAM	19.7	23.6	95.0	75.6	92.6	75.1	90.3	74.5	3188	1745
RICHLANDS ELLIS	19.5	24.7	94.6	77.5	92.0	76.7	90.3	76.0	2876	1825
SEYMOUR JOHNSON AFB	21.2	25.4	96.4	76.2	93.6	76.1	91.4	75.3	2687	2055
SIMMONS AAF	21.2	25.2	96.1	75.4	93.6	75.2	91.4	74.7	2733	2085
WILMINGTON	24.2	27.5	93.4	77.7	91.2	76.9	89.1	76.3	2355	2075
WINSTON-SALEM REYNOLDS	19.1	23.1	92.2	73.5	90.3	73.0	88.3	72.4	3398	1535
North Dakota										
BISMARCK	-17.5	-11.8	93.1	70.3	89.4	69.3	86.1	68.0	8414	555
FARGO HECTOR	-18.7	-13.9	90.0	72.4	87.0	70.4	84.3	68.8	8685	571
GRAND FORKS AFB	-20.1	-15.3	89.1	72.1	86.0	70.4	83.1	68.5	9281	414
GRAND FORKS INTL	-21.6	-16.8	88.9	71.9	85.9	69.9	83.3	68.3	9345	427
MINOT AFB	-22.2	-17.2	90.4	69.1	86.8	68.2	83.7	66.5	9356	357
MINOT INTL	-17.7	-13.0	91.0	69.2	87.7	68.5	84.2	66.5	8733	477

Climatic Design Conditions for Selected Locations (*Continued*)

Station	Heating DB		Cooling DB/MCWB						Heat./Cool. Degree-Days	
			0.4%		1%		2%			
	99.6%	99%	DB / MCWB		DB / MCWB		DB / MCWB		HDD / CDD 65	
Ohio										
AKRON-CANTON	2.2	7.3	88.8	72.8	86.3	71.6	84.0	70.2	5923	768
CINCINNATI LUNKEN	7.1	12.6	92.4	75.0	89.8	74.4	87.6	73.5	4776	1135
CLEVELAND HOPKINS	3.6	9.0	89.7	73.6	87.2	72.4	84.6	71.1	5737	853
COLUMBUS GLENN	4.5	9.8	91.1	73.4	88.9	72.5	86.6	71.3	5161	1098
COLUMBUS RICKENBACKER	4.7	10.1	92.2	73.9	90.2	73.3	88.0	72.4	5030	1152
DAYTON INTL	1.7	7.5	90.1	73.7	87.9	72.8	85.5	71.4	5442	994
FAIRFIELD COUNTY AP	1.3	8.6	90.3	74.1	88.2	73.3	85.8	72.0	5378	852
FINDLAY	0.5	5.8	90.5	73.7	88.2	72.5	85.7	71.0	5825	889
MANSFIELD LAHM	0.7	5.9	88.2	73.1	85.9	71.8	83.6	70.5	6056	717
OHIO STATE UNIVERSITY	3.5	9.1	90.3	73.7	88.1	72.9	85.8	71.6	5398	967
TOLEDO EXPRESS	0.4	5.8	91.2	74.1	88.5	72.4	85.8	70.9	6028	838
WRIGHT-PATTERSON AFB	2.5	8.6	90.8	74.3	88.5	73.2	86.2	71.9	5327	980
YOUNGSTOWN-WARREN	2.1	7.1	88.1	72.6	85.6	71.2	83.3	69.7	6113	620
Oklahoma										
LAWTON FORT SILL NORTH	15.8	20.1	103.6	72.9	100.4	73.5	97.6	73.7	3094	2343
LAWTON FORT SILL SOUTH	16.4	20.3	104.1	73.0	101.2	73.2	98.9	73.5	3123	2379
OKLAHOMA CITY POST	14.4	18.7	100.3	73.5	97.9	73.8	94.9	74.1	3418	2148
OKLAHOMA CITY ROGERS	14.6	19.0	100.6	73.9	97.6	74.2	94.7	74.3	3398	2038
STILLWATER	12.3	17.8	102.0	74.6	99.1	75.1	95.6	75.3	3576	2079
TINKER AFB	13.9	18.4	100.0	73.4	97.0	73.7	93.8	74.0	3382	2006
TULSA INTL	13.6	18.2	100.1	75.5	97.2	76.2	94.6	76.0	3411	2152
TULSA JONES	14.5	18.7	100.6	75.9	98.3	76.6	95.3	76.4	3455	2108
VANCE AFB	10.9	15.6	101.7	73.4	99.1	73.6	96.2	74.1	3908	2017

Climatic Design Conditions for Selected Locations (*Continued*)

Station	Heating DB		Cooling DB/MCWB						Heat./Cool. Degree-Days	
			0.4%		1%		2%			
	99.6%	99%	DB / MCWB		DB / MCWB		DB / MCWB		HDD / CDD 65	
Oregon										
AURORA	25.4	28.2	92.4	67.1	88.5	66.5	84.3	64.9	4380	410
CORVALLIS	24.8	27.5	92.9	67.2	89.8	66.3	85.5	64.7	4290	397
EUGENE	23.7	27.2	92.2	66.7	88.3	65.7	84.6	64.4	4629	298
MCMINNVILLE	25.8	28.2	92.8	67.0	88.9	66.1	84.4	64.7	4580	322
MEDFORD	23.9	26.7	98.9	66.8	95.5	65.6	92.3	64.4	4195	922
PORTLAND HILLSBORO	23.1	26.6	92.4	67.6	88.3	66.5	84.1	65.0	4768	290
PORTLAND INTL	25.9	29.4	91.7	67.4	87.5	66.3	83.8	64.9	4179	484
REDMOND	6.1	12.4	93.6	61.3	90.7	60.6	87.8	59.7	6456	264
SALEM	24.7	27.8	92.6	66.8	88.5	65.9	84.6	64.5	4436	379
Pennsylvania										
ALLEGHENY COUNTY AP	5.2	9.8	88.5	72.2	86.2	71.0	83.9	69.8	5385	847
ALTOONA-BLAIR COUNTY AP	5.5	9.8	88.2	71.9	85.6	70.8	83.0	69.7	5832	651
CAPITAL CITY	11.0	15.5	92.2	74.2	89.7	72.8	87.3	71.7	4974	1136
ERIE	4.8	9.7	86.9	73.0	84.4	71.8	82.1	70.6	6021	700
HARRISBURG	10.4	14.8	91.8	75.2	89.5	74.0	86.8	72.9	5026	1160
LEHIGH VALLEY	8.1	12.5	91.2	74.1	88.5	72.7	86.0	71.4	5435	902
NORTHEAST PHILADELPHIA	12.8	17.2	93.3	75.0	90.8	73.8	88.4	72.6	4628	1279
PHILADELPHIA INTL	13.8	17.8	93.4	75.0	90.8	73.9	88.4	72.5	4410	1403
PITTSBURG-BUTLER	2.6	8.0	88.1	72.3	84.5	70.9	82.3	69.4	6021	596
PITTSBURGH INTL	4.3	9.2	88.9	71.9	86.4	70.8	84.3	69.6	5518	816
READING	9.5	13.6	92.3	74.6	89.6	73.6	87.0	72.2	5125	1047
WASHINGTON COUNTY AP	1.2	7.9	88.3	71.8	85.6	71.0	83.2	69.6	5848	586
WILKES-BARRE SCRANTON	4.2	8.9	89.2	72.1	86.5	70.7	83.8	69.2	5965	688
WILLOW GROVE NAS	12.5	16.6	91.9	73.9	89.4	72.6	86.8	71.5	4935	1034

Climatic Design Conditions for Selected Locations (*Continued*)

Station	Heating DB		Cooling DB/MCWB						Heat./Cool. Degree-Days	
			0.4%		1%		2%			
	99.6%	99%	DB / MCWB		DB / MCWB		DB / MCWB		HDD / CDD 65	
Rhode Island										
PROVIDENCE GREEN	8.1	12.8	90.0	73.5	86.8	72.1	84.0	70.6	5477	798
South Carolina										
CHARLESTON INTL	27.2	30.6	94.4	77.8	92.3	77.4	90.3	76.9	1821	2429
COLUMBIA METRO	23.5	27.0	97.2	75.3	94.8	74.9	92.8	74.6	2374	2297
FLORENCE	23.6	27.0	96.0	76.5	93.6	75.9	91.5	75.5	2392	2168
FOLLY ISLAND	30.9	34.4	87.4	78.2	86.2	78.2	85.1	78.0	1878	2173
GREENVILLE-SPARTANBURG	21.6	25.4	94.1	73.4	91.8	73.2	89.5	72.7	2950	1718
SHAW AFB	23.3	27.0	96.2	75.7	93.8	75.5	91.5	75.0	2390	2163
South Dakota										
ELLSWORTH AFB	-7.5	-2.3	95.3	66.6	91.3	66.0	88.2	65.6	7002	712
RAPID CITY	-8.4	-3.0	96.6	66.1	92.4	65.9	88.8	65.3	7113	660
SIOUX FALLS	-11.1	-6.3	91.2	74.2	88.3	73.1	85.6	71.7	7442	762
Tennessee										
CHATTANOOGA	19.2	23.4	94.8	73.9	92.6	73.8	90.6	73.4	3037	1872
KNOXVILLE TYSON	16.4	21.0	92.7	73.6	90.4	73.3	88.4	72.7	3486	1585
MCKELLAR-SIPES	15.0	19.4	94.8	76.8	92.8	76.8	90.8	76.2	3444	1762
MEMPHIS INTL	19.0	23.2	96.4	77.0	94.3	76.5	92.4	76.1	2856	2321
MILLINGTON-MEMPHIS	17.8	21.3	99.5	80.8	97.1	79.6	93.4	77.9	3083	2107
NASHVILLE INTL	14.9	19.5	94.4	74.7	92.3	74.5	90.4	73.9	3430	1800
TRI-CITIES	12.8	17.4	90.5	71.9	88.4	71.4	86.5	70.9	4131	1095
Texas										
ABILENE	20.1	24.4	100.5	70.8	98.4	70.9	96.2	71.0	2413	2551
AMARILLO NWS	10.8	16.0	98.8	65.6	96.1	65.9	93.6	66.1	3952	1526
ANGELINA COUNTY AP	27.0	29.9	99.0	76.0	96.4	76.2	94.3	76.3	1792	2759

Climatic Design Conditions for Selected Locations (*Continued*)

Station	Heating DB		Cooling DB/MCWB						Heat./Cool. Degree-Days	
			0.4%		1%		2%			
	99.6%	99%	DB	MCWB	DB	MCWB	DB	MCWB	HDD	CDD 65
AUSTIN-BERGSTROM	26.6	29.9	100.3	74.3	98.4	74.6	96.5	74.7	1648	3030
BROWNSVILLE	38.6	42.4	96.2	78.4	94.9	78.3	93.7	78.2	499	4181
COLLEGE STATION EASTWOOD	28.6	31.9	99.9	75.5	98.1	75.6	96.0	75.7	1526	3165
CORPUS CHRISTI INTL	34.6	38.1	96.9	77.9	95.4	77.9	93.9	77.9	821	3697
CORPUS CHRISTI NAS	37.1	41.0	92.8	80.0	91.6	80.0	90.8	79.8	714	3786
DALLAS EXECUTIVE	24.8	28.0	101.5	74.2	99.2	74.7	96.9	74.5	2082	2862
DALLAS FORT WORTH	23.4	27.4	101.4	74.2	99.1	74.6	96.9	74.7	2113	2956
DALLAS HENSLEY FIELD	21.5	27.2	99.6	75.5	97.5	75.4	95.3	75.0	2171	2723
DALLAS LOVE FIELD	24.7	28.5	101.6	74.7	99.4	75.3	97.4	75.1	1996	3104
DEL RIO	31.5	34.5	102.4	72.3	100.5	72.5	98.8	72.6	1269	3565
DRAUGHON-MILLER CENTRAL TEXAS	25.0	27.9	100.1	74.2	98.9	74.3	96.9	74.5	1953	2807
DYESS AFB	19.0	23.1	102.3	72.0	100.1	71.8	98.0	71.8	2482	2688
EAST TEXAS	25.4	28.2	99.9	75.1	97.5	75.6	95.0	75.7	2098	2665
EL PASO	25.7	28.8	101.2	63.6	99.1	63.4	96.9	63.3	2203	2631
ELLINGTON FIELD	33.7	36.6	97.1	78.0	94.9	78.4	93.0	78.4	1159	3247
FORT WORTH ALLIANCE	21.1	25.3	102.3	74.0	99.9	74.5	97.5	74.3	2350	2774
FORT WORTH NAS	24.6	28.4	102.7	73.1	100.4	73.7	98.3	73.8	2019	3109
FT WORTH MEACHAM	22.6	26.8	101.6	74.0	99.4	74.6	97.3	74.6	2193	2851
GALVESTON	36.5	39.6	92.1	79.4	90.9	79.5	90.1	79.4	957	3438
GEORGETOWN	26.3	28.3	99.2	73.2	97.2	73.5	95.1	74.0	1918	2790
HOUSTON BUSH	31.4	34.3	97.6	76.6	95.7	76.8	93.9	76.8	1297	3200
HOUSTON HOBBY	33.5	36.6	96.3	77.2	94.4	77.3	92.8	77.2	1115	3304
HOUSTON HOOKS	29.8	33.4	98.1	75.9	95.8	76.4	93.5	76.5	1404	3071
KILLEEN REGIONAL	25.4	29.3	100.4	73.0	99.0	73.2	96.8	73.2	1805	2929
KILLEEN SKYLARK	25.6	28.7	100.1	74.2	99.0	74.3	96.9	74.5	1847	2909

Climatic Design Conditions for Selected Locations (*Continued*)

Station	Heating DB		Cooling DB/MCWB						Heat./Cool. Degree-Days	
			0.4%		1%		2%			
	99.6%	99%	DB / MCWB		DB / MCWB		DB / MCWB		HDD / CDD 65	
LACKLAND AFB	29.7	33.0	100.5	74.2	99.1	74.2	97.1	74.2	1338	3342
LAREDO	36.0	39.0	105.1	74.7	102.9	74.7	101.2	74.7	768	4541
LAUGHLIN AFB	30.5	33.9	104.3	72.0	102.1	72.6	100.0	72.7	1207	3706
LUBBOCK	15.9	20.1	99.7	66.2	97.3	67.0	94.9	67.0	3217	1959
MCALLEN	38.5	42.0	101.4	76.4	99.7	76.8	98.1	76.7	517	4667
MCGREGOR	24.7	27.7	101.7	74.6	99.6	74.8	97.7	74.9	2032	2862
MCKINNEY	20.9	25.2	100.5	74.6	98.7	75.0	96.4	75.0	2471	2559
MIDLAND INTL	20.7	24.6	101.6	67.2	99.2	67.4	97.0	67.5	2475	2528
NACOGDOCHES	24.9	27.6	99.1	75.8	96.8	76.0	93.3	75.9	2093	2496
NEW BRAUNFELS	28.7	31.8	100.3	74.1	98.6	74.2	96.7	74.4	1464	3125
PORT ARANSAS PIER	37.4	41.3	86.2	78.2	85.5	78.6	85.1	78.5	805	3136
PORT ARTHUR	31.4	34.9	95.1	77.8	93.4	78.0	91.9	78.0	1286	3024
RANDOLPH AFB	28.6	32.0	100.1	73.8	98.6	73.8	96.6	74.0	1433	3141
REESE AFB	14.7	19.4	101.0	67.0	97.8	67.3	95.1	67.2	3182	1831
SABINE PASS	32.2	36.0	89.2	77.3	87.7	77.7	86.8	77.6	1407	2710
SAN ANGELO	22.1	25.8	102.2	70.3	100.0	70.2	97.9	70.2	2138	2731
SAN ANTONIO INTL	30.0	33.1	99.3	73.6	97.7	73.6	95.9	73.8	1352	3270
SAN ANTONIO STINSON	31.0	34.0	101.3	73.9	99.4	74.2	97.5	73.9	1238	3480
SAN MARCOS	27.5	30.2	100.0	74.3	98.9	74.4	97.0	74.5	1600	3107
VALLEY	37.0	40.7	98.9	77.6	97.3	77.7	95.9	77.6	586	4161
VICTORIA	31.3	34.4	98.1	76.6	96.1	76.7	94.3	76.7	1156	3286
WACO	24.4	27.9	101.4	74.1	99.3	74.7	97.3	74.8	2003	2946
WICHITA FALLS SHEPPARD AFB	18.6	22.5	103.8	72.7	101.2	72.9	98.5	73.1	2774	2574
Utah										
HILL AFB	9.4	13.0	94.3	60.8	91.8	60.1	89.7	59.7	5892	996

Climatic Design Conditions for Selected Locations (*Continued*)

Station	Heating DB		Cooling DB/MCWB						Heat./Cool. Degree-Days	
			0.4%		1%		2%			
	99.6%	99%	DB	MCWB	DB	MCWB	DB	MCWB	HDD	CDD 65
LOGAN-CACHE	-4.5	1.0	94.9	61.6	92.4	61.0	90.0	60.3	7061	519
PROVO	8.8	13.2	95.2	62.5	92.5	62.2	90.2	62.0	5835	867
SALT LAKE CITY INTL	11.4	15.6	98.3	62.6	95.9	61.9	93.4	61.3	5329	1350
ST GEORGE	25.3	27.8	106.2	66.1	103.6	65.2	100.9	64.5	2931	2724
Vermont										
BURLINGTON INTL	-7.1	-1.7	88.5	71.3	85.7	69.9	83.0	68.6	7145	573
Virginia										
DANVILLE	18.0	21.6	93.5	74.5	91.2	74.3	89.4	73.7	3618	1466
DAVISON AAF	13.9	18.4	95.3	75.2	92.7	74.3	90.2	73.5	4207	1377
DINWIDDIE	15.8	19.2	97.2	76.8	93.4	75.9	91.2	74.9	3692	1590
LANGLEY AFB	19.4	23.8	92.5	76.3	90.4	75.8	88.3	75.0	3415	1632
LESSBURG	13.9	18.1	94.9	76.6	91.4	75.1	90.2	74.5	4396	1369
LYNCHBURG	14.7	18.8	91.7	73.5	89.5	72.9	87.2	72.0	4216	1133
MANASSAS	11.1	15.9	93.0	74.8	90.8	74.4	88.5	73.5	4752	1153
NEWPORT NEWS WILLIAMSBURG	19.4	23.3	94.3	77.1	91.7	76.2	89.8	75.4	3389	1691
NORFOLK INTL	21.8	25.8	93.5	76.8	91.2	76.0	89.0	75.3	3139	1783
NORFOLK NAS	22.5	26.8	93.9	77.0	91.5	76.1	89.7	75.5	2974	1926
OCEANA NAS	20.9	25.1	93.0	77.1	90.6	76.3	88.4	75.4	3259	1665
QUANTICO MCAF	15.9	19.6	92.5	76.3	90.2	75.8	87.9	75.0	4109	1436
RICHMOND	17.4	21.2	94.9	75.5	92.4	75.0	90.1	74.2	3635	1609
ROANOKE-BLACKSBURG	15.5	19.8	92.1	72.6	89.7	71.9	87.5	71.2	3927	1300
SHENANDOAH VALLEY	10.6	16.0	93.0	73.8	90.6	73.3	88.3	72.5	4480	1113
VIRGINIA TECH MONTGOMERY	10.3	15.7	88.8	72.3	86.3	71.3	83.9	70.6	4730	817
WASHINGTON DULLES	12.3	16.6	93.2	74.5	90.7	73.7	88.3	72.7	4557	1238
WASHINGTON RONALD REAGAN	17.1	20.7	94.5	75.6	92.0	74.7	89.6	73.7	3856	1660

Climatic Design Conditions for Selected Locations *(Continued)*

Station	Heating DB		Cooling DB/MCWB						Heat./Cool. Degree-Days	
			0.4%		1%		2%			
	99.6%	99%	DB / MCWB		DB / MCWB		DB / MCWB		HDD / CDD 65	
Washington										
ARLINGTON	19.4	23.6	83.4	66.7	80.6	64.9	76.6	63.0	5388	73
BELLINGHAM	20.5	24.7	80.2	65.4	76.8	63.9	73.6	62.2	5265	65
BREMERTON	22.8	26.7	86.4	65.6	82.1	63.9	79.1	62.5	5542	109
FAIRCHILD AFB	6.5	11.7	92.6	62.0	89.6	61.2	86.0	60.5	6707	432
GRAY AFF	20.9	24.8	87.8	66.1	83.7	64.8	80.5	63.4	5118	164
KELSO-LONGVIEW	23.4	27.0	88.3	67.3	83.7	66.2	80.6	64.7	4732	213
MCCHORD AFB	21.0	24.8	86.9	65.7	83.0	64.4	79.5	62.9	5137	139
OLYMPIA	21.0	24.6	87.7	65.7	83.8	64.6	80.1	63.3	5319	122
PASCO TRI-CITIES	11.2	17.1	99.2	69.1	96.3	67.7	92.7	66.5	4952	830
SANDERSON FIELD	22.1	25.8	88.3	65.7	83.9	64.4	79.9	63.0	5356	124
SEATTLE KING COUNTY INTL	26.8	29.8	85.9	65.2	82.2	63.9	79.2	62.7	4299	294
SEATTLE PAINE	25.4	29.0	80.9	63.8	77.2	62.3	73.8	61.1	5088	101
SEATTLE TACOMA	26.6	30.0	86.1	65.1	82.2	63.9	78.7	62.7	4621	226
SEATTLE WEST POINT	30.1	33.6	70.4	61.2	68.0	60.4	66.1	59.7	4919	8
SPOKANE FELTS FIELD	9.4	15.0	94.7	64.0	91.3	63.1	88.2	62.2	6042	508
SPOKANE INTL	6.1	11.8	93.2	62.6	90.1	61.6	86.6	60.5	6539	505
TACOMA NARROWS	27.7	31.0	83.8	64.3	80.6	63.0	76.9	61.8	4755	152
VANCOUVER PEARSON	24.4	27.4	91.4	66.7	87.7	66.1	83.6	64.7	4359	413
WALLA WALLA	12.2	18.2	98.5	66.1	94.8	64.7	91.1	63.6	4762	975
YAKIMA	9.2	14.4	97.4	66.0	94.1	65.3	90.7	63.9	5730	624
West Virginia										
HUNTINGTON TRI-STATE	9.4	14.7	91.4	74.0	89.1	73.3	86.9	72.4	4383	1171
MID-OHIO VALLEY	6.8	12.0	90.5	73.7	88.1	72.7	86.0	71.6	4871	980
YEAGER	9.6	14.8	91.1	72.9	88.8	72.4	86.7	71.7	4385	1108
Wisconsin										
APPLETON	-6.0	-0.3	88.3	75.1	84.5	72.3	82.2	70.6	7210	602

Climatic Design Conditions for Selected Locations (*Continued*)

Station	Heating DB		Cooling DB/MCWB						Heat./Cool. Degree-Days	
			0.4%		1%		2%			
	99.6%	99%	DB / MCWB		DB / MCWB		DB / MCWB		HDD / CDD 65	
CENTRAL WISCONSIN	-11.0	-7.3	86.3	72.3	83.4	70.5	81.2	68.1	8305	360
CHIPPEWA VALLEY	-13.6	-8.5	89.8	73.0	86.6	71.0	83.9	69.3	7810	592
DANE COUNTY REGIONAL	-6.8	-1.9	89.2	74.0	86.4	72.4	83.9	71.1	7053	653
FOND DU LAC	-6.4	-1.7	88.5	73.4	85.7	71.6	83.0	70.2	7144	607
GREEN BAY STRAUBEL	-8.2	-3.2	87.9	73.7	85.0	71.9	82.5	70.3	7519	500
KENOSHA AP	-3.3	1.3	90.1	74.5	87.1	73.1	84.0	71.4	6693	639
LA CROSSE	-9.2	-4.5	91.4	75.0	88.6	73.0	85.9	71.5	6929	866
MANITOWOC COUNTY AP	-4.9	0.0	85.0	71.8	82.0	70.5	79.8	68.8	7512	372
MILWAUKEE MITCHELL	-1.7	2.8	89.5	74.3	86.4	72.3	83.5	70.6	6647	715
OSHKOSH WHITTMAN	-6.3	-1.8	88.2	73.6	85.1	71.7	82.4	70.1	7309	575
SHEBOYGAN	-2.5	2.2	83.0	71.1	79.5	70.3	76.6	69.6	7259	343
SHEBOYGAN COUNTY AP	-5.1	-0.3	88.1	73.9	84.3	71.5	81.8	70.0	7439	443
WAUSAU	-12.0	-7.4	87.6	71.5	84.5	69.5	81.9	67.8	7975	469
Wyoming										
CASPER NATRONA COUNTY INTL	-7.9	-1.0	94.0	59.4	91.4	58.9	88.6	58.3	7336	472
CHEYENNE	-3.1	3.1	89.8	58.1	87.3	57.6	84.5	57.3	6972	387
Canada										
Alberta										
BOW ISLAND	-20.8	-14.3	89.3	64.4	85.9	63.1	82.5	62.3	8518	216
CALGARY INTL	-17.9	-12.0	83.8	60.8	80.3	59.9	77.0	58.8	9098	78
CANADIAN OLYMPIC PARK UPPER	-16.9	-11.4	82.9	59.5	79.3	58.4	75.9	57.4	9006	83
EDMONTON BLATCHFORD	-19.1	-13.7	83.2	63.9	80.0	62.4	77.1	61.1	9376	139
EDMONTON INTL	-26.2	-20.1	82.0	64.4	79.0	63.2	76.1	61.5	10465	43
EDMONTON NAMAO	-21.6	-16.1	82.0	63.9	79.0	62.4	76.0	60.8	10027	70
FORT MCMURRAY	-32.2	-27.2	84.0	63.3	80.4	61.7	77.2	60.2	11273	88

Climatic Design Conditions for Selected Locations *(Continued)*

Station	Heating DB		Cooling DB/MCWB						Heat./Cool. Degree-Days	
			0.4%		1%		2%			
	99.6%	99%	DB / MCWB		DB / MCWB		DB / MCWB		HDD / CDD 65	
GRANDE PRAIRIE	-30.8	-23.2	81.4	61.7	78.1	60.5	75.1	59.1	10627	46
LACOMBE	-24.9	-18.5	82.6	64.5	79.2	62.9	76.1	61.3	10225	43
LETHBRIDGE CDA	-17.8	-11.9	89.2	62.6	85.6	61.6	82.1	60.7	8020	217
MEDICINE HAT	-21.6	-14.8	91.4	63.2	88.0	62.4	84.5	61.5	8416	328
RED DEER	-24.5	-17.8	82.3	63.0	79.0	61.4	75.9	60.1	10272	44
SPRINGBANK	-22.9	-16.4	81.5	60.0	78.1	58.8	74.9	57.8	10170	13
British Columbia										
ABBOTSFORD	19.7	24.1	86.2	67.3	82.4	66.1	78.9	64.6	5154	164
AGASSIZ	19.8	23.9	86.8	68.2	83.4	67.0	80.1	65.8	5069	232
BALLENAS ISLAND	30.7	33.3	74.3	65.9	72.2	65.0	70.4	63.9	4719	109
COMOX	24.3	27.6	80.8	64.1	77.3	63.0	74.1	61.8	5465	120
DISCOVERY ISLAND	30.0	33.9	72.8	60.4	69.2	58.7	66.3	57.7	5021	19
ENTRANCE ISLAND	30.0	32.5	74.4	64.6	72.0	63.7	70.1	63.0	4772	111
ESQUIMALT HARBOUR	28.0	31.1	71.8	60.3	68.9	59.3	66.4	58.4	5370	12
HOWE SOUND PAM ROCKS	27.5	30.8	76.4	65.9	73.6	64.7	71.5	63.9	4773	148
KAMLOOPS	-0.6	5.7	93.5	64.3	89.8	63.3	86.0	62.0	6295	527
KELOWNA	1.5	8.3	91.8	64.4	88.4	63.3	84.9	62.1	6917	273
MALAHAT	22.4	26.1	81.8	62.3	78.4	61.4	75.4	60.4	5820	188
PENTICTON	8.9	14.0	91.5	65.4	88.2	64.5	85.0	63.2	6095	434
PITT MEADOWS	19.2	23.6	86.7	67.3	83.1	66.1	79.6	64.9	5275	165
POINT ATKINSON	28.7	31.5	75.8	63.7	73.6	63.7	71.6	63.1	4438	174
PRINCE GEORGE	-19.4	-12.2	82.2	61.1	78.5	59.8	75.0	58.1	9221	36
SANDHEADS	26.7	30.2	72.3	N/A	70.3	N/A	68.7	N/A	4917	62
SUMMERLAND	6.9	12.4	91.3	63.4	88.1	62.6	84.8	61.6	6264	489
UNIVERSITY OF VICTORIA	27.6	31.1	80.7	64.4	77.3	63.3	74.2	62.1	4971	68

Climatic Design Conditions for Selected Locations *(Continued)*

Station	Heating DB		Cooling DB/MCWB						Heat./Cool. Degree-Days	
			0.4%		1%		2%			
	99.6%	99%	DB / MCWB		DB / MCWB		DB / MCWB		HDD / CDD 65	
VANCOUVER HARBOUR	27.2	30.5	78.8	64.6	76.2	63.6	73.8	62.5	4762	137
VANCOUVER INTL	22.7	26.6	77.2	65.3	74.7	64.3	72.5	63.2	5171	89
VERNON	2.8	8.3	91.3	65.0	87.8	64.0	84.1	62.7	6757	387
VICTORIA GONZALES	27.4	30.9	76.0	62.1	72.0	60.5	68.9	59.2	5148	39
VICTORIA HARTLAND	25.3	29.1	83.2	65.7	79.9	64.2	76.7	63.1	5124	173
VICTORIA INTL	25.6	28.4	80.3	63.8	76.6	62.4	73.6	61.1	5324	54
WEST VANCOUVER	22.7	26.6	81.1	64.4	77.8	63.9	74.8	62.7	5288	157
WHITE ROCK	22.8	26.9	77.0	65.6	74.0	64.3	71.8	63.2	4951	62
YOHO PARK	-21.7	-15.3	78.2	56.2	74.5	55.0	70.8	53.6	11554	2
Manitoba										
WINNIPEG INTL	-25.5	-21.2	86.6	70.2	83.6	68.5	80.9	66.8	10254	303
New Brunswick										
FREDERICTON INTL	-9.5	-4.5	85.9	69.8	82.6	68.1	79.7	66.3	8174	269
MONCTON ROMEO LEBLANC	-6.7	-2.5	83.9	69.7	80.9	67.8	78.2	66.3	8265	223
SAINT JOHN	-7.5	-2.7	79.3	66.1	76.5	64.3	73.8	62.9	8371	64
Newfoundland and Labrador										
ST JOHN'S INTL	7.4	10.3	77.0	66.7	74.3	65.3	71.8	64.0	8497	69
Northwest Territories										
YELLOWKNIFE	-39.9	-35.8	78.0	61.0	75.0	59.6	72.2	58.4	14491	69
Nova Scotia										
HALIFAX STANFIELD	0.4	4.6	82.2	68.9	79.2	67.0	76.6	65.8	7548	215
SHEARWATER	3.8	8.1	79.7	67.4	76.9	65.9	74.3	64.8	7192	160
SYDNEY	2.0	6.5	81.8	68.9	78.8	67.3	75.9	65.8	7978	168
Nunavut										
IQALUIT	-34.7	-32.1	62.8	52.6	57.8	50.4	54.1	48.4	17349	0

Climatic Design Conditions for Selected Locations *(Continued)*

Station	Heating DB		Cooling DB/MCWB						Heat./Cool. Degree-Days	
			0.4%		1%		2%			
	99.6%	99%	DB / MCWB		DB / MCWB		DB / MCWB		HDD / CDD 65	
Ontario										
BEAUSOLEIL	-12.1	-5.7	85.9	74.0	82.6	71.7	79.7	70.3	7855	387
BELLE RIVER	5.7	10.1	88.9	75.6	86.0	74.6	83.3	73.0	5952	818
CFB TRENTON	-7.5	-1.9	84.8	72.0	82.2	70.6	79.9	69.3	7341	419
ERIEAU	4.0	8.5	80.5	73.3	78.8	72.2	77.2	71.1	6457	533
GUELPH TURFGRASS INSTITUTE	-6.7	-1.4	85.5	70.7	82.7	69.4	80.1	68.0	7917	271
HAMILTON INTL	-1.7	3.3	86.9	72.5	84.2	71.1	81.5	69.8	7024	470
LONDON INTL	-2.2	3.0	86.5	72.2	83.8	71.0	81.2	69.3	7018	465
NORTH BAY	-17.8	-12.5	82.5	68.1	79.6	66.6	77.0	65.1	9227	235
OTTAWA INTL	-11.4	-6.5	87.5	71.6	84.5	69.7	81.6	68.4	8012	457
PETERBOROUGH TRENT UNIVERSITY	-9.7	-3.7	87.4	70.4	84.3	69.1	81.5	67.4	7784	347
PORT WELLER	8.0	12.0	84.8	72.6	82.1	71.6	79.7	70.5	6241	609
REGION OF WATERLOO INTL	-5.5	0.2	87.0	71.2	84.1	70.0	81.4	68.7	7541	358
SAULT STE MARIE	-13.3	-7.5	83.3	70.0	80.2	68.0	77.4	66.4	8813	176
SUDBURY	-18.4	-12.6	84.2	68.1	81.1	66.2	78.2	64.6	9328	233
THUNDER BAY	-21.1	-16.1	84.1	68.7	80.9	66.6	77.9	65.0	9926	135
TIMMINS	-27.7	-21.7	85.1	67.7	81.6	65.4	78.5	64.0	10707	162
TORONTO BILLY BISHOP	3.2	8.1	83.0	70.9	80.3	70.0	77.7	69.1	6588	459
TORONTO BUTTONVILLE	-3.9	1.6	88.9	72.1	85.6	70.2	82.6	68.8	7141	516
TORONTO PEARSON	-1.3	3.8	88.7	72.4	85.5	70.8	82.6	69.4	6803	610
WINDSOR	2.5	7.6	89.5	73.7	86.8	72.4	84.3	71.0	6128	819
Prince Edward Island										
CHARLOTTETOWN	-2.7	1.3	80.6	69.5	78.0	67.7	75.6	66.3	8119	214
Québec										
BAGOTVILLE	-20.3	-15.7	84.9	67.2	81.3	65.5	78.0	64.2	9956	197

Climatic Design Conditions for Selected Locations *(Continued)*

Station	Heating DB		Cooling DB/MCWB						Heat./Cool. Degree-Days	
			0.4%		1%		2%			
	99.6%	99%	DB / MCWB		DB / MCWB		DB / MCWB		HDD / CDD 65	
BIG TROUT LAKE	-33.9	-29.6	80.4	65.3	77.3	63.6	74.2	62.3	13145	91
JONQUIERE	-20.5	-15.7	84.1	67.5	80.8	66.1	77.6	64.9	9816	186
LA BAIE	-22.5	-17.8	84.2	67.4	80.6	66.4	77.3	64.9	10238	135
LAC SAINT-PIERRE	-11.2	-6.2	82.2	70.1	79.7	68.9	77.5	67.7	8145	386
L'ACADIE	-11.4	-6.7	86.2	71.1	83.5	69.8	80.9	68.5	7865	426
L'ASSOMPTION	-14.2	-8.7	86.9	71.6	83.9	69.7	81.2	68.3	8247	410
MONT JOLI	-9.4	-5.1	80.6	68.0	77.4	66.0	74.7	64.4	9401	139
MONT-ORFORD	-19.0	-13.2	77.2	65.3	74.3	63.9	71.6	62.8	10130	98
MONTREAL MCTAVISH	-6.9	-2.3	86.4	71.2	83.6	69.5	81.2	68.1	7400	583
MONTREAL MIRABEL INTL	-14.2	-9.0	85.5	71.7	82.6	69.7	80.0	68.1	8405	352
MONTREAL ST-HUBERT	-9.8	-5.0	86.4	72.0	83.7	70.2	81.2	68.8	7850	460
MONTREAL TRUDEAU	-9.1	-4.3	86.5	71.8	83.7	70.0	81.3	68.6	7662	542
NICOLET	-13.5	-8.5	83.8	72.3	81.1	70.5	78.7	68.9	8368	320
POINTE-AU-PERE	-7.2	-2.5	73.6	65.5	70.8	63.8	68.4	62.0	9561	21
QUEBEC CITY JEAN LESAGE	-14.4	-9.4	83.8	70.0	81.1	68.3	78.4	66.7	8933	249
QUEBEC CITY SAINTE-FOY	-11.2	-6.6	84.3	69.0	81.5	67.4	78.8	66.0	8658	292
SHERBROOKE AP	-16.8	-11.1	84.2	70.4	81.5	68.6	78.9	67.2	8729	210
SHERBROOKE LENNOXVILLE	-13.7	-8.1	85.0	70.7	82.3	69.1	79.8	67.8	8216	285
ST-ANICET	-12.4	-7.1	87.3	72.6	84.6	71.2	82.0	69.7	7894	421
STE-ANNE-DE-BELLEVUE	-10.5	-5.5	86.1	71.4	83.4	69.8	80.8	68.4	7871	443
TROIS-RIVIERES	-10.8	-6.1	81.3	70.3	79.2	69.4	77.2	68.3	8208	358
VARENNES	-10.4	-5.9	86.5	71.2	83.6	69.6	80.9	68.1	8012	390
Saskatchewan										
MOOSE JAW	-23.7	-18.4	89.2	65.4	85.4	64.4	81.8	63.1	9638	222
PRINCE ALBERT	-31.0	-25.7	83.8	66.3	80.6	64.7	77.8	62.8	11085	120

Climatic Design Conditions for Selected Locations *(Continued)*

Station	Heating DB		Cooling DB/MCWB						Heat./Cool. Degree-Days	
			0.4%		1%		2%			
	99.6%	99%	DB / MCWB		DB / MCWB		DB / MCWB		HDD / CDD 65	
REGINA	-26.9	-21.9	87.7	66.5	83.9	65.1	80.7	63.7	10296	202
SASKATOON INTL	-28.6	-23.3	86.4	65.9	82.9	64.5	79.7	63.3	10535	175
SASKATOON KERNEN FARM	-28.3	-23.0	87.2	63.8	83.4	62.4	80.2	61.0	10581	184
Yukon Territory										
WHITEHORSE	-36.5	-28.3	78.4	57.8	74.4	56.0	70.8	54.6	11982	16
Albania										
TIRANA RINAS	26.0	28.7	95.1	72.5	92.9	72.9	90.8	73.3	2724	1330
Algeria										
CONSTANTINE BOUDIAF INTL	31.6	33.4	102.4	68.1	98.9	68.0	95.5	67.6	2921	1581
DAR EL BEIDA	35.3	37.4	96.0	72.3	92.9	72.5	89.8	72.7	1735	1654
ORAN ES SENIA	36.8	39.1	93.9	70.1	91.0	70.6	88.0	71.0	1549	1715
Argentina										
BUENOS AIRES EZEIZA	32.0	35.0	93.1	72.4	90.2	71.9	87.9	71.0	2079	1231
BUENOS AIRES NEWBERY	40.6	42.7	88.9	73.8	86.1	73.4	84.2	72.5	1551	1412
CORDOBA	30.7	34.0	95.0	70.7	91.8	70.1	89.4	69.6	1752	1333
CORRIENTES	40.0	42.8	98.5	76.1	96.3	76.4	93.6	75.8	678	2978
MAR DEL PLATA	30.0	32.2	88.3	70.2	84.8	68.9	81.4	68.0	3299	457
MENDOZA	31.5	33.8	96.6	67.6	93.6	67.4	91.5	66.8	2157	1677
PARANA	36.9	39.2	94.0	73.7	91.5	73.0	89.3	72.3	1459	1663
POSADAS	41.3	44.6	97.0	75.2	95.2	75.1	93.4	75.0	527	3255
RESISTENCIA	35.5	39.1	99.0	75.6	96.8	76.0	94.7	75.9	802	2919
ROSARIO	31.3	34.0	94.2	73.9	91.6	73.1	89.5	72.5	1764	1502
SALTA	30.2	33.4	91.7	65.4	89.2	65.9	86.3	65.8	1621	1075
SAN JUAN	28.3	31.1	100.6	67.7	98.1	67.4	95.4	66.8	2074	2093
SAN MIGUEL DE TUCUMAN	38.0	40.9	98.1	74.4	95.1	74.2	92.8	73.7	976	2314

Climatic Design Conditions for Selected Locations (*Continued*)

Station	Heating DB		Cooling DB/MCWB						Heat./Cool. Degree-Days	
			0.4%		1%		2%			
	99.6%	99%	DB / MCWB		DB / MCWB		DB / MCWB		HDD / CDD 65	
SANTA FE	33.7	37.1	95.2	75.6	92.5	74.3	89.9	73.5	1385	1918
SANTIAGO DEL ESTERO	30.9	34.8	102.6	74.4	99.8	74.2	96.9	73.7	1028	2736
Armenia										
YEREVAN ARABKIR	8.4	12.7	97.0	70.9	94.7	69.8	91.8	68.8	4932	1388
Aruba										
QUEEN BEATRIX INTL	75.0	75.9	93.1	80.9	91.8	80.6	91.4	80.5	0	7003
Australia										
ADELAIDE AP	39.0	41.0	98.2	65.4	93.4	64.2	89.5	63.5	2032	923
ADELAIDE KENT TOWN	40.2	42.2	100.6	66.5	96.5	65.5	92.3	64.7	1890	1159
ADELAIDE MOUNT LOFTY	36.4	37.6	89.2	61.1	85.5	60.1	82.0	58.9	4458	371
BRISBANE AP	42.8	45.6	87.5	73.5	85.5	73.6	84.0	72.6	577	1868
BRISBANE ARCHERFIELD	41.8	44.1	91.3	73.1	88.8	72.7	86.7	72.0	630	1990
CANBERRA AP	25.5	27.7	94.1	64.5	90.0	63.7	86.3	62.5	3646	548
CANBERRA TUGGERANONG	25.3	27.3	93.7	65.3	89.7	64.5	86.1	63.2	3667	550
COOLANGATTA	42.8	46.0	85.5	73.9	84.0	73.9	82.5	72.9	543	1759
GOLD COAST SEAWAY	49.3	51.4	86.9	74.1	84.9	73.8	83.3	73.2	327	2071
MELBOURNE AP	37.1	38.9	95.8	64.6	91.2	64.1	86.3	63.3	2943	528
MELBOURNE LAVERTON	35.3	37.3	95.7	66.3	90.5	65.3	85.4	64.6	2912	474
MELBOURNE MOORABBIN	36.9	39.2	94.4	66.7	89.4	65.5	84.8	64.9	2773	466
MELBOURNE REGIONAL OFFICE	40.4	42.3	95.0	65.8	90.4	64.9	85.9	64.2	2233	649
MELBOURNE SCORESBY	36.1	38.1	94.1	67.0	89.8	66.2	85.9	65.5	2896	524
NEWCASTLE NOBBYS HEAD	45.8	47.5	87.8	67.2	82.6	67.2	79.0	68.8	1032	1084
NEWCASTLE WILLIAMTOWN	39.0	41.0	95.4	69.5	90.8	69.2	86.8	69.0	1440	1150
PERTH AP	38.9	41.0	99.4	66.9	96.2	66.6	92.9	66.2	1358	1512
PERTH JANDAKOT	35.6	38.1	97.8	67.7	94.5	67.2	91.1	66.5	1649	1274

Climatic Design Conditions for Selected Locations *(Continued)*

Station	Heating DB		Cooling DB/MCWB						Heat./Cool. Degree-Days	
			0.4%		1%		2%			
	99.6%	99%	DB	MCWB	DB	MCWB	DB	MCWB	HDD	CDD 65
PERTH METRO	38.9	41.2	97.5	68.3	94.0	67.6	90.7	67.1	1329	1421
PERTH SWANBOURNE	43.8	45.7	95.0	67.8	90.9	67.4	87.3	66.9	1121	1278
SYDNEY AP	44.1	45.6	91.9	67.0	87.6	68.1	84.1	68.3	1145	1291
SYDNEY BANKSTOWN	37.9	40.0	93.8	68.7	89.5	68.9	85.9	68.2	1584	1095
SYDNEY CANTERBURY	38.6	40.5	91.4	68.1	87.3	68.6	83.9	68.2	1588	988
SYDNEY OBSERVATORY	45.0	46.4	89.0	67.6	84.8	68.1	81.8	68.4	1099	1190
SYDNEY OLYMPIC PARK ARCHERY	41.0	42.9	93.5	69.1	89.2	68.6	85.8	68.4	1325	1221
Austria										
GUMPOLDSKIRCHEN	15.1	19.0	89.4	70.6	85.9	69.2	82.8	67.6	5222	542
TULLN LANGENLEBARN	12.8	17.8	90.0	71.1	86.4	69.6	83.4	68.0	5466	463
WIEN HOHE WARTE	15.9	19.8	89.2	71.2	85.8	69.8	82.7	68.2	5189	552
WIEN INNERE STADT	18.2	21.7	90.4	71.1	87.1	69.8	84.1	68.4	4705	773
WIEN SCHWECHAT	14.0	17.9	89.3	69.8	85.9	68.7	82.6	67.1	5391	491
Bahamas										
NASSAU INTL	58.9	61.7	92.9	79.7	91.5	79.4	90.0	78.9	10	5053
Bahrain										
BAHRAIN INTL	54.4	56.8	106.1	74.6	104.2	76.1	102.3	77.2	131	6258
Bangladesh										
DHAKA HAZRAT SHAHJALAL INTL	55.1	57.1	97.0	78.8	95.3	79.1	93.7	79.2	30	5714
Barbados										
GRANTLEY ADAMS INTL	72.8	73.5	88.2	79.4	88.1	79.4	87.8	79.3	0	6022
Belarus										
BREST SHEBRIN	1.3	7.9	87.3	67.9	83.9	66.5	80.5	64.9	6600	300
GOMEL	-4.6	1.2	87.7	68.5	84.3	67.4	81.3	65.8	7244	363
GRODNO	-2.5	3.8	85.0	68.0	81.2	66.3	78.3	64.6	7216	200

Climatic Design Conditions for Selected Locations (*Continued*)

Station	Heating DB		Cooling DB/MCWB						Heat./Cool. Degree-Days	
			0.4%		1%		2%			
	99.6%	99%	DB / MCWB		DB / MCWB		DB / MCWB		HDD / CDD 65	
MINSK	-2.6	3.0	85.3	68.0	82.2	66.1	78.9	64.7	7525	236
MOGILEV	-7.3	-1.3	84.4	67.9	80.9	66.2	78.0	65.1	7937	192
VITEBSK	-6.8	-0.8	83.9	68.0	80.5	66.2	77.3	64.5	7896	213
Belgium										
ANTWERP INTL	21.0	24.6	85.6	69.0	81.6	67.2	78.1	65.4	4897	222
BRUSSELS AP	21.0	24.6	84.9	68.6	81.0	66.8	77.5	65.1	5076	192
UCCLE	21.7	25.0	84.8	67.3	81.1	65.9	77.6	64.1	5012	224
Belize										
LADYVILLE GOLDSON INTL	62.9	65.3	91.5	80.8	90.0	80.4	89.7	80.3	0	5705
Benin										
COTONOU	71.7	73.1	91.4	80.4	90.3	80.7	89.8	80.7	0	6225
Bermuda										
BERMUDA INTL	55.1	56.9	86.8	77.9	86.0	77.8	84.6	77.0	183	2799
Bolivia										
COCHABAMBA	35.7	38.8	86.3	58.3	84.5	57.9	82.8	57.5	833	558
LA PAZ EL ALTO	22.9	24.9	64.5	42.3	62.8	42.1	61.2	41.9	6914	0
SANTA CRUZ DE LA SIERRA	49.7	52.0	95.1	74.3	93.4	74.7	91.7	75.0	143	4054
Bosnia and Herzegovina										
BJELASNICA	-1.7	2.7	67.2	54.9	64.6	54.2	62.2	53.2	10717	3
SARAJEVO	8.9	14.2	91.6	67.4	88.1	67.3	84.6	66.6	5521	447
SARAJEVO-BJELAVE	11.8	16.5	91.8	67.6	88.3	66.9	84.9	66.0	5237	555
Botswana										
GABORONE	35.4	37.8	98.4	62.5	95.8	62.6	93.5	62.7	805	2496
Brazil										
ANAPOLIS	55.3	57.2	91.2	64.6	89.3	65.2	87.5	66.0	17	2852

Climatic Design Conditions for Selected Locations (*Continued*)

Station	Heating DB		Cooling DB/MCWB						Heat./Cool. Degree-Days	
			0.4%		1%		2%			
	99.6%	99%	DB / MCWB		DB / MCWB		DB / MCWB		HDD / CDD 65	
ARACAJU	69.7	71.3	89.8	79.8	88.7	79.4	87.9	79.1	0	5517
BELEM	73.0	73.2	91.8	78.5	91.3	78.4	90.0	78.3	0	6100
BELO HORIZONTE CONFINS	51.4	53.3	89.8	67.2	87.9	67.7	86.1	67.9	110	2215
BELO HORIZONTE PAMPULHA	51.8	53.7	91.5	67.4	89.7	67.6	88.0	67.8	39	2881
BRASILIA	50.2	52.2	91.0	63.4	89.3	63.7	87.5	64.6	29	2586
CAMPINAS	48.2	51.4	92.8	68.4	91.0	68.9	89.3	69.1	166	2632
CAMPO GRANDE	46.4	49.9	95.1	68.4	93.1	69.1	91.4	69.6	156	3893
CUIABA	55.5	59.0	101.2	71.2	99.3	71.6	97.8	72.2	22	6052
CURITIBA	37.6	41.4	87.7	68.2	85.8	68.5	83.9	68.4	1094	1078
FLORIANOPOLIS	46.7	50.0	89.9	77.6	87.9	77.1	86.0	76.1	351	2388
FORTALEZA	73.0	73.4	89.8	76.7	89.2	76.4	88.1	76.0	0	6063
GOIANIA	55.3	57.3	96.6	66.4	94.7	66.8	92.9	67.6	5	4353
GUARULHOS	46.3	48.6	91.2	70.9	89.2	70.8	87.4	70.5	370	1939
LONDRINA	46.7	50.1	93.6	71.0	91.7	71.4	89.8	71.7	196	3035
MACAPA	73.0	73.3	95.4	79.6	95.2	79.6	94.7	79.7	0	6678
MACEIO	65.3	66.3	91.5	77.9	89.9	77.2	89.3	77.0	0	4800
MANAUS GOMES	71.2	71.5	96.5	78.9	95.0	78.3	93.4	78.3	0	6077
MANAUS PONTA PELADA	72.1	73.1	95.0	78.4	93.5	78.4	92.6	78.4	0	6230
NATAL	69.5	69.9	90.9	77.8	89.8	77.3	89.2	77.2	0	5568
PORTO ALEGRE	39.5	42.8	94.8	76.2	91.6	75.2	89.4	74.6	819	2110
PORTO VELHO	66.0	68.2	96.8	75.2	95.2	75.7	93.6	76.3	1	6013
RECIFE	70.7	71.5	93.1	80.8	91.7	79.9	91.0	79.5	0	5965
RIO DE JANEIRO GALEAO	58.8	60.6	96.9	76.3	94.9	76.5	92.9	76.5	10	4226
RIO DE JANEIRO SANTOS DUMONT	62.2	62.9	94.6	78.3	91.6	77.9	89.7	77.4	5	4235
SALVADOR	69.4	70.2	90.0	79.9	89.5	79.6	88.1	79.0	0	5415

Climatic Design Conditions for Selected Locations (*Continued*)

Station	Heating DB		Cooling DB/MCWB						Heat./Cool. Degree-Days	
			0.4%		1%		2%			
	99.6%	99%	DB / MCWB		DB / MCWB		DB / MCWB		HDD / CDD 65	
SAO LUIS	73.1	73.6	91.9	77.9	91.4	77.7	90.0	77.0	0	6456
SAO PAULO CONGONHAS	48.4	51.4	90.0	68.2	88.1	68.2	86.3	68.2	361	2126
TERESINA	71.4	72.6	102.1	72.1	100.6	72.7	99.0	73.2	0	7249
VITORIA	61.8	63.5	93.4	77.9	91.7	77.4	90.4	77.1	0	4682
Brunei Darussalam										
BRUNEI INTL	73.2	73.8	92.9	78.4	91.7	78.7	91.1	78.8	0	6373
Bulgaria										
CHERNI VRAH	-2.5	1.0	63.2	51.7	60.6	51.0	58.4	50.2	11495	0
PLOVDIV	13.9	19.1	94.9	69.5	91.7	69.0	89.4	68.3	4447	1041
SOFIA	10.0	14.3	91.6	66.6	87.9	65.9	85.2	65.4	5324	581
VARNA	15.6	19.7	89.6	71.7	87.0	71.6	84.5	70.9	4440	841
Burkina Faso										
BOBO-DIOULASSO	64.7	66.8	100.8	68.7	99.9	68.8	98.4	69.1	0	6303
OUAGADOUGOU	61.1	63.0	105.7	68.9	104.1	68.9	102.4	69.1	0	7006
Cameroon										
YAOUNDE	62.5	64.5	89.9	72.9	89.2	73.0	87.8	73.4	0	4093
Central African Republic										
BANGUI M'POKO INTL	60.6	62.8	97.2	73.4	95.9	73.7	94.8	74.0	0	5522
Chad										
N'DJAMENA INTL	55.9	58.8	109.6	70.9	107.9	71.0	106.1	70.7	0	7086
Chile										
ANTOFAGASTA	50.0	51.7	75.6	66.1	74.9	65.5	73.5	64.6	1279	331
SANTIAGO PUDAHUEL	30.5	32.7	89.8	62.6	87.8	62.4	85.9	62.3	2572	550
China										
ANQING	28.2	30.3	96.2	81.1	94.3	80.9	92.4	80.3	2795	2398

Climatic Design Conditions for Selected Locations (*Continued*)

Station	Heating DB		Cooling DB/MCWB						Heat./Cool. Degree-Days	
			0.4%		1%		2%			
	99.6%	99%	DB / MCWB		DB / MCWB		DB / MCWB		HDD / CDD 65	
ANYANG	16.7	20.0	95.9	73.4	93.4	74.6	91.1	74.7	4150	1841
BAODING	12.6	16.0	95.8	73.1	93.0	73.6	90.7	73.7	4755	1738
BAOJI	21.7	24.0	95.6	70.9	93.1	70.5	90.7	70.5	4107	1552
BEIJING	11.1	14.3	95.3	71.7	93.0	72.0	90.0	72.2	5115	1613
BENGBU	23.5	26.0	96.1	79.9	93.9	79.2	91.5	77.9	3373	2067
BENXI	-7.8	-3.8	89.4	72.0	86.8	71.4	84.7	70.8	7283	945
CANGZHOU	15.1	18.1	93.6	73.7	91.4	74.3	89.4	74.1	4769	1668
CHANGCHUN	-14.4	-9.7	88.2	69.6	86.0	69.8	83.9	69.2	8698	794
CHANGDE	29.8	31.8	97.6	79.8	95.4	79.7	93.2	79.2	2627	2408
CHANGSHA	29.8	31.8	97.5	78.7	95.6	78.7	93.6	78.6	2583	2510
CHAOYANG	-1.9	1.9	93.5	70.3	90.6	70.4	88.1	69.7	6577	1211
CHENGDE	-0.9	2.5	92.1	69.3	89.4	69.3	86.9	68.8	6815	971
CHENGDU SHUANGLIU	33.7	35.7	93.5	76.8	91.6	76.2	89.5	75.3	2311	1946
CHIFENG	-5.0	-1.6	91.6	67.2	88.6	66.6	86.0	65.6	7574	820
CHONGQING	37.0	38.9	99.4	77.0	96.9	77.2	94.6	77.0	2074	2377
DANDONG	3.0	6.5	86.4	75.2	84.0	73.9	81.9	72.9	6478	855
DATONG	-6.1	-2.3	89.6	63.9	86.8	63.0	84.3	62.9	7567	629
DEZHOU	17.1	19.7	93.6	75.7	91.3	75.8	89.4	75.2	4492	1738
FUZHOU	40.7	42.7	95.8	79.8	93.5	79.5	91.6	79.2	1232	3004
GANYU	19.3	22.2	92.4	79.7	89.8	78.8	87.5	78.2	4093	1594
GAOYAO	43.5	45.7	95.2	79.5	93.7	79.3	92.2	79.1	669	3777
GUANGZHOU	42.6	44.6	96.7	79.2	95.0	79.1	93.3	79.0	667	3834
GUILIN	33.9	36.1	95.4	78.1	93.6	77.9	91.8	77.7	1804	2747
GUIYANG	26.3	28.6	87.2	71.0	85.1	70.5	83.2	69.8	3097	1194
HAIKOU	51.3	54.2	95.2	80.3	93.6	80.1	92.2	79.8	183	4575

Climatic Design Conditions for Selected Locations (*Continued*)

Station	Heating DB		Cooling DB/MCWB						Heat./Cool. Degree-Days	
			0.4%		1%		2%			
	99.6%	99%	DB	MCWB	DB	MCWB	DB	MCWB	HDD	CDD 65
HANGZHOU	28.4	30.5	98.4	79.7	96.4	79.5	93.9	79.2	2712	2402
HARBIN	-17.3	-13.3	88.8	69.0	86.2	70.0	83.8	69.6	9345	763
HEFEI	24.5	26.8	96.6	82.1	94.5	81.3	92.0	80.2	3215	2178
HOHHOT	-9.7	-4.5	89.7	63.3	87.2	62.8	84.5	62.2	7949	630
HUAIYIN	22.2	24.7	93.4	80.6	91.4	79.8	89.3	78.5	3677	1795
HUICHUAN	31.1	33.0	90.8	72.9	88.8	72.6	86.9	72.1	2891	1546
JIANGLING	28.7	30.7	95.3	82.0	93.6	81.1	91.8	80.0	2791	2275
JINAN	16.8	20.0	95.3	74.0	93.1	74.2	90.9	73.7	4022	1985
JINGDEZHEN	30.1	32.1	97.4	79.8	95.7	79.4	93.9	79.0	2311	2639
JINZHOU	3.3	6.8	89.9	71.8	87.5	71.3	85.4	71.0	6218	1174
JIXI	-12.2	-8.8	87.2	69.6	84.5	68.9	81.9	68.3	9371	536
KUNMING WUJIABA	32.2	35.3	82.6	61.5	80.7	61.6	79.0	61.7	2026	644
LANZHOU	11.6	14.3	90.7	64.5	87.9	63.3	85.4	62.3	5516	811
LINGXIAN	12.9	16.5	95.1	74.6	92.7	75.2	90.3	75.2	4621	1674
LIUZHOU	37.7	40.2	95.4	78.4	93.9	78.3	92.5	78.0	1265	3393
MENGJIN	20.8	23.1	95.2	71.8	92.6	72.2	90.0	72.2	3847	1751
MUDANJIANG	-15.2	-11.3	88.6	70.4	86.1	69.2	83.4	68.5	9236	637
NANCHANG	30.9	32.9	96.7	80.0	95.0	79.9	93.3	79.6	2371	2708
NANJING	23.4	26.4	96.8	80.3	94.7	79.8	92.0	79.2	3251	2093
NANNING	40.6	42.9	95.1	79.6	93.5	79.3	91.8	78.9	880	3535
NEIJIANG	36.1	38.3	96.0	78.6	93.6	78.1	91.5	77.4	2114	2149
SANJIAZI	-18.3	-14.5	89.9	69.6	86.8	68.9	84.2	68.4	9688	764
SHANGHAI BAOSHAN	28.6	30.8	95.9	80.0	93.6	79.7	91.4	79.2	2815	2197
SHANGHAI HONGQIAO INTL	27.5	30.0	97.1	81.0	94.8	80.7	92.8	80.3	2760	2343
SHANTOU	45.1	47.9	94.8	80.6	93.0	80.6	91.2	80.4	566	3541

Climatic Design Conditions for Selected Locations *(Continued)*

Station	Heating DB		Cooling DB/MCWB						Heat./Cool. Degree-Days	
			0.4%		1%		2%			
	99.6%	99%	DB	MCWB	DB	MCWB	DB	MCWB	HDD	CDD 65
SHAOGUAN	36.2	38.3	95.6	78.6	94.0	78.4	92.4	78.1	1366	3139
SHENGYANG TAOXIAN	-11.1	-6.1	89.7	73.9	87.7	73.6	85.7	72.4	7390	1040
SHENYANG	-9.0	-4.8	89.4	74.0	87.3	72.9	85.4	72.0	7357	1019
SHENZHEN	44.9	47.9	93.2	79.5	91.6	79.5	90.1	79.4	425	4057
SHIJIAZHUANG	17.6	20.3	97.1	71.8	94.2	72.7	91.7	73.0	4296	1944
SIPING	-11.0	-7.1	88.2	71.1	86.0	70.7	84.1	70.2	8092	889
TAI SHAN	2.0	5.7	73.1	63.5	71.4	63.7	70.0	64.2	7918	95
TAIYUAN	6.2	10.0	93.0	67.5	89.9	67.3	87.8	67.0	5616	1063
TANGSHAN	7.3	11.2	92.9	73.8	90.5	73.8	88.3	73.3	5312	1514
TIANHE	27.5	30.0	97.2	81.7	95.3	81.2	93.4	80.6	2826	2442
TIANJIN	13.1	16.2	94.7	73.8	92.2	73.9	89.9	73.5	4841	1760
TIANJIN BINHAI INTL	12.3	15.7	94.9	73.1	92.8	73.5	89.8	73.1	4905	1726
URUMQI	-7.8	-3.7	92.6	62.0	89.8	61.3	87.2	60.7	7723	1032
URUMQI DIWOPU INTL	-11.4	-7.3	96.7	64.9	93.5	64.1	91.3	63.4	7643	1474
WEIFANG	13.3	16.4	94.3	75.5	91.9	75.2	89.6	74.7	4700	1564
WENZHOU	34.3	37.0	93.0	81.2	91.2	80.7	89.6	80.0	1937	2350
WUHUXIAN	26.5	28.8	97.2	81.4	95.2	80.9	92.9	80.2	2984	2236
XIAMEN	44.4	46.4	94.9	79.3	93.2	79.5	91.5	79.2	751	3342
XIANYANG	16.0	19.5	98.2	73.9	95.2	73.5	92.9	73.0	4226	1656
XIHUA	22.6	25.0	95.5	78.1	93.4	77.9	91.3	77.1	3599	1946
XINGTAI	18.9	21.5	96.6	72.1	93.8	72.9	91.4	73.3	4149	1932
XINING	0.8	3.9	82.4	59.8	79.2	58.1	76.3	56.6	7574	98
XINYANG	24.1	26.3	95.1	79.8	92.8	78.7	90.7	77.6	3306	1994
XINZHENG	21.0	23.2	96.3	74.3	93.6	74.8	91.5	74.7	3778	1889
XUZHOU	21.0	23.8	95.1	78.7	92.9	77.9	90.7	76.7	3735	1941

Climatic Design Conditions for Selected Locations (*Continued*)

Station	Heating DB		Cooling DB/MCWB						Heat./Cool. Degree-Days	
			0.4%		1%		2%			
	99.6%	99%	DB	MCWB	DB	MCWB	DB	MCWB	HDD	CDD 65
YANGJIANG	45.0	47.2	91.5	80.0	90.0	79.7	88.8	79.4	477	3717
YANJI	-7.2	-3.6	88.5	71.2	85.4	69.8	82.5	68.7	8463	554
YICHANG	29.9	31.9	96.3	79.8	94.1	78.9	91.8	77.9	2647	2190
YINCHUAN	3.5	7.0	91.3	65.6	89.0	65.3	86.7	64.5	6072	982
YINGKOU	0.5	4.3	87.2	75.9	85.2	75.0	83.6	74.2	6484	1139
YUEYANG	30.0	32.0	94.2	81.1	92.7	80.6	91.4	80.1	2585	2451
YUNCHENG	16.4	19.8	97.8	72.2	95.3	72.2	92.8	71.7	4101	1905
ZHANGJIAKOU	1.0	4.4	91.6	66.1	88.8	65.5	86.2	65.3	6675	987
ZHANJIANG	45.8	48.3	93.2	80.2	91.7	80.2	90.4	80.1	383	4051
ZHOUSHUIZI	10.0	13.2	89.4	74.5	86.4	73.7	84.3	73.1	5508	1207
Colombia										
CALI	63.8	64.3	91.0	71.9	89.5	71.9	88.0	71.7	0	4029
BARRANQUILLA	73.1	73.7	94.2	81.4	93.0	81.2	91.6	80.7	0	6671
BOGOTA	39.0	41.3	70.8	55.6	69.7	55.5	68.3	55.3	2906	0
CARTAGENA	73.8	75.0	91.7	81.7	91.2	81.5	90.0	80.9	0	6617
RIONEGRO	50.4	51.9	75.2	60.5	73.8	60.1	73.5	60.0	644	52
Congo										
BRAZZAVILLE MAYA MAYA INTL	64.6	66.2	93.6	76.3	92.7	76.3	91.4	76.2	0	5177
Congo, the Democratic Republic of the										
KINSHASA N'DJILI INTL	66.0	67.7	93.5	77.2	92.2	76.9	91.3	76.6	0	5304
Costa Rica										
SAN JOSE SANTAMARIA INTL	62.4	63.8	87.5	69.1	86.1	68.7	84.6	68.6	0	3368
Côte d'Ivoire										
ABIDJAN	71.1	71.9	91.2	81.2	90.0	80.6	89.4	80.4	0	5912

Climatic Design Conditions for Selected Locations *(Continued)*

Station	Heating DB		Cooling DB/MCWB						Heat./Cool. Degree-Days	
			0.4%		1%		2%			
	99.6%	99%	DB / MCWB		DB / MCWB		DB / MCWB		HDD / CDD 65	
Croatia										
ZAGREB MAKSIMIR	15.3	19.9	91.1	71.1	88.2	70.1	85.3	68.9	4783	682
ZAGREB PLESO	12.6	17.7	91.5	71.6	88.2	70.5	85.8	69.8	4985	625
Cuba										
CAMAGUEY INTL	59.0	62.0	92.9	74.5	91.6	74.8	90.7	74.8	6	4860
HAVANA JOSE MARTI	50.3	53.7	91.6	76.8	91.1	76.8	89.8	76.7	48	4164
SANTIAGO DE CUBA	65.9	67.6	89.8	76.8	89.2	77.0	88.1	77.1	0	5185
Cyprus										
NICOSIA ERCAN	35.8	38.9	102.3	70.1	100.3	69.9	98.4	69.9	1552	2705
Czech Republic										
BRNO-TURANY	10.8	15.0	88.3	68.7	85.0	67.6	81.8	66.2	5924	403
OSTRAVA MOSNOV	5.8	11.3	87.4	68.6	83.8	67.4	80.7	65.9	6254	266
PRAHA-KBELY	10.2	14.8	86.6	67.4	83.0	66.1	80.0	65.0	6025	296
PRAHA-LIBUS	11.0	15.5	88.5	67.1	84.6	65.8	81.3	64.5	5950	328
PRAHA-RUZYNE	9.2	14.0	86.2	66.8	82.5	65.5	79.2	64.3	6398	225
Denmark										
DROGDEN FYR	22.6	25.0	73.0	65.6	71.0	64.7	69.2	63.4	5982	74
KOEBENHAVNS AP	19.6	22.6	78.4	65.3	75.5	64.4	73.0	63.2	6216	108
ROSKILDE AP	15.6	19.5	78.7	65.0	75.5	64.4	73.0	63.2	6579	68
VAERLOSE	14.0	18.6	80.3	65.3	77.1	64.5	73.7	63.3	6792	82
Dominican Republic										
LAS AMERICAS INTL	64.7	66.2	91.5	79.3	90.0	79.1	89.6	79.0	0	5261
SANTO DOMINGO	67.9	69.2	90.9	81.0	89.9	80.9	89.1	80.6	0	5587
Ecuador										
GUAYAQUIL	66.0	66.6	91.3	75.1	89.8	75.4	89.2	75.4	0	5072

Climatic Design Conditions for Selected Locations (*Continued*)

Station	Heating DB		Cooling DB/MCWB						Heat./Cool. Degree-Days	
			0.4%		1%		2%			
	99.6%	99%	DB	MCWB	DB	MCWB	DB	MCWB	HDD	CDD 65
QUITO	43.4	45.0	71.4	53.3	70.0	53.3	69.4	53.4	2550	0
Egypt										
ALEXANDRIA INTL	44.7	46.6	93.0	71.7	89.7	73.8	88.0	74.4	761	2556
ASSIUT INTL	40.6	42.6	107.1	70.0	104.1	69.8	101.9	69.4	822	3935
CAIRO INTL	46.7	48.6	101.8	69.9	98.8	70.6	96.7	70.9	560	3574
LUXOR INTL	42.9	44.9	110.8	74.1	108.4	73.3	106.6	72.9	435	5265
PORT SAID EL GAMIL	49.3	51.4	89.9	77.5	88.2	77.7	87.5	77.5	525	2892
El Salvador										
EL SALVADOR INTL	67.6	68.4	95.4	73.4	94.7	73.9	93.3	74.7	0	6190
Equatorial Guinea										
MALABO	71.2	71.5	90.0	79.9	89.6	79.9	88.8	79.8	0	5443
Estonia										
TALLINN	-1.3	4.8	80.4	66.9	76.9	64.7	73.6	63.0	8110	81
Ethiopia										
ADDIS ABABA BOLE INTL	45.5	48.0	79.1	56.9	77.9	57.0	76.8	57.1	835	196
Faroe Islands										
TORSHAVN	25.6	27.8	57.7	54.3	56.4	53.4	55.4	52.8	7457	0
Fiji										
SUVA	67.0	68.2	87.4	N/A	86.5	N/A	85.6	N/A	0	4607
Finland										
HELSINKI VANTAA	-6.7	-0.7	81.0	65.1	78.1	63.4	75.0	61.9	8347	106
ISOSAARI	-0.8	5.1	73.4	66.3	71.2	65.3	69.3	63.8	8083	65
France										
CAP COURONNE	27.3	32.7	87.3	72.7	85.0	72.2	83.0	71.3	2822	1021
CAP FERRAT	39.3	41.4	84.4	72.3	82.6	72.3	80.9	71.8	2286	1008

Climatic Design Conditions for Selected Locations (*Continued*)

Station	Heating DB		Cooling DB/MCWB						Heat./Cool. Degree-Days	
			0.4%		1%		2%			
	99.6%	99%	DB / MCWB		DB / MCWB		DB / MCWB		HDD / CDD 65	
CAP POMEGUES	29.4	35.2	83.5	71.6	81.1	71.5	79.3	70.7	2741	823
LYON ST EXUPERY AP	21.6	24.9	91.5	68.0	88.0	67.3	84.8	66.5	4322	655
LYON-BRON AP	22.5	25.6	92.9	68.4	89.3	67.7	86.1	66.9	4181	720
MARSEILLE PROVENCE AP	28.0	30.6	91.6	69.7	89.3	69.3	87.2	68.8	2858	1215
NICE COTE D'AZUR AP	35.8	38.0	85.5	72.8	83.8	72.4	82.2	71.9	2416	1059
PARIS CHARLES DE GAULLE AP	23.2	26.3	88.0	67.8	84.1	66.5	80.6	65.2	4518	344
PARIS LE BOURGET AP	24.2	27.1	88.4	68.1	84.3	66.8	80.7	65.4	4445	326
PARIS MONTSOURIS	26.8	29.0	88.9	68.7	84.9	67.0	81.6	65.7	4060	458
PARIS ORLY AP	23.5	26.6	88.6	68.4	84.7	67.0	81.3	65.7	4521	363
TOULOUSE BLAGNAC AP	25.3	28.4	92.0	69.4	88.6	68.5	85.7	67.6	3581	751
TRAPPES	23.7	26.5	86.9	67.8	82.8	66.2	79.4	64.9	4749	271
VELIZY-VILLACOUBLAY AB	23.6	26.5	86.7	67.7	83.0	66.2	79.7	64.9	4802	302
French Guiana										
CAYENNE MATOURY	70.9	71.4	91.2	77.4	90.0	77.3	89.6	77.3	0	5568
Gabon										
LIBREVILLE INTL	71.6	73.0	89.2	81.2	88.1	80.8	87.6	80.6	0	5505
Gambia										
BANJUL YUNDUM	61.7	63.0	100.1	68.5	97.0	68.7	95.0	69.6	0	5684
Georgia										
TBILISI INTL	19.7	23.7	95.2	71.4	93.0	70.8	90.1	70.7	4032	1355
Germany										
BERLIN DAHLEM	10.4	15.6	84.7	66.2	81.1	64.7	78.1	63.3	6102	213
BERLIN SCHONEFELD	10.8	17.2	88.1	66.9	84.5	65.7	80.9	64.9	5693	331
BERLIN TEGEL	13.6	19.0	88.2	66.6	84.5	65.5	81.0	64.6	5473	385
BERLIN TEMPELHOF	11.7	17.0	86.4	66.3	82.7	65.2	79.5	63.9	5728	294

Climatic Design Conditions for Selected Locations *(Continued)*

Station	Heating DB		Cooling DB/MCWB						Heat./Cool. Degree-Days	
			0.4%		1%		2%			
	99.6%	99%	DB / MCWB		DB / MCWB		DB / MCWB		HDD / CDD 65	
BREMEN	16.1	19.7	85.7	67.4	81.2	66.2	77.8	64.6	5745	192
CELLE	13.9	18.4	87.4	67.0	83.6	65.4	80.0	64.1	5705	248
DRESDEN	11.8	17.2	87.7	66.7	84.0	65.2	80.5	64.7	5763	324
DUSSELDORF	20.8	24.6	88.0	67.5	83.9	66.0	80.4	64.8	4897	310
ESSEN MULHEIM	14.3	19.5	82.8	66.7	79.8	65.2	76.7	63.7	5720	186
FRANKFURT AM MAIN	17.2	21.4	89.7	67.9	86.0	66.6	82.4	65.1	5137	419
FURSTENFELDBRUCK	4.8	10.2	84.3	66.0	80.7	64.6	77.4	63.0	6670	147
GUTERSLOH	16.2	20.9	86.4	66.7	82.4	65.6	78.8	64.4	5539	220
HAMBURG FUHLSBUTTEL	17.2	21.0	84.5	66.6	80.7	66.1	77.2	64.2	5668	182
HANNOVER	15.8	19.7	86.3	67.5	82.5	66.2	78.9	64.6	5516	231
HEIDELBERG	17.3	21.5	89.9	68.8	86.3	67.5	82.8	65.7	4897	497
ITZEHOE	14.7	18.8	83.2	65.7	79.0	65.0	75.5	63.9	6274	112
KOELN BONN	17.7	21.6	87.9	67.6	84.0	66.0	80.4	64.8	5188	271
LEIPZIG HALLE	12.1	17.5	88.1	67.3	84.4	66.2	80.8	65.2	5597	338
LEIPZIG HOLZHAUSEN	12.2	17.2	86.5	66.8	83.0	65.2	79.6	64.2	5704	276
MUNICH INTL	8.8	14.3	86.2	66.8	82.6	65.7	79.2	64.6	6185	214
NORVENICH	19.0	22.9	87.9	67.4	83.9	66.3	80.2	64.8	5101	261
NURNBERG	12.3	17.7	89.4	67.3	85.6	66.2	82.0	64.9	5802	308
POTSDAM	9.2	14.0	85.5	66.0	81.8	64.9	78.7	63.8	6186	214
QUICKBORN	14.5	18.7	82.9	66.0	79.2	65.2	75.8	63.8	6229	101
ROTH	8.4	14.0	88.1	66.7	84.2	65.2	80.8	64.1	6336	216
STUTTGART ECHTERDINGEN	14.0	19.1	88.1	67.2	84.3	66.2	80.9	65.3	5511	319
STUTTGART SCHNARREN	11.3	15.8	85.2	67.3	82.0	65.5	79.0	64.3	5674	288
WUNSTORF	15.4	19.6	87.6	67.3	83.3	65.9	79.6	64.4	5504	259

Climatic Design Conditions for Selected Locations *(Continued)*

Station	Heating DB		Cooling DB/MCWB						Heat./Cool. Degree-Days	
			0.4%		1%		2%			
	99.6%	99%	DB / MCWB		DB / MCWB		DB / MCWB		HDD / CDD 65	
Ghana										
ACCRA	72.3	73.2	92.6	78.3	91.6	78.4	91.0	78.4	0	6287
Greece										
ATHINAI HELLINIKON	35.4	38.5	96.5	70.1	93.8	70.1	91.7	70.1	1882	2149
ELEFSIS	33.5	36.0	98.6	69.2	95.6	68.9	93.4	68.3	2108	2183
THESSALONIKI MAKEDONIA	26.5	29.8	94.9	71.0	91.8	70.7	89.8	70.1	3080	1596
Guatemala										
GUATEMALA LA AURORA	51.6	53.5	82.5	64.2	80.8	64.4	79.2	64.3	104	1314
Guyana										
TIMEHRI	69.5	70.5	92.4	78.5	91.5	78.3	90.0	77.9	0	5578
Honduras										
SAN PEDRO SULA MORALES	64.1	65.8	98.3	78.6	96.0	79.0	94.7	79.1	0	5809
TEGUCIGALPA TONCONTIN	53.4	55.4	89.7	67.0	87.9	67.6	86.2	67.5	19	2750
Hong Kong										
HONG KONG INTL	47.9	50.3	93.3	79.8	91.8	79.5	91.2	79.3	311	4328
HONG KONG OBSERVATORY	49.3	51.6	90.0	79.7	89.0	79.6	88.1	79.4	426	3556
Hungary										
BUDAORS	11.8	15.8	87.8	68.2	84.8	67.4	82.0	66.5	5530	443
BUDAPEST FERIHEGY	10.8	15.8	91.6	71.6	88.1	70.0	85.3	68.9	5494	560
BUDAPEST PESTSZENTLORINC	14.4	18.1	92.0	69.4	88.8	68.3	85.7	67.2	5112	718
India										
AHMEDABAD	51.6	53.7	109.6	73.4	107.5	73.2	104.9	73.1	18	6387
AKOLA	53.5	55.9	110.3	71.7	108.4	71.1	106.4	70.9	2	6528
AURANGABAD	51.9	54.4	104.6	73.0	103.0	72.9	101.2	72.5	8	5177
BELGAUM	55.5	57.7	97.7	66.9	95.9	67.1	94.2	67.2	0	4084

Climatic Design Conditions for Selected Locations *(Continued)*

Station	Heating DB		Cooling DB/MCWB						Heat./Cool. Degree-Days	
			0.4%		1%		2%			
	99.6%	99%	DB / MCWB		DB / MCWB		DB / MCWB		HDD / CDD 65	
BENGALURU	59.9	61.2	93.8	68.0	92.4	67.8	90.8	67.8	0	3964
BHOPAL	48.5	51.0	107.6	71.5	105.5	70.7	103.3	70.4	119	4956
BHUBANESHWAR	56.9	58.9	102.7	81.1	100.4	81.0	98.2	80.4	1	6151
BIKANER	43.1	45.7	111.4	70.8	109.1	71.6	106.9	72.3	317	6268
CHENNAI INTL	68.0	69.6	102.2	78.8	100.2	79.1	98.3	78.9	0	7034
COIMBATORE INTL	65.2	66.9	98.1	72.0	96.5	72.0	94.8	72.6	0	5774
GUWAHATI INTL	51.8	53.5	95.4	82.1	93.9	81.7	92.6	81.2	78	4543
GWALIOR	42.7	44.6	110.8	74.2	108.7	74.0	106.3	74.0	343	5500
HYDERABAD BEGUMPET	56.1	58.7	105.9	71.5	103.8	71.5	101.7	71.5	1	5667
INDORE INTL	49.4	51.8	105.5	69.6	103.5	68.8	101.5	68.5	81	4799
JABALPUR	47.0	49.3	108.4	69.5	106.3	69.3	104.1	69.4	148	5148
JAIPUR	45.0	47.6	108.9	69.7	106.2	70.0	104.0	70.1	285	5474
JAMSHEDPUR	50.1	52.2	107.8	72.7	105.1	73.3	102.3	74.2	45	5613
JODHPUR	47.7	49.8	109.0	71.1	106.7	71.3	104.4	71.6	130	6105
KOLKATA BOSE INTL	52.1	54.0	100.2	81.2	98.3	81.5	96.6	81.0	38	5695
KOZHIKODE	72.7	73.7	95.3	82.7	94.0	82.1	92.9	81.5	0	6589
LUCKNOW	43.6	46.2	109.1	74.2	106.1	74.2	103.8	74.7	360	5193
MANGALORE INTL	69.7	71.2	94.0	76.9	93.1	77.0	92.1	76.8	0	6085
MUMBAI SHIVAJI INTL	62.9	65.9	96.8	72.9	95.0	73.4	93.4	74.1	0	6428
NAGPUR AMBEDKAR INTL	52.1	55.1	111.6	72.6	109.6	72.4	107.6	72.1	9	6060
NELLORE	69.4	70.5	105.6	80.8	103.1	81.0	100.8	80.6	0	7496
NEW DELHI INDIRA GANDHI INTL	42.6	44.5	110.8	72.0	107.7	72.1	105.5	72.3	512	5379
NEW DELHI SAFDARJUNG	42.8	44.7	108.2	73.8	105.7	74.5	103.3	74.6	475	5169
PATIALA	41.4	43.4	107.2	76.2	104.6	75.9	101.7	76.1	695	4491
PATNA	45.9	48.0	106.4	73.7	103.9	74.2	100.7	75.5	260	5298

Climatic Design Conditions for Selected Locations (*Continued*)

Station	Heating DB		Cooling DB/MCWB						Heat./Cool. Degree-Days	
			0.4%		1%		2%			
	99.6%	99%	DB / MCWB		DB / MCWB		DB / MCWB		HDD / CDD 65	
PUNE	49.9	52.1	101.3	67.8	99.4	67.7	97.5	67.9	11	4370
RAJKOT	53.7	56.0	106.4	71.7	104.4	71.7	102.3	72.4	8	6285
SOLAPUR	59.5	62.1	106.3	72.1	104.5	72.1	102.7	72.0	0	6433
SURAT	57.5	59.7	100.7	72.6	98.1	73.2	96.0	73.9	1	6225
THIRUVANANTHAPURAM	72.1	73.1	93.6	79.2	92.5	78.8	91.5	78.4	0	6259
TIRUCHIRAPPALLI	68.1	69.6	102.6	78.8	101.8	78.6	100.3	78.3	0	7399
VISHAKHAPATNAM CWC	68.1	69.4	93.1	80.9	91.7	81.6	90.8	81.5	0	6264
Indonesia										
DENPASAR NGURAH RAI	71.5	73.1	90.5	79.9	89.7	79.7	88.9	79.6	0	6099
JAKARTA SOEKARNO-HATTA	72.1	73.2	93.2	77.8	91.8	78.0	91.5	78.1	0	6333
JUANDA SURABAYA	70.2	71.7	93.4	76.5	92.4	76.7	91.5	77.0	0	6426
KUALANAMU MEDAN	72.7	73.2	93.5	79.0	92.6	79.1	91.6	79.0	0	6228
MENADO SAM RATULANGI	69.4	70.7	93.1	76.4	91.6	76.4	90.8	76.5	0	5699
MIA PADANG	71.1	72.1	90.0	79.0	89.5	79.0	88.9	78.8	0	5719
PEKAN BARU SIMPANGTIGA	71.7	72.5	94.2	79.2	93.3	79.2	92.6	79.1	0	6367
UJUNG PANDANG HASANUDDIN	68.2	69.8	94.2	75.0	93.2	75.8	91.8	76.6	0	6008
Iran, Islamic Republic of										
ABADAN	39.4	42.5	118.8	72.8	116.9	72.6	115.0	72.0	701	6095
AHWAZ	40.8	43.1	118.5	74.3	116.7	73.9	114.9	73.2	721	6096
ANZALI	34.3	37.0	88.8	78.1	87.2	77.5	85.8	77.0	2630	1697
ARAK	7.3	15.1	98.0	60.6	95.9	60.0	93.9	59.3	4236	1653
BANDAR ABBASS INTL	48.4	51.5	107.7	75.9	104.4	78.1	102.3	79.0	117	5919
HAMEDAN	1.2	8.7	97.2	60.9	95.2	60.5	93.2	59.8	5001	1026
ISFAHAN SHAHID BEHESHTI INTL	17.2	19.8	102.4	62.2	100.6	61.3	98.6	60.7	3641	1856
KASHAN	24.4	28.3	108.0	66.3	105.8	66.0	103.7	65.5	2591	3400

Climatic Design Conditions for Selected Locations (*Continued*)

Station	Heating DB		Cooling DB/MCWB						Heat./Cool. Degree-Days	
			0.4%		1%		2%			
	99.6%	99%	DB	MCWB	DB	MCWB	DB	MCWB	HDD	CDD 65
KERMAN	19.3	22.8	100.5	60.3	98.7	59.4	96.8	58.9	2869	1861
KERMANSHAH	19.0	22.8	104.1	62.3	102.2	62.0	100.2	61.4	3626	1878
MASHHAD INTL	15.9	21.5	100.1	63.6	97.2	63.1	95.2	62.4	3569	1951
MEHRABAD INTL	26.3	29.8	102.2	63.7	100.2	63.4	98.2	63.2	2797	2848
SHIRAZ SHAHID DASTGHAIB INTL	28.1	30.4	102.6	63.0	100.8	62.1	99.1	61.5	2417	2588
TABRIZ INTL	11.6	15.7	97.1	62.2	94.9	61.8	92.6	61.2	4698	1551
URMIA INTL	10.6	15.4	93.4	63.6	91.1	63.5	88.2	63.1	5085	887
ZAHEDAN INTL	23.0	26.5	102.5	61.8	100.6	61.1	98.7	60.1	2071	2676
ZANJAN	7.4	12.6	95.2	61.0	92.6	60.7	89.8	60.4	5147	909
Iraq										
BAGHDAD INTL	35.3	37.6	116.8	71.4	114.7	70.9	112.7	70.1	1171	5157
Ireland										
CASEMENT	26.5	29.3	73.2	63.6	70.2	61.9	67.9	60.7	5588	15
DUBLIN AP	27.1	29.8	71.7	62.7	69.1	61.4	67.0	60.2	5696	8
Israel										
TEL AVIV BEN GURION	43.2	45.8	95.4	68.8	92.4	71.4	90.0	73.1	854	2723
TEL AVIV SDE DOV	47.3	49.1	88.2	75.9	86.9	76.1	86.0	75.8	809	2463
Italy										
BARI PALESE	33.7	35.7	93.5	71.9	90.2	71.4	87.8	71.0	2612	1278
BOLOGNA	24.9	28.0	94.8	72.6	91.7	72.0	89.5	71.3	3721	1279
CATANIA FONTANAROSSA	34.5	37.1	94.5	73.1	91.2	73.0	88.4	72.6	1984	1501
CATANIA SIGONELLA	35.3	37.5	98.5	71.9	95.1	71.9	92.8	71.8	1964	1775
FIRENZE PERETOLA	26.5	29.5	96.4	71.2	93.3	70.7	91.0	70.1	2984	1330
GENOVA SESTRI	35.2	37.4	86.3	73.1	84.3	73.7	82.6	73.5	2369	1223
GRAZZANISE	30.7	33.4	91.9	76.0	89.8	75.6	87.8	75.2	2664	1244

Climatic Design Conditions for Selected Locations (*Continued*)

Station	Heating DB		Cooling DB/MCWB						Heat./Cool. Degree-Days	
			0.4%		1%		2%		HDD / CDD 65	
	99.6%	99%	DB / MCWB		DB / MCWB		DB / MCWB			
MILANO LINATE	24.8	27.1	92.6	74.8	89.9	73.3	87.9	72.1	3723	1219
NAPOLI CAPODICHINO	34.1	36.9	91.5	73.3	89.5	73.1	87.6	73.1	2238	1475
PALERMO PUNTA RAISI	44.2	46.0	91.6	72.1	88.0	73.5	85.8	74.4	1425	1732
PRATICA DI MARE	33.5	35.7	88.0	73.8	86.1	74.0	84.4	74.2	2384	1147
ROMA CIAMPINO	30.4	33.4	93.3	70.8	91.2	70.8	88.2	70.1	2731	1275
ROMA FIUMICINO	31.8	33.9	89.0	71.4	86.6	71.9	85.1	71.8	2610	1061
TORINO BRIC DELLA CROCE	23.3	26.4	82.8	69.4	80.8	68.6	78.8	67.6	4636	534
TORINO CASELLE	22.9	25.2	88.1	72.4	86.0	71.1	84.0	69.9	4248	781
TRIESTE	29.2	32.2	89.6	74.4	87.4	74.1	85.5	73.2	3085	1239
Jamaica										
KINGSTON MANLEY	72.9	73.5	91.8	79.0	91.3	79.1	90.1	78.7	0	6529
Japan										
AKITA	23.3	25.0	89.3	76.1	86.7	75.0	84.1	74.0	5003	989
ASAHIKAWA	0.6	4.6	85.8	72.9	82.9	70.6	80.5	69.1	7697	466
ASHIYA AB	30.4	32.3	91.0	78.4	88.2	78.4	86.4	77.9	3065	1537
ATSUGI AB	30.3	32.2	91.7	78.1	89.7	77.1	87.8	76.7	2953	1678
CHIBA	32.8	34.3	90.7	78.4	88.9	77.9	87.2	77.3	2865	1667
FUJISAN	-19.7	-16.2	53.7	42.3	51.2	41.4	48.7	40.5	15902	0
FUKUOKA AP	31.9	33.8	93.3	78.3	91.5	77.9	89.6	77.2	2716	1961
FUKUYAMA	27.3	29.2	93.3	78.0	91.5	77.8	89.7	77.3	3301	1731
FUSHIKI	27.7	29.2	92.5	77.2	89.7	77.1	87.1	76.6	3919	1383
FUTENMA MCAS	51.8	53.4	90.3	79.9	89.5	79.8	88.2	79.5	336	3402
GIFU AB	26.3	28.1	94.9	78.2	91.8	77.2	89.7	76.5	3499	1714
HAMAMATSU AB	30.5	32.2	91.6	78.4	89.4	77.8	87.5	77.5	2833	1691
HANEDA AP	33.7	35.5	91.3	78.9	89.5	78.0	87.6	77.7	2794	1679
HIMEJI	28.2	29.8	92.4	78.2	90.6	77.6	88.7	77.0	3337	1674

Climatic Design Conditions for Selected Locations (*Continued*)

Station	Heating DB		Cooling DB/MCWB						Heat./Cool. Degree-Days	
			0.4%		1%		2%			
	99.6%	99%	DB	MCWB	DB	MCWB	DB	MCWB	HDD	CDD 65
HIROSHIMA	30.6	32.2	93.1	77.3	91.4	77.1	89.6	76.4	2930	1923
IIZUKA	28.8	30.7	92.7	78.4	90.9	78.1	89.0	77.4	3073	1738
IRUMA AB	26.5	28.3	94.6	77.7	91.6	76.9	89.4	76.3	3539	1501
KADENA AB	48.0	50.4	91.5	80.4	90.0	80.5	89.3	80.5	405	3362
KAGOSHIMA	34.8	36.8	92.4	78.8	90.9	78.4	89.4	78.1	1912	2393
KANAZAWA	29.8	31.1	91.8	76.7	90.0	76.4	88.1	76.0	3586	1539
KANSAI INTL	35.2	37.0	91.5	77.9	89.7	77.6	87.9	77.4	2699	1929
KOBE	32.3	34.2	92.1	77.5	90.1	77.1	88.3	76.6	2786	2018
KOCHI	30.4	32.4	91.5	77.9	90.0	77.6	88.4	77.1	2461	1960
KOMATSU AB	28.5	30.2	91.8	76.1	89.7	76.0	87.7	75.7	3750	1396
KUMAGAYA	28.1	29.9	96.2	77.9	93.6	77.4	90.9	76.2	3288	1697
KUMAMOTO	29.1	31.1	94.5	77.8	92.7	77.4	90.8	76.8	2669	2139
KURE	32.0	33.7	90.8	77.6	89.1	77.2	87.5	76.6	2855	1793
KYOTO	30.5	32.0	95.5	76.6	93.4	76.1	91.3	75.6	3102	1979
MATSUYAMA	32.0	33.7	92.4	76.9	90.9	76.6	89.3	76.2	2782	1897
MINAMITORISHIMA	64.5	65.8	89.3	79.6	88.5	79.4	87.8	79.1	0	5021
MIYAZAKI	31.9	34.0	92.7	78.3	90.5	78.3	88.6	78.0	2222	2009
NAGANO	19.9	22.1	91.7	74.8	89.2	74.0	86.6	73.0	4842	1218
NAGASAKI	33.4	35.3	91.4	78.4	89.6	78.3	87.9	77.7	2420	1973
NAGOYA AP	28.4	30.2	95.4	77.5	93.3	77.1	91.3	76.3	3135	1980
NAHA AP	54.0	55.6	90.0	79.8	89.6	79.8	88.2	79.8	201	3755
NARA	28.3	29.7	93.6	77.1	91.8	76.7	89.7	76.2	3434	1645
NAZE	49.0	50.6	91.2	79.1	90.0	78.9	88.9	78.8	617	2962
NIIGATA	28.9	30.2	91.4	77.4	89.1	76.8	86.7	76.1	4012	1362
NYUTABARU AB	30.0	32.2	91.2	78.3	88.2	78.6	86.4	78.3	2403	1778
OITA	31.5	33.3	92.5	77.8	90.8	77.5	88.8	77.0	2711	1817
OKAYAMA	29.7	31.5	94.3	77.7	92.4	77.2	90.6	76.7	3096	1942

Climatic Design Conditions for Selected Locations (*Continued*)

Station	Heating DB		Cooling DB/MCWB						Heat./Cool. Degree-Days	
			0.4%		1%		2%			
	99.6%	99%	DB / MCWB		DB / MCWB		DB / MCWB		HDD / CDD 65	
OMAEZAKI	32.3	34.2	87.0	79.2	85.6	78.6	84.3	77.9	2589	1575
ONAHAMA	27.9	29.7	84.6	75.8	82.6	75.4	81.0	74.6	3813	950
OSAKA	33.2	34.8	94.2	76.9	92.4	76.5	90.6	76.1	2751	2130
OSAKA INTL	29.9	31.6	94.9	78.1	93.0	77.4	91.2	76.9	3121	1994
OTARU	14.9	17.1	83.1	72.3	80.2	70.8	77.7	69.4	6620	424
OZUKI AB	31.6	33.4	91.2	79.0	89.4	78.6	87.6	78.6	3029	1651
SAPPORO	14.2	16.6	85.1	73.0	82.3	71.2	79.8	69.6	6425	566
SENDAI	25.6	27.4	89.0	76.2	86.3	75.3	83.8	74.2	4418	965
SHIMOFUSA AB	28.4	30.2	92.9	79.0	89.9	77.7	87.9	77.3	3262	1533
SHIMONOSEKI	34.8	36.8	90.3	78.4	88.7	78.1	87.1	77.6	2533	1850
SHIZUHAMA AB	31.6	33.4	90.0	78.7	88.0	78.6	86.1	77.8	2702	1617
SHIZUOKA	31.7	33.7	91.4	77.6	89.1	77.4	87.3	76.9	2557	1745
SUMOTO	32.0	33.6	89.6	78.1	87.8	77.6	85.8	77.0	3101	1566
TADOTSU	31.9	33.8	92.6	77.5	90.8	77.1	89.0	76.6	2915	1865
TAKAMATSU	31.4	33.1	94.2	77.5	92.4	77.2	90.5	76.9	2913	1980
TOKUSHIMA	32.8	34.5	92.2	78.1	90.4	77.8	88.7	77.3	2740	1905
TOKYO	33.2	34.7	92.6	78.0	90.6	77.3	88.7	76.5	2806	1775
TOYAMA	27.7	29.3	93.1	78.0	90.9	77.5	88.4	76.7	3805	1479
TSUIKI AB	28.4	30.2	91.2	78.2	89.3	78.1	87.5	78.1	3275	1529
UTSUNOMIYA	24.5	26.4	92.8	78.0	90.4	77.1	87.8	76.0	3787	1405
WAKAYAMA	32.8	34.4	92.5	76.8	90.5	76.8	88.8	76.6	2764	1969
YOKOHAMA	33.2	34.7	91.1	78.3	89.1	77.4	87.3	76.7	2818	1657
YOKOSUKA	35.4	37.2	93.5	78.6	89.8	77.2	86.4	76.6	2547	1727
YOKOTA AB	25.2	27.5	93.2	78.6	91.1	77.8	88.1	76.4	3534	1446
Jordan										
AMMAN	35.2	37.3	97.0	64.9	94.7	64.8	91.8	64.3	2067	2141

Climatic Design Conditions for Selected Locations (*Continued*)

Station	Heating DB		Cooling DB/MCWB						Heat./Cool. Degree-Days	
			0.4%		1%		2%			
	99.6%	99%	DB / MCWB		DB / MCWB		DB / MCWB		HDD / CDD 65	
IRBID	35.2	38.1	94.6	67.0	91.6	66.9	89.4	66.7	1931	1977
QUEEN ALIA INTL	31.6	33.6	98.8	67.0	96.4	66.1	93.5	65.7	2363	1573
Kazakhstan										
ALMATY	-3.6	1.7	93.9	65.4	91.1	64.6	88.1	64.0	6250	932
KARAGANDY	-27.5	-21.8	89.8	62.3	86.3	61.4	82.8	60.3	10177	276
NUR-SULTAN	-27.3	-22.1	90.2	64.0	86.8	63.2	83.7	62.3	10263	348
PAVLODAR	-31.1	-25.3	91.4	64.9	87.9	64.4	84.4	63.6	10267	440
SHYMKENT	4.3	10.4	100.7	65.9	98.4	65.4	95.4	64.6	4556	1616
TARAZ	-5.0	1.4	97.1	63.8	94.6	63.5	91.7	62.7	5629	1132
Kenya										
MOMBASA INTL	68.8	69.7	91.7	77.5	91.1	77.4	89.9	77.1	0	5547
NAIROBI JOMO KENYATTA INTL	50.4	53.1	84.6	60.8	83.2	60.7	82.1	60.8	126	1151
Korea, Democratic People's Republic of										
CHONGJIN	9.8	12.6	81.9	73.2	79.6	72.2	77.5	71.3	6708	452
HAMHUNG	8.9	12.2	89.9	76.0	86.8	74.8	84.0	73.3	5621	846
KAESONG	8.8	12.3	89.0	78.4	86.3	76.5	84.0	74.9	5420	1119
NAMPO	8.8	12.2	87.7	79.2	85.3	77.4	83.2	76.0	5616	1124
PYONGYANG SUNAN INTL	5.7	9.2	89.0	77.0	86.8	75.6	84.9	74.6	5759	1190
SINUIJU	4.0	7.6	88.4	75.8	85.7	74.6	83.5	73.5	6203	1007
WONSAN	13.5	16.9	89.9	74.8	86.9	73.9	84.0	72.9	5137	908
Korea, Republic of										
BUSAN	22.7	25.9	88.7	78.1	86.7	77.4	84.7	76.5	3317	1346
BUSAN GIMHAE INTL	21.0	23.2	91.5	78.6	89.4	77.9	86.4	76.7	3728	1454
CHANGWON	22.2	25.5	90.7	78.7	88.5	77.7	86.2	76.6	3563	1457
CHEONGJU	13.0	16.4	91.7	76.1	89.4	74.9	87.1	73.6	4692	1433

Climatic Design Conditions for Selected Locations (*Continued*)

Station	Heating DB		Cooling DB/MCWB						Heat./Cool. Degree-Days	
			0.4%		1%		2%			
	99.6%	99%	DB / MCWB		DB / MCWB		DB / MCWB		HDD / CDD 65	
CHEONGJU INTL	8.2	12.1	91.8	78.8	89.8	77.4	87.7	76.3	5115	1319
DAEGU AFB	19.4	22.3	94.2	75.3	91.7	74.7	89.3	73.8	3921	1592
DAEGU INTL	17.4	19.8	94.9	77.6	91.8	76.5	89.6	75.3	4164	1517
GIMPO INTL	8.3	11.9	91.2	77.4	88.1	75.9	86.1	74.4	5339	1262
GWANGJU	20.1	22.9	91.4	77.8	89.2	76.8	87.1	75.6	4009	1520
GWANGJU AP	19.3	21.5	93.4	79.3	91.1	78.1	88.2	76.6	4287	1509
INCHEON	13.3	16.9	88.8	77.6	86.3	76.5	84.1	75.1	4820	1221
JEJU	32.6	34.3	89.9	77.9	88.1	77.8	86.4	77.5	2902	1552
JEJU INTL	31.8	33.7	89.7	78.6	87.7	79.0	86.0	78.3	3110	1419
JEONJU	16.4	19.7	92.1	77.5	89.9	76.8	87.8	75.3	4329	1512
JINJU	16.7	19.4	91.8	76.6	89.4	75.9	87.1	74.9	4288	1327
OSAN AB	8.4	12.1	92.2	78.8	89.6	77.7	87.4	76.4	5129	1328
POHANG AP	19.2	21.6	93.2	78.6	90.9	77.8	87.8	76.6	4019	1234
PYEONGTAEK AB	10.2	13.7	91.6	78.9	89.4	77.6	87.0	76.5	5046	1349
SEOGWIPO	32.7	35.0	88.6	79.9	87.1	79.6	85.5	79.0	2473	1653
SEOUL AB	9.5	13.6	92.8	78.5	89.8	76.9	87.6	75.6	5032	1345
SEOUL OBSERVATORY	11.1	14.9	91.1	76.0	88.6	74.4	86.3	72.9	4798	1415
SEOUL SINYONGSAN	10.8	13.9	91.7	77.3	89.6	76.0	87.4	75.3	4716	1433
SUWON	11.7	15.2	90.9	77.3	88.5	76.2	86.2	74.7	4928	1361
TAEJON	12.8	16.1	91.6	78.5	89.2	76.8	86.7	75.3	4767	1325
ULSAN	21.4	24.3	91.8	77.0	89.5	76.5	87.1	75.5	3722	1337
WANDO	24.7	27.2	89.0	79.5	87.0	78.6	84.9	77.5	3753	1324
YEOSU	23.2	26.0	87.6	77.6	85.6	77.0	83.7	76.2	3584	1311
Kosovo										
PRISTINA INTL	8.2	14.0	92.8	65.4	89.4	65.1	86.1	64.3	5289	553

Climatic Design Conditions for Selected Locations *(Continued)*

Station	Heating DB		Cooling DB/MCWB						Heat./Cool. Degree-Days	
			0.4%		1%		2%			
	99.6%	99%	DB / MCWB		DB / MCWB		DB / MCWB		HDD / CDD 65	
Kuwait										
KUWAIT INTL	39.4	42.7	118.6	70.1	116.8	69.6	115.0	69.2	668	6357
Kyrgyzstan										
BISHKEK	1.3	7.2	95.9	65.7	93.2	64.5	90.7	63.8	5262	1210
Lao People's Democratic Republic										
VIENTIANE WATTAY INTL	57.8	60.8	99.4	79.2	97.1	78.8	95.1	78.5	7	5892
Latvia										
RIGA	-1.0	5.4	83.9	68.0	80.5	67.1	77.0	64.8	7389	161
Lebanon										
BEIRUT RAFIC HARIRI INTL	47.1	49.7	91.1	74.1	88.7	75.7	87.6	76.0	685	2764
Libyan Arab Jamahiriya										
BENGHAZI	44.4	46.2	98.8	68.9	95.4	69.0	92.9	68.6	1039	2504
MISRATA	46.8	48.6	98.9	71.3	94.6	70.9	91.1	71.2	757	2611
TRIPOLI INTL	40.2	42.5	107.7	72.8	104.0	72.1	100.4	71.4	1105	3079
Liechtenstein										
VADUZ	15.3	19.2	86.4	68.0	83.2	66.8	80.2	65.6	5247	394
Lithuania										
KAUNAS	-1.7	4.2	83.5	67.8	80.3	66.0	77.2	64.5	7296	168
VILNIUS	-2.8	3.1	83.9	67.1	80.5	65.5	77.2	63.9	7591	177
Luxembourg										
LUXEMBOURG AP	18.2	21.5	85.7	66.2	82.0	64.8	78.7	63.5	5729	264
Macao										
MACAU INTL	46.2	48.4	91.0	80.6	89.6	80.5	88.2	80.4	476	3661
Madagascar										
ANTANANARIVO IVATO	46.4	48.2	86.1	67.1	84.3	67.4	82.7	67.4	503	1345

Climatic Design Conditions for Selected Locations *(Continued)*

Station	Heating DB		Cooling DB/MCWB						Heat./Cool. Degree-Days	
			0.4%		1%		2%			
	99.6%	99%	DB / MCWB		DB / MCWB		DB / MCWB		HDD / CDD 65	
Malaysia										
KOTA KINABALU INTL	73.1	73.5	93.4	82.9	92.6	82.5	91.6	81.9	0	6396
KUALA LUMPUR SUBANG	73.3	74.1	95.0	79.4	93.6	79.2	93.1	79.1	0	6779
KUCHING INTL	71.8	72.7	93.4	79.2	92.4	79.1	91.5	79.1	0	6015
PAHANG	71.3	72.0	93.4	80.9	92.6	80.8	91.6	80.5	0	6135
SANDAKAN	73.3	73.9	93.1	80.0	91.7	79.8	91.0	79.8	0	6295
TAWAU	72.2	73.0	91.3	79.0	90.0	79.2	89.6	79.3	0	5919
Mali										
BAMAKO	59.0	61.2	105.0	67.4	103.7	67.5	102.1	67.8	0	6365
Malta										
MALTA LUQA	44.4	46.3	93.5	70.5	91.1	71.3	88.2	71.6	1300	1928
Mauritania										
NOUAKCHOTT	55.2	57.3	106.6	68.1	103.3	67.9	100.0	67.8	4	5415
Mexico										
ACAPULCO INTL	66.6	69.4	91.8	79.9	91.4	79.7	90.0	78.8	0	5864
CANCUN INTL	55.7	58.8	93.2	80.6	91.7	80.1	91.1	79.9	5	5125
CHETUMAL INTL	59.8	63.1	93.8	80.5	92.7	80.4	91.5	80.1	0	6013
GUADALAJARA INTL	35.4	37.7	91.6	59.4	89.9	58.8	88.1	58.3	627	1319
GUANAJUATO INTL	39.2	42.5	93.3	58.4	91.3	58.3	89.3	58.2	502	1389
HERMOSILLO	40.9	44.2	109.1	72.9	107.0	73.5	104.4	73.1	339	4951
MAZATLAN INTL	47.7	49.8	92.9	77.6	91.6	77.4	91.0	77.3	55	3803
MERIDA INTL	56.8	60.2	101.8	76.0	99.4	76.1	97.6	76.2	2	5971
MEXICO CITY INTL	37.6	40.9	84.4	54.2	82.5	53.8	80.6	53.7	1023	389
MONTERREY INTL	37.3	40.8	101.9	73.0	100.0	72.8	98.3	72.8	679	3844
PUERTO VALLARTA INTL	57.5	59.3	91.8	80.3	91.5	80.1	90.1	79.5	1	4610

Climatic Design Conditions for Selected Locations (*Continued*)

Station	Heating DB		Cooling DB/MCWB						Heat./Cool. Degree-Days	
			0.4%		1%		2%			
	99.6%	99%	DB / MCWB		DB / MCWB		DB / MCWB		HDD / CDD 65	
SAN LUIS POTOSI	33.5	36.0	90.0	57.3	87.8	57.5	85.7	57.5	1150	797
TAMPICO INTL	50.0	53.4	94.3	80.6	92.8	80.1	91.4	79.7	137	4753
TAPACHULA	68.2	69.7	96.0	79.0	94.8	78.9	93.7	78.9	0	6335
TIJUANA	42.4	44.3	91.0	63.4	87.4	63.2	84.1	63.1	1258	934
TOLUCA INTL	28.4	30.6	79.1	53.9	77.1	53.4	75.2	52.8	3133	4
TORREON	39.2	42.6	100.4	68.6	98.5	68.3	96.8	68.1	542	3792
VERACRUZ INTL	58.7	60.7	95.3	80.2	93.5	80.3	91.8	79.8	6	4972
Moldova, Republic of										
CHISINAU	6.4	11.2	91.0	67.5	87.7	66.6	85.1	65.7	5649	795
Mongolia										
ULAANBAATAR	-33.1	-29.2	87.9	59.8	84.1	58.7	80.4	57.6	12719	183
Montenegro										
PODGORICA GRAD	26.7	29.5	98.6	71.4	95.6	70.7	93.2	70.2	3029	1677
Morocco										
AGADIR AL MASSIRA INTL	40.9	43.0	102.1	68.1	95.2	66.5	90.0	66.1	709	1731
AGADIR INEZGANE	41.0	43.6	95.3	66.9	89.3	65.9	84.1	65.2	936	1171
CASABLANCA ANFA	44.3	46.2	85.1	70.8	81.7	71.4	79.4	71.2	1078	1224
CASABLANCA NOUASSEUR	37.3	39.5	96.8	70.9	92.1	70.5	88.3	69.7	1427	1504
FES SAIS	33.7	35.8	104.1	67.4	100.5	67.5	96.9	67.2	2021	1717
MARRAKECH MENARA	39.2	41.4	107.8	67.9	104.0	67.9	100.4	67.8	1080	2675
MEKNES	36.7	38.9	103.0	68.7	98.8	68.8	95.1	68.3	1901	1668
OUJDA ANGADS	33.8	36.1	100.7	69.1	96.9	69.2	93.6	68.9	1894	1718
SALE	40.6	42.6	91.1	69.9	86.0	69.8	82.5	69.9	1431	998
TANGIER IBN BATTUTA	39.5	42.4	91.8	70.3	89.4	70.2	86.4	69.7	1373	1382
TETOUAN	42.7	45.0	92.2	68.2	88.9	68.4	85.9	68.4	1064	1584

Climatic Design Conditions for Selected Locations *(Continued)*

Station	Heating DB		Cooling DB/MCWB						Heat./Cool. Degree-Days	
			0.4%		1%		2%			
	99.6%	99%	DB / MCWB		DB / MCWB		DB / MCWB		HDD / CDD 65	
Mozambique										
MAPUTO	53.5	55.4	96.8	75.2	93.3	74.8	91.0	74.6	24	3689
Myanmar										
YANGON	63.6	65.8	100.7	78.6	98.9	78.1	97.1	77.6	0	6393
Namibia										
WINDHOEK	39.2	42.6	93.6	58.8	91.7	58.2	90.0	57.7	555	2119
Nepal										
TRIBHUVAN INTL	35.9	37.6	87.4	69.1	85.8	69.5	84.3	70.3	1258	1733
Netherlands										
AMSTERDAM AP SCHIPHOL	21.5	25.0	82.6	68.0	78.6	66.5	75.0	64.6	5161	146
HOEK VAN HOLLAND	23.3	26.5	81.4	66.9	76.9	65.4	73.4	64.5	4867	144
IJMUIDEN	20.5	24.6	78.0	65.7	74.4	64.1	71.3	63.6	5257	92
ROTTERDAM THE HAGUE AP	21.3	24.9	83.1	68.1	79.0	66.6	75.5	64.8	5150	145
VALKENBURG	21.2	24.7	80.9	67.6	76.8	65.8	73.3	64.2	5247	105
WOENSDRECHT	19.1	23.3	84.7	67.7	80.4	66.3	76.9	64.6	5271	150
New Caledonia										
NOUMEA	61.2	62.3	89.1	76.9	87.5	76.6	85.9	76.1	3	3376
New Zealand										
AUCKLAND	39.4	41.6	78.5	68.1	76.7	67.2	75.1	66.2	2149	327
CHRISTCHURCH	26.9	28.7	82.7	62.5	79.0	61.0	75.4	60.0	4619	109
Nicaragua										
MANAGUA INTL	68.0	69.7	96.8	75.9	95.3	75.6	94.7	75.6	0	6327
Niger										
NIAMEY	60.7	62.6	109.0	68.6	107.5	68.4	105.8	68.5	0	7739

Climatic Design Conditions for Selected Locations (*Continued*)

Station	Heating DB		Cooling DB/MCWB						Heat./Cool. Degree-Days	
			0.4%		1%		2%			
	99.6%	99%	DB / MCWB		DB / MCWB		DB / MCWB		HDD / CDD 65	
Nigeria										
LAGOS IKEJA	69.9	71.5	94.7	78.6	93.4	79.1	92.7	79.1	0	6200
North Macedonia										
SKOPJE INTL	11.8	17.6	97.0	68.4	93.8	68.1	91.2	67.4	4551	1007
Norway										
HAKADAL	-2.7	2.0	80.6	63.4	77.1	62.3	73.6	60.5	8473	70
OSLO BLINDERN	7.0	10.9	80.5	63.1	77.0	62.1	73.7	60.3	7473	101
Oman										
AL BURAIMI	51.0	53.5	112.8	69.4	111.3	69.6	109.7	69.8	96	6917
Pakistan										
ISLAMABAD INTL	36.2	38.4	105.9	73.1	102.6	73.4	100.4	73.0	1103	3771
JINNAH INTL	50.4	53.4	102.2	72.8	98.9	73.5	96.9	74.3	38	5896
LAHORE ALLAMA IQBAL INTL	37.8	40.8	109.7	74.0	107.4	73.9	104.2	73.9	780	4741
Palestinian Territory, Occupied										
JERUSALEM ATAROT	35.6	38.2	92.0	65.0	89.6	65.0	87.4	64.8	2195	1514
Panama										
PANAMA PACIFICO	71.9	73.2	95.0	77.8	93.5	77.5	92.9	77.4	0	6418
TOCUMEN INTL	69.6	71.2	93.5	77.7	92.9	77.5	91.6	77.1	0	6107
Paraguay										
ASUNCION	41.4	44.9	99.0	75.4	97.1	75.6	95.3	75.6	432	3870
Peru										
AREQUIPA	42.9	44.5	75.2	48.4	73.7	47.8	73.2	47.6	2038	5
CHICLAYO	58.8	59.4	89.9	75.5	88.2	74.8	87.3	74.4	2	2900
CUSCO	32.4	34.1	73.6	47.5	72.0	47.4	71.3	47.3	3516	0
IQUITOS	66.6	69.4	93.6	79.3	92.9	79.3	91.5	79.1	0	5575

Climatic Design Conditions for Selected Locations (*Continued*)

Station	Heating DB		Cooling DB/MCWB						Heat./Cool. Degree-Days	
			0.4%		1%		2%			
	99.6%	99%	DB / MCWB		DB / MCWB		DB / MCWB		HDD / CDD 65	
LIMA	57.2	58.2	84.1	73.4	82.3	72.5	80.6	71.8	318	1448
PIURA	60.6	61.6	93.3	77.6	91.9	76.9	90.9	76.4	0	4357
PUCALLPA	64.6	67.6	94.7	79.2	93.3	79.0	92.1	78.7	1	5700
TRUJILLO	57.9	58.7	82.5	74.6	80.9	73.8	79.2	72.7	209	1276
Philippines										
CAGAYAN DE ORO	71.8	73.0	94.3	81.5	93.3	81.3	92.5	81.1	0	6482
DAVAO FRANCISCO BANGOY INTL	73.1	73.7	93.3	80.2	92.2	80.1	91.5	80.1	0	6478
GENERAL SANTOS	73.0	73.4	95.0	81.1	93.8	80.8	92.8	80.7	0	6387
ILOILO	73.0	73.8	94.4	82.3	93.1	81.9	91.8	81.5	0	6340
MACTAN CEBU INTL	74.1	75.0	91.7	80.6	91.1	80.5	89.9	80.3	0	6409
MANILA	73.7	74.8	94.0	79.5	92.8	79.4	91.7	79.4	0	6721
MANILA NINOY AQUINO INTL	71.3	73.0	95.2	78.6	93.8	78.5	92.9	78.4	0	6511
QUEZON CITY SCIENCE GARDEN	68.5	70.1	95.1	78.7	93.8	78.6	92.6	78.6	0	6162
SANGLEY POINT	73.9	75.0	95.6	83.4	94.4	83.1	93.4	82.8	0	6927
ZAMBOANGA	72.9	73.8	93.5	81.3	92.9	81.1	91.7	80.8	0	6556
Poland										
BALICE	3.9	9.5	86.7	69.0	83.4	67.6	80.2	66.2	6424	264
GDANSK LECHA WALESY	5.0	10.5	81.0	66.4	78.5	65.1	75.1	63.9	6978	109
GDANSK-SWIBNO	2.7	10.8	79.8	68.0	76.1	65.8	72.7	64.4	6882	93
HEL	15.6	19.3	78.1	68.7	75.3	67.0	72.8	65.7	6364	118
KATOWICE MUCHOWEC	5.3	10.9	86.2	68.0	82.6	66.3	79.5	65.0	6491	225
LODZ	5.5	10.8	86.5	67.7	82.9	66.2	80.0	64.9	6537	254
LUBLIN RADAWIEC	2.6	8.3	85.2	68.8	81.8	67.6	78.7	65.9	6831	226
POZNAN LAWICA	7.8	13.5	87.4	67.1	83.9	65.9	80.6	64.6	6200	288
RACIBORZ	5.4	11.0	86.8	68.4	83.2	67.1	80.2	65.8	6164	265

Climatic Design Conditions for Selected Locations (*Continued*)

Station	Heating DB		Cooling DB/MCWB						Heat./Cool. Degree-Days	
			0.4%		1%		2%			
	99.6%	99%	DB / MCWB		DB / MCWB		DB / MCWB		HDD / CDD 65	
SZCZECIN	10.4	16.0	85.0	68.4	81.4	66.8	78.2	65.4	6139	195
TERESPOL	0.0	6.4	86.4	69.2	83.1	67.6	80.0	66.0	6786	249
WARSZAWA OKECIE	4.1	10.0	86.4	68.6	83.1	67.0	80.2	65.6	6454	297
WROCLAW STRACHOWICE	7.8	13.5	87.7	68.8	84.2	67.2	80.9	65.9	5995	291
Portugal										
LISBOA GAGO COUTINHO	40.5	42.6	92.7	68.2	89.0	67.3	85.4	66.5	1799	1046
Puerto Rico										
ROOSEVELT ROADS	68.4	70.1	90.2	79.5	89.4	79.0	88.4	78.4	0	5717
SAN JUAN MARIN INTL	70.0	71.0	91.6	77.5	89.8	77.8	89.0	77.9	0	5755
Qatar										
DOHA INTL	54.2	56.8	111.7	72.2	109.6	72.5	107.6	73.4	73	6943
Romania										
BUCURESTI BANEASA	8.5	13.8	94.0	69.8	91.1	69.2	88.1	68.1	5277	777
BUCURESTI AFUMATI	8.3	13.7	93.4	70.3	90.6	70.2	87.8	68.9	5142	873
CLUJ NAPOCA	6.7	12.0	88.5	68.8	85.7	68.1	82.5	66.5	6030	392
CONSTANTA	15.5	19.8	86.7	73.9	84.5	73.0	82.6	72.1	4503	931
CRAIOVA	10.1	14.6	93.5	69.5	90.6	68.9	87.8	68.4	5038	900
IASI	3.9	9.7	92.2	69.7	89.1	68.8	86.2	67.9	5671	712
MIHAIL KOGALNICEANU	12.1	16.1	91.7	70.1	89.2	69.5	86.1	69.1	4948	871
TIMISOARA	11.8	16.2	93.6	69.3	91.1	69.5	87.7	68.3	4997	748
Russian Federation										
ARKHANGELSK TALAGI	-25.9	-19.6	82.0	67.0	77.4	64.5	73.6	62.4	11039	84
ASTRAKHAN	-1.4	4.8	98.4	69.4	95.2	68.8	92.7	68.2	5943	1353
BARNAUL	-29.1	-23.6	86.2	65.8	83.1	64.8	80.5	63.7	10460	294
BOSTOVO CHEREPOVETS	-20.9	-14.9	82.8	68.0	79.3	66.3	75.9	64.5	9766	112

Climatic Design Conditions for Selected Locations (*Continued*)

Station	Heating DB		Cooling DB/MCWB						Heat./Cool. Degree-Days	
			0.4%		1%		2%			
	99.6%	99%	DB / MCWB		DB / MCWB		DB / MCWB		HDD / CDD 65	
BRYANSK	-7.3	-1.1	85.2	67.6	82.1	66.0	79.1	64.3	7910	263
CHELYABINSK MEZHDUNARODNYY	-20.6	-15.1	87.5	66.6	84.0	65.6	80.6	64.4	10036	272
CHITA KADALA	-34.9	-31.2	88.0	65.2	84.4	63.9	80.9	62.3	12596	192
IM E K FEDOROVA	-24.0	-19.5	60.5	55.8	55.7	52.7	52.2	49.9	14879	0
IRKUTSK	-32.4	-25.8	84.4	64.2	80.9	63.5	78.3	62.4	11752	117
IZHEVSK	-20.2	-14.1	85.6	68.0	82.3	66.4	79.1	65.0	10079	238
KALUGA	-12.9	-6.6	83.4	67.1	80.5	65.7	77.7	64.9	8540	161
KAZAN	-17.7	-11.5	88.0	67.6	84.4	66.7	80.9	65.2	9304	352
KEMEROVO	-29.2	-23.9	84.2	66.4	80.8	64.9	78.3	63.7	11103	214
KHABAROVSK	-22.1	-18.6	86.4	72.6	83.8	71.2	80.7	69.7	10879	411
KHRABROVO	2.5	8.5	83.0	68.3	79.3	66.4	76.4	65.0	6811	147
KIROV	-20.5	-14.4	84.8	68.5	81.4	66.5	78.2	64.8	10052	215
KRASNODAR	6.6	13.4	94.9	72.5	91.5	71.6	88.3	70.5	4937	1062
KRASNOYARSK	-28.6	-23.9	83.1	65.0	79.9	63.7	76.6	62.3	11257	122
KRASNOYARSK MININO	-33.9	-28.8	84.8	66.6	81.5	65.4	78.3	63.8	11039	193
KURGAN	-26.7	-21.1	88.7	66.8	85.2	66.1	82.0	64.9	10470	316
KURSK	-7.5	-1.9	87.6	66.9	84.1	65.4	81.0	64.4	7697	416
MAGNITOGORSK	-21.4	-16.8	87.5	65.1	84.2	64.0	81.2	62.8	10329	278
MAKHACHKALA	10.3	16.6	89.1	73.4	86.8	73.8	84.8	73.2	4831	1095
MOSKVA SHEREMETYEVO	-10.9	-4.4	85.9	66.6	82.4	65.3	78.9	64.5	8589	230
MOSKVA VDNH	-7.4	-1.6	85.9	69.9	82.4	68.4	79.2	66.9	8244	272
MOSKVA VNUKOVO	-9.4	-3.9	84.6	66.3	82.1	65.7	78.8	64.6	8538	244
MURMANSK	-27.3	-21.2	76.7	61.4	71.8	59.0	67.9	57.1	12026	21
NIZHNY NOVGOROD STRIGINO	-15.2	-9.4	86.3	68.2	82.8	66.9	80.2	65.8	8952	256
NIZHNY TAGIL	-24.4	-19.5	83.2	67.3	80.1	65.6	77.1	63.9	10945	119

Climatic Design Conditions for Selected Locations (*Continued*)

Station	Heating DB		Cooling DB/MCWB						Heat./Cool. Degree-Days	
			0.4%		1%		2%			
	99.6%	99%	DB / MCWB		DB / MCWB		DB / MCWB		HDD / CDD 65	
NOVOKUZNETSK	-27.7	-23.1	85.1	67.0	81.9	65.5	78.8	64.4	10624	197
NOVOSIBIRSK TOLMACHEVO	-33.1	-27.6	85.7	66.1	82.5	64.8	79.4	63.5	11020	218
OMSK	-27.5	-22.9	87.8	65.7	84.2	64.9	80.9	63.7	10858	296
ORENBURG	-21.1	-15.2	94.7	66.9	91.3	66.1	87.8	65.2	9134	609
ORYOL	-10.2	-4.1	86.8	67.9	83.4	66.8	80.5	65.4	7937	326
PENZA	-16.8	-10.7	89.7	67.9	86.0	66.9	82.6	65.5	8729	375
PERM BOLSHOYE SAVINO	-23.4	-16.9	86.0	68.6	82.5	66.7	79.0	65.0	10262	209
PSKOV	-9.6	-2.6	83.9	68.7	80.5	66.6	77.2	64.9	8071	164
ROSTOV-ON-DON	-0.1	5.2	95.2	70.0	91.6	69.4	88.2	68.2	6024	994
RYAZAN	-11.2	-5.6	87.0	67.7	83.2	66.2	80.0	64.9	8483	298
SAMARA OGMS	-15.1	-9.6	91.2	67.0	87.6	66.2	84.2	64.9	8792	495
SARATOV TSENTRALNY	-9.9	-5.3	92.3	67.7	88.9	67.2	85.6	66.3	7970	727
SMOLENSK	-7.6	-1.8	82.6	68.2	79.5	66.4	76.5	65.0	8330	162
SOCHI	28.7	31.7	87.7	74.9	85.6	74.7	83.8	73.8	3349	1020
ST PETERSBURG PULKOVO	-9.2	-3.6	83.1	67.3	79.4	65.7	76.4	64.1	8454	135
STAVROPOL	1.4	8.3	92.9	66.9	89.6	66.2	86.2	65.5	5880	781
SURGUT	-40.3	-35.2	83.8	65.5	80.4	64.2	76.8	63.3	13166	154
TOMSK	-33.6	-28.0	83.7	67.3	80.8	65.7	77.9	64.3	11404	189
TRUBCHEVSK	-8.8	-2.3	86.2	68.6	82.9	67.3	79.8	66.1	7740	273
TULA	-11.7	-5.7	86.3	68.0	82.7	66.5	79.8	65.4	8393	265
TVER	-12.9	-6.8	85.6	67.1	81.9	66.2	78.5	64.7	8668	214
TYUMEN	-25.9	-20.9	85.5	67.5	82.3	66.2	79.3	64.7	10741	221
UFA	-23.7	-18.1	89.2	68.9	85.8	68.0	82.4	66.3	9721	309
ULAN-UDE BAIKAL	-33.0	-28.8	89.7	64.3	85.9	63.7	82.2	62.5	12259	275
VELIKIYE LUKI	-9.0	-2.6	82.8	67.1	79.9	66.0	77.1	64.6	8098	154

Climatic Design Conditions for Selected Locations *(Continued)*

Station	Heating DB		Cooling DB/MCWB						Heat./Cool. Degree-Days	
			0.4%		1%		2%			
	99.6%	99%	DB	MCWB	DB	MCWB	DB	MCWB	HDD	CDD 65
VLADIKAVKAZ	6.8	12.5	88.0	68.6	84.8	67.7	81.9	66.7	5934	517
VLADIMIR	-13.3	-7.6	85.4	69.7	81.8	68.3	78.6	66.8	8874	249
VLADIVOSTOK	-11.3	-6.3	82.6	70.4	79.1	68.9	76.3	67.8	8867	291
VOLGOGRAD GUMRAK	-8.3	-3.1	96.4	65.9	92.9	65.6	89.5	65.0	7189	932
VORONEZH	-9.2	-3.5	89.9	68.0	86.4	66.9	83.2	65.6	7543	509
VORONEZH CHERTOVITSKY	-11.6	-5.7	91.4	66.4	87.6	65.5	84.0	64.5	7693	434
YEKATERINBURG KOLTSOVO	-23.8	-18.0	85.8	67.5	82.3	65.8	78.9	64.3	10532	181
YELABUGA TATARSTAN	-19.2	-13.2	88.4	68.7	84.6	68.0	81.2	65.9	9442	349
Rwanda										
KIGALI INTL	58.7	59.3	86.3	65.5	84.9	65.4	84.0	65.3	0	2278
Saudi Arabia										
ABHA	44.3	46.3	89.6	56.6	88.0	56.2	86.4	56.3	765	1617
DHAHARAN KING ABDULAZIZ AB	46.5	49.0	114.7	73.2	112.6	73.3	109.8	73.5	272	6370
GASSIM	39.1	42.6	113.3	N/A	111.6	N/A	110.8	N/A	656	5616
JEDDAH KING ABDULAZIZ INTL	61.1	63.0	105.8	74.7	103.8	75.6	102.0	76.2	0	7091
KHAMIS MUSHAIT	45.5	47.9	90.7	58.5	89.4	58.9	87.9	59.1	499	1998
MAKKAH	62.7	64.7	113.4	76.2	111.5	76.0	109.7	76.0	0	8911
MEDINA PRINCE ABDULAZIZ INTL	49.9	52.3	113.4	65.9	111.8	65.3	110.8	65.0	107	7013
RIYADH KING SALMAN AB	43.2	46.3	112.8	67.1	111.2	66.3	109.7	65.7	457	6173
TABUK	35.8	38.8	107.3	66.0	104.4	65.1	102.4	64.5	1107	4001
Senegal										
DAKAR	62.4	63.0	91.0	72.0	88.8	76.4	87.8	77.8	0	4421
Serbia										
BEOGRAD	16.5	20.5	94.3	70.6	91.2	70.1	88.2	69.1	4294	1072
BEOGRAD SURCIN	13.8	18.0	94.7	70.6	91.3	70.5	88.0	69.2	4627	878

Climatic Design Conditions for Selected Locations *(Continued)*

Station	Heating DB		Cooling DB/MCWB						Heat./Cool. Degree-Days	
			0.4%		1%		2%			
	99.6%	99%	DB / MCWB		DB / MCWB		DB / MCWB		HDD / CDD 65	
Singapore										
SINGAPORE CHANGI INTL	73.9	74.9	91.8	79.3	91.3	79.2	90.0	79.1	0	6565
Slovakia										
BRATISLAVA-LETISKO	13.8	18.3	90.8	69.4	87.5	68.2	84.3	67.0	5283	584
Slovenia										
LJUBLJANA BEZIGRAD	16.9	20.3	89.7	70.2	86.7	68.8	83.8	67.6	5021	591
South Africa										
BLOEMFONTEIN INTL	23.3	26.0	93.4	59.8	91.2	59.7	89.2	59.7	2445	966
CAPE TOWN INTL	39.3	41.6	89.4	67.6	85.8	66.7	82.6	65.7	1526	786
DE AAR	31.0	33.5	95.0	60.1	92.9	60.1	90.8	59.8	1985	1422
DURBAN	48.5	50.7	86.4	75.0	84.6	74.3	83.4	73.8	258	1969
EAST LONDON	46.3	48.2	87.4	68.0	84.0	68.9	81.1	69.2	726	1066
JOHANNESBURG INTL	32.8	35.9	84.4	58.6	82.5	58.8	80.6	59.2	1869	541
PORT ELIZABETH INTL	41.4	44.2	85.1	65.8	81.6	67.0	79.1	67.5	1163	742
PRETORIA EENDRACHT	37.0	39.0	90.0	63.2	88.0	63.1	86.1	63.2	1077	1537
Spain										
LA CORUNA	40.3	42.4	78.6	66.5	75.5	65.5	73.3	64.6	2448	232
ALICANTE AP	38.1	40.7	91.0	70.1	88.6	70.7	86.8	71.0	1570	1650
BARCELONA AP	35.4	37.6	87.6	74.3	85.6	74.1	84.0	73.6	2222	1258
BILBAO AP	31.7	34.0	89.9	69.5	85.5	68.5	81.9	67.5	2728	635
GRAN CANARIA	56.9	58.0	86.8	67.6	83.8	68.2	81.8	69.1	97	2055
MADRID TORREJON AB	23.4	26.5	98.4	66.8	95.3	65.5	93.2	64.6	3656	1145
MADRID-BARAJAS AP	25.7	28.1	98.2	65.1	95.9	64.5	93.4	63.8	3436	1245
MALAGA AP	39.6	42.5	96.1	68.2	91.8	68.2	88.2	68.2	1373	1692
MURCIA	36.8	39.3	97.9	71.7	95.2	71.2	92.8	71.0	1533	2113

Climatic Design Conditions for Selected Locations (*Continued*)

Station	Heating DB		Cooling DB/MCWB						Heat./Cool. Degree-Days	
			0.4%		1%		2%			
	99.6%	99%	DB / MCWB		DB / MCWB		DB / MCWB		HDD / CDD 65	
PALMA DE MALLORCA AP	33.2	35.4	92.7	72.2	89.8	72.5	87.7	72.4	2174	1355
SEVILLA AP	36.0	38.8	102.6	70.6	100.1	70.0	97.2	69.2	1502	2296
VALENCIA AP	33.4	35.8	92.7	69.3	89.7	70.4	87.7	70.9	1904	1555
VALLADOLID	25.5	27.6	94.2	64.7	91.3	64.1	88.1	63.2	4218	687
ZARAGOZA AP	28.4	31.4	97.9	69.4	94.8	68.7	91.5	67.9	2988	1329
Sri Lanka										
KATUNAYAKE	69.8	71.6	91.7	76.4	90.4	77.2	89.7	77.6	0	6157
Sudan										
KHARTOUM INTL	58.7	61.0	109.8	67.2	108.9	67.1	107.3	66.9	2	8169
Suriname										
ZANDERIJ	69.5	70.5	93.6	76.3	93.1	76.4	91.7	76.6	0	5884
Sweden										
GOTEBORG	11.3	16.0	80.7	64.6	77.7	63.7	74.6	62.3	6384	122
MALMO	15.6	19.9	79.9	65.9	77.0	65.2	73.9	63.5	6200	88
STOCKHOLMN BROMMA	5.0	10.4	81.1	64.6	77.8	63.2	74.9	61.9	7398	107
UPPSALA	-2.2	3.9	80.9	65.8	77.4	63.9	74.2	62.3	8022	63
Switzerland										
BERN ZOLLIKOFEN	15.1	18.9	86.2	67.1	83.0	66.4	79.7	65.1	5927	259
LAEGEREN	13.0	16.8	80.4	64.0	77.1	62.6	74.2	61.7	6882	152
ZUERICH-FLUNTERN	17.4	20.8	85.6	67.2	82.0	65.8	78.9	64.5	5660	302
Syrian Arab Republic										
ALEPPO INTL	28.5	31.2	103.7	67.8	100.5	67.6	98.1	67.5	2647	2546
DAMASCUS INTL	26.4	29.8	104.0	66.1	101.2	65.3	98.8	64.9	2488	2226
DARAA	33.9	36.7	97.6	66.7	94.9	66.9	92.5	67.2	2010	1997
HAMA	31.6	33.9	103.2	70.1	100.3	69.5	97.7	68.7	2175	2636

Climatic Design Conditions for Selected Locations (*Continued*)

Station	Heating DB		Cooling DB/MCWB						Heat./Cool. Degree-Days	
			0.4%		1%		2%			
	99.6%	99%	DB	MCWB	DB	MCWB	DB	MCWB	HDD	CDD 65
LATAKIA	39.8	42.6	90.6	74.5	88.8	76.0	87.6	76.4	1183	2325
Taiwan										
GANGSHAN	49.9	52.2	91.8	80.9	91.2	80.8	89.9	80.4	143	4071
CHIANG KAI SHEK INTL	48.6	51.4	94.9	80.4	93.2	80.6	91.6	80.2	452	3600
HENGCHUN	60.9	62.5	90.9	80.6	90.0	80.2	89.2	79.9	11	4834
HSINCHU	48.4	50.3	91.7	82.3	90.7	81.9	89.7	81.4	496	3323
HSINCHU CITY	48.4	50.6	91.7	80.0	90.6	79.8	89.4	79.5	480	3262
KAOHSIUNG	55.2	57.3	90.9	80.9	90.0	80.7	89.1	80.5	55	4575
KAOHSIUNG INTL	53.8	56.9	92.4	80.3	91.5	80.2	90.3	79.8	51	4813
KEELUNG	50.9	52.7	93.0	78.6	91.3	78.4	89.9	78.4	426	3316
KINMEN	44.8	46.6	91.3	83.2	89.8	82.7	88.9	82.3	894	2865
MATSU NANGAN	40.1	42.1	88.9	81.9	87.6	81.6	86.1	80.8	1795	2155
PINGTUNG NORTH	52.0	54.8	93.9	81.1	93.2	80.9	91.8	80.4	72	4520
PINGTUNG SOUTH	53.3	55.3	94.9	81.2	93.5	80.8	92.7	80.5	57	4721
TAICHUNG INTL	46.6	48.5	91.1	80.0	89.8	79.6	89.2	79.5	481	3245
TAICHUNG SHUINAN AP	46.3	48.6	93.6	82.1	92.9	82.0	91.6	81.5	326	3744
TAICHUNG WUQI	50.6	52.5	91.1	81.2	90.2	80.9	89.3	80.6	347	3574
TAINAN AP	51.4	53.5	91.8	81.6	91.3	81.4	89.9	80.5	127	4201
TAIPEI	49.7	51.7	94.6	79.4	93.1	79.1	91.7	78.8	419	3601
TAIPEI SONGSHAN	49.6	51.7	96.4	80.2	94.7	79.8	93.2	79.6	375	3928
TAOYUAN	47.7	49.6	93.2	82.8	91.7	82.2	90.9	81.8	593	3252
Tajikistan										
DUSHANBE	15.6	21.4	100.8	66.9	98.7	65.9	96.7	65.4	3386	1736
Tanzania, United Republic of										
DAR ES SALAAM INTL	65.0	66.2	92.3	79.4	91.4	79.0	90.2	78.3	0	5457

Climatic Design Conditions for Selected Locations (*Continued*)

Station	Heating DB		Cooling DB/MCWB						Heat./Cool. Degree-Days	
			0.4%		1%		2%			
	99.6%	99%	DB / MCWB		DB / MCWB		DB / MCWB		HDD / CDD 65	
Thailand										
BANGKOK DON MUEANG INTL	67.2	69.8	98.9	79.7	97.4	79.8	96.5	79.8	0	7224
PHUKET	75.0	75.7	94.7	79.1	93.5	78.9	92.5	78.8	0	6947
Togo										
LOME	71.2	72.3	91.8	78.9	91.4	79.4	90.6	79.5	0	6260
Trinidad and Tobago										
PIARCO INTL	69.6	71.2	93.2	78.4	91.8	77.9	91.4	77.8	0	6115
Tunisia										
TUNIS CARTHAGE	41.6	44.2	100.3	72.2	96.7	72.3	93.4	72.0	1284	2335
Turkey										
ADANA INCIRLIK	33.6	35.9	98.2	72.3	95.3	73.3	93.4	73.8	1755	2499
ADANA SAKIRPASA	34.2	37.4	97.5	72.4	95.2	73.7	93.4	74.3	1592	2690
ANKARA ESENBOGA	8.3	13.9	93.1	62.6	89.8	62.0	87.2	61.6	5466	586
ANKARA ETIMESGUT	14.2	18.1	95.0	63.8	91.7	63.5	89.3	63.0	4822	866
ANTALYA HAVALIMANI	36.3	38.9	101.5	68.2	98.5	68.2	95.1	68.5	1679	2419
BURSA	26.4	28.8	94.4	71.9	91.7	71.6	89.5	70.9	3296	1298
DIYARBAKIR	17.2	22.6	105.2	66.0	102.6	65.8	100.7	65.5	3695	2263
ERZURUM	-18.6	-13.1	87.8	58.2	84.7	57.9	82.3	57.9	8593	174
ESKISEHIR HAVALIMANI	14.1	18.0	92.3	66.0	89.5	65.3	86.4	64.4	4978	655
ISTANBUL ATATURK	29.5	31.9	89.7	70.7	87.7	70.3	85.7	70.0	3089	1396
IZMIR ADNAN MENDERES	27.8	30.3	99.0	69.5	96.7	69.2	94.6	68.8	2665	1927
IZMIR CIGLI	29.8	31.9	98.4	70.6	95.4	70.3	93.4	69.7	2323	1932
KAYSERI ERKILET	5.3	12.0	94.7	62.7	91.4	62.1	88.2	61.2	5287	596
KONYA	12.0	16.7	93.5	61.7	91.2	61.5	88.2	60.9	4862	955
MALATYA ERHAC	12.9	17.5	100.6	66.3	98.5	65.1	95.9	64.4	4512	1532

Climatic Design Conditions for Selected Locations (*Continued*)

Station	Heating DB		Cooling DB/MCWB						Heat./Cool. Degree-Days	
			0.4%		1%		2%			
	99.6%	99%	DB / MCWB		DB / MCWB		DB / MCWB		HDD / CDD 65	
OGUZELI	24.3	26.8	102.4	69.3	100.3	68.3	98.2	67.6	3331	2141
SAMSUN	31.4	33.7	84.6	72.5	83.1	72.2	81.8	71.6	3031	1009
VAN FERITMELEN	9.0	12.5	84.4	63.8	82.4	64.2	80.7	64.5	6120	414
Turkmenistan										
ASHGABAT	18.0	23.4	105.7	67.8	103.0	67.1	100.7	66.7	3229	2826
Uganda										
ENTEBBE INTL	62.8	64.1	84.5	70.2	83.6	70.7	82.4	71.1	4	2914
Ukraine										
CHERNIHIV	-2.7	2.4	87.8	68.7	84.6	67.6	81.5	66.2	7111	387
DNIPROPETROVSK	-0.2	5.3	93.4	69.6	89.9	68.7	86.7	67.8	6372	787
DONETSK	-2.3	3.2	92.5	66.6	88.9	66.3	85.6	65.6	6747	650
KARHIV	-3.0	2.3	91.4	67.0	87.8	66.1	84.5	65.3	6879	615
KHERSON	4.0	9.5	94.4	70.2	91.1	69.2	87.9	68.1	5669	874
KRYVYI RIH	-0.3	5.2	92.9	68.6	89.5	67.7	86.2	66.9	6334	697
KYIV	1.5	6.5	88.1	68.5	85.3	67.7	82.3	66.3	6652	479
LUHANSK	-5.7	0.5	95.0	69.1	91.4	68.3	87.6	67.2	6586	717
LVIV	1.4	7.4	85.8	68.8	82.4	67.0	79.2	65.3	6722	250
MARIUPOL'	3.6	8.8	89.9	70.5	87.3	70.1	84.6	69.5	6090	828
ODESA	8.2	13.5	91.2	69.2	87.9	68.3	84.8	67.7	5490	823
POLTAVA	-1.7	3.6	89.7	68.2	86.4	67.2	83.5	66.2	6791	569
SIMFEROPOL	10.0	15.2	92.8	68.8	89.6	68.2	86.4	67.1	5137	795
VINNYTSIA	-1.4	4.7	86.3	67.5	83.2	66.4	80.5	65.2	6922	333
ZAPORIZHZHIA	0.1	5.8	94.0	68.6	91.0	68.0	87.7	66.9	6208	805
United Arab Emirates										
ABU DHABI INTL	53.6	55.7	113.2	73.5	111.1	73.9	108.8	74.1	35	6856

Climatic Design Conditions for Selected Locations (*Continued*)

Station	Heating DB		Cooling DB/MCWB						Heat./Cool. Degree-Days	
			0.4%		1%		2%			
	99.6%	99%	DB / MCWB		DB / MCWB		DB / MCWB		HDD / CDD 65	
ABU DHABI BATEEN	57.2	59.1	112.5	74.1	109.6	74.6	107.5	75.0	10	7065
AL AIN INTL	51.9	53.7	114.8	72.6	113.1	72.6	111.5	72.6	68	7208
DUBAI INTL	56.8	58.7	109.9	74.4	107.7	74.9	105.7	75.5	17	6966
SHARJAH INTL	51.4	53.6	111.7	74.3	109.7	74.7	107.7	75.4	50	6497
United Kingdom										
AUGHTON	26.8	29.3	76.0	63.3	72.3	62.1	68.9	60.6	5748	33
BINGLEY	25.2	27.4	75.3	63.4	71.5	61.5	68.2	59.9	6345	19
BIRMINGHAM	24.4	26.7	80.2	64.6	75.8	62.9	73.1	61.8	5486	62
BRISTOL	26.3	28.4	76.6	64.1	73.0	62.7	69.7	61.4	5485	33
BRISTOL WEATHER CENTRE	28.5	31.1	80.1	65.0	76.6	63.0	73.4	61.9	4670	106
CARDIFF WEATHER CENTRE	30.6	32.5	79.7	65.4	76.1	63.7	73.1	62.2	4500	114
CHURCH LAWFORD	24.8	27.3	80.2	65.7	76.3	63.6	73.0	62.0	5498	62
CILFYNYDD	24.5	27.3	78.0	64.3	74.2	62.2	70.8	60.9	5899	40
CROSBY	26.1	29.2	76.2	65.1	72.3	63.4	69.3	62.1	5142	39
EDINBURGH AP	22.7	26.2	71.9	62.2	69.5	61.2	66.6	59.3	6138	7
EMLEY MOOR	26.3	28.1	74.9	63.5	71.3	62.0	68.3	60.3	6215	26
GLASGOW AP	21.2	24.9	73.7	62.9	70.2	61.2	67.9	60.0	6034	13
GRAVESEND-BROADNESS	27.5	29.8	82.3	67.3	78.5	65.5	75.3	63.8	4667	141
HAWARDEN	24.5	27.4	77.5	64.8	73.7	63.3	70.8	61.9	5362	36
KENLEY AF	26.3	28.4	79.8	65.0	76.0	63.2	72.8	61.8	5314	80
LECONFIELD	26.1	28.7	77.2	65.2	73.9	63.6	71.0	61.9	5592	34
LEEDS BRADFORD	26.2	28.2	75.2	64.0	71.6	62.0	68.2	60.4	6152	23
LEEDS WEATHER CENTRE	28.2	30.1	79.8	64.7	75.8	62.8	72.7	61.2	5249	84
LIVERPOOL JOHN LENNON	28.3	30.3	77.2	64.2	73.6	62.6	71.2	61.9	5053	56
LONDON HEATHROW	27.9	30.0	83.7	65.7	79.7	64.1	76.4	62.8	4562	183

Climatic Design Conditions for Selected Locations (*Continued*)

Station	Heating DB		Cooling DB/MCWB						Heat./Cool. Degree-Days	
			0.4%		1%		2%			
	99.6%	99%	DB / MCWB		DB / MCWB		DB / MCWB		HDD / CDD 65	
LONDON WC CLERKENWELL	30.8	32.8	83.2	65.2	79.6	63.9	76.4	62.5	4134	236
MANCHESTER AP	25.0	28.2	78.5	64.5	74.8	62.9	71.5	61.4	5488	53
NORTHOLT	25.2	27.7	83.1	65.5	79.2	63.9	75.8	62.6	4894	134
NOTTINGHAM EAST MIDLANDS	26.4	28.4	80.2	65.0	75.5	62.9	73.0	61.8	5373	73
VALLEY ANGLESEY	29.4	31.7	73.1	62.8	69.3	60.9	66.4	59.7	5112	17
Uruguay										
MONTEVIDEO CARRASCO	34.8	37.4	89.3	71.2	86.1	70.7	83.3	70.1	2115	880
MONTEVIDEO PRADO	37.4	39.8	89.1	72.8	86.4	71.8	84.1	71.2	1952	1035
Uzbekistan										
NAMANGAN	16.6	21.0	98.9	69.4	96.7	68.9	94.7	68.4	3943	2080
SAMARKAND	13.7	19.2	98.5	66.1	95.8	65.4	93.5	64.7	3881	1630
TASHKENT INTL	14.2	19.1	102.2	67.5	100.0	66.8	97.1	66.1	3700	2011
Venezuela										
SAN ANTONIO DEL TACHIRA	67.8	69.4	95.4	74.3	94.6	74.1	93.2	73.8	0	5961
MAIQUETIA	69.5	71.2	93.1	82.1	91.6	81.4	91.0	81.1	0	6134
Viet Nam										
DA NANG INTL	62.2	63.8	98.0	79.5	96.2	79.4	94.6	79.4	5	5395
HA NOI	49.9	51.9	97.2	81.3	95.3	81.2	93.5	81.2	294	4374
HO CHI MINH TAN SON NHAT INTL	68.2	70.1	96.5	78.2	94.8	78.3	93.4	78.2	0	6580
PHU LIEN	49.7	51.7	93.8	84.0	91.9	83.7	90.4	83.1	304	4004
Western Sahara										
LAAYOUNE	50.3	53.1	97.0	69.2	92.8	69.0	88.2	68.5	207	2286
Yemen										
ADEN INTL	70.1	71.7	98.6	76.7	97.1	77.1	96.5	77.2	0	7168

Climatic Design Conditions for Selected Locations *(Continued)*

Station	Heating DB		Cooling DB/MCWB						Heat./Cool. Degree-Days	
			0.4%		1%		2%			
	99.6%	99%	DB / MCWB		DB / MCWB		DB / MCWB		HDD / CDD 65	
Zambia										
LUSAKA	44.9	46.6	93.4	64.9	91.5	65.4	89.5	65.3	325	2110
Zimbabwe										
HARARE	42.7	44.6	88.2	61.3	86.3	61.2	84.5	61.4	650	1376

INDEX